MARKINGS
1999

Peter R. March

Ian Allan
PUBLISHING

Contents

Photographs by Peter R. March (PRM) unless otherwise credited

This twentieth edition published 1999

ISBN 0 7110 2641 6

Published by Ian Allan Publishing

an imprint of Ian Allan Publishing Ltd,
Terminal House, Shepperton, Surrey TW17 8AS.

Printed by Ian Allan Printing Ltd,
Riverdene Business Park, Hersham, Surrey KT12 4RG

Code: 9903/F2

Front cover: A No1 Squadron Harrier GR7. *Richard Cooper*

Back cover: Griffin HT1 ZJ239 used by No 66(R) Squadron as an advanced trainer. *PRM*

This twentieth annual edition of *abc Military Aircraft Markings*, a companion to *abc Civil Aircraft Markings*, lists in alphabetical and numerical order all of the aircraft that carry a United Kingdom military serial, and **which are based, or might be seen, in the UK**. It also includes airworthy and current RAF/RN/Army aircraft that are based permanently or temporarily overseas. The term *aircraft* used here covers powered, manned aeroplanes, helicopters, airships and gliders. Included are all the current Royal Air Force, Royal Navy, Army Air Corps, Ministry of Defence (Procurement Executive), Defence Evaluation & Research Agency, manufacturers' test aircraft and civilian-owned aircraft with military markings.

Aircraft withdrawn from operational use but which are retained in the UK for ground training purposes or otherwise preserved by the Services and in the numerous museums and collections are listed. The serials of some incomplete aircraft have been included, such as the cockpit sections of machines displayed by the RAF, aircraft used by airfield fire sections and for service battle damage repair training (BDRT), together with significant parts of aircraft held by preservation groups and societies. Where only part of the aircraft fuselage remains the abbreviation <ff> for front fuselage/cockpit section or <rf> for rear fuselage is shown after the type. Many of these aircraft are allocated, and sometimes wear, a secondary identity, such as an RAF Logistics Command 'M' maintenance number. These numbers are listed against those aircraft to which they have been allocated.

A serial 'missing' is either because it was never issued as it formed part of a 'black-out block' (a practice that has now ceased) or because the aircraft is written off, scrapped, sold abroad or allocated an alternative marking. Aircraft used as targets on MoD ranges to which access is restricted, and un-manned target drones, are omitted, as are UK military aircraft that have been permanently grounded and are based overseas and unlikely to return to Britain.

In the main, the serials listed are those markings presently displayed on the aircraft. Where an aircraft carries a false serial it is quoted in *italic type*. Very often these serials are carried by replicas, that are denoted by <R> after the type. The manufacturer and aircraft type are given, together with recent alternative, previous, secondary or civil identity shown in round brackets. Complete records of multiple previous identities are only included where space permits. The operating unit and its based location, along with any known unit and base code markings in square brackets, are given as accurately as possible. The unit markings are normally carried boldly on the sides of the fuselage or on the aircraft's fin. In the case of RAF and AAC machines currently in service, they are usually one or two letters or numbers, while the RN continues to use a well-established system of three-figure codes between 000 and 999 together with a fin letter code denoting the aircraft's operational base. RN squadrons, units and bases are allocated blocks of numbers from which individual aircraft codes are issued. To help identification of RN bases and landing platforms on ships, a list of tail-letter codes with their appropriate name, helicopter code number, ship pennant number and type of vessel, is included; as is a helicopter code number/ships' tail-letter code grid cross-reference.

Codes change, for example when aircraft move between units, and therefore the markings currently painted on a particular aircraft might not be those shown in this edition because of subsequent events. The implementation of the Government's continuing civilian contractorisation and the reductions in service manpower, again account for many of the changes in this new edition. Aircraft currently under manufacture or not yet delivered to the Service, such as the C-130Js temporarily stored at Cambridge, most of which carry civil registrations, are listed under their allocated RAF serial. Those airframes which may not appear in the next edition because of sale, accident, etc, have their fates, where known, given in italic type in the *locations* column.

The Irish Army Air Corps fleet is listed, together with the serials of other overseas air arms whose aircraft might be seen visiting the UK from time to time. The serial numbers are as usually presented on the individual machine or as they are normally identified. Where possible, the aircraft's base and operating unit have been shown.

USAF, US Army and US Navy aircraft based in the UK and in Western Europe, and types that regularly visit the UK from the USA, are each listed in separate sections by aircraft type. The serial number actually displayed on the aircraft is shown in full, with additional Fiscal Year (FY) or full serial information also provided. Where appropriate, details of the operating wing, squadron allocation and base are added. The USAF is, like the RAF, in a continuing period of change, resulting in the adoption of new unit titles, squadron and equipment changes and the closure of bases. Only details that concern changes effected by January 1999 are shown.

Veteran and vintage aircraft which carry overseas military markings but which are based in the UK have been separately listed showing their principal means of identification. This has been extended in this edition with the addition of warbirds based on mainland Europe that are likely to be seen visiting the UK. The growing list of aircraft in government or military service, often under contract to private operating companies, that carry civil registrations has again been included.

With the use of the Internet now well established as a rich source of information, a new section has been added to this edition, listing a selection of military aviation 'world wide web' sites. Although only a few of these provide details of aircraft serials and markings, they do give interesting insights into air arms and their operating units, aircraft, museums and a broad range of associated topics.

Information shown is believed to be correct at 31 January 1999, and significant changes can be monitored through the monthly 'Military Markings' column in *Aircraft Illustrated*.

Acknowledgements

The compilers again wish to thank the many people who have taken trouble to send comments, criticism and other useful information following the publication of the previous editions of *abc Military Aircraft Markings*. In particular the following correspondents: A. Allen, W. Allen, B. Dunnell, R. Fitton, H. W. Gandy, P. Jones, I. Logan, M. V. Lowe, A. P. March, D. J. March, B. Martin, T. McGhee, D. Moore, D. Stretton and M. Thomas, along with the Mil-Spotters Forum mailing list..

The compilation has relied heavily on the publications of the following aviation groups and societies: *Air-Britain News* (Air-Britain), *Airfield Review* (Airfield Research Group), *Air Link* (Lincolnshire Aviation Society), *BAC News* (Bristol Aero Collection), *British Aviation Review* (British Aviation Research Group), *International Auster Club News*, *Irish Air Letter*, *Military Aviation Review* (MAP), *Osprey* (Solent Aviation Society), *RAF News*, *Scramble* (Dutch Aviation Society), *Stansted Aviation News* (Stansted Aviation Society), *SWAG MAG* (South West Aviation Group), *Ulster Air Mail* (Ulster Aviation Society) and *Update* (British Aviation Preservation Council) and *Warbirds Worldwide*.

This fully revised edition of *abc Military Aircraft Markings* has been researched and collated by Howard Curtis, to whom I am indebted.

PRM   January 1999

845 Naval Air Squadron's Sea King HC4 ZA298 carrying SFOR markings. *PRM*

Abbreviations

AAC	Army Air Corps	CC	County Council
AACS	Airborne Air Control Squadron	CCF	Combined Cadet Force/Canadian Car &
AACTS	Airborne Air Control Training Squadron		Foundry Company
AAS	Aeromedical Airlift Squadron	CDE	Chemical Defence Establishment
ABS	Air Base Squadron	CEAM	Centre d'Expérimentation Aériennes
ACC	Air Combat Command		Militaires (Military Air Experimental Centre)
ACCGS	Air Cadets Central Gliding School	CEV	Centre d'Essais en Vol (Flight Test Centre)
ACCS	Airborne Command and Control Squadron	CFS	Central Flying School
ACW	Airborne Control Wing	CIFAS	Centre d'Instruction des Forces Aériennes
AD&StA	Aberdeen, Dundee & St Andrews		Stratégiques (Air Strategic Training
AEF	Air Experience Flight		Centre)
AESS	Air Engineering & Survival School	CinC	Commander in Chief
AEW	Airborne Early Warning	CinCAFSE	Commander in Chief, Allied Forces
AF	Arméflyget (Army Air Battalion)		Southern Europe
AFB	Air Force Base	CinCLANT	Commander in Chief Atlantic
AFD	Air Fleet Department	CITac	Centre d'Instruction Tactique (Tactical
AFRC	Air Force Reserve Command		Training Centre)
AFSC	Air Force Systems Command	Co	Company
AFSK	Armeflygskolan (Army Flying School)	Comp	Composite with
AFWF	Advanced Fixed Wing Flight	CT	College of Technology
AG	Airlift Group	CTE	Central Training Establishment
AGA	Academia General del Aire (General Air	CTTS	Civilian Technical Training School
	Academy)	CV	Chance-Vought
AkG	Aufklärüngsgeschwader (Reconnaissance	D-BA	Daimler-Benz Aerospace
	Wing)	D-BD	Dassault-Breguet Dornier
AMC	Air Mobility Command	D&G	Dumfries and Galloway
AMD-BA	Avions Marcel Dassault-Breguet Aviation	DEODS	Defence Explosives Ordnance Disposal
AMF	Aircraft Maintenance Flight		School
AMG	Aircraft Maintenance Group	DERA	Defence Evaluation and Research Agency
AMIF	Aircraft Maintenance Instruction Flight	Det	Detachment
AMS	Air Movements School	DH	de Havilland
AMW	Air Mobility Wing	DHC	de Havilland Canada
ANG	Air National Guard	DHFS	Defence Helicopter Flying School
APS	Aircraft Preservation Society	dlt	dopravni letka (Transport Squadron)
ARS	Air Refuelling Squadron	DTI	Department of Trade and Industry
ARW	Air Refuelling Wing	EA	Escadron Aérien (Air Squadron)
ARWS	Advanced Rotary Wing Squadron	EAC	Ecole de l'Aviation de Chasse (Fighter
AS	Airlift Squadron/Air Squadron		Aviation School)
ASCW	Airborne Surveillance Control Wing	EAP	European Aircraft Project
ASF	Aircraft Servicing Flight	EAT	Ecole de l'Aviation de Transport (Transport
AS&RU	Aircraft Salvage and Repair Unit		Aviation School)
ATC	Air Training Corps	EC	Escadre de Chasse (Fighter Wing)
ATCC	Air Traffic Control Centre	ECS	Electronic Countermeasures Squadron
Avn	Aviation	EDA	Escadre de Detection Aéroportée (Air
Avn Co	Aviation Company		Detection Wing)
AW	Airlift Wing/Armstrong Whitworth Aircraft	EdC	Escadron de Convoyage
AWC	Air Warfare Centre	EDCA	Escadron de Détection et de Control
BAC	British Aircraft Corporation		Aéroportée (Airborne Detection & Control
BAe	British Aerospace PLC		Sqn)
BAOR	British Army of the Rhine	EE	English Electric
BAPC	British Aviation Preservation Council	EET	Escadron Electronique Tactique (Tactical
BATUS	British Army Training Unit Support		Electronics Flight)
BBMF	Battle of Britain Memorial Flight	EH	Escadron d'Helicoptères (Helicopter Flight)
BDRF	Battle Damage Repair Flight	EHI	European Helicopter Industries
BDRT	Battle Damage Repair Training	EL	Escadre de Liaison (Liaison Wing)
Be	Beech	EMA	East Midlands Airport
Bf	Bayerische Flugzeugwerke	EMVO	Elementaire Militaire Vlieg Opleiding
BFWF	Basic Fixed Wing Flight		(Elementary Flying Training)
BG	Bomber Group	ENOSA	Ecole des Navigateurs Operationnelles
BGA	British Gliding & Soaring Association		Systemes d'Armees (Navigation School)
bk	black (squadron colours and markings)	EoN	Elliot's of Newbury
bl	blue (squadron colours and markings)	EPAA	Ecole de Pilotage Elementaire de l'Armée
BNFL	British Nuclear Fuels Ltd		de l'Air (Air Force Elementary Flying
BnHAtk	Helicopter Attack Battalion		School)
BnHLn	Liaison Battalion	EPE	Ecole de Pilotage Elementaire (Elementary
BP	Boulton & Paul		Flying School)
br	brown (squadron colours and markings)	EPTT	Exhibition, Production & Transportation
BS	Bomber Squadron		Team
B-V	Boeing-Vertol	ER	Escadre de Reconnaissance
BW	Bomber Wing		(Reconnaissance Wing)
CAC	Commonwealth Aircraft Corporation	ERS	Escadron de Reconnaissance Stratégique
CARG	Cotswold Aircraft Restoration Group		(Strategic Reconnaissance Squadron)
CASA	Construcciones Aeronautics SA	ERV	Escadre de Ravitaillement en Vol (Air
Cav	Cavalry		Refuelling Wing)

ES	Escadrille de Servitude
Esc	Escuadron (Squadron)
Esk	Eskadrille (Squadron)
Eslla	Escuadrilla (Squadron)
Esq	Esquadra (Squadron)
ET	Escadre de Transport (Transport Squadron)
ETE	Escadron de Transport et Entrainement (Transport Training Squadron)
ETEC	Escadron de Transport d'Entrainement et de Calibration (Transport Training & Calibration Sqn)
ETL	Escadron de Transport Légère (Light Transport Squadron)
ETO	Escadron de Transition Operationnelle
ETOM	Escadron de Transport Outre Mer (Overseas Transport Squadron)
ETPS	Empire Test Pilots' School
ETS	Engineering Training School
FAA	Fleet Air Arm/Federal Aviation Administration
FACF	Forward Air Control Flight
FBS	Flugbereitschaftsstaffel
FBW	Fly by wire
FC	Forskokcentralen (Flight Centre)
FE	Further Education
FETC	Fire and Emergency Training Centre
ff	Front fuselage
FG	Fighter Group
FH	Fairchild-Hiller
FI	Falkland Islands
FISt	Flieger Staffel (Flight Squadron)
Flt	Flight
FMA	Fabrica Militar de Aviones
FMT	Flotila Militara de Transport (Transport Regiment)
FMV	Forsvarets Materielwerk
FONA	Flag Officer Naval Aviation
FRADU	Fleet Requirements and Air Direction Unit
FRA	FR Aviation
FS	Fighter Squadron
FSAIU	Flight Safety & Accident Investigation Unit
FSCTE	Fire School Central Training Establishment
FTS	Flying Training School
FTW	Flying Training Wing
Fw	Focke Wulf
FW	Fighter Wing/Foster Wickner
FWTS	Fixed Wing Test Squadron
FY	Fiscal Year
F3 OCU	Tornado F3 Operational Conversion Unit
GAL	General Aircraft Ltd
GAM	Groupe Aerien Mixte (Composite Air Group)
gd	gold (squadron colours and markings)
GD	General Dynamics
GHL	Groupe d'Helicopteres Legeres (Light Helicopter Group)
GI	Ground Instruction/Groupement d'Instruction (Instructional Group)
GKNW	GKN Westland
gn	green (squadron colours and markings)
GRD	Gruppe fur Rustunggdienste (Group for Service Preparation)
GT	Grupo de Transporte (Transport Wing)
GTT	Grupo de Transporte de Tropos (Troop Carrier Wing)
gy	grey (squadron colours and markings)
H&W	Hereford and Worcester
HAF	Historic Aircraft Flight
HC	Helicopter Combat Support Squadron
HF	Historic Flying Ltd
HFR	Heeresfliegerregiment (Army Air Regiment)
HFWS	Heeresflieger Waffenschule (Army Air Weapons School)
Hkp Div	Helikopterdivisionen (Helicopter Division)
HMA	Helicopter Maritime Attack
HMF	Harrier Maintenance Flight/Helicopter Maintenance Flight
HMS	Her Majesty's Ship
HOCU	Harrier OCU
HP	Handley-Page
HQ	Headquarters
HS	Hawker Siddeley
HSF	Harrier Servicing Flight
IAF	Israeli Air Force
INTA	Instituto Nacional de Tecnica Aerospacial
IOW	Isle Of Wight
IWM	Imperial War Museum
JATE	Joint Air Transport Establishment
JbG	Jagdbombergeschwader (Fighter Bomber Wing)
JFACSTU	Joint Forward Air Control Students Training Unit
JG	Jagdgeschwader (Fighter Wing)
Kridlo	Wing
Letka	Squadron
ltBVr	letka Bitevnich Vrtulníkù (Attack Helicopter Squadron)
LTG	Lufttransportgeschwader (Air Transport Wing)
LTV	Ling-Temco-Vought
LVG	Luftwaffen Versorgungs Geschwader (Air Force Maintenance Wing)/Luft Verkehrs Gesellschaft
LZO	Letecky Zkusební Odbor (Aviation Test Department)
m	multi-coloured (squadron colours and markings)
MAPK	Mira Anachestisis Pantos Kerou (All Weather Interception Sqn)
MARPAT	Maritime Patrouillegroep (Maritime Patrol Group)
MBB	Messerschmitt Bolkow-Blohm
MCAS	Marine Corps Air Station
McD	McDonnell Douglas
Med	Medical
MFG	Marine Flieger Geschwader (Naval Air Wing)
MH	Max Holste
MIB	Military Intelligence Battalion
MiG	Mikoyan — Gurevich
MoD(PE)	Ministry of Defence (Procurement Executive)
Mod	Modified
MR	Maritime Reconnaissance
MRF	Meteorological Research Flight
MS	Morane-Saulnier
MTM	Mira Taktikis Metaforon (Tactical Transport Sqn)
MU	Maintenance Unit
Mus'm	Museum
NA	North American
NACDS	Naval Air Command Driving School
NAEWF	NATO Airborne Early Warning Force
NAF	Naval Air Facility
NAS	Naval Air Station
NASU	Naval Air Support Unit
NATO	North Atlantic Treaty Organisation
NAWC	Naval Air Warfare Center
NAWC-AD	Naval Air Warfare Center Aircraft Division
NBC	Nuclear, Biological and Chemical
NE	North-East
NI	Northern Ireland
NMSU	Nimrod Major Servicing Unit
NWTSPM	Naval Weapons Test Squadron, Point Mugu
NYARC	North Yorks Aircraft Restoration Centre
OCU	Operational Conversion Unit
OEU	Operation Evaluation Unit
OFMC	Old Flying Machine Company
or	orange (squadron colours and markings)
OSAC	Operational Support Airlift Command
OVH Kmp	Observations-Helicopter Kompagni

PASF	Puma Aircraft Servicing Flight
PAT	Priority Air Transport Detachment
PBN	Pilatus Britten-Norman
PLM	Pulk Lotnictwa Mysliwskiego (Fighter Regiment)
pr	purple (squadron colours and markings)
PRU	Photographic Reconnaissance Unit
PVH Kmp	Panservaerns-Helicopter Kompagni
pzdlt	prùzkumná dopravni letka (Reconnaissance & Transport Squadron)
r	red (squadron colours and markings)
R	Replica
RAeS	Royal Aeronautical Society
RAF	Royal Aircraft Factory/Royal Air Force
RAFC	Royal Air Force College
RAFM	Royal Air Force Museum
RAFGSA	Royal Air Force Gliding and Soaring Association
RAOC	Royal Army Ordnance Corps
RCAF	Royal Canadian Air Force
RE	Royal Engineers
Regt	Regiment
REME	Royal Electrical & Mechanical Engineers
rf	Rear fuselage
RJAF	Royal Jordanian Air Force
RM	Royal Marines
RMB	Royal Marines Base
RMC of S	Royal Military College of Science
RN	Royal Navy
RNAS	Royal Naval Air Station
RNAW	Royal Naval Aircraft Workshop
RNAY	Royal Naval Aircraft Yard
RNEC	Royal Naval Engineering College
RNGSA	Royal Navy Gliding and Soaring Association
ROF	Royal Ordnance Factory
RQS	Rescue Squadron
R-R	Rolls-Royce
RS	Reid & Sigrist/Reconnaissance Squadron
RSV	Reparto Sperimentale Volo (Experimental Flight Squadron)
RW	Reconnaissance Wing
SA	Scottish Aviation
Saab	Svenska Aeroplan Aktiebolag
SAH	School of Air Handling
SAL	Scottish Aviation Limited
SAM	School of Aviation Medicine
SAOEU	Strike/Attack Operational Evaluation Unit
SAR	Search and Rescue
Saro	Saunders-Roe
SARTU	Search and Rescue Training Unit
SBoLK	Stíhacie Bombardovacie Letecké Kridlo (Fighter Bomber Air Wing)
SCW	Sea Control Wing
SEAE	School of Electrical & Aeronautical Engineering
SEPECAT	Société Européenne de Production de l'avion Ecole de Combat et d'Appui Tactique
SFDO	School of Flight Deck Operations
SHAPE	Supreme Headquarters Allied Forces Europe
si	silver (squadron colours and markings)
SKTU	Sea King Training Unit
Skv	Skvadron (Squadron)
SLK	Stíhacie Letecké Kridlo (Fighter Air Wing)
slt	stíhací letka (Fighter Squadron)
SLV	School Licht Vliegwezen (Flying School)
Sm	Smaldeel (Squadron)
SNCAN	Société Nationale de Constructions Aéronautiques du Nord
SOES	Station Operations & Engineering Squadron
SOG	Special Operations Group
SOS	Special Operations Squadron
SoTT	School of Technical Training
SOW	Special Operations Wing
SPAD	Société Pour les Appareils Deperdussin
Sqn	Squadron
SSF	Station Servicing Flight
SWWAPS	Second World War Aircraft Preservation Society
TA	Territorial Army
TAP	Transporten Avio Polk (Air Transport Regiment)
T&EE	Test & Evaluation Establishment
TFC	The Fighter Collection
TGp	Test Groep
TIARA	Tornado Integrated Avionics Research Aircraft
tlt	taktická letka (Tactical Squadron)
TMF	Tornado Maintenance Flight
TMTS	Trade Management Training School
tpzlt	taktická a prùzkumná letka (Tactical & Reconnaissance Squadron)
TS	Test Squadron
TsAGI	Tsentral'ny Aerogidrodinamicheski Instut (Central Aero & Hydrodynamics Institute)
TsLw	Technische Schule der Luftwaffe (Luftwaffe Technical School)
TSW	Tactical Supply Wing
TTTE	Tri-national Tornado Training Establishment
TW	Test Wing
UAS	University Air Squadron
Uberwg	Uberwachunggeschwader (Surveillance Wing)
UK	United Kingdom
UKAEA	United Kingdom Atomic Energy Authority
UNFICYP	United Nations' Forces in Cyprus
US	United States
USAF	United States Air Force
USAFE	United States Air Forces in Europe
USAREUR	US Army Europe
USCGS	US Coast Guard Station
USEUCOM	United States European Command
USMC	United States Marine Corps
USN	United States Navy
VAAC	Vectored thrust Advanced Aircraft flight Control
VFW	Vereinigte Flugtechnische Werke
VGS	Volunteer Gliding School
vlt	vycviková letka (Training Squadron)
VMGR	Marine Aerial Refuelling/Transport Squadron
VMGRT	Marine Aerial Refuelling/Transport Training Squadron
VQ	Fleet Air Reconnaissance Squadron
VR	Fleet Logistic Support Squadron
VS	Vickers-Supermarine
VSD	Vegyes Szàllitorepülö Dandàr (Aircraft Transport Brigade)
VSL	Vycvikové Stredisko Letectva (Flying Training Centre)
w	white (squadron colours and markings)
Wg	Wing
WLT	Weapons Loading Training
WRS	Weather Reconnaissance Squadron
WS	Westland
WTD	Wehrtechnische Dienstelle (Technical Support Unit)
WW2	World War II
y	yellow (squadron colours and markings)
zDL	základna Dopravního Letectva (Air Transport Base)
ZmDK	Zmiesany Dopravny Kridlo (Mixed Transport Wing)
zSL	základna Skolního Letectva (Training Air Base)
zTL	základna Taktického Letectva (Tactical Air Base)
zVrL	základna Vrtulníkového Letectva (Helicopter Air Base)

A Guide to the Location of Operational Bases in the UK

This section is to assist the reader to locate the places in the United Kingdom where operational military aircraft are based. The term *aircraft* also includes helicopters and gliders.

The alphabetical order listing gives each location in relation to its county and to its nearest classified road(s) (*by* means adjoining; *of* means proximate to), together with its approximate direction and mileage from the centre of a nearby major town or city. Some civil airports are included where active military units are also based, but **excluded** are MoD sites with non-operational aircraft (eg *gate guardians*), the bases of privately-owned civil aircraft that wear military markings and museums.

User	Base name	County/Region	Location	Distance/direction from (town)
DERA	Aberporth	Dyfed	N of A487	6m ENE of Cardigan
Army	Abingdon	Oxfordshire	W by B4017, W of A34	5m SSW of Oxford
RAF	Aldergrove/Belfast Airport	Co Antrim	W by A26	13m W of Belfast
RM	Arbroath	Angus	E of A933	2m NW of Arbroath
RAF/ Hunting	Barkston Heath	Lincolnshire	W by B6404, S of A153	5m NNE of Grantham
RAF	Benson	Oxfordshire	E by A423	1m NE of Wallingford
DERA/ RAF	Boscombe Down	Wiltshire	S by A303, W of A338	6m N of Salisbury
RAF	Boulmer	Northumberland	E of B1339	4m E of Alnwick
RAF	Brize Norton	Oxfordshire	W of A4095	5m SW of Witney
Marshall	Cambridge Airport/ Teversham	Cambridgeshire	S by A1303	2m E of Cambridge
RM/RAF	Chivenor	Devon	S of A361	4m WNW of Barnstaple
RAF	Church Fenton	Yorkshire North	S of B1223	7m WNW of Selby
RAF	Colerne	Wiltshire	S of A420, E of Fosse Way	5m NE of Bath
RAF	Coltishall	Norfolk	W of B1150	9m NNE of Norwich
RAF	Coningsby	Lincolnshire	S of A153, W by B1192	10m NW of Boston
RAF	Cosford	Shropshire	W of A41, N of A464	9m WNW of Wolverhampton
RAF	Cottesmore	Leicestershire	W of A1, N of B668	9m NW of Stamford
RAF	Cranwell	Lincolnshire	N by A17, S by B1429	5m WNW of Sleaford
RN	Culdrose	Cornwall	E by A3083	1m SE of Helston
Army	Dishforth	Yorkshire North	E by A1	4m E of Ripon
BAe	Dunsfold	Surrey	W of A281, S of B2130	9m S of Guildford
USAF	Fairford	Gloucestershire	S of A417	9m ESE of Cirencester
RN	Fleetlands	Hampshire	E by A32	2m SE of Fareham
RAF	Glasgow Airport	Strathclyde	N by M8 jn 28	7m W of city
RAF	Halton	Buckinghamshire	N of A4011, S of B4544	4m ESE of Aylesbury
RAF	Henlow	Bedfordshire	E of A600, W of A6001	1m SW of Henlow
RAF	Honington	Suffolk	E of A134, W of A1088	6m S of Thetford
Army	Hullavington	Wiltshire	W of A429	1m N of M4 jn 17
RAF	Kenley	Greater London	W of A22	1m W of Warlingham
RAF	Kinloss	Grampian	E of B9011, N of B9089	3m NE of Forres
RAF	Kirknewton	Lothian	E by B7031, N by A70	8m SW of Edinburgh
USAF	Lakenheath	Suffolk	W by A1065	8m W of Thetford
RAF	Leeming	Yorkshire North	E by A1	5m SW of Northallerton
RAF	Leuchars	Fife	E of A919	7m SE of Dundee
RAF	Linton-on-Ouse	Yorkshire North	E of B6265	10m NW of York
DERA	Llanbedr	Gwynedd	W of A496	7m NNW of Barmouth
RAF	Lossiemouth	Grampian	W of B9135, S of B9040	4m N of Elgin
RAF	Lyneham	Wiltshire	W of A3102, S of A420	10m WSW of Swindon
RAF	Marham	Norfolk	N by A1122	6m W of Swaffham
Army	Middle Wallop	Hampshire	S by A343	6m SW of Andover
USAF	Mildenhall	Suffolk	S by A1101	9m NNE of Newmarket
RAF	Newton	Nottinghamshire	N of A52, W of A46	7m E of Nottingham
RAF	Northolt	Greater London	N by A40	3m E of M40 jn 1
RAF	Odiham	Hampshire	E of A32	2m S of M3 jn 5
RN	Predannack	Cornwall	W by A3083	7m S of Helston
RN	Prestwick Airport	Strathclyde	E by A79	3m N of Ayr
RAF	St Athan	South Glamorgan	N of B4265	13m WSW of Cardiff
RAF	St Mawgan/Newquay	Cornwall	N of A3059	4m ENE of Newquay
RAF	Sealand	Flint	W by A550	6m WNW of Chester
RAF	Shawbury	Shropshire	W of B5063	7m NNE of Shrewsbury
RAF	Syerston	Nottinghamshire	W by A46	5m SW of Newark
RAF	Ternhill	Shropshire	SW by A41	3m SW of Market DTEO
RAF/ Army	Topcliffe	Yorkshire North	E of A167, W of A168	3m SW of Thirsk

User	Base name	County/Region	Location	Distance/direction from (town)
RAF	Valley	Gwynedd	S of A5 on Anglesey	5m SE of Holyhead
RAF	Waddington	Lincolnshire	E by A607, W by A15	5m S of Lincoln
BAe	Warton	Lancashire	S by A584	8m SE of Blackpool
Army/ RAF	Wattisham	Suffolk	N of B1078	5m SSW of Stowmarket
DERA	West Freugh	Dumfries & Galloway	S by A757, W by A715	5m SE of Stranraer
RAF	Weston-on-the-Green	Oxfordshire	E by A43	9m N of Oxford
RAF	Wittering	Cambridgeshire	W by A1, N of A47	3m S of Stamford
RAF	Woodvale	Merseyside	W by A565	5m SSW of Southport
RAF	Wyton	Cambridgeshire	E of A141, N of B1090	3m NE of Huntingdon
WS	Yeovil	Somerset	N of A30, S of A3088	1m W of Yeovil
RN	Yeovilton	Somerset	S by B3151, S of A303	5m N of Yeovil

British Military Aircraft Serials

The Committee of Imperial Defence through its Air Committee introduced a standardised system of numbering aircraft in November 1912. The Air Department of the Admiralty was allocated the first batch 1-200 and used these to cover aircraft already in use and those on order. The Army was issued with the next block from 201-800, which included the number 304 which was given to the Cody Biplane now preserved in the Science Museum. By the outbreak of World War 1 the Royal Navy was on its second batch of serials 801-1600 and this system continued with alternating allocations between the Army and Navy until 1916 when number 10000, a Royal Flying Corps BE2C, was reached.

It was decided not to continue with five digit numbers but instead to start again from 1, prefixing RFC aircraft with the letter A and RNAS aircraft with the prefix N. The RFC allocations commenced with A1 an FE2D and before the end of the year had reached A9999 an Armstrong Whitworth FK8. The next group commenced with B1 and continued in logical sequence through the C, D, E and F prefixes. G was used on a limited basis to identify captured German aircraft, while H was the last block of wartime-ordered aircraft. To avoid confusion I was not used, so the new postwar machines were allocated serials in the J range. A further minor change was made in the serial numbering system in August 1929 when it was decided to maintain four numerals after the prefix letter, thus omitting numbers 1 to 999. The new K series therefore commenced at K1000, which was allocated to an AW Atlas.

The Naval N prefix was not used in such a logical way. Blocks of numbers were allocated for specific types of aircraft such as seaplanes or flying-boats. By the late 1920s the sequence had largely been used up and a new series using the prefix S was commenced. In 1930 separate naval allocations were stopped and subsequent serials were issued in the 'military' range which had by this time reached the K series. A further change in the pattern of allocations came in the L range. Commencing with L7272 numbers were issued in blocks with smaller blocks of serials between not used. These were known as blackout blocks. As M had already been used as a suffix for Maintenance Command instructional airframes it was not used as a prefix. Although N had previously been used for naval aircraft it was used again for serials allocated from 1937.

With the build-up to World War 2 the rate of allocations quickly accelerated and the prefix R was being used when war was declared. The letters O and Q were not allotted, and nor was S which had been used up to S1865 for naval aircraft before integration into the RAF series. By 1940 the serial Z9999 had been reached, as part of a blackout block, with the letters U and Y not used to avoid confusion. The option to recommence serial allocation at A1000 was not taken up; instead it was decided to use an alphabetical two-letter prefix with three numerals running from 100 to 999. Thus AA100 was allocated to a Blenheim IV.

This two-letter, three-numeral serial system which started in 1940 continues today. The letters C, I, O, Q, U and Y were, with the exception of NC, not used. For various reasons the following letter combinations were not issued: DA, DB, DH, EA, GA to GZ, HA, HT, JE, JH, JJ, KR to KT, MR, NW, NZ, SA to SK, SV, TN, TR and VE. The first postwar serials issued were in the VP range while the end of the WZs had been reached by the Korean War. The current new issues are in the ZJ range and there are now no blackout blocks of unallocated serials. This being so, and at the current rate of issue the Z range will last well into the 21st century.

Note: Whilst every effort has been made to ensure the accuracy of this publication, no part of the contents has been obtained from official sources. The compiler will be pleased to continue to receive comments, corrections and further information for inclusion in subsequent editions of *Military Aircraft Markings* and the monthly up-date of additions and amendments that is published in *Aircraft Illustrated*. Please send your information to Military Aircraft Markings, PO Box 46, Westbury-on-Trym, Bristol BS9 1TF; fax to 0117 968 3928 or e-mail to prmavia@aol.com

British Military Aircraft Markings

A serial in *italics* denotes that it is not the genuine marking for that airframe.

Serial	Type (other identity) [code]	Owner/operator, location or fate	Notes
164	Bleriot Type XI (BAPC 106/9209M)	RAF Museum Restoration Centre, Cardington	
168	Sopwith Tabloid Scout <R> (G-BFDE)	RAF Museum, Hendon	
304	Cody Biplane (BAPC 62)	Science Museum, South Kensington	
433	Bleriot Type XXVII (BAPC 107/9202M)	RAF Museum, Hendon	
687	RAF BE2b <R> (BAPC 181)	RAF Museum, Hendon	
1701	RAF BE2c <R> (BAPC 117)	Privately owned, Orpington	
2345	Vickers FB5 Gunbus <R> (G-ATVP)	RAF Museum, Hendon	
2699	RAF BE2c	Imperial War Museum, Lambeth	
2882	Vickers FB5 Gunbus <R> (BAPC 234)	Barton Aviation Heritage Society, Barton	
3066	Caudron GIII (G-AETA/9203M)	RAF Museum, Hendon	
5894	DH2 <R> (G-BFVH)	Privately owned, Withybush	
5964	DH2 <R> (BAPC 112)	Museum of Army Flying, stored Middle Wallop	
6232	RAF BE2c <R> (BAPC 41)	Yorkshire Air Museum, stored Elvington	
8359	Short 184 <ff>	FAA Museum, RNAS Yeovilton	
A301	Morane BB (frame)	RAF Museum Restoration Centre, Cardington	
A1325	RAF BE2e (G-BVGR)	Aero Vintage, Hatch	
A1742	Bristol Scout D <R> (BAPC 38)	Privately owned, Solihull	
A4850	RAF SE5a <R> (BAPC 176)	Barton Aviation Heritage Society, Barton	
A7317	Sopwith Pup <R> (BAPC 179)	Midland Air Museum, Coventry	
A8226	Sopwith 1_ Strutter <R> (G-BIDW)	RAF Museum, Hendon	
B1807	Sopwith Pup (G-EAVX) [A7]	Privately owned, Keynsham, Avon	
B2458	Sopwith 1F.1 Camel <R> (G-BPOB/*F542*) [R]	Privately owned, Booker	
B3459	Nieuport Scout 17/23 <R> (G-BWMJ) [21]	Privately owned, Fairoaks	
B6401	Sopwith 1F.1 Camel <R> (G-AWYY/C1701)	FAA Museum, RNAS Yeovilton	
B7270	Sopwith 1F.1 Camel <R> (G-BFCZ)	Brooklands Museum, Weybridge	
C1904	RAF SE5a <R> (G-PFAP) [Z]	Privately owned, Syerston	
C3011	Phoenix Currie Super Wot (G-SWOT) [S]	The Real Aeroplane Company, Breighton	
C3988	Sopwith 5F.1 Dolphin	RAF Museum Restoration Centre, Cardington	
C4451	Avro 504J <R> (BAPC 210)	Southampton Hall of Aviation	
C4918	Bristol M1C <R> (G-BWJM)	The Shuttleworth Collection, Old Warden	
C4940	Bristol M1C <R>	Privately owned	
C4994	Bristol M1C <R> (G-BLWM)	RAF Museum, Hendon	
C9533	RAF SE5a <R> (G-BUWE) [M]	Privately owned, DERA Boscombe Down	
D276	RAF SE5a <R> (BAPC 208) [A]	Prince's Mead Shopping Centre, Farnborough	
D3419	Sopwith 1F.1 Camel <R> (BAPC 59)	RAF Cosford Aerospace Museum	
D7560	Avro 504K	Museum of Army Flying, Middle Wallop	
D7889	Bristol F2b Fighter (G-AANM/BAPC 166)	Aero Vintage, St Leonards-on-Sea	
D8084	Bristol F2b Fighter (G-ACAA/F4516) [S]	The Fighter Collection, Duxford	
D8096	Bristol F2b Fighter (G-AEPH) [D]	The Shuttleworth Collection, Old Warden	
D8781	Avro 504K <R> (G-ECKE)	Privately owned, Rougham	
E373	Avro 504K <R> (BAPC 178)	Privately owned,	
E449	Avro 504K (G-EBJE/9205M)	RAF Museum, Hendon	
E2466	Bristol F2b Fighter (BAPC 165) [I]	RAF Museum, Hendon	
E2581	Bristol F2b Fighter [13]	Imperial War Museum, Duxford	

F141 – L1070

Notes	Serial	Type (other identity) [code]	Owner/operator, location or fate
	F141	RAF SE5a <R> (G-SEVA) [G]	Privately owned, DERA Boscombe Down
	F235	RAF SE5a <R> (G-BMDB) [B]	Privately owned, Boscombe Down
	F760	SE5a Microlight <R> [A]	Privately owned, Redhill
	F904	RAF SE5a (G-EBIA)	The Shuttleworth Collection, Old Warden
	F938	RAF SE5a (G-EBIC/9208M)	RAF Museum, Hendon
	F943	RAF SE5a <R> (G-BIHF) [S]	Museum of Army Flying, Middle Wallop
	F943	RAF SE5a <R> (G-BKDT)	Yorkshire Air Museum, Elvington
	F1010	Airco DH9A [C]	RAF Museum, Hendon
	F3556	RAF RE8	Imperial War Museum, Duxford
	F4013	Sopwith 1F.1 Camel <R>	Privately owned, Coventry
	F5447	RAF SE5a <R> (G-BKER) [N]	Privately owned, Cumbernauld
	F5459	RAF SE5a <R> (G-INNY) [Y]	Privately owned, Goodwood
	F5475	RAF SE5a <R> (BAPC 250)	Brooklands Museum, Weybridge
	F6314	Sopwith 1F.1 Camel (9206M) [B]	RAF Museum, Hendon
	F8010	RAF SE5a <R> (G-BDWJ) [Z]	Privately owned, Graveley
	F8614	Vickers FB27A Vimy IV <R> (G-AWAU)	RAF Museum, Hendon
	H1968	Avro 504K <R> (BAPC 42)	Yorkshire Air Museum, stored Elvington
	H2311	Avro 504K (G-ABAA)	Gr Manchester Mus of Science & Industry
	H3426	Hawker Hurricane <R> (BAPC 68)	Privately owned,
	H5199	Avro 504K (BK892/3118M/G-ACNB/ G-ADEV)	The Shuttleworth Collection, Old Warden
	J7326	DH53 Humming Bird (G-EBQP)	Privately owned, Audley End
	J8067	Westland Pterodactyl 1a	Science Museum, South Kensington
	J9941	Hawker Hart 2 (G-ABMR)	RAF Museum, Hendon
	K1786	Hawker Tomtit (G-AFTA)	The Shuttleworth Collection, Old Warden
	K2050	Isaacs Fury II (G-ASCM)	Privately owned, Brize Norton
	K2059	Isaacs Fury II (G-PFAR)	Privately owned, Dunkeswell
	K2060	Isaacs Fury II (G-BKZM)	Privately owned, Haverfordwest
	K2075	Isaacs Fury II (G-BEER)	Privately owned, Temple Bruer
	K2227	Bristol 105 Bulldog IIA (G-ABBB)	RAF Museum/Skysport Engineering, Hatch
	K2567	DH82A Tiger Moth (DE306/ 7035M/G-MOTH)	Privately owned, Tadlow
	K2572	DH82A Tiger Moth (NM129/ G-AOZH)	Privately owned, Shoreham
	K2572	DH82A Tiger Moth <R>	The Aircraft Restoration Company, Duxford
	K2587	DH82A Tiger Moth <R> (G-BJAP)	Privately owned, Shobdon
	K3215	Avro 621 Tutor (G-AHSA)	The Shuttleworth Collection, Old Warden
	K3661	Hawker Nimrod II (G-BURZ)	Aero Vintage, St Leonards-on-Sea
	K3731	Isaacs Fury <R> (G-RODI)	Privately owned, Hailsham
	K4232	Avro 671 Rota I (SE-AZB)	To Spain, 1997
	K4235	Avro 671 Rota I (G-AHMJ) [KX-H]	Sold to the USA, June 1998
	K4259	DH82A Tiger Moth (G-ANMO) [21]	Privately owned, White Waltham
	K4972	Hawker Hart Trainer IIA (1764M)	RAF Cosford Aerospace Museum
	K5054	Supermarine Spitfire <R> (BAPC 190/EN398)	Privately owned, Sevenoaks, Kent
	K5054	Supermarine Spitfire <R> (BAPC 214)	Tangmere Military Aviation Museum
	K5054	Supermarine Spitfire <R> (G-BRDV)	Privately owned, Hullavington
	K5054	Supermarine Spitfire <R>	Kent Battle of Britain Museum, Hawkinge
	K5414	Hawker Hind (G-AENP/ BAPC 78) [XV]	The Shuttleworth Collection, Old Warden
	K5600	Hawker Audax I (2015M/G-BVVI)	Aero Vintage, St Leonards-on-Sea
	K5673	Hawker Fury I <R> (BAPC 249)	Brooklands Museum, Weybridge
	K6035	Westland Wallace II (2361M)	RAF Museum, Hendon
	K7271	Hawker Fury II <R> (BAPC 148)	Privately owned, High Ercall
	K8042	Gloster Gladiator II (8372M)	RAF Museum, Hendon
	K8203	Hawker Demon I (G-BTVE/2292M)	Demon Displays, Hatch
	K9853	VS300 Spitfire IA (AR213/G-AIST) [QV-H]	Privately owned, Booker
	K9926	VS300 Spitfire I <R> (BAPC 217) [JH-C]	RAF Bentley Priory, on display
	K9942	VS300 Spitfire I (8383M) [SD-V]	Medway Aircraft Preservation Society, Rochester
	K9962	VS300 Spitfire I <R>	Privately owned, Greenford, W. London
	L1070	VS300 Spitfire I <R> (BAPC 227) [XT-A]	Edinburgh Airport, on display

Serial	Type (other identity) [code]	Owner/operator, location or fate	Notes
L1592	Hawker Hurricane I [KW-Z]	Science Museum, South Kensington	
L1679	Hawker Hurricane I <R> (BAPC 241) [JX-G]	Tangmere Military Aviation Museum	
L1710	Hawker Hurricane I <R> (BAPC 219) [AL-D]	RAF Biggin Hill, on display	
L2301	VS Walrus I (G-AIZG)	FAA Museum, RNAS Yeovilton	
L2940	Blackburn Skua I	FAA Museum, RNAS Yeovilton	
L5343	Fairey Battle I [VO-S]	RAF Museum, Hendon	
L6906	Miles M14A Magister I (G-AKKY/ T9841/BAPC 44)	Museum of Berkshire Aviation, Woodley	
L8756	Bristol 149 Bolingbroke IVT (RCAF 10001) [XD-E]	RAF Museum, Hendon	
L8841	Bristol 149 Bolingbroke IVT (G-BPIV/Z5722) [QY-C]	The Aircraft Restoration Company, Duxford	
N248	Supermarine S6A [S1596]	Southampton Hall of Aviation	
N500	Sopwith LC-1T Triplane <R> (G-PENY/G-BWRA)	Privately owned, Dunkeswell	
N546	Wright Quadruplane 1 <R> (BAPC 164)	Southampton Hall of Aviation	
N1671	Boulton Paul P82 Defiant I] (8370M) [EW-D]	RAF Museum, Hendon	
N1854	Fairey Fulmar II (G-AIBE)	FAA Museum, RNAS Yeovilton	
N2078	Sopwith Baby (8214/8215)	FAA Museum, RNAS Yeovilton	
N2276	Gloster Sea Gladiator II (N5903/ G-GLAD) [H]	Repainted as N5903	
N2980	Vickers Wellington IA [R]	Brooklands Museum, Weybridge	
N3177	RAF BE2e <R>	Barton Aviation Heritage Society, Barton	
N3194	VS300 Spitfire I <R> (BAPC 220) [GR-Z]	RAF Biggin Hill, on display	
N3289	VS300 Spitfire I <R> (BAPC 65) [DW-K]	Kent Battle of Britain Museum, Hawkinge	
N3313	VS300 Spitfire I <R> (BAPC 69) [KL-B]	Kent Battle of Britain Museum, Hawkinge	
N3378	Boulton Paul P82 Defiant I	Boulton Paul Association, Wolverhampton	
N4389	Fairey Albacore (N4172) [4M]	FAA Museum, RNAS Yeovilton	
N4877	Avro 652A Anson I (G-AMDA) [VX-F]	Imperial War Museum, Duxford	
N5182	Sopwith Pup <R> (G-APUP/ 9213M)	RAF Museum, Hendon	
N5195	Sopwith Pup (G-ABOX)	Museum of Army Flying, Middle Wallop	
N5419	Bristol Scout D <R> (N5419)	FAA Museum, RNAS Yeovilton	
N5492	Sopwith Triplane <R> (BAPC 111)		
N5628	Gloster Gladiator II	RAF Museum, Hendon	
N5903	Gloster Sea Gladiator II (N2276/G-GLAD)	The Fighter Collection, Duxford	
N5912	Sopwith Triplane (8385M)	RAF Museum, Hendon	
N6181	Sopwith Pup (G-EBKY/N5180)	The Shuttleworth Collection, Old Warden	
N6290	Sopwith Triplane <R> (G-BOCK)	The Shuttleworth Collection, Old Warden	
N6452	Sopwith Pup <R> (G-BIAU)	FAA Museum, RNAS Yeovilton	
N6466	DH82A Tiger Moth (G-ANKZ)	Privately owned, Sywell	
N6537	DH82A Tiger Moth (G-AOHY)	AAC Historic Aircraft Flt, Middle Wallop	
N6720	DH82A Tiger Moth (7014M) [RUO-B]	Privately owned, Hatch	
N6797	DH82A Tiger Moth (G-ANEH)	Privately owned, Goodwood	
N6812	Sopwith 2F.1 Camel	Imperial War Museum, Lambeth	
N6847	DH82A Tiger Moth (G-APAL)	Privately owned, Little Gransden	
N6848	DH82A Tiger Moth (G-BALX)	Disappeared over the English Channel, 19 April 1998	
N6965	DH82A Tiger Moth (G-AJTW) [FL-J]	Privately owned, Tibenham	
N6985	DH82A Tiger Moth (G-AHMN)	AAC Historic Aircraft Flt, Middle Wallop	
N9191	DH82A Tiger Moth (G-ALND)	Privately owned, Abergavenny	
N9192	DH82A Tiger Moth (G-BSTJ) [RCO-N]	Privately owned, Sywell	
N9389	DH82A Tiger Moth (G-ANJA)	Privately owned, Seething	
N9899	Supermarine Southampton I (fuselage)	RAF Museum, Hendon	
P1344	HP52 Hampden I (9175M) [PL-K]	RAF Museum Restoration Centre, Cardington .	

Notes	Serial	Type (other identity) [code]	Owner/operator, location or fate
	P1344	HP52 Hampden I <rf> (parts Hereford L6012)	RAF Museum, Hendon
	P2617	Hawker Hurricane I (8373M) [AF-A]	RAF Museum, Hendon
P2793		Hawker Hurricane I <R> (BAPC 236) [SD-M]	Eden Camp Theme Park, Malton, North Yorkshire
	P2902	Hawker Hurricane I (G-ROBT) [DX-X]	Privately owned, Milden
P3059		Hawker Hurricane I <R> (BAPC 64) [SD-N]	Kent Battle of Britain Museum, Hawkinge
	P3175	Hawker Hurricane I (wreck)	RAF Museum, Hendon
P3208		Hawker Hurricane I <R> (BAPC 63/*L1592*) [SD-T]	Kent Battle of Britain Museum, Hawkinge
P3386		Hawker Hurricane I <R> (BAPC 218) [FT-A]	RAF Bentley Priory, on display
P3395		Hawker Hurricane IV (KX829) [JX-B]	Birmingham Mus of Science & Industry
	P3554	Hawker Hurricane I (composite)	The Air Defence Collection, Salisbury
	P3717	Hawker Hurricane I (composite) (DR348)	Privately owned, Hinckley, Leics
P4139		Fairey Swordfish II (HS618) [5H]	FAA Museum, RNAS Yeovilton
	P6382	Miles M14A Hawk Trainer 3 (G-AJRS) [C]	The Shuttleworth Collection, Old Warden
	P7350	VS329 Spitfire IIA (G-AWIJ) [BA-Y]	RAF BBMF, Coningsby
	P7540	VS329 Spitfire IIA [DU-W]	Dumfries & Galloway Avn Mus, Dumfries
	P8140	VS329 Spitfire II <R> (BAPC 71) [ZF-K]	Norfolk & Suffolk Avn Museum, Flixton
P8196		Curtiss P-40M Kittyhawk (F-AZPJ/ G-KITT) [34]	*Repainted in US markings, 1998*
P8448		VS329 Spitfire II <R> (BAPC 225) [UM-D]	RAF Cranwell, on display
	P9444	VS300 Spitfire IA [RN-D]	Science Museum, South Kensington
	R1914	Miles M14A Magister (G-AHUJ)	Privately owned, Strathallan
	R4907	DH82A Tiger Moth II (G-ANCS)	Privately owned, Cambridge
R5136		DH82A Tiger Moth II (G-APAP)	The Aircraft Restoration Co, Duxford
	R5250	DH82A Tiger Moth II (G-AODT)	Privately owned, Tibenham
	R5868	Avro 683 Lancaster I (7325M) [PO-S]	RAF Museum, Hendon
R6690		VS300 Spitfire I <R> (BAPC 254)	Yorkshire Air Museum, Elvington
	R6915	VS300 Spitfire I	Imperial War Museum, Lambeth
	R9125	Westland Lysander III (8377M) [LX-L]	RAF Museum, Hendon
	R9371	HP59 Halifax II <ff>	Cotswold Aircraft Rest'n Grp, Innsworth
S1287		Fairey Flycatcher <R> (G-BEYB) [5]	FAA Museum, RNAS Yeovilton
S1579		Hawker Nimrod I <R> (G-BBVO) [571]	Privately owned, Basingstoke
	S1581	Hawker Nimrod I (G-BWWK) (fuselage)	Aero Vintage, St Leonards-on-Sea
	S1595	Supermarine S6B	Science Museum, South Kensington
	T5298	Bristol 156 Beaufighter I (4552M) <ff>	Midland Air Museum, Coventry
	T5424	DH82A Tiger Moth II (G-AJOA)	Privately owned, Chiseldon
	T5672	DH82A Tiger Moth II (G-ALRI)	Privately owned, Chalmington
	T5854	DH82A Tiger Moth II (G-ANKK)	Privately owned, Welshpool
	T5879	DH82A Tiger Moth II (G-AXBW)	Privately owned, Frensham
	T5968	DH82A Tiger Moth II (G-ANNN)	Privately owned, Hollybush
	T6296	DH82A Tiger Moth II (8387M)	RAF Museum, Hendon
	T6313	DH82A Tiger Moth II (G-AHVU)	Privately owned, Liphook
T6390		DH82A Tiger Moth II (G-ANIX)	*Returned to Germany, 1998*
	T6818	DH82A Tiger Moth II (G-ANKT) [91]	The Shuttleworth Collection, Old Warden
T6991		DH82A Tiger Moth II (G-ANOR/ DE694)	Privately owned, Paddock Wood
	T7109	DH82A Tiger Moth II (G-AOIM)	*Repainted as G-AOIM*
	T7230	DH82A Tiger Moth II (G-AFVE)	Privately owned, Boscombe Down
	T7281	DH82A Tiger Moth II (G-ARTL)	Privately owned, Egton, nr Whitby
	T7404	DH82A Tiger Moth II (G-ANMV) [04]	Privately owned, Booker
	T7793	DH82A Tiger Moth II (G-ANKV)	Privately owned, Croydon, on display
	T7842	DH82A Tiger Moth II (G-AMTF)	Privately owned, Boughton, Suffolk
	T7909	DH82A Tiger Moth II (G-ANON)	Privately owned, Sherburn-in-Elmet
T7997		DH82A Tiger Moth II (NL750/ G-AHUF)	Privately owned, Edburton

Serial	Type (other identity) [code]	Owner/operator, location or fate	Notes
T8191	DH82A Tiger Moth II (G-BWMK)	Privately owned, Welshpool	
T9707	Miles M14A Magister I (G-AKKR/ 8378M/T9708)	RAF Museum, Hendon	
T9738	Miles M14A Magister I (G-AKAT)	Privately owned, Breighton	
V1075	Miles M14A Magister I (G-AKPF)	Front Line Aviation Museum, Sandown	
V3388	Airspeed AS10 Oxford I (G-AHTW)	Imperial War Museum, Duxford	
V6028	Bristol 149 Bolingbroke IVT (G-MKIV) [GB-D] <rf>	The Aircraft Restoration Co, stored Duxford	
V7350	Hawker Hurricane I (fuselage)	Brenzett Aeronautical Museum	
V7467	Hawker Hurricane I <R> (BAPC 223) [LE-D]	RAF Coltishall, on display	
V7767	Hawker Hurricane I <R> (BAPC 72)	Jet Age Museum, Staverton	
V9441	WS Lysander IIIA (G-AZWT) [AR-A]	The Shuttleworth Collection, Old Warden	
V9545	WS Lysander IIIA (G-BCWL/V9281) [BA-C]	Sold to the USA, October 1998	
V9673	WS Lysander IIIA (V9300/G-LIZY) [MA-J]	Imperial War Museum, Duxford	
W1048	HP59 Halifax II (8465M) [TL-S]	RAF Museum, Hendon	
W2068	Avro 652A Anson I (VH-ASM) [68]	RAF Museum, Hendon	
W2718	VS Walrus I (G-RNLI)	Dick Melton Aviation, Great Yarmouth	
W4041	Gloster E28/39 [G]	Science Museum, South Kensington	
W4050	DH98 Mosquito	Mosquito Aircraft Museum, London Colney	
W5856	Fairey Swordfish II (G-BMGC) [A2A]	RN Historic Flight, Yeovilton	
W9385	DH87B Hornet Moth (G-ADND) [YG-L,3]	The Shuttleworth Collection, Old Warden	
X4590	VS300 Spitfire I (8384M) [PR-F]	RAF Museum, Hendon	
X7688	Bristol 156 Beaufighter I (3858M/ G-DINT)	Privately owned, Hatch	
Z2033	Fairey Firefly I (G-ASTL) [275]	Imperial War Museum, Duxford	
Z2389	Hawker Hurricane IIA	Brooklands Museum, Weybridge	
Z5053	Hawker Hurricane IIB (G-BWHA)	Repainted as Z5252	
Z5207	Hawker Hurricane IIB (G-BYDL)	Privately owned, Billingshurst	
Z5252	Hawker Hurricane IIB (G-BWHA/ Z5053) [GO-B]	Privately owned, Dursley, Glos	
Z7015	Hawker Sea Hurricane IB (G-BKTH) [7-L]	The Shuttleworth Collection, Old Warden	
Z7197	Percival P30 Proctor III (G-AKZN/ 8380M)	RAF Museum, Hendon	
Z7258	DH89A Dragon Rapide (NR786/ G-AHGD)	Privately owned, Membury (wreck)	
Z7381	Hawker Hurricane XIIA (G-HURI) [XR-T]	The Fighter Collection, Duxford	
AA550	VS349 Spitfire VB <R> (BAPC 230/ AA908) [GE-P]	Eden Camp Theme Park, Malton, North Yorkshire	
AB130	VS349 Spitfire VA (parts)	Privately owned,	
AB910	VS349 Spitfire VB (G-AISU) [ZD-C]	RAF BBMF, Coningsby	
AD540	VS349 Spitfire VB (wreck)	Dumfries & Galloway Avn Mus, Dumfries	
AE436	HP52 Hampden I (parts)	Lincolnshire Avn Heritage Centre, E Kirkby	
AE977	Hawker Sea Hurricane X (G-TWTD)	Hawker Restorations Ltd, Milden	
AL246	Grumman Martlet I	FAA Museum, RNAS Yeovilton	
AM561	Lockheed Hudson V (parts)	Cornwall Aero Park, Helston	
AP506	Cierva C30A (G-ACWM)	The Helicopter Museum, Weston-super-Mare	
AP507	Cierva C30A (G-ACWP) [KX-P]	Science Museum, South Kensington	
AR501	VS349 Spitfire LF VC (G-AWII) [NN-A]	The Shuttleworth Collection, Old Warden	
AR614	VS349 Spitfire VC (5378M/ 7555M/G-BUWA) [DU-Z]	Privately owned, Earls Colne	
BB807	DH82A Tiger Moth (G-ADWO)	Southampton Hall of Aviation	
BE417	Hawker Hurricane XIIB (G-HURR) [LK-A]	The Real Aeroplane Company, Breighton	
BE421	Hawker Hurricane IIC <R> (BAPC 205) [XP-G]	RAF Museum, Hendon	
BL614	VS349 Spitfire VB (4354M) [ZD-F]	RAF Museum, Hendon	

Notes	Serial	Type (other identity) [code]	Owner/operator, location or fate
	BL655	VS349 Spitfire VB (wreck)	Lincolnshire Avn Heritage Centre, East Kirkby
	BL924	VS349 Spitfire VB <R> (BAPC 242) [AZ-G]	Tangmere Military Aviation Museum
	BM597	VS349 Spitfire LF VB (5718M/ G-MKVB) [JH-C]	Historic Aircraft Collection, Audley End
	BN230	Hawker Hurricane IIC (LF751/ 5466M) [FT-A]	RAF Manston, Memorial Pavilion
	BR600	VS361 Spitfire IX <R> (BAPC 222) [SH-V]	RAF Uxbridge, on display
	BR600	VS361 Spitfire IX <R> (BAPC 224) [JP-A]	
	BR600	VS361 Spitfire IX <R> (fuselage)	Privately owned, Dunkeswell, derelict
	BW881	Hawker Hurricane XIIA (G-KAMM)	Privately owned, Eye, Suffolk
	CB733	SA122 Bulldog (G-BCUV/G-112)	Privately owned, Hurstbourne Tarrant, Hants
	DD931	Bristol 152 Beaufort VIII (9131M) [L]	RAF Museum, Hendon
	DE208	DH82A Tiger Moth II (G-AGYU)	Privately owned, Ronaldsway
	DE363	DH82A Tiger Moth II (G-ANFC)	*Repainted as G-ANFC*
	DE470	DH82A Tiger Moth II (G-ANMY)	Privately owned, Oaksey Park, Wilts
	DE623	DH82A Tiger Moth II (G-ANFI)	Privately owned, Cardiff
	DE673	DH82A Tiger Moth II (6948M/ G-ADNZ)	Privately owned, Swanton Morley
	DE992	DH82A Tiger Moth II (G-AXXV)	Privately owned, Upavon
	DF112	DH82A Tiger Moth II (G-ANRM)	Privately owned, Clacton
	DF128	DH82A Tiger Moth II (G-AOJJ) [RCO-U]	Privately owned, White Waltham
	DF155	DH82A Tiger Moth II (G-ANFV)	Privately owned, Shempston Fm, Lossiemouth
	DF198	DH82A Tiger Moth II (G-BBRB)	Privately owned, Biggin Hill
	DG202	Gloster F9/40 (5758M) [G]	RAF Cosford Aerospace Museum
	DG590	Miles M2H Hawk Major (8379M/ G-ADMW)	RAF Museum Restoration Centre, Cardington
	DP872	Fairey Barracuda II (fuselage)	FAA Museum, stored Yeovilton
	DR613	Foster-Wikner GM1 Wicko (G-AFJB)	Privately owned, stored Berkswell, W Midlands
	DV372	Avro 683 Lancaster I <ff>	Imperial War Museum, Lambeth
	EE416	Gloster Meteor F3 <ff>	Martin Baker Aircraft, Chalgrove
	EE425	Gloster Meteor F3 <ff>	Meteor Flight, Yatesbury
	EE531	Gloster Meteor F4 (7090M)	Midland Air Museum, Coventry
	EE549	Gloster Meteor F4 (7008M) [A]	Tangmere Military Aviation Museum
	EF545	VS349 Spitfire VC <ff>	Privately owned, High Wycombe
	EJ693	Hawker Tempest V (N7027E) [SA-J]	Privately owned, Booker
	EJ922	Hawker Typhoon IB <ff>	RAF Manston History Museum
	EM720	DH82A Tiger Moth II (G-AXAN)	Privately owned, Little Gransden
	EM727	DH82A Tiger Moth II (G-AOXN)	Privately owned, Yeovil
	EM903	DH82A Tiger Moth II (G-APBI)	*Repainted as G-APBI*
	EN224	VS366 Spitfire F XII (G-FXII)	Privately owned, Newport Pagnell
	EN343	VS365 Spitfire PR XI <R> (BAPC 226)	RAF Benson, on display
	EN398	VS361 Spitfire F IX <R> (BAPC 184) [WO-A]	Privately owned, North Weald
	EP120	VS349 Spitfire LF VB (5377M/ 8070M/G-LFVB) [AE-A]	The Fighter Collection, Duxford
	EX976	NA AT-6D Harvard III (FAP.1657)	FAA Museum, RNAS Yeovilton
	EZ259	NA AT-6D Harvard III (G-BMJW)	Privately owned, Wakefield, West Yorkshire
	FB226	Bonsall Mustang <R> (G-BDWM) [MT-A]	Privately owned, Swansea
	FE695	Noorduyn AT-16 Harvard IIB (G-BTXI) [94]	The Fighter Collection, Duxford
	FE905	Noorduyn AT-16 Harvard IIB (LN-BNM)	RAF Museum, Hendon
	FE992	Noorduyn AT-16 Harvard IIB (G-BDAM) [K-T]	Privately owned, Duxford
	FH153	Noorduyn AT-16 Harvard IIB (G-BBHK) [GW-A]	Privately owned, stored Cardiff
	FJ992	Boeing-Stearman PT-17 Kaydet (442/G-BPTB)	Privately owned, Audley End

Serial	Type (other identity) [code]	Owner/operator, location or fate	Notes
FM118	Avro 683 Lancaster B X <ff>	Privately owned, Gosport, Hants	
FR886	Piper L-4J Cub (G-BDMS)	Privately owned, Old Sarum	
FS668	Noorduyn AT-16 Harvard IIB (PH-TBR)	Privately owned, The Netherlands	
FS890	Noorduyn AT-16 Harvard IIB (7554M)	MoD(PE), stored DERA Boscombe Down	
FT239	CCF T-6J Texan (G-BIWX)	Repainted as KF584, 1998	
FT323	NA AT-6D Harvard III (FAP 1513)	Air Engineering Services, Swansea	
FT391	Noorduyn AT-16 Harvard IIB (G-AZBN)	Privately owned, Shoreham	
FX301	NA AT-6D Harvard III (EX915/ G-JUDI)	Privately owned, Bryngwyn Bach, Clwyd	
FX360	Noorduyn AT-16 Harvard IIB (KF435)	Booker Aircraft Museum	
FX442	Noorduyn AT-16 Harvard IIB [TO-M]	Privately owned, South Gorley, Hants	
FX760	Curtiss P-40N Kittyhawk IV (9150M) [GA-?]	RAF Museum Restoration Centre, Cardington	
HB275	Beech C-45 Expeditor II (G-BKGM)	Privately owned, North Weald	
HB751	Fairchild Argus III (G-BCBL)	Privately owned, Little Gransden	
HD346	NA B-25J Mitchell (44-29507/ N320SQ) [NO-V]	Dukes of Brabant AF, Eindhoven, The Netherlands	
HH379	GAL48 Hotspur II <rf>	Museum of Army Flying, Middle Wallop	
HH982	Taylorcraft Plus D (LB312/G-AHXE)	Repainted as LB312	
HJ711	DH98 Mosquito NF II [VI-C]	Night-Fighter Preservation Tm, Elvington	
HM354	Percival P34 Proctor III (G-ANPP)	Privately owned, Stansted	
HM580	Cierva C-30A (G-ACUU)	Imperial War Museum, Duxford	
HS503	Fairey Swordfish IV (BAPC 108)	RAFM Restoration Centre, Cardington	
JR505	Hawker Typhoon IB <rf>	Midland Air Museum, Coventry	
JV482	Grumman Wildcat V	Ulster Aviation Society, Langford Lodge	
JV579	Grumman FM-2 Wildcat (N4845V/ G-RUMW) [F]	The Fighter Collection, Duxford	
KB889	Avro 683 Lancaster B X (G-LANC) [NA-I]	Imperial War Museum, Duxford	
KB976	Avro 683 Lancaster B X (G-BCOH)	Sold to the USA, February 1993	
KB994	Avro 683 Lancaster B X (G-BVBP)	Privately owned, North Weald	
KD345	Goodyear FG-1D Corsair (88297/ G-FGID) [130-A]	The Fighter Collection, Duxford	
KD431	CV Corsair IV [E2-M]	FAA Museum, RNAS Yeovilton	
KE209	Grumman Hellcat II	FAA Museum, RNAS Yeovilton	
KE418	Hawker Tempest <rf>	RAF Museum Store, Cardington	
KF183	Noorduyn AT-16 Harvard IIB [3]	MoD(PE)/AFD, DERA Boscombe Down	
KF435	Noorduyn AT-16 Harvard IIB <ff>	Privately owned, Swindon	
KF487	Noorduyn AT-16 Harvard IIB	The Aircraft Restoration Co, Duxford, spares use	
KF488	Noorduyn AT-16 Harvard IIB <ff>	Privately owned, Bournemouth	
KF532	Noorduyn AT-16 Harvard IIB <ff>	Newark Air Museum, Winthorpe	
KF584	CCF T-6J Texan (FT239/G-BIWX/ G-RAIX) [RAI-X]	Privately owned, North Weald	
KG374	Douglas Dakota IV (KN645/ 8355M) [YS]	RAF Cosford Aerospace Museum	
KJ351	Airspeed AS58 Horsa II (TL659/ BAPC 80) [23]	Museum of Army Flying, Middle Wallop	
KK995	Sikorsky Hoverfly I [E]	RAF Museum, Hendon	
KL161	NA B-25D Mitchell II (N88972/ G-BXXV) [VO-B]	The Fighter Collection, Duxford	
KL216	Republic P-47D Thunderbolt (45-49295/9212M) [RS-L]	RAF Cosford Aerospace Museum	
KN442	Douglas Dakota C4 (G-AMPZ)	Atlantic Airlines, Coventry	
KN448	Douglas Dakota C4 <ff>	Science Museum, South Kensington	
KN751	Consolidated Liberator C VI (IAF HE807) [F]	RAF Cosford Aerospace Museum	
KP208	Douglas Dakota IV [YS]	Airborne Forces Museum, Aldershot	
KZ191	Hawker Hurricane IV (frame only)	Privately owned, North Weald	
KZ321	Hawker Hurricane IV (G-HURY) (frame only)	The Fighter Collection, stored Duxford	
LA198	VS356 Spitfire F21 (7118M) [RAI-G]	Royal Scottish Mus'm of Flight, E Fortune	

Notes	Serial	Type (other identity) [code]	Owner/operator, location or fate
	LA226	VS356 Spitfire F21 (7119M)	RAF Museum Restoration Centre, Cardington
	LA255	VS356 Spitfire F21 (6490M) [JX-U]	RAF No 1 Sqn, Wittering (preserved)
	LA546	VS Seafire F46	Charleston Aviation Services, Colchester
	LA564	VS Seafire F46	Privately owned, Newport Pagnell
	LB294	Taylorcraft Plus D (G-AHWJ)	Museum of Army Flying, Whitchurch, Hants
	LB312	Taylorcraft Plus D (*HH982*/G-AHXE)	Privately owned, Old Sarum
	LB367	Taylorcraft Plus D (G-AHGZ)	Privately owned, Old Sarum
	LB375	Taylorcraft Plus D (G-AHGW)	Privately owned, Edge Hill
	LF363	Hawker Hurricane IIC [US-C]	RAF BBMF, Coningsby
	LF738	Hawker Hurricane IIC (5405M) [UH-A]	RAF Cosford Aerospace Museum
	LF789	DH82 Queen Bee (BAPC 186) [R2-K]	Mosquito Aircraft Museum, London Colney
	LF858	DH82 Queen Bee (G-BLUZ)	Privately owned, Rush Green
	LS326	Fairey Swordfish II (G-AJVH) [L2]	RN Historic Flight, Yeovilton
	LV907	HP59 Halifax III (HR792) [NP-F]	Yorkshire Air Museum, Elvington
	LZ551	DH100 Vampire [P]	FAA Museum, RNAS Yeovilton
	LZ551	DH100 Vampire FB6 (J-1173/G-DHXX) [P]	*Repainted as VT871 by June 1998*
	LZ766	Percival P34 Proctor III (G-ALCK)	Imperial War Museum, Duxford
	MA863	VS349 Spitfire VC	Aero Vintage, St Leonards-on-Sea
	MF628	Vickers Wellington T10 (9210M)	RAF Museum, Hendon
	MH434	VS361 Spitfire LF IXB (G-ASJV) [PK-K]	The Old Flying Machine Company, Duxford
	MH486	VS361 Spitfire LF IX <R> (BAPC 206) [FF-A]	RAF Museum, Hendon
	MH777	VS361 Spitfire IX <R> (BAPC 221) [RF-N]	RAF Northolt, on display
	MJ147	VS361 Spitfire LF IX	Privately owned, Kent
	MJ627	VS509 Spitfire T9 (G-BMSB) [9G-P]	Privately owned, Coventry
	MJ730	VS361 Spitfire HF IXE (G-HFIX) [GZ-?]	Privately owned, Staverton
	MJ751	VS361 Spitfire IX <R> (BAPC 209) [DU-V]	D-Day Museum, Shoreham Airport
	MJ832	VS361 Spitfire IX <R> (BAPC 229) [DN-Y]	RAF Digby, on display
	MK178	VS361 Spitfire LF XVIE (TE311/*X4474*/7241M) [LZ-V]	RAF EPTT, St Athan
	MK356	VS361 Spitfire LF IXC (5690M) [2I-V]	RAF BBMF, Coningsby
	MK356	VS361 Spitfire LF IXC <R> [21-V]	Kent Battle of Britain Museum, Hawkinge
	MK673	VS361 Spitfire LF XVIE (TB382/*X4277*/7244M) [SK-E]	RAF EPTT, St Athan
	MK732	VS361 Spitfire LF IXC (8633M/G-HVDM) [OU-U]	Dutch Spitfire Flight, Lelystad, The Netherlands
	MK805	VS361 Spitfire LF IX <R> [SH-B]	Privately owned, Chiseldon
	MK912	VS361 Spitfire LF IXE (G-BRRA) [MN-P]	Historic Flying Ltd, stored Audley End
	ML407	VS509 Spitfire T9 (G-LFIX) [OU-V]	Privately owned, Duxford
	ML411	VS361 Spitfire LF IXE	Privately owned, Kent
	ML417	VS361 Spitfire LF IXE (G-BJSG) [2I-T]	The Fighter Collection, Duxford
	ML427	VS361 Spitfire IX (6457M) [ST-I]	Birmingham Mus of Science & Industry
	ML796	Short S25 Sunderland V	Imperial War Museum, Duxford
	ML824	Short S25 Sunderland V [NS-Z]	RAF Museum, Hendon
	MN235	Hawker Typhoon IB	RAF Museum, Hendon
	MP425	Airspeed AS10 Oxford I (G-AITB) [G]	RAF Museum, Hendon
	MS902	Miles M25 Martinet TT1 (TF-SHC)	Museum of Berkshire Aviation, Woodley
	MT197	Auster IV (G-ANHS)	Privately owned, Spanhoe Lodge
	MT438	Auster III (G-AREI)	Privately owned, Petersfield
	MT847	VS379 Spitfire FR XIVE (6960M) [AX-H]	Gr Manchester Mus of Science & Industry
	MT928	VS359 Spitfire HF VIIIC (G-BKMI/*MV154*)[ZX-M]	Privately owned, Filton
	MV262	VS379 Spitfire FR XIV (G-CCVV)	Privately owned, Booker
	MV293	VS379 Spitfire FR XIV (G-SPIT) [0I-C]	The Fighter Collection, Duxford

Serial	Type (other identity) [code]	Owner/operator, location or fate	Notes
MW401	Hawker Tempest II (IAF HA604/ G-PEST)	Tempest Two Ltd, Sandtoft, S Yorks	
MW404	Hawker Tempest II (IAF HA557)	Privately owned	
MW758	Hawker Tempest II (IAF HA580)	Privately owned	
MW763	Hawker Tempest II (IAF HA586/ G-TEMT) [HF-A]	Tempest Two Ltd, Sandtoft, S Yorks	
NF370	Fairey Swordfish III	Imperial War Museum, Duxford	
NF389	Fairey Swordfish III [D]	RN Historic Flight, BAe Brough (rebuild)	
NJ673	Auster 5D (G-AOCR)	Privately owned, Canterbury	
NJ695	Auster 4 (G-AJXV)	Privately owned, Newark	
NJ703	Auster 5 (G-AKPI)	Privately owned, Croft, Lincs	
NJ719	Auster 5 (TW385/G-ANFU)	Privately owned, Newcastle	
NL750	DH82A Tiger Moth II (T7997/ G-AOBH)	Privately owned, Thruxton	
NL772	DH82A Tiger Moth II (G-BXMN)	Privately owned, Blackpool	
NL846	DH82A Tiger Moth II (F-BGEQ)	Brooklands Museum, Weybridge	
NL985	DH82A Tiger Moth I (7015M/ G-BWIK)	Privately owned, Sywell	
NM181	DH82A Tiger Moth II (G-AZGZ)	Privately owned, Dunkeswell	
NP294	Percival P31 Proctor IV [TB-M]	Lincolnshire Avn Heritage Centre, E Kirkby	
NP303	Percival P31 Proctor IV (G-ANZJ)	Privately owned, Byfleet, Surrey	
NV778	Hawker Tempest TT5 (8386M)	RAF Museum Restoration Centre, Cardington	
NX534	Auster III (G-BUDL)	Privately owned, Middle Wallop	
NX611	Avro 683 Lancaster B VII (8375M/ G-ASXX) [LE-C/DX-C]	Lincolnshire Avn Heritage Centre, E Kirkby	
PA474	Avro 683 Lancaster B I [WS-J]	RAF BBMF, Coningsby	
PF179	HS Gnat T1 (XR541/8602M)	Privately owned, Binbrook	
PK624	VS356 Spitfire F22 (8072M) [RAU-T]	The Fighter Collection, Duxford	
PK664	VS356 Spitfire F22 (7759M) [V6-B]	RAF Museum Restoration Centre, Cardington	
PK683	VS356 Spitfire F24 (7150M)	Southampton Hall of Aviation	
PK724	VS356 Spitfire F24 (7288M)	RAF Museum, Hendon	
PL344	VS361 Spitfire LF IXE (G-IXCC) [Y2-B]	Privately owned, Booker	
PL965	VS365 Spitfire PR XI (G-MKXI) [R]	The Real Aeroplane Company, Breighton	
PM631	VS390 Spitfire PR XIX [S]	RAF BBMF, Coningsby	
PM651	VS390 Spitfire PR XIX (7758M) [X]	RAF Museum Restoration Centre, Cardington	
PN323	HP Halifax VII <ff>	Imperial War Museum, Lambeth	
PP566	Fairey Firefly I (fuselage)	South Yorkshire Avn Museum, Firbeck	
PP972	VS358 Seafire LF IIIC (G-BUAR)	Flying A Services, Earls Colne	
PR536	Hawker Tempest II (IAF HA457) [OQ-H]	RAF Museum, Hendon	
PS853	VS390 Spitfire PR XIX (G-MXIX/ G-RRGN) [C]	Rolls-Royce, Filton	
PS915	VS390 Spitfire PR XIX (7548M/ 7711M) [UM-G]	RAF BBMF, Coningsby	
PT462	VS509 Spitfire T9 (G-CTIX/ N462JC) [SW-A]	Privately owned, Caernarfon/Duxford	
PV202	VS509 Spitfire T9 (G-TRIX) [5R-Q]	Privately owned, Goodwood	
PZ865	Hawker Hurricane IIC (G-AMAU) [J]	RAF BBMF, Coningsby	
RA848	Slingsby Cadet TX1	The Aeroplane Collection, stored Wigan	
RA854	Slingsby Cadet TX1	Privately owned, Wigan	
RA897	Slingsby Cadet TX1	Newark Air Museum store, Hucknall	
RD253	Bristol 156 Beaufighter TF X (7931M)	RAF Museum, Hendon	
RF342	Avro 694 Lincoln B II (G-29-1/ G-APRJ)	Privately owned, North Weald	
RF398	Avro 694 Lincoln B II (8376M)	RAF Cosford Aerospace Museum	
RG333	Miles M38 Messenger IIA (G-AIEK)	Privately owned, Felton, Bristol	
RG333	Miles M38 Messenger IIA (G-AKEZ)	Sold to New Zealand, 1997	
RH377	Miles M38 Messenger 4A (G-ALAH)	Privately owned, Stretton, Cheshire	
RH746	Bristol 164 Brigand TF1 (fuselage)	North-East Aircraft Museum, stored Usworth	
RL958	DH89A Dominie II (G-AKRP)	Restored as G-AKRP, 1998	
RL962	DH89A Dominie II (G-AHED)	RAF Museum Store, Cardington	

Notes	Serial	Type (other identity) [code]	Owner/operator, location or fate
	RM221	Percival P31 Proctor IV (G-ANXR)	Privately owned, Biggin Hill
	RM689	VS379 Spitfire F XIV (G-ALGT) (remains)	Rolls-Royce, Derby
	RM694	VS379 Spitfire F XIV (6640M)	Privately owned, High Wycombe
	RM927	VS379 Spitfire F XIV	Privately owned, High Wycombe
	RN218	Isaacs Spitfire <R> (G-BBJI) [N]	Privately owned, Langham
	RR232	VS361 Spitfire HF IXC (G-BRSF)	Sussex Spraying Services, Lancing, W Sussex
	RT486	Auster 5 (G-AJGJ) [PF-A]	Privately owned, Henstridge, Somerset
	RT610	Auster 5A-160 (G-AKWS)	Privately owned, Bournemouth
	RW388	VS361 Spitfire LF XVIE (6946M) [U4-U]	Stoke-on-Trent City Museum, Hanley
	RW393	VS361 Spitfire LF XVIE (7293M) [XT-A]	RAF Cosford Aerospace Museum
	RX168	VS358 Seafire L IIIC (IAC 157/ G-BWEM)	Privately owned, Norwich
	SL611	VS361 Spitfire LF XVIE	Supermarine Aero Engineering, Stoke-on-Trent
	SL674	VS361 Spitfire LF IX (8392M) [RAS-H]	RAF Museum Restoration Centre, Cardington
	SM520	VS361 Spitfire LF IX (G-BXHZ)	Privately owned, Oxford
	SM832	VS379 Spitfire F XIVE (G-WWII/ F-AZSJ) [YB-A]	Privately owned, Dijon, France
	SM845	VS394 Spitfire FR XVIII (G-BUOS)	Privately owned, Audley End
	SX137	VS384 Seafire F XVII	FAA Museum, RNAS Yeovilton
	SX300	VS384 Seafire F XVII	Privately owned, Twyford, Bucks
	SX336	VS384 Seafire F XVII (G-BRMG)	Privately owned, Twyford, Bucks
	TA122	DH98 Mosquito FB VI [UP-G]	Mosquito Aircraft Museum, London Colney
	TA634	DH98 Mosquito TT35 (G-AWJV) [8K-K]	Mosquito Aircraft Museum, London Colney
	TA639	DH98 Mosquito TT35 (7806M) [AZ-E]	RAF Cosford Aerospace Museum
	TA719	DH98 Mosquito TT35 (G-ASKC) [6T]	Imperial War Museum, Duxford
	TA805	VS361 Spitfire HF IX (G-PMNF)	Privately owned, Sandown
	TB252	VS361 Spitfire LF XVIE (G-XVIE) [GW-H]	Historic Flying Ltd, Audley End
	TB752	VS361 Spitfire LF XVIE (8086M) [KH-Z]	RAF Manston, Memorial Pavilion
	TB885	VS361 Spitfire LF XVIE<ff>(R1247)	Shoreham Aircraft Preservation Society
	TD248	VS361 Spitfire LF XVIE (7246M/ G-OXVI) [D]	Privately owned, Antwerp, Belgium
	TD314	VS361 Spitfire LF IX (*N601DA*)	Privately owned, Norwich
	TE184	VS361 Spitfire LF XVIE (6850M/ G-MXVI)	De Cadanet Motor Racing, North Weald
	TE462	VS361 Spitfire LF XVIE (7243M)	Royal Scottish Mus'm of Flight, E Fortune
	TE517	VS361 Spitfire LF XVIE (G-CCIX)	Privately owned, stored Booker
	TE566	VS361 Spitfire LF IXE (G-BLCK) [DU-A]	*Sold as ZU-SPT, August 1998*
	TG263	Saro SR A1 (G-12-1) [P]	Southampton Hall of Aviation
	TG511	HP67 Hastings C1 (8554M)	RAF Cosford Aerospace Museum
	TG517	HP67 Hastings T5	Newark Air Museum, Winthorpe
	TG528	HP67 Hastings C1A	Imperial War Museum, Duxford
	TJ118	DH98 Mosquito TT35 <ff>	Mosquito Aircraft Museum, stored London Colney
	TJ138	DH98 Mosquito B35 (7607M) [VO-L]	RAF Museum, Hendon
	TJ324	Auster 5 (G-APAH)	Privately owned, Cumbernauld
	TJ343	Auster 5 (G-AJXC)	Privately owned, stored Hook
	TJ398	Auster AOP6 (BAPC 70)	Aircraft Pres'n Soc of Scotland, E Fortune
	TJ569	Auster 5 (G-AKOW)	Museum of Army Flying, Middle Wallop
	TJ672	Auster 5D (G-ANIJ)	Privately owned, Whitchurch, Hants
	TJ704	Beagle A61 Terrier 2 (VW993/ G-ASCD) [JA]	Yorkshire Air Museum, Elvington
	TJ707	Auster 5 (frame)	South Yorkshire Avn Museum, Firbeck
	TK718	GAL59 Hamilcar I	National Tank Museum, Bovington
	TK777	GAL59 Hamilcar I (fuselage)	Museum of Army Flying, Middle Wallop
	TL615	Airspeed AS58 Horsa II	Robertsbridge Aviation Society, Mayfield
	TS291	Slingsby Cadet TX1 (BGA852)	Royal Scottish Mus'm of Flight, E Fortune

Serial	Type (other identity) [code]	Owner/operator, location or fate	Notes
TS423	Douglas C-47A Dakota C3 (G-DAKS/N147DC) [A]	Privately owned, North Weald	
TS798	Avro 685 York C1 (G-AGNV)	RAF Cosford Aerospace Museum	
TV959	DH98 Mosquito T III [AF-V]	The Fighter Collection, stored Duxford	
TV959	DH98 Mosquito T III <R>	Privately owned, Heald Green, Cheshire	
TW384	Auster 5 (G-ANHZ)	Sold to Switzerland, 1995	
TW439	Auster 5 (G-ANRP)	The Real Aeroplane Company, Breighton	
TW448	Auster 5 (G-ANLU)	Privately owned, Hedge End	
TW462	Beagle A61 Terrier 1 (G-ARLO)	Privately owned, Chandlers Ford, Hants	
TW467	Auster 5 (G-ANIE) [ROD-F]	Privately owned, Bassingbourn	
TW511	Auster 5 (G-APAF)	Privately owned, North Coates	
TW533	Beagle A61 Terrier 2 (G-ASAX)	Privately owned, Netherley, Grampian	
TW536	Auster AOP6 (7704M/G-BNGE) [TS-V]	Privately owned, Netheravon	
TW591	Auster 6A (G-ARIH) [N]	Privately owned, Abbots Bromley	
TW641	Beagle A61 Terrier 2 (G-ATDN)	Privately owned, Biggin Hill	
TX183	Avro 652A Anson C19 (G-BSMF)	Privately owned, Arbroath	
TX213	Avro 652A Anson C19 (G-AWRS)	North-East Aircraft Museum, Usworth	
TX214	Avro 652A Anson C19 (7817M)	RAF Cosford Aerospace Museum	
TX226	Avro 652A Anson C19 (7865M)	Air Atlantique Historic Flight, Coventry	
TX235	Avro 652A Anson C19	Caernarfon Air World	
VD165	Slingsby T7 Kite (BGA 400) [F]	Privately owned, Dunstable	
VF301	DH100 Vampire F1 (7060M) [RAL-G]	Midland Air Museum, Coventry	
VF512	Auster 6A (G-ARRX) [PF-M]	Privately owned, White Waltham	
VF516	Beagle A61 Terrier 2 (G-ASMZ) [T]	Privately owned, Bagby	
VF526	Auster 6A (G-ARXU) [T]	Privately owned, Middle Wallop	
VF548	Beagle A61 Terrier 1 (G-ASEG)	Privately owned, Dunkeswell	
VF611	Beagle A61 Terrier 2 (G-ATBU)	Privately owned, Hucknall	
VH127	Fairey Firefly TT4 [200/R]	FAA Museum, RNAS Yeovilton	
VL348	Avro 652A Anson C19 (G-AVVO)	Newark Air Museum, Winthorpe	
VL349	Avro 652A Anson C19 (G-AWSA)	Norfolk & Suffolk Avn Mus'm, Flixton	
VM325	Avro 652A Anson C19	Privately owned, Staverton	
VM360	Avro 652A Anson C19 (G-APHV)	Royal Scottish Mus'm of Flight, E Fortune	
VM791	Slingsby Cadet TX3 (XA312/8876M)	No 450 Sqn ATC, RAF Kenley	
VN148	Grunau Baby IIb (BAPC 33/BGA2400)	Privately owned, Dunstable	
VN485	VS356 Spitfire F24 (7326M)	Imperial War Museum, Duxford	
VP293	Avro 696 Shackleton T4 <ff>	Avro Aircraft Heritage Society, Woodford	
VP519	Avro 652A Anson C19 (G-AVVR) <ff>	Privately owned, Wolverhampton	
VP952	DH104 Devon C2 (8820M)	RAF Cosford Aerospace Museum	
VP955	DH104 Devon C2 (G-DVON)	Privately owned, Little Staughton	
VP957	DH104 Devon C2 (8822M) <ff>	No 1137 Sqn ATC, Belfast	
VP959	DH104 Devon C2 (G-BWFB) [L]	Sold as N959VP, 1998	
VP967	DH104 Devon C2 (G-KOOL)	East Surrey Technical College, Redhill	
VP971	DH104 Devon C2 (8824M)	Burnt at Manston, 1997	
VP975	DH104 Devon C2 [M]	Science Museum, Wroughton	
VP978	DH104 Devon C2 (8553M)	RAF Brize Norton, instructional use	
VP981	DH104 Devon C2 (G-DHDV)	Air Atlantique Historic Flight, Coventry	
VR137	Westland Wyvern TF1	FAA Museum, stored RNAS Yeovilton	
VR192	Percival P40 Prentice T1 (G-APIT)	SWWAPS, Lasham	
VR249	Percival P40 Prentice T1 (G-APIY) [FA-EL]	Newark Air Museum, Winthorpe	
VR259	Percival P40 Prentice T1 (G-APJB) [M]	Air Atlantique Historic Flight, Coventry	
VR930	Hawker Sea Fury FB11 (8382M) [110/O]	RN Historic Flight, Yeovilton	
VS356	Percival P40 Prentice T1 (G-AOLU)	Privately owned, Montrose	
VS562	Avro 652A Anson T21 (8012M)	Maes Artro Craft Village, Llanbedr	
VS610	Percival P40 Prentice T1 (G-AOKL) [K-L]	Privately owned, Sandy, Beds	
VS623	Percival P40 Prentice T1 (G-AOKZ) [KQ-F]	Midland Air Museum, Coventry	
VT409	Fairey Firefly AS5 <rf>	North-East Aircraft Museum, stored Usworth	
VT812	DH100 Vampire F3 (7200M) [N]	RAF Museum Restoration Centre, Cardington	
VT871	DH100 Vampire FB6 (J-1173/LZ551/G-DHXX)	Source Classic Jet Flight, Bournemouth	

Notes	Serial	Type (other identity) [code]	Owner/operator, location or fate
	VT935	Boulton Paul P111A (VT769)	Midland Air Museum, Coventry
	VT987	Auster AOP6 (G-BKXP)	Aerobuild Ltd, Little Gransden, Cambs
	VV106	Supermarine 510 (7175M)	FAA Museum, stored Wroughton
	VV217	DH100 Vampire FB5 (7323M)	North-East Aircraft Museum, stored Usworth
	VV901	Avro 652A Anson T21	Yorkshire Air Museum, Elvington
	VW453	Gloster Meteor T7 (8703M) [Z]	RAF Innsworth, on display
	VW985	Auster AOP6 (G-ASEF)	Privately owned, Upper Arncott, Oxon
	VX118	Auster AOP6 (G-ASNB)	Vliegend Museum Seppe, The Netherlands
	VX147	Alon A2 Aircoupe (G-AVIL)	Privately owned, Headcorn
	VX185	EE Canberra B(I)8 (7631M) <ff>	Royal Scottish Mus'm of Flight, E Fortune
	VX250	DH103 Sea Hornet 21 [48] <rf>	Mosquito Aircraft Museum, London Colney
	VX272	Hawker P.1052 (7174M)	FAA Museum, stored Wroughton
	VX275	Slingsby T21B Sedbergh TX1 (8884M/BGA 572)	RAF Museum Restoration Centre, Cardington
	VX461	DH100 Vampire FB5 (7646M)	RAF Museum Restoration Centre, Cardington
	VX573	Vickers Valetta C2 (8389M)	RAF Cosford Aerospace Museum, stored
	VX580	Vickers Valetta C2	Norfolk & Suffolk Avn Museum, Flixton
	VX595	WS51 Dragonfly HR1	FAA Museum, RNAS Yeovilton
	VX665	Hawker Sea Fury FB11 <rf>	RN Historic Flight, at BAe Brough
	VX926	Auster T7 (G-ASKJ)	Privately owned, Little Gransden
	VZ345	Hawker Sea Fury T20S	RN Historic Flight, Yeovilton (stored)
	VZ467	Gloster Meteor F8 (G-METE) [01]	Classic Jets Flying Museum, Kemble
	VZ477	Gloster Meteor F8 (7741M) <ff>	Midland Air Museum, Coventry
	VZ608	Gloster Meteor FR9	Newark Air Museum, Winthorpe
	VZ634	Gloster Meteor T7 (8657M)	Newark Air Museum, Winthorpe
	VZ638	Gloster Meteor T7 (G-JETM) [HF]	Vallance By-Ways, Charlwood, Surrey
	VZ728	RS4 Desford Trainer (G-AGOS)	Snibston Discovery Park, stored Coalville
	VZ962	WS51 Dragonfly HR1 [904]	The Helicopter Museum, Weston-super-Mare
	VZ965	WS51 Dragonfly HR5	To Cyprus
	WA473	VS Attacker F1 [102/J]	FAA Museum, RNAS Yeovilton
	WA576	Bristol 171 Sycamore 3 (7900M/ G-ALSS)	Dumfries & Galloway Avn Mus, Dumfries
	WA577	Bristol 171 Sycamore 3 (7718M/ G-ALST)	North-East Aircraft Museum, Usworth
	WA591	Gloster Meteor T7 (7917M/ G-BWMF) [W]	Meteor Flight, Yatesbury
	WA630	Gloster Meteor T7 (69) <ff>	Robertsbridge Aviation Society, Newhaven
	WA634	Gloster Meteor T7/8	RAF Cosford Aerospace Museum
	WA638	Gloster Meteor T7(mod)	Martin Baker Aircraft, Chalgrove, spares use
	WA662	Gloster Meteor T7	South Yorkshire Avn Museum, Firbeck
	WA984	Gloster Meteor F8 [A]	Tangmere Military Aviation Museum
	WB188	Hawker Hunter F3 (7154M)	Tangmere Military Aviation Museum
	WB271	Fairey Firefly AS5 [204/R]	RN Historic Flight, BAe Dunsfold
	WB440	Fairey Firefly AS6 <ff>	Privately owned, Newton-le-Willows
	WB491	Avro 706 Ashton 2 (TS897/ G-AJWJ) <ff>	Avro Aircraft Heritage Society, BAe Woodford
	WB556	DHC1 Chipmunk T10	RAFGSA, Bicester
	WB560	DHC1 Chipmunk T10	South Yorkshire Avn Museum, Firbeck
	WB565	DHC1 Chipmunk T10 (G-PVET) [X]	Privately owned, Kemble
	WB584	DHC1 Chipmunk T10 (7706M) <ff>	RAF Manston History Museum
	WB585	DHC1 Chipmunk T10 (G-AOSY) [RCU-X]	Privately owned, Blackbushe
	WB588	DHC1 Chipmunk T10 (G-AOTD) [D]	Privately owned, Biggin Hill
	WB615	DHC1 Chipmunk T10 (G-BXIA) [E]	Privately owned, Blackpool
	WB624	DHC1 Chipmunk T10 <ff>	Newark Air Museum, Winthorpe
	WB626	DHC1 Chipmunk T10 <ff>	Privately owned, South Molton, Devon
	WB627	DHC1 Chipmunk T10 (9248M) [N]	Dulwich College CCF
	WB645	DHC1 Chipmunk T10 (8218M)	RAFGSA, Bicester, spares use
	WB647	DHC1 Chipmunk T10 [R]	Sold as ZK-XUK, 1997
	WB652	DHC1 Chipmunk T10 (G-CHPY) [V]	Privately owned, Cardiff
	WB654	DHC1 Chipmunk T10 (G-BXGO) [U]	Privately owned, Booker
	WB657	DHC1 Chipmunk T10 [908]	RN Historic Flight, Yeovilton
	WB660	DHC1 Chipmunk T10 (G-ARMB)	Privately owned, Shipdham
	WB670	DHC1 Chipmunk T10 (8361M) <ff>	No 1312 Sqn ATC, Southend Airport
	WB685	DHC1 Chipmunk T10 (comp WP969/G-ATHC)	North-East Aircraft Museum, Usworth

Serial	Type (other identity) [code]	Owner/operator, location or fate	Notes
WB693	DHC1 Chipmunk T10 [S]	*Sold as ZK-RFS, 1997*	
WB697	DHC1 Chipmunk T10 (G-BXCT) [95]	Privately owned, Wickenby	
WB702	DHC1 Chipmunk T10 (G-AOFE)	Privately owned, Goodwood	
WB703	DHC1 Chipmunk T10 (G-ARMC)	Privately owned, White Waltham	
WB711	DHC1 Chipmunk T10 (G-APPM)	The Aircraft Restoration Co, Duxford	
WB726	DHC1 Chipmunk T10 (G-AOSK)	Privately owned, Essex	
WB733	DHC1 Chipmunk T10 (comp WG422)	South Yorkshire Avn Museum, Firbeck	
WB754	DHC1 Chipmunk T10 [H]	*Sold as ZU-BJZ, June 1997*	
WB758	DHC1 Chipmunk T10 (7729M) [P]	Privately owned, Torbay	
WB763	DHC1 Chipmunk T10 (G-BBMR) [14]	Privately owned, Camberley	
WB922	Slingsby T21B Sedbergh TX1 (BGA 4366)	Privately owned, Kingston Deverill	
WB938	Slingsby T21B Sedbergh TX1	Privately owned, Halton	
WB943	Slingsby T21B Sedbergh TX1 (BGA 2941)	Privately owned, Rufforth	
WB971	Slingsby T21B Sedbergh TX1 (BGA 3324)	Privately owned, Thame	
WB975	Slingsby T21B Sedbergh TX1 (BGA 3288)	Privately owned, Drumshade, Fife	
WB981	Slingsby T21B Sedbergh TX1 (BGA 3238)	Privately owned, Aston Down	
WD286	DHC1 Chipmunk T10 (G-BBND) [J]	Privately owned, Croydon, Cambs	
WD288	DHC1 Chipmunk T10 (G-AOSO) [38]	Privately owned, Charlton Park, Wilts	
WD292	DHC1 Chipmunk T10 (G-BCRX)	Privately owned, White Waltham	
WD293	DHC1 Chipmunk T10 (7645M) <ff>	No 1367 Sqn ATC, Caerleon, Gwent	
WD305	DHC1 Chipmunk T10 (G-ARGG)	Privately owned, Coventry	
WD310	DHC1 Chipmunk T10 (G-BWUN) [B]	Privately owned, Ringmer, E Sussex	
WD318	DHC1 Chipmunk T10 (8207M) <ff>	No 145 Sqn ATC, Timperley, Gr Manchester	
WD325	DHC1 Chipmunk T10 [N]	AAC Historic Aircraft Flight, Middle Wallop	
WD331	DHC1 Chipmunk T10 (G-BXDH) [J]	Privately owned, Kemble	
WD355	DHC1 Chipmunk T10 (WD335) <ff>	No 1955 Sqn ATC, Wells, Somerset	
WD356	DHC1 Chipmunk T10 (7625M)	Privately owned, St Ives, Cambridgeshire	
WD363	DHC1 Chipmunk T10 (G-BCIH) [5]	Privately owned, Andrewsfield	
WD370	DHC1 Chipmunk T10 <ff>	Privately owned, Brighton	
WD373	DHC1 Chipmunk T10 (G-BXDI) [12]	Privately owned, Perth	
WD377	DHC1 Chipmunk T10 <ff>	RAF Millom Museum, Haverigg	
WD379	DHC1 Chipmunk T10 (WB696/ G-APLO) [K]	Privately owned, Jersey	
WD386	DHC1 Chipmunk T10 (comp WD377)	Dumfries & Galloway Avn Mus, Dumfries	
WD390	DHC1 Chipmunk T10 (G-BWNK) [68]	Privately owned, Breighton	
WD413	Avro 652A Anson T21 (7881M/ G-BFIR/G-VROE)	Air Atlantique Historic Flight, Coventry	
WD646	Gloster Meteor TT20 (8189M) [R]	RAF Manston History Museum	
WD686	Gloster Meteor NF11	Muckleburgh Collection, Weybourne	
WD790	Gloster Meteor NF11 (8743M)<ff>	North-East Aircraft Museum, Usworth	
WD889	Fairey Firefly AS5 <ff>	North-East Aircraft Museum, Usworth	
WD931	EE Canberra B2 <ff>	RAF Cosford Aerospace Museum	
WD935	EE Canberra B2 (8440M) <ff>	Privately owned, Bridgnorth	
WD954	EE Canberra B2 <ff>	Privately owned, Romford, Essex	
WE113	EE Canberra T4 <ff>	Privately owned, Woodhurst, Cambridgeshire	
WE122	EE Canberra TT18 [845] <ff>	Blyth Valley Aviation Collection, Walpole, Suffolk	
WE139	EE Canberra PR3 (8369M)	RAF Museum, Hendon	
WE168	EE Canberra PR3 (8049M) <ff>	Privately owned, Colchester	
WE173	EE Canberra PR3 (8740M) <ff>	Robertsbridge Aviation Society, Mayfield	
WE188	EE Canberra T4	Solway Aviation Society, Carlisle	
WE192	EE Canberra T4 <ff>	Blyth Valley Aviation Collection, Walpole, Suffolk	
WE275	DH112 Venom FB50 (J-1601/ G-VIDI)	BAe Hawarden, Fire Section	
WE402	DH112 Venom FB50 (J-1523/ G-VENI)	Source Classic Jet Flight, Bournemouth	

Notes	Serial	Type (other identity) [code]	Owner/operator, location or fate
	WE569	Auster T7 (G-ASAJ)	Privately owned, Sandy, Beds
	WE600	Auster T7 Antarctic (7602M)	RAF Cosford Aerospace Museum
	WE724	Hawker Sea Fury FB11 (VX653/ G-BUCM) [062]	The Fighter Collection, Duxford
	WE925	Gloster Meteor F8	Classic Jet Aircraft Group, Loughborough
	WE982	Slingsby T30B Prefect TX1 (8781M)	RAF Cosford Aerospace Museum, stored
	WE990	Slingsby T30B Prefect TX1 (BGA 2583)	Privately owned, RAF Swanton Morley
	WF118	Percival P57 Sea Prince T1 (G-DACA)	Vallance By-Ways, Charlwood, Surrey
	WF122	Percival P57 Sea Prince T1 [575/CU]	Flambards Village Theme Park, Helston
	WF128	Percival P57 Sea Prince T1 (8611M)	Norfolk & Suffolk Avn Museum, Flixton
	WF137	Percival P57 Sea Prince C1	SWWAPS, Lasham
	WF145	Hawker Sea Hawk F1 <ff>	Privately owned, Welshpool
	WF225	Hawker Sea Hawk F1 [CU]	RNAS Culdrose, at main gate
	WF259	Hawker Sea Hawk F2 [171/A]	Royal Scottish Mus'm of Flight,E Fortune
	WF369	Vickers Varsity T1 [F]	Newark Air Museum, Winthorpe
	WF372	Vickers Varsity T1 [A]	Brooklands Museum, Weybridge
	WF376	Vickers Varsity T1	Bristol Airport Fire Section
	WF408	Vickers Varsity T1 (8395M)	Privately owned, East Grinstead
	WF410	Vickers Varsity T1 [F]	Brunel Technical College, Lulsgate
	WF643	Gloster Meteor F8 [X]	Norfolk & Suffolk Avn Museum, Flixton
	WF714	Gloster Meteor F8 (WK914)	Front Line Aviation Museum, Sandown
	WF784	Gloster Meteor T7 (7895M)	Jet Age Museum, Staverton
	WF825	Gloster Meteor T7 (8359M) [A]	Avon Air Museum, stored Malmesbury
	WF877	Gloster Meteor T7 (G-BPOA)	Privately owned, Kemble
	WF911	EE Canberra B2 <ff>	The Griffin Trust, Hooton Park, Cheshire
	WF922	EE Canberra PR3	Midland Air Museum, Coventry
	WG300	DHC1 Chipmunk T10 <ff>	RAFGSA, Bicester
	WG303	DHC1 Chipmunk T10 (8208M) <ff>	RAFGSA, Bicester
	WG307	DHC1 Chipmunk T10 (G-BCYJ)	Privately owned, Shempston Fm, Lossiemouth
	WG310	DHC1 Chipmunk T10 (G-BWUN)	Privately owned, Ringmer
	WG316	DHC1 Chipmunk T10 (G-BCAH)	Privately owned, Shoreham
	WG323	DHC1 Chipmunk T10 (G-BXHS) [F]	Sold as C-GBRW, 1997
	WG348	DHC1 Chipmunk T10 (G-BBMV)	Privately owned, Croydon, Cambs
	WG350	DHC1 Chipmunk T10 (G-BPAL)	Privately owned, Thruxton
	WG407	DHC1 Chipmunk T10 (G-BWMX)	Privately owned, Spanhoe Lodge
	WG418	DHC1 Chipmunk T10 (8209M/ G-ATDY) <ff>	No 1940 Sqn ATC, Levenshulme, Gr Manchester
	WG419	DHC1 Chipmunk T10 (8206M) <ff>	No 1053 Sqn ATC, Armthorpe
	WG422	DHC1 Chipmunk T10 (8394M/ G-BFAX) [116]	The Aircraft Restoration Co, Duxford
	WG430	DHC1 Chipmunk T10 [3]	Sold as C-GBNM, March 1998
	WG432	DHC1 Chipmunk T10 [L]	Museum of Army Flying, Middle Wallop
	WG465	DHC1 Chipmunk T10 (G-BCEY)	Privately owned, White Waltham
	WG469	DHC1 Chipmunk T10 (G-BWJY) [72]	Privately owned, Newtownards
	WG471	DHC1 Chipmunk T10 (8210M) <ff>	No 301 Sqn ATC, Bury St Edmunds
	WG472	DHC1 Chipmunk T10 (G-AOTY)	Privately owned, Netherthorpe
	WG477	DHC1 Chipmunk T10 (8362M/ G-ATDP) <ff>	No 281 Sqn ATC, Birkdale, Merseyside
	WG482	DHC1 Chipmunk T10 (VH-ZOT)[01]	Privately owned, Duxford
	WG483	DHC1 Chipmunk T10 (G-AOTY)	Privately owned, Netherthorpe
	WG486	DHC1 Chipmunk T10 (WG393/ VH-ZIT)	Privately owned, Duxford
	WG511	Avro 696 Shackleton T4 (fuselage)	Flambards Village Theme Park, Helston
	WG718	WS51 Dragonfly HR3 [934]	Privately owned, Elvington
	WG719	WS51 Dragonfly HR5 (G-BRMA) [902]	The Helicopter Museum, Weston-super-Mare
	WG724	WS51 Dragonfly HR5 [932]	North-East Aircraft Museum, Usworth
	WG751	WS51 Dragonfly HR5	Privately owned, Condover, Shropshire
	WG754	WS51 Dragonfly HR3 (WG725/ 7703M) [912/CU]	Flambards Village Theme Park, Helston
	WG760	EE P1A (7755M)	RAF Cosford Aerospace Museum
	WG763	EE P1A (7816M)	Gr Manchester Mus of Science & Industry
	WG768	Short SB5 (8005M)	RAF Cosford Aerospace Museum
	WG774	BAC 221	Science Museum, RNAS Yeovilton

Serial	Type (other identity) [code]	Owner/operator, location or fate	Notes
WG777	Fairey FD2 (7986M)	RAF Cosford Aerospace Museum	
WG789	EE Canberra B2/6 <ff>	Privately owned, Mendlesham, Suffolk	
WH132	Gloster Meteor T7 (7906M) [J]	No 276 Sqn ATC, Chelmsford	
WH166	Gloster Meteor T7 (8052M) [A]	Privately owned, Birlingham, Worcs	
WH291	Gloster Meteor F8	SWWAPS, Lasham	
WH301	Gloster Meteor F8 (7930M) [T]	RAF Museum, Hendon	
WH364	Gloster Meteor F8 (8169M)	Privately owned, Kemble	
WH453	Gloster Meteor D16 [L]	MoD(PE), stored DERA Llanbedr	
WH646	EE Canberra T17A <ff>	Midland Air Museum, Coventry	
WH657	EE Canberra B2	Brenzett Aeronautical Museum	
WH665	EE Canberra T17 (8763M) [J]	BAe Filton, Fire Section	
WH725	EE Canberra B2	Imperial War Museum, Duxford	
WH734	EE Canberra B2(mod)	MoD(PE), DERA Llanbedr	
WH739	EE Canberra B2 <ff>	No 2475 Sqn ATC, Ammanford, Dyfed	
WH740	EE Canberra T17 (8762M) [K]	Privately owned, East Midlands Airport	
WH773	EE Canberra PR7 (8696M)	Vallance By-Ways, Charlwood, Surrey	
WH775	EE Canberra PR7 (8128M/8868M) <ff>	Privately owned, Welshpool	
WH779	EE Canberra PR7 [BP]	RAF, stored Marham	
WH780	EE Canberra T22 <rf>	RAF St Athan, Fire Section	
WH791	EE Canberra PR7 (8165M/8176M/8187M)	Newark Air Museum, Winthorpe	
WH796	EE Canberra PR7 <ff>	Privately owned, Stock, Essex	
WH797	EE Canberra T22 <rf>	RAF St Athan, Fire Section	
WH803	EE Canberra T22 <ff>	Privately owned, Stock, Essex	
WH840	EE Canberra T4 (8350M) <ff>	Privately owned, Flixton	
WH846	EE Canberra T4	Yorkshire Air Museum, Elvington	
WH849	EE Canberra T4	RAF No 39(1 PRU) Sqn, Marham	
WH850	EE Canberra T4 <ff>	Barton Aviation Heritage Society, Barton	
WH854	EE Canberra T4 <ff>	Martin Baker Aircraft, Chalgrove	
WH863	EE Canberra T17 (8693M) [CP] <ff>	Newark Air Museum, Winthorpe	
WH876	EE Canberra B2(mod)	DERA Aberporth, instructional use	
WH887	EE Canberra TT18 [847]	MoD(PE), stored DERA Llanbedr	
WH903	EE Canberra B2 <ff>	Yorkshire Air Museum, Elvington	
WH903	EE Canberra B2 (8584M) <ff>	Vallance By-Ways, Charlwood, Surrey	
WH904	EE Canberra T19	Newark Air Museum, Winthorpe	
WH946	EE Canberra B6(mod) (8185M) <ff>	Privately owned, Tetney, Grimsby	
WH953	EE Canberra B6(mod) <ff>	Blyth Valley Aviation Collection, Walpole, Suffolk	
WH957	EE Canberra E15 (8869M) <ff>	Lincolnshire Avn Heritage Centre, East Kirkby	
WH960	EE Canberra B15 (8344M) <ff>	Privately owned, Hucknall	
WH964	EE Canberra E15 (8870M) <ff>	Privately owned, Hants	
WH984	EE Canberra B15 (8101M) <ff>	RAF Sealand	
WH991	WS51 Dragonfly HR3	Privately owned, Elvington	
WJ231	Hawker Sea Fury FB11 (WE726) [115/O]	FAA Museum, Yeovilton	
WJ358	Auster AOP6 (G-ARYD)	Museum of Army Flying, stored Middle Wallop	
WJ565	EE Canberra T17 (8871M) <ff>	Privately owned, Binbrook	
WJ567	EE Canberra B2 <ff>	Privately owned, Houghton, Cambs	
WJ576	EE Canberra T17 <ff>	Phoenix Aviation, Bruntingthorpe	
WJ581	EE Canberra PR7 <ff>	Privately owned, Canterbury	
WJ603	EE Canberra B2 (8664M) <ff>	Privately owned, Stock, Essex	
WJ630	EE Canberra T17 [ED]		
WJ633	EE Canberra T17 [EF] <ff>	RAF Wyton	
WJ639	EE Canberra TT18 [39]	North-East Aircraft Museum, Usworth	
WJ640	EE Canberra B2 (8722M) <ff>	Pinewood Studios, Bucks	
WJ676	EE Canberra B2 (7796M) <ff>	Privately owned, Heswall, Merseyside	
WJ677	EE Canberra B2 <ff>	Privately owned, Redruth	
WJ680	EE Canberra TT18 (G-BURM) [CT]	Canberra Flight, Kemble	
WJ717	EE Canberra TT18 (9052M) <ff>	RAF St Athan, Fire Section	
WJ721	EE Canberra TT18 [21] <ff>	Dundonald Aviation Centre, Strathclyde	
WJ731	EE Canberra B2T [BK] <ff>	Privately owned, Beds	
WJ775	EE Canberra B6 (8581M) [J] (fuselage)	Stanford Training Area, Bodney Camp, Norfolk	
WJ821	EE Canberra PR7 (8668M)	Army, Bassingbourn, on display	
WJ863	EE Canberra T4 <ff>	Cambridge Airport Fire Section	
WJ865	EE Canberra T4	Privately owned, Stamford, Lincs	
WJ866	EE Canberra T4 [AV]	RAF, stored Shawbury	
WJ872	EE Canberra T4 (8492M) <ff>	No 327 Sqn ATC, Kilmarnock	

Notes	Serial	Type (other identity) [code]	Owner/operator, location or fate
	WJ874	EE Canberra T4 [AS]	RAF No 39(1 PRU) Sqn, Marham
	WJ876	EE Canberra T4 <ff>	
	WJ880	EE Canberra T4 (8491M) <ff>	Dumfries & Galloway Avn Mus, Dumfries
	WJ893	Vickers Varsity T1	DERA Aberporth Fire Section
	WJ903	Vickers Varsity T1 [C] <ff>	South Yorkshire Avn Museum, Firbeck
	WJ945	Vickers Varsity T1 (G-BEDV) [21]	Imperial War Museum, Duxford
	WJ975	EE Canberra T19 [S]	Bomber County Aviation Museum, Hemswell
	WJ992	EE Canberra T4	Bournemouth Int'l Airport, Fire Section
	WK102	EE Canberra T17 (8780M) <ff>	Privately owned, Welshpool
	WK118	EE Canberra TT18 <ff>	Privately owned, Worcester
	WK122	EE Canberra TT18 [22]	Flambards Village Theme Park, Helston
	WK124	EE Canberra TT18 (9093M) [CR]	FSCTE, RAF Manston
	WK126	EE Canberra TT18 (N2138J) [843]	Jet Age Museum, Staverton
	WK127	EE Canberra TT18 (8985M) <ff>	No 2484 Sqn ATC, Bassingbourn
	WK128	EE Canberra B2	MoD(PE), DERA Llanbedr
	WK143	EE Canberra B2	Scrapped at Llanbedr, 1996
	WK163	EE Canberra B6(mod) (G-BVWC)	Classic Aviation Projects, Bruntingthorpe
	WK198	VS Swift F4 (7428M) (fuselage)	North-East Aircraft Museum, Usworth
	WK275	VS Swift F4	Privately owned, Upper Hill, nr Leominster
	WK277	VS Swift FR5 (7719M) [N]	Newark Air Museum, Winthorpe
	WK281	VS Swift FR5 (7712M) [S]	Tangmere Military Aviation Museum
	WK511	DHC1 Chipmunk T10 (G-BVBT) [905]	Kennet Aviation, Cranfield
	WK512	DHC1 Chipmunk T10 (G-BXIM) [A]	Privately owned, Brize Norton
	WK517	DHC1 Chipmunk T10 (G-ULAS) [84]	Privately owned, Booker
	WK518	DHC1 Chipmunk T10	RAF BBMF, Coningsby
	WK522	DHC1 Chipmunk T10 (G-BCOU)	Privately owned, High Easter
	WK549	DHC1 Chipmunk T10 (G-BTWF) [Y]	Privately owned, Rufforth
	WK550	DHC1 Chipmunk T10 [G]	Sold as VH-KMF, February 1997
	WK558	DHC1 Chipmunk T10 (G-ARMG)	Privately owned, Wellesbourne Mountford
	WK559	DHC1 Chipmunk T10 [M]	Sold as N559WK, 1997
	WK570	DHC1 Chipmunk T10 (8211M) <ff>	Southampton Hall of Aviation
	WK576	DHC1 Chipmunk T10 (8357M) <ff>	No 1206 Sqn ATC, Lichfield
	WK584	DHC1 Chipmunk T10 (7556M) <ff>	No 216 Sqn ATC, Bawtry
	WK585	DHC1 Chipmunk T10	RAF, stored Newton
	WK586	DHC1 Chipmunk T10 (G-BXGX) [V]	Privately owned, Shoreham
	WK608	DHC1 Chipmunk T10 [906]	RN Historic Flight, Yeovilton
	WK609	DHC1 Chipmunk T10 (G-BXDN) [93]	Privately owned, Halton
	WK611	DHC1 Chipmunk T10 (G-ARWB)	Privately owned, Thruxton
	WK613	DHC1 Chipmunk T10 [P]	
	WK620	DHC1 Chipmunk T10 [T] (fuselage)	Privately owned, Twyford, Bucks
	WK622	DHC1 Chipmunk T10 (G-BCZH)	Privately owned, Horsford
	WK624	DHC1 Chipmunk T10 (G-BWHI) [M]	The Aircraft Restoration Co, Duxford
	WK626	DHC1 Chipmunk T10 (8213M) <ff>	South Yorkshire Avn Museum, Firbeck
	WK628	DHC1 Chipmunk T10 (G-BBMW)	Privately owned, Shoreham
	WK630	DHC1 Chipmunk T10 (G-BXDG) [11]	Privately owned, Swanton Morley
	WK633	DHC1 Chipmunk T10 (G-BXEC) [B]	Privately owned, Spanhoe Lodge
	WK638	DHC1 Chipmunk T10 (G-BWJZ) [83]	Privately owned, Breighton
	WK640	DHC1 Chipmunk T10 (G-BWUV) [C]	Privately owned, Bagby
	WK642	DHC1 Chipmunk T10 (G-BXDP) [94]	Privately owned, Eire
	WK643	DHC1 Chipmunk T10 [G]	Sold as C-GBNJ, March 1998
	WK654	Gloster Meteor F8 (8092M) [X]	City of Norwich Aviation Museum
	WK800	Gloster Meteor D16 [Z]	MoD(PE), DERA Llanbedr
	WK864	Gloster Meteor F8 (WL168/7750M) [C]	Yorkshire Air Museum, Elvington
	WK935	Gloster Meteor Prone Pilot (7869M)	RAF Cosford Aerospace Museum
	WK991	Gloster Meteor F8 (7825M)	Imperial War Museum, Duxford
	WL131	Gloster Meteor F8 (7751M) <ff>	South Yorkshire Avn Museum, Firbeck
	WL181	Gloster Meteor F8 [X]	North-East Aircraft Museum, Usworth
	WL332	Gloster Meteor T7 [888]	Privately owned, Long Marston
	WL345	Gloster Meteor T7	St Leonard's Motors, Hollington, E Sussex
	WL349	Gloster Meteor T7 [Z]	On display, Gloucestershire Airport
	WL360	Gloster Meteor T7 (7920M) [G]	Meteor Flight, Yatesbury
	WL375	Gloster Meteor T7(mod)	Dumfries & Galloway Avn Mus, Dumfries

Serial	Type (other identity) [code]	Owner/operator, location or fate	Notes
WL405	Gloster Meteor T7	Martin Baker Aircraft, Chalgrove, spares use	
WL419	Gloster Meteor T7	Martin Baker Aircraft, Chalgrove	
WL505	DH100 Vampire FB9 (7705M/ G-FBIX)	De Havilland Aviation, Swansea	
WL505	DH100 Vampire FB6 (J-1167/VZ304/G-MKVI)	De Havilland Aviation, Swansea	
WL626	Vickers Varsity T1 (G-BHDD) [P]	Privately owned, East Midlands Airport	
WL627	Vickers Varsity T1 (8488M) [D] <ff>	Privately owned, Preston, E Yorkshire	
WL679	Vickers Varsity T1 (9155M)	RAF Cosford Aerospace Museum	
WL732	BP P108 Sea Balliol T21	RAF Cosford Aerospace Museum	
WL756	Avro 696 Shackleton AEW2 (9101M)	RAF St Mawgan, Fire Section	
WL795	Avro 696 Shackleton MR2C (8753M) [T]	RAF St Mawgan, on display	
WL798	Avro 696 Shackleton MR2C (8114M) <ff>	Privately owned, Elgin	
WL925	Slingsby T31B Cadet TX3 (WV925) <ff>	RAF No 633 VGS, Cosford	
WM145	AW Meteor NF11 <ff>	N Yorks Aircraft Recovery Centre, Chop Gate	
WM167	AW Meteor NF11 (G-LOSM)	Jet Heritage Ltd, Bournemouth	
WM223	AW Meteor TT20	Scrapped at Lasham	
WM267	Gloster Meteor NF11 <ff>	Blyth Valley Aviation Collection, Walpole, Suffolk	
WM292	AW Meteor TT20 [841]	Phoenix Aviation, Bruntingthorpe	
WM311	AW Meteor TT20 (WM224/8177M)	Privately owned, North Weald	
WM366	AW Meteor NF13 (4X-FNA) (comp VZ462)	SWWAPS, Lasham	
WM367	AW Meteor NF13 <ff>	South Yorkshire Avn Museum, Firbeck	
WM571	DH112 Sea Venom FAW21 [VL]	Southampton Hall of Aviation	
WM729	DH113 Vampire NF10 [A] <ff>	Mosquito Aircraft Museum, Staverton	
WM913	Hawker Sea Hawk FB5 (8162M) [456/J]	Newark Air Museum, Winthorpe	
WM961	Hawker Sea Hawk FB5 [J]	Caernarfon Air World	
WM969	Hawker Sea Hawk FB5 [10/Z]	Imperial War Museum, Duxford	
WM993	Hawker Sea Hawk FB5 [034]	Privately owned, Peasedown St John, Avon	
WN105	Hawker Sea Hawk FB3 (WF299/ 8164M)	Privately owned, Birlingham, Worcs	
WN108	Hawker Sea Hawk FB5 [033]	Ulster Aviation Society, Langford Lodge	
WN149	BP P108 Balliol T2	Boulton Paul Association, Wolverhampton	
WN411	Fairey Gannet AS1 (fuselage)	Privately owned, Southampton	
WN493	WS51 Dragonfly HR5	FAA Museum, RNAS Yeovilton	
WN499	WS51 Dragonfly HR5 [Y]	Caernarfon Air World	
WN516	BP P108 Balliol T2 <ff>	North-East Aircraft Museum, Usworth	
WN534	BP P108 Balliol T2 <ff>	Boulton Paul Association, Wolverhampton	
WN890	Hawker Hunter F2 <ff>	Robertsbridge Aviation Society, Mayfield	
WN904	Hawker Hunter F2 (7544M) [3]	RE 39 Regt, Waterbeach, on display	
WN907	Hawker Hunter F2 (7416M) <ff>	Blyth Valley Aviation Collection, Walpole, Suffolk	
WP185	Hawker Hunter F5 (7583M)	Privately owned, Great Dunmow, Essex	
WP190	Hawker Hunter F5 (7582M/8473M/ WP180) [K]	Privately owned, Quedgeley, Glos.	
WP250	DH113 Vampire NF10 <ff>	Privately owned, Warwickshire	
WP255	DH113 Vampire NF10 <ff>	RAF Millom Museum, Haverigg	
WP270	EoN Eton TX1 (8598M)	RAF Museum Restoration Centre, Cardington	
WP271	EoN Eton TX1	Privately owned, stored Keevil	
WP313	Percival P57 Sea Prince T1 [568/CU]	FAA Museum, stored Wroughton	
WP314	Percival P57 Sea Prince T1 (8634M) [573/CU]	Privately owned, Carlisle Airport	
WP321	Percival P57 Sea Prince T1 (G-BRFC) [750/CU]	Privately owned, North Weald	
WP503	WS51 Dragonfly HR3 [901]	Privately owned, Carnforth, Lancs	
WP515	EE Canberra B2 <ff>	Privately owned, Welshpool	
WP772	DHC1 Chipmunk T10 [Q] (wreck)	No 2491 Sqn ATC, RAF Lyneham	
WP784	DHC1 Chipmunk T10 <ff>	Privately owned, Long Marston	
WP788	DHC1 Chipmunk T10 (G-BCHL)	Privately owned, Sleap	
WP790	DHC1 Chipmunk T10 (G-BBNC) [T]	Mosquito Aircraft Museum, London Colney	

Notes	Serial	Type (other identity) [code]	Owner/operator, location or fate
	WP795	DHC1 Chipmunk T10 (G-BVZZ) [901]	Privately owned, Lee-on-Solent
	WP800	DHC1 Chipmunk T10 (G-BCXN) [2]	Privately owned, Halton
	WP803	DHC1 Chipmunk T10 (G-HAPY) [G]	Privately owned, Booker
	WP805	DHC1 Chipmunk T10 (G-MAJR) [D]	Privately owned, Fareham
	WP808	DHC1 Chipmunk T10 (G-BDEU)	Privately owned, Binham
	WP809	DHC1 Chipmunk T10 (G-BVTX) [778]	Privately owned, Husbands Bosworth
	WP831	DHC1 Chipmunk T10 (G-BBMT)	*Repainted as G-BBMT*
	WP833	DHC1 Chipmunk T10 [H]	RAF, stored Newton
	WP837	DHC1 Chipmunk T10 [L]	*Sold as VH-WPO, February 1997*
	WP839	DHC1 Chipmunk T10 [A]	Privately owned, Thornton-Cleveleys, Lancs
	WP840	DHC1 Chipmunk T10 (G-BXDM) [9]	Privately owned, Halton
	WP843	DHC1 Chipmunk T10 (G-BDBP)	Privately owned, Booker
	WP844	DHC1 Chipmunk T10 (G-BWOX) [85]	Privately owned, Kings Coughton
	WP845	DHC1 Chipmunk T10 <ff>	Privately owned, Leicestershire
	WP856	DHC1 Chipmunk T10 (G-BVWP) [904]	Privately owned, Cuckfield
	WP857	DHC1 Chipmunk T10 (G-BDRJ) [24]	Privately owned, Elstree
	WP859	DHC1 Chipmunk T10 (G-BXCP) [E]	Privately owned, Eire
	WP860	DHC1 Chipmunk T10 (G-BXDA) [6]	Privately owned, Cumbernauld
	WP863	DHC1 Chipmunk T10 (8360M/ G-ATJI) <ff>	FR Aviation, Bournemouth
	WP864	DHC1 Chipmunk T10 (8214M) <ff>	RAF, stored Newton
	WP869	DHC1 Chipmunk T10 (8215M) <ff>	*To Poland*
	WP871	DHC1 Chipmunk T10 [W]	AAC, Middle Wallop, for display
	WP872	DHC1 Chipmunk T10	*Sold as C-GBNI, February 1997*
	WP896	DHC1 Chipmunk T10 (G-BWVY) [M]	Privately owned, London
	WP901	DHC1 Chipmunk T10 (G-BWNT) [B]	Privately owned, East Midlands Airport
	WP903	DHC1 Chipmunk T10 (G-BCGC)	Privately owned, Shoreham
	WP907	DHC1 Chipmunk T10 <ff> (7970M)	Privately owned, Reading
	WP912	DHC1 Chipmunk T10 (8467M)	RAF Cosford Aerospace Museum
	WP920	DHC1 Chipmunk T10 (G-BXCR) [10]	Privately owned, Rendcomb
	WP921	DHC1 Chipmunk T10 (G-ATJJ) <ff>	Privately owned, Brooklands
	WP925	DHC1 Chipmunk T10 (G-BXHA) [C]	Privately owned, Camberley
	WP927	DHC1 Chipmunk T10 (8216M/ G-ATJK) <ff>	No 247 Sqn ATC, Ashton-under-Lyne, Gr Manchester
	WP928	DHC1 Chipmunk T10 (G-BXGM) [D]	Privately owned, Shoreham
	WP929	DHC1 Chipmunk T10 (G-BXCV) [F]	Privately owned, Duxford
	WP930	DHC1 Chipmunk T10 (G-BXHF) [J]	Privately owned, Redhill
	WP962	DHC1 Chipmunk T10 [C]	RAF, stored Newton
	WP964	DHC1 Chipmunk T10 [Y]	AAC Historic Aircraft Flight, Middle Wallop
	WP971	DHC1 Chipmunk T10 (G-ATHD)	Privately owned, Denham
	WP976	DHC1 Chipmunk T10 (WP791/ G-APTS)	Privately owned, Booker
	WP977	DHC1 Chipmunk T10 (G-BHRD) [N]	Privately owned, Kidlington
	WP978	DHC1 Chipmunk T10 (7467M) <ff>	Privately owned, Bournemouth
	WP983	DHC1 Chipmunk T10 (G-BXNN) [B]	Privately owned, London
	WP984	DHC1 Chipmunk T10 (G-BWTO) [H]	Privately owned, Duxford
	WR410	DH112 Venom FB50 (J-1539/ G-DHUU/*WE410*)	Source Classic Jet Flight, Bournemouth
	WR410	DH112 Venom FB54 (J-1790/ G-BLKA) [N]	Source Classic Jet Flight, stored Bournemouth
	WR421	DH112 Venom FB50 (J-1611/ G-DHTT)	Source Classic Jet Flight, Bournemouth
	WR539	DH112 Venom FB4 (8399M) [F]	Mosquito Aircraft Museum, Staverton
	WR960	Avro 696 Shackleton AEW2 (8772M)	Gr Manchester Mus of Science & Industry
	WR963	Avro 696 Shackleton AEW2	Air Atlantique Historic Flight, Coventry
	WR971	Avro 696 Shackleton MR3 (8119M) [Q]	Fenland & W Norfolk Aviation Museum, Wisbech

Serial	Type (other identity) [code]	Owner/operator, location or fate	Notes
WR974	Avro 696 Shackleton MR3 (8117M) [K]	Vallance By-Ways, Charlwood, Surrey	
WR977	Avro 696 Shackleton MR3 (8186M) [B]	Newark Air Museum, Winthorpe	
WR982	Avro 696 Shackleton MR3 (8106M) [J]	Vallance By-Ways, Charlwood, Surrey	
WR985	Avro 696 Shackleton MR3 (8103M) [H]	Privately owned, Long Marston	
WS103	Gloster Meteor T7 [709/VL]	FAA Museum, stored Wroughton	
WS692	Gloster Meteor NF12 (7605M) [C]	Newark Air Museum, Winthorpe	
WS726	Gloster Meteor NF14 (7960M) [G]	No 1855 Sqn ATC, Royton, Gr Manchester	
WS739	Gloster Meteor NF14 (7961M)	Newark Air Museum, Winthorpe	
WS760	Gloster Meteor NF14 (7964M)	Meteor Flight, stored Yatesbury	
WS774	Gloster Meteor NF14 (7959M)	Privately owned, Quedgeley, Glos	
WS776	Gloster Meteor NF14 (7716M) [K]	Privately owned, North Coates	
WS788	Gloster Meteor NF14 (7967M) [Z]	Yorkshire Air Museum, Elvington	
WS792	Gloster Meteor NF14 (7965M) [K]	Brighouse Bay Caravan Park, Borgue, D&G	
WS807	Gloster Meteor NF14 (7973M) [N]	Jet Age Museum, Staverton	
WS832	Gloster Meteor NF14 [W]	Solway Aviation Society, Carlisle	
WS838	Gloster Meteor NF14	Midland Air Museum, Coventry	
WS843	Gloster Meteor NF14 (7937M) [Y]	RAF Cosford Aerospace Museum, stored	
WT121	Douglas Skyraider AEW1 (WT983) [415/CU]	FAA Museum, RNAS Yeovilton	
WT205	EE Canberra B15	No 2431 Sqn ATC, Eastwood, Essex	
WT308	EE Canberra B(I)6	RN, Predannack Fire School	
WT309	EE Canberra B(I)6 <ff>	Privately owned, Farnborough	
WT327	EE Canberra B(I)8 (G-BXMO)	*Sold as N30UP, December 1997*	
WT333	EE Canberra B6(mod) (G-BVXC)	Privately owned, Bruntingthorpe	
WT339	EE Canberra B(I)8 (8198M)	RAF Barkston Heath Fire Section	
WT480	EE Canberra T4 [AT]	RAF, stored Shawbury	
WT482	EE Canberra T4 <ff>	Privately owned	
WT483	EE Canberra T4 [83]	Privately owned, Long Marston	
WT486	EE Canberra T4 (8102M) <ff>	Flight Experience Workshop, Belfast	
WT488	EE Canberra T4	*Scrapped at Dunsfold*	
WT507	EE Canberra PR7 (8131M/8548M) [44] <ff>	No 384 Sqn ATC, Mansfield	
WT509	EE Canberra PR7 [BR]	RAF, stored Marham	
WT510	EE Canberra T22 <ff>	Privately owned, Stock, Essex	
WT519	EE Canberra PR7 [CH]	RAF Wyton, Fire Section	
WT520	EE Canberra PR7 (8094M/8184M)	No 946 Sqn ATC, Preston	
WT525	EE Canberra T22 <ff>	Privately owned, South Woodham Ferrers	
WT532	EE Canberra PR7 (8728M/8890M) [Z]	Bournemouth Int'l Airport, Fire Section	
WT534	EE Canberra PR7 (8549M) [43] <ff>	No 492 Sqn ATC, Shirley, W. Midlands	
WT536	EE Canberra PR7 (8063M) <ff>	Privately owned, Portsmouth	
WT537	EE Canberra PR7	BAe Samlesbury, on display	
WT538	EE Canberra PR7 <ff> [CJ]	RAF St Athan	
WT555	Hawker Hunter F1 (7499M)	Vanguard Haulage, Greenford, London	
WT569	Hawker Hunter F1 (7491M)	No 2117 Sqn ATC, Kenfig Hill, Mid-Glamorgan	
WT612	Hawker Hunter F1 (7496M)	RAF Henlow, on display	
WT619	Hawker Hunter F1 (7525M)	Gr Manchester Mus of Science & Industry	
WT648	Hawker Hunter F1 (7530M) <ff>	The Air Defence Collection, Salisbury	
WT651	Hawker Hunter F1 [C]	Newark Air Museum, Winthorpe	
WT660	Hawker Hunter F1 (7421M) [C]	Privately owned, Cullen, Grampian	
WT680	Hawker Hunter F1 (7533M) [J]	No 1429 Sqn ATC, at DERA Aberporth	
WT684	Hawker Hunter F1 (7422M)	S Yorkshire Aviation Museum, Firbeck	
WT694	Hawker Hunter F1 (7510M)	Caernarfon Air World	
WT711	Hawker Hunter GA11 [833/DD]	Air Atlantique, Coventry	
WT720	Hawker Hunter F51 (RDAF E-408/8565M) [B]	RAF Sealand, on display	
WT722	Hawker Hunter T8C (G-BWGN) [878/VL]	Classic Jet Aircraft Co, Exeter	
WT723	Hawker Hunter PR11 (N723WT) [866/VL,3]	Classic Jet Aircraft Co, Exeter	
WT744	Hawker Hunter GA11 [868/VL]	South West Aviation Heritage, Eaglescott	
WT746	Hawker Hunter F4 (7770M) [A]	Army, Saighton, Cheshire	
WT799	Hawker Hunter T8C [879]	McCarthy Aviation, North Weald	
WT804	Hawker Hunter GA11 [831/DD]	FETC, Moreton-in-Marsh, Glos	
WT806	Hawker Hunter GA11	Privately owned, Sproughton	

Notes	Serial	Type (other identity) [code]	Owner/operator, location or fate
	WT859	Supermarine 544 <ff>	Brooklands Museum, Weybridge
	WT867	Slingsby T31B Cadet TX3	Privately owned, Eaglescott
	WT898	Slingsby T31B Cadet TX3 (BGA 3284/BGA 4412)	Privately owned, Rufforth
	WT899	Slingsby T31B Cadet TX3	Privately owned, Swindon
	WT902	Slingsby T31B Cadet TX3 (BGA 3147)	Privately owned, Lleweni Parc, Clwyd
	WT905	Slingsby T31B Cadet TX3	Privately owned
	WT910	Slingsby T31B Cadet TX3 (BGA 3953)	Privately owned, Challock
	WT933	Bristol 171 Sycamore 3 (G-ALSW/ 7709M)	Newark Air Museum, Winthorpe
	WV106	Douglas Skyraider AEW1 [427/C]	FAA Museum, at RNAS Culdrose
	WV198	Sikorsky S55 Whirlwind HAR21 (G-BJWY) [K]	Solway Aviation Society, Carlisle
	WV256	Hawker Hunter GA11 [862/VL]	RN, stored Shawbury
	WV276	Hawker Hunter F4 (7847M) [D]	Front Line Aviation Museum, Sandown
	WV318	Hawker Hunter T7B (G-FFOX)	Delta Engineering Aviation, Kemble
	WV322	Hawker Hunter T8C (9096M) [Y]	AMIF, RAFC Cranwell
	WV332	Hawker Hunter F4 (7673M) <ff>	No 1254 Sqn ATC, Godalming
	WV372	Hawker Hunter T7 (G-BXFI) [R]	Privately owned, Kemble
	WV381	Hawker Hunter GA11 [732/VL]	UKAEA, Culham, Oxon
	WV382	Hawker Hunter GA11 [830/VL]	Jet Avn Preservation Grp, Long Marston
	WV383	Hawker Hunter T7	MoD(PE)/AFD, DERA Boscombe Down
	WV395	Hawker Hunter F4 (8001M)	*Scrapped at Dunsfold*
	WV396	Hawker Hunter T8C (9249M) [91]	RAF Valley, at main gate
	WV483	Percival P56 Provost T1 (7693M) [N-E]	Privately owned
	WV486	Percival P56 Provost T1 (7694M) [N-D]	*Scrapped at Grazeley by 1997*
	WV493	Percival P56 Provost T1 (G-BDYG/7696M) [29]	Royal Scottish Mus'm of Flight, stored E Fortune
	WV499	Percival P56 Provost T1 (7698M) [P-G]	Privately owned, Sandtoft
	WV562	Percival P56 Provost T1 (7606M) [P-C]	RAF Cosford Aerospace Museum, stored
	WV605	Percival P56 Provost T1 [T-B]	Norfolk & Suffolk Avn Museum, Flixton
	WV606	Percival P56 Provost T1 (7622M) [P-B]	Newark Air Museum, Winthorpe
	WV666	Percival P56 Provost T1 (7925M/ G-BTDH) [O-D]	Privately owned, Shoreham
	WV679	Percival P56 Provost T1 (7615M) [O-J]	Wellesbourne Wartime Museum
	WV703	Percival P66 Pembroke C1 (8108M/*G-IIIM*)	Privately owned, Tattershall Thorpe
	WV705	Percival P66 Pembroke C1 <ff>	Southampton Hall of Aviation, stored
	WV740	Percival P66 Pembroke C1 (G-BNPH)	Privately owned, Jersey
	WV746	Percival P66 Pembroke C1 (8938M)	RAF Cosford Aerospace Museum
	WV781	Bristol 171 Sycamore HR12 (G-ALTD/7839M)	Caernarfon Air World
	WV783	Bristol 171 Sycamore HR12 (G-ALSP/7841M)	RAF Museum Restoration Centre, Cardington
	WV787	EE Canberra B2/8 (8799M)	Newark Air Museum, Winthorpe
	WV795	Hawker Sea Hawk FGA6 (8151M)	Kennet Aviation, Cranfield
	WV797	Hawker Sea Hawk FGA6 (8155M) [491/J]	Midland Air Museum, Coventry
	WV798	Hawker Sea Hawk FGA6 [026/CU]	SWWAPS, Lasham
	WV838	Hawker Sea Hawk FGA4	Privately owned, Chippenham, Wilts
	WV856	Hawker Sea Hawk FGA6 [163]	FAA Museum, RNAS Yeovilton
	WV903	Hawker Sea Hawk FGA4 (8153M) [128/C]	RN Historic Flight, stored Yeovilton
	WV906	Hawker Sea Hawk FGA6 (WV826) [182]	Kennet Aviation, Cranfield
	WV908	Hawker Sea Hawk FGA6 (8154M) [188/A]	RN Historic Flight, at BAe Dunsfold
	WW138	DH112 Sea Venom FAW22 [227/Z]	FAA Museum, RNAS Yeovilton
	WW145	DH112 Sea Venom FAW22 [680/LM]	Royal Scottish Mus'm of Flight, E Fortune
	WW217	DH112 Sea Venom FAW22 [351]	Newark Air Museum, Winthorpe

Serial	Type (other identity) [code]	Owner/operator, location or fate	Notes
WW388	Percival P56 Provost T1 (7616M) [O-F]	Bomber County Aviation Museum, Hemswell	
WW421	Percival P56 Provost T1 (7688M) [P-B]	Privately owned, Sandtoft	
WW442	Percival P56 Provost T1 (7618M) [N]	Privately owned, Kings Langley, Herts	
WW444	Percival P56 Provost T1 [D]	Privately owned, Rugeley, Staffs	
WW447	Percival P56 Provost T1	Privately owned, Grazeley, Berks	
WW453	Percival P56 Provost T1 (G-TMKI) [W-S]	Kennet Aviation, Cranfield	
WW654	Hawker Hunter GA11 [834/DD]	Privately owned, Oving, W Sussex	
WX643	DHC1 Chipmunk T10 (8437M/ 8630M/WG362) [80] <ff>	RAF Newton, instructional use	
WX788	DH112 Venom NF3	Night-Fighter Preservation Team, Elvington	
WX853	DH112 Venom NF3 (7443M)	Mosquito Aircraft Museum, London Colney	
WX905	DH112 Venom NF3 (7458M)	Newark Air Museum, Winthorpe	
WZ425	DH115 Vampire T11	Privately owned, Birlingham, Worcs	
WZ450	DH115 Vampire T11 <ff>	Lashenden Air Warfare Museum, Headcorn	
WZ458	DH115 Vampire T11 (7728M) [31] <ff>	Blyth Valley Aviation Collection, Walpole, Suffolk	
WZ464	DH115 Vampire T11 (N62430) [40]	Vintage Aircraft Team, Bruntingthorpe	
WZ507	DH115 Vampire T11 (G-VTII)	De Havilland Aviation, Swansea	
WZ515	DH115 Vampire T11 [60]	Solway Aviation Society, Carlisle	
WZ518	DH115 Vampire T11	North-East Aircraft Museum, Usworth	
WZ549	DH115 Vampire T11 (8118M) [F]	Ulster Aviation Society, Langford Lodge	
WZ553	DH115 Vampire T11 (G-DHYY) [40]	Source Classic Jet Flight, stored Bournemouth	
WZ557	DH115 Vampire T11	N Yorks Aircraft Recovery Centre, Chop Gate	
WZ581	DH115 Vampire T11 <ff>	The Vampire Collection, Hemel Hempstead	
WZ584	DH115 Vampire T11 [K]	Privately owned, Sandtoft	
WZ589	DH115 Vampire T11 [19]	Lashenden Air Warfare Museum, Headcorn	
WZ589	DH115 Vampire T55 (U-1230/ G-DHZZ)	Source Classic Jet Flight, Bournemouth	
WZ590	DH115 Vampire T11 [19]	Imperial War Museum, Duxford	
WZ608	DH115 Vampire T11 [56] <ff>	Privately owned,	
WZ620	DH115 Vampire T11 [68]	Avon Aviation Museum, Yatesbury	
WZ662	Auster AOP9 (G-BKVK)	Privately owned, Middle Wallop	
WZ706	Auster AOP9 (7851M/G-BURR)	Privately owned, Middle Wallop	
WZ711	Auster AOP9/Beagle E3 (G-AVHT)	Privately owned, Middle Wallop	
WZ721	Auster AOP9	Museum of Army Flying, Middle Wallop	
WZ724	Auster AOP9 (7432M)	AAC Middle Wallop, at main gate	
WZ729	Auster AOP9 (G-BXON)	Privately owned, Newark-on-Trent	
WZ736	Avro 707A (7868M)	Gr Manchester Mus of Science & Industry	
WZ744	Avro 707C (7932M)	RAF Cosford Aerospace Museum	
WZ753	Slingsby T38 Grasshopper TX1	Southampton Hall of Aviation	
WZ765	Slingsby T38 Grasshopper TX1 (BGA 3662)	To Luftwaffenmuseum, Germany, by November 1997	
WZ767	Slingsby T38 Grasshopper TX1	North-East Aircraft Museum, stored Usworth	
WZ768	Slingsby T38 Grasshopper TX1 (comp XK820)	Privately owned, Kirton-in-Lindsey, Lincs	
WZ769	Slingsby T38 Grasshopper TX1	Privately owned, stored Rufforth	
WZ772	Slingsby T38 Grasshopper TX1	Museum of Army Flying, Middle Wallop	
WZ779	Slingsby T38 Grasshopper TX1	Privately owned, Old Sarum	
WZ784	Slingsby T38 Grasshopper TX1	Privately owned, Thurrock College	
WZ791	Slingsby T38 Grasshopper TX1 (8944M)	RAF Museum, Hendon	
WZ792	Slingsby T38 Grasshopper TX1	Privately owned, Sproughton	
WZ793	Slingsby T38 Grasshopper TX1	Whitgift School, Croydon	
WZ796	Slingsby T38 Grasshopper TX1	Privately owned, stored Nympsfield, Glos	
WZ816	Slingsby T38 Grasshopper TX1 (BGA 3979)	Privately owned, stored Ashford, Kent	
WZ819	Slingsby T38 Grasshopper TX1 (BGA 3498)	Privately owned, Halton	
WZ822	Slingsby T38 Grasshopper TX1	South Yorkshire Avn Museum, Firbeck	
WZ824	Slingsby T38 Grasshopper TX1	Privately owned, stored Strathaven, Strathclyde	
WZ825	Slingsby T38 Grasshopper TX1	RAF Cosford Aerospace Museum, stored	
WZ826	Vickers Valiant B(K)1 (XD826/ 7872M) <ff>	Privately owned, Foulness	

Notes	Serial	Type (other identity) [code]	Owner/operator, location or fate
	WZ827	Slingsby T38 Grasshopper TX1	RAFGSA, stored Bicester
	WZ828	Slingsby T38 Grasshopper TX1 (BGA 4421)	Privately owned, Bicester
	WZ829	Slingsby T38 Grasshopper TX1	RAFGSA, stored Bicester
	WZ831	Slingsby T38 Grasshopper TX1	Privately owned, stored Nympsfield, Glos
	WZ846	DHC1 Chipmunk T10 (G-BCSC/ 8439M) <ff>	No 1404 Sqn ATC, Chatham
	WZ847	DHC1 Chipmunk T10 (G-CPMK) [F]	Privately owned, Ashbourne
	WZ866	DHC1 Chipmunk T10 (8217M/ G-ATEB) <ff>	South Yorkshire Avn Museum, Firbeck
	WZ868	DHC1 Chipmunk T10 (G-BCIW) [H]	Privately owned, Sandtoft
	WZ868	DHC1 Chipmunk T10 (WG322/ G-ARMF) [H]	Privately owned, Twyford, Bucks
	WZ869	DHC1 Chipmunk T10 [R] <ff>	No 395 Sqn ATC, Handforth, Cheshire
	WZ872	DHC1 Chipmunk T10 [E]	RAF, stored Newton
	WZ876	DHC1 Chipmunk T10 (G-BBWN) <ff>	Privately owned, South Molton, Devon
	WZ877	DHC1 Chipmunk T10 [75]	*Sold as F-AZLI, 1997*
	WZ879	DHC1 Chipmunk T10 (G-BWUT) [73]	Aero Vintage, Rye
	WZ882	DHC1 Chipmunk T10 (G-BXGP) [K]	Privately owned, Eaglescott
	WZ884	DHC1 Chipmunk T10 (G-BXGL) [P]	*Repainted as G-BXGL by May 1998*
	XA109	DH115 Sea Vampire T22	Royal Scottish Mus'm of Flight, E Fortune
	XA127	DH115 Sea Vampire T22 <ff>	FAA Museum, stored RNAS Yeovilton
	XA129	DH115 Sea Vampire T22	FAA Museum, stored Wroughton
	XA225	Slingsby T38 Grasshopper TX1	Churchers College, Petersfield, Hants
	XA230	Slingsby T38 Grasshopper TX1 (BGA 4098)	Privately owned, Henlow
	XA231	Slingsby T38 Grasshopper TX1 (8888M)	E Cheshire & S Manchester Wg ATC, Sealand
	XA241	Slingsby T38 Grasshopper TX1	Shuttleworth Collection, Old Warden
	XA243	Slingsby T38 Grasshopper TX1 (8886M)	Privately owned, Gransden Lodge, Cambs
	XA244	Slingsby T38 Grasshopper TX1	RAF, stored Cosford
	XA282	Slingsby T31B Cadet TX3	Caernarfon Air World
	XA286	Slingsby T31B Cadet TX3	Privately owned, stored Rufforth
	XA289	Slingsby T31B Cadet TX3	Privately owned, Eaglescott
	XA290	Slingsby T31B Cadet TX3	Privately owned, stored Rufforth
	XA293	Slingsby T31B Cadet TX3	Privately owned, Breighton
	XA302	Slingsby T31B Cadet TX3 (BGA3786)	Privately owned, Syerston
	XA454	Fairey Gannet COD4	RNAS Yeovilton Fire Section
	XA459	Fairey Gannet ECM6 [E]	Privately owned, Cirencester
	XA460	Fairey Gannet ECM6 [768/BY]	NE Wales Institute, Connah's Quay, Clwyd
	XA466	Fairey Gannet COD4 [777/LM]	FAA Museum, stored Wroughton
	XA508	Fairey Gannet T2 [627/GN]	FAA Museum, at Midland Air Museum, Coventry
	XA553	Gloster Javelin FAW1 (7470M)	*Sold to South Africa, 1998*
	XA564	Gloster Javelin FAW1 (7464M)	RAF Cosford Aerospace Museum
	XA634	Gloster Javelin FAW4 (7641M)	RAF Leeming, on display
	XA699	Gloster Javelin FAW5 (7809M)	Midland Air Museum, Coventry
	XA847	EE P1B (8371M)	Privately owned
	XA862	WS55 Whirlwind HAR1 (G-AMJT)	The Helicopter Museum, Weston-super-Mare
	XA864	WS55 Whirlwind HAR1	FAA Museum, stored Wroughton
	XA868	WS55 Whirlwind HAR1	
	XA870	WS55 Whirlwind HAR1	Flambards Village Theme Park, Helston
	XA880	DH104 Devon C2 (G-BVXR)	Privately owned, Staverton
	XA893	Avro 698 Vulcan B1 (8591M) <ff>	RAF Cosford Aerospace Museum
	XA896	Avro 698 Vulcan B1 <ff>	Privately owned, Reigate
	XA903	Avro 698 Vulcan B1 <ff>	Privately owned, Sidcup, Kent
	XA917	HP80 Victor B1 (7827M) <ff>	Privately owned, Guardbridge, Fife
	XB259	Blackburn B101 Beverley C1 (G-AOAI)	Museum of Army Transport, Beverley
	XB261	Blackburn B101 Beverley C1 <ff>	Duxford Aviation Society, Duxford
	XB446	Grumman TBM-3 Avenger ECM6B	FAA Museum, Yeovilton
	XB480	Hiller HT1 [537]	FAA Museum, stored Wroughton
	XB812	Canadair CL-13 Sabre F4 (9227M) [U]	RAF Museum, Hendon

Serial	Type (other identity) [code]	Owner/operator, location or fate	Notes
XD145	Saro SR53	RAF Cosford Aerospace Museum	
XD163	WS55 Whirlwind HAR10 (8645M) [X]	The Helicopter Museum, Weston-super-Mare	
XD165	WS55 Whirlwind HAR10 (8673M) [B]	AAC Wattisham, instructional use	
XD186	WS55 Whirlwind HAR10 (8730M)	*To Germany*	
XD215	VS Scimitar F1 <ff>	Privately owned, Cheltenham	
XD234	VS Scimitar F1 [834]	DERA, derelict Farnborough	
XD235	VS Scimitar F1 <ff>	No 424 Sqn ATC, Southampton	
XD317	VS Scimitar F1 [112/R]	FAA Museum, RNAS Yeovilton	
XD332	VS Scimitar F1 [194/C]	Flambards Village Theme Park, Helston	
XD375	DH115 Vampire T11 (7887M) [72]	Privately owned, Yorkshire	
XD377	DH115 Vampire T11 (8203M) [A] <ff>	Privately owned, Barton	
XD382	DH115 Vampire T11 (8033M)	Anchor Surplus, Ripley, Derbys	
XD425	DH115 Vampire T11 <ff>	RAF Millom Museum, Haverigg	
XD434	DH115 Vampire T11 [25]	Fenland & W Norfolk Aviation Museum, Wisbech	
XD435	DH115 Vampire T11 [26] <ff>	*Scrapped*	
XD445	DH115 Vampire T11	Bomber County Aviation Museum, Hemswell	
XD447	DH115 Vampire T11 [50]	Jet Avn Preservation Grp, Long Marston	
XD452	DH115 Vampire T11 (7990M) [47] <ff>	Vampire Support Team, RAF Sealand	
XD453	DH115 Vampire T11 (7890M) [64] <ff>	*Scrapped at Millom, 1997*	
XD459	DH115 Vampire T11 [63] <ff>	Privately owned, Bruntingthorpe	
XD463	DH115 Vampire T11 (8023M)	Privately owned, Nottingham	
XD506	DH115 Vampire T11 (7983M)	Jet Age Museum, Staverton	
XD515	DH115 Vampire T11 (7998M/ XM515)	Privately owned, Rugeley, Staffs	
XD525	DH115 Vampire T11 (7882M) <ff>	Campbell College CCF, Belfast	
XD528	DH115 Vampire T11 (8159M) <ff>	Gamston Aerodrome Fire Section	
XD534	DH115 Vampire T11 [41]	Military Aircraft Pres'n Grp, Barton	
XD535	DH115 Vampire T11 <ff>	Barton Aviation Heritage Society, Barton	
XD536	DH115 Vampire T11 (7734M) [H]	Alleyn's School CCF, Northolt	
XD542	DH115 Vampire T11 (7604M) [28]	Montrose Air Station Museum	
XD547	DH115 Vampire T11 [Z] (composite)	Dumfries & Galloway Avn Mus, Dumfries	
XD593	DH115 Vampire T11 [50]	Newark Air Museum, Winthorpe	
XD595	DH115 Vampire T11 <ff>	Privately owned, Glentham, Lincs	
XD596	DH115 Vampire T11 (7939M)	Southampton Hall of Aviation	
XD599	DH115 Vampire T11	Privately owned, Shobdon	
XD602	DH115 Vampire T11 (7737M) <ff>	Privately owned, Brands Hatch	
XD614	DH115 Vampire T11 (8124M) <ff>	Privately owned, Southampton	
XD616	DH115 Vampire T11 [56]	Mosquito Aircraft Museum, Staverton	
XD622	DH115 Vampire T11 (8160M)	No 2214 Sqn ATC, Usworth	
XD624	DH115 Vampire T11 [O]	Macclesfield Technical College	
XD626	DH115 Vampire T11 [Q]	Midland Air Museum, Coventry	
XD674	Hunting Jet Provost T1 (7570M) [T]	RAF Cosford Aerospace Museum	
XD693	Hunting Jet Provost T1 (XM129/ G-AOBU) [Z-Q]	Kennet Aviation, Cranfield	
XD816	Vickers Valiant B(K)1 <ff>	Brooklands Museum, Weybridge	
XD818	Vickers Valiant B(K)1 (7894M)	RAF Museum, Hendon	
XD857	Vickers Valiant B(K)1 <ff>	Privately owned, Foulness	
XD875	Vickers Valiant B(K)1 <ff>	British Aviation Heritage, Bruntingthorpe	
XE317	Bristol 171 Sycamore HR14 (G-AMWO) [S-N]	South Yorkshire Avn Museum, Firbeck	
XE327	Hawker Sea Hawk FGA6 [644/LH]	Privately owned, Kings Langley, Herts	
XE339	Hawker Sea Hawk FGA6 (8156M) [149/E]	RN Historic Flight, stored Yeovilton	
XE340	Hawker Sea Hawk FGA6 [131/Z]	FAA Museum, at Montrose Air Station Museum	
XE368	Hawker Sea Hawk FGA6 [200/J]	Flambards Village Theme Park, Helston	
XE489	Hawker Sea Hawk FGA6 (G-JETH)	Vallance By-Ways, Charlwood, Surrey	
XE521	Fairey Rotodyne Y (parts)	The Helicopter Museum, Weston-super-Mare	
XE584	Hawker Hunter FGA9 <ff>	Barton Aviation Heritage Society, Barton	
XE597	Hawker Hunter FGA9 (8874M) <ff>		
XE601	Hawker Hunter FGA9	MoD(PE)/AFD, DERA Boscombe Down	
XE624	Hawker Hunter FGA9 (8875M) [G]	Army, Cawdor Barracks, Brawdy, on display	

Notes	Serial	Type (other identity) [code]	Owner/operator, location or fate
	XE627	Hawker Hunter F6A [T]	Imperial War Museum, Duxford
	XE643	Hawker Hunter FGA9 (8586M) <ff>	RAF EPTT, Aldergrove
	XE650	Hawker Hunter F6 (G-9-449) <ff>	*Actually IF68*
	XE656	Hawker Hunter F6 (8678M)	*Sold to Germany, 26 October 1998*
	XE665	Hawker Hunter T8C (G-BWGM) [876/VL]	Classic Jet Aircraft Co, Exeter
	XE668	Hawker Hunter GA11 [832/DD]	RN, Predannack Fire School
	XE670	Hawker Hunter F4 (7762M/8585M) <ff>	RAF Cosford Aerospace Museum
	XE677	Hawker Hunter F4 (G-HHUN)	*Crashed 5 June 1998, Dunsfold*
	XE685	Hawker Hunter GA11 (G-GAII) [861/VL]	Classic Jet Aircraft Co, Exeter
	XE689	Hawker Hunter GA11 (G-BWGK) [864/VL]	Classic Jet Aircraft Co, Exeter
	XE712	Hawker Hunter GA11 [708]	*Burnt at Predannack by April 1998*
	XE786	Slingsby T31B Cadet TX3	RAF, stored Arbroath
	XE793	Slingsby T31B Cadet TX3 (8666M)	Privately owned
	XE796	Slingsby T31B Cadet TX3	Privately owned, stored North Weald
	XE799	Slingsby T31B Cadet TX3 (8943M) [R]	RAFGSA, Syerston
	XE802	Slingsby T31B Cadet TX3	Privately owned, stored Cupar, Fife
	XE807	Slingsby T31B Cadet TX3 (BGA3545)	Privately owned, Halesland
	XE849	DH115 Vampire T11 (7928M) [V3]	Privately owned,Shobdonl
	XE852	DH115 Vampire T11 [H]	No 2247 Sqn ATC, Hawarden
	XE855	DH115 Vampire T11 <ff>	Midland Air Museum, Coventry
	XE856	DH115 Vampire T11	Privately owned, Henlow
	XE864	DH115 Vampire T11(composite with XD435)	Privately owned, Shobdon
	XE872	DH115 Vampire T11 [62]	Midland Air Museum, Coventry
	XE874	DH115 Vampire T11 (8582M) [61]	Montrose Air Station Museum
	XE897	DH115 Vampire T11 (XD403)	Privately owned, Errol, Tayside
	XE897	DH115 Vampire T55 (U-1214/ G-DHVV)	Source Classic Jet Flight, Bournemouth
	XE920	DH115 Vampire T11 (8196M/ G-VMPR) [D]	Vampire Support Team, Swansea
	XE921	DH115 Vampire T11 [64] <ff>	South Yorkshire Avn Museum, stored Firbeck
	XE935	DH115 Vampire T11 [30]	South Yorkshire Avn Museum, Firbeck
	XE946	DH115 Vampire T11 (7473M) <ff>	Privately owned, Heath Farm, North Rauceby, Lincs
	XE956	DH115 Vampire T11 (G-OBLN)	De Havilland Aviation, Swansea
	XE979	DH115 Vampire T11 [54]	Privately owned, Birlingham, Worcs
	XE982	DH115 Vampire T11 (7564M) [01]	Privately owned, Dunkeswell
	XE985	DH115 Vampire T11 (*WZ476*)	De Havilland Aviation, Swansea
	XE993	DH115 Vampire T11 (8161M)	Privately owned, Cosford
	XE995	DH115 Vampire T11 [53]	Privately owned, High Halden, Kent
	XE998	DH115 Vampire T11 (*U-1215*)	Privately owned, Brooklands Museum, Weybridge
	XF113	VS Swift F7 [19] <ff>	The Air Defence Collection, Salisbury
	XF114	VS Swift F7 (G-SWIF)	Privately owned, Scampton
	XF300	Hawker Hunter GA11 [860/VL]	RN, stored Shawbury
	XF303	Hawker Hunter F58A (J-4105/ G-BWOU) [A/105]	The Old Flying Machine Company, stored Scampton
	XF310	Hawker Hunter T8C [869/VL,2]	*Sold to Australia, 1997*
	XF314	Hawker Hunter F51 (RDAF E-412) [N]	Front Line Aviation Museum, Sandown
	XF321	Hawker Hunter T7	Classic Jet Aircraft Co, Exeter (spares use)
	XF324	Hawker Hunter F51 (RDAF E-427) [D]	British Aviation Heritage, Bruntingthorpe
	XF357	Hawker Hunter T8C (G-BWGL) [871/VL]	Classic Jet Aircraft Co, Exeter
	XF358	Hawker Hunter T8C [870/VL]	MoD(PE)/AFD, DERA Boscombe Down
	XF368	Hawker Hunter GA11 [863/VL]	RN, stored Shawbury
	XF375	Hawker Hunter F6A (8736M/ G-BUEZ) [05]	The Old Flying Machine Co, Duxford
	XF382	Hawker Hunter F6A [15]	Midland Air Museum, Coventry
	XF383	Hawker Hunter F6 (8706M) <ff>	Privately owned, Kidlington
	XF509	Hawker Hunter F6 (8708M)	Humbrol Paints, Marfleet, E Yorkshire
	XF515	Hawker Hunter F6A (8830M/ G-KAXF) [R]	Kennet Aviation, Cranfield

Serial	Type (other identity) [code]	Owner/operator, location or fate	Notes
XF516	Hawker Hunter F6A (8685M/ G-BVVC) [F]	Privately owned, Exeter	
XF519	Hawker Hunter FGA9 (8677M/ 8738M/9183M) (comp XJ695) [J]	FSCTE, RAF Manston	
XF522	Hawker Hunter F6 <ff>	No 1365 Sqn ATC, Aylesbury	
XF526	Hawker Hunter F6 (8679M) [78/E]	Privately owned, Birlingham, Worcs	
XF527	Hawker Hunter F6 (8680M)	RAF Halton, on display	
XF545	Percival P56 Provost T1 (7957M) [O-K]	Privately owned, Thatcham	
XF597	Percival P56 Provost T1 (G-BKFW) [AH]	Privately owned, Thatcham	
XF603	Percival P56 Provost T1 (G-KAPW)	Kennet Aviation, Cranfield	
XF690	Percival P56 Provost T1 (8041M/ G-MOOS)	Kennet Aviation, Cranfield	
XF708	Avro 716 Shackleton MR3 [203/C]	Imperial War Museum, Duxford	
XF785	Bristol 173 (7648M/G-ALBN)	RAF Cosford Aerospace Museum, stored	
XF836	Percival P56 Provost T1 (8043M/ G-AWRY) [JG]	Privately owned, Thatcham	
XF844	Percival P56 Provost T1 [70]	British Aviation Heritage, Bruntingthorpe	
XF877	Percival P56 Provost T1 (G-AWVF) [JX]	Privately owned, Sandown	
XF926	Bristol 188 (8368M)	RAF Cosford Aerospace Museum	
XF967	Hawker Hunter T8C (9186M) [T]	AMIF, RAFC Cranwell	
XF994	Hawker Hunter T8C [873/VL]	MoD(PE)/AFD, DERA Boscombe Down	
XF995	Hawker Hunter T8B (9237M) [K]	AMIF, RAFC Cranwell	
XG154	Hawker Hunter FGA9 (8863M) [54]	RAF Museum, Hendon	
XG160	Hawker Hunter F6A (8831M/ G-BWAF) [U]	Royal Jordanian AF Historic Flt, stored Bournemouth	
XG164	Hawker Hunter F6 (8681M)	RAF, stored Shawbury	
XG172	Hawker Hunter F6A (8832M) [A]	McCarthy Aviation, North Weald	
XG193	Hawker Hunter FGA9 (XG297) (comp with WT741)	Bomber County Aviation Museum, Hemswell	
XG196	Hawker Hunter F6A (8702M) [31]	Army, Mytchett, Surrey, on display	
XG209	Hawker Hunter F6 (8709M) <ff>	Privately owned, Chelmsford	
XG210	Hawker Hunter F6	Privately owned, Beck Row, Suffolk	
XG225	Hawker Hunter F6A (8713M) [S]	RAF Cosford on display	
XG226	Hawker Hunter F6A (8800M) [28] <ff>	No 1242 Sqn ATC, Faversham, Kent	
XG252	Hawker Hunter FGA9 (8840M) [U]	Privately owned, Hereford	
XG254	Hawker Hunter FGA9 (8881M)	RAF Coltishall Fire Section	
XG274	Hawker Hunter F6 (8710M) [71]	Privately owned, Sproughton	
XG290	Hawker Hunter F6 (8711M) [74] (fuselage)	The Air Defence Collection, Salisbury	
XG297	Hawker Hunter FGA9 <ff>	South Yorkshire Avn Museum, stored Firbeck	
XG325	EE Lightning F1 <ff>	No 1476 Sqn ATC, Southend	
XG329	EE Lightning F1 (8050M)	Privately owned, Flixton	
XG331	EE Lightning F1 <ff>	Jet Age Museum, Staverton	
XG337	EE Lightning F1 (8056M) [M]	RAF Cosford Aerospace Museum	
XG452	Bristol 192 Belvedere HC1 (7997M/G-BRMB)	The Helicopter Museum, Weston-super-Mare	
XG454	Bristol 192 Belvedere HC1 (8366M)	Gr Manchester Mus of Science & Industry	
XG462	Bristol 192 Belvedere HC1 <ff>	The Helicopter Museum, stored Weston-super-Mare	
XG474	Bristol 192 Belvedere HC1 (8367M) [O]	RAF Museum, Hendon	
XG496	DH104 Devon C2 (G-ANDX) [K]	Privately owned, Newcastle	
XG502	Bristol 171 Sycamore HR14	Museum of Army Flying, Middle Wallop	
XG506	Bristol 171 Sycamore HR14 (7852M) [S-P]	Bomber County Aviation Museum, Hemswell	
XG518	Bristol 171 Sycamore HR14 (8009M) [S-E]	Norfolk & Suffolk Avn Museum, Flixton	
XG523	Bristol 171 Sycamore HR14 <ff> [K]	Norfolk & Suffolk Avn Museum, Flixton	
XG540	Bristol 171 Sycamore HR14 (7899M/8345M) [Y-S]	Botany Bay Village, Chorley, Lancs	
XG544	Bristol 171 Sycamore HR14	Privately owned, Tremar, Cornwall	
XG547	Bristol 171 Sycamore HR14 (G-HAPR) [S-T]	The Helicopter Museum, Weston-super-Mare	
XG574	WS55 Whirlwind HAR3 [752/PO]	FAA Museum, RNAS Yeovilton	
XG577	WS55 Whirlwind HAR3 (9050M)	RAF Leconfield Crash Rescue Training	

Notes	Serial	Type (other identity) [code]	Owner/operator, location or fate
	XG588	WS55 Whirlwind HAR3 (G-BAMH/VR-BEP)	Privately owned, East Midlands Airport
	XG594	WS55 Whirlwind HAS7 [517/PO]	FAA Museum, at R. Scottish Mus'm of Flt, E Fortune
	XG596	WS55 Whirlwind HAS7 [66]	THM/GKN Westland, Yeovil (under restoration)
	XG597	WS55 Whirlwind HAS7	Privately owned, Siddal, West Yorkshire
	XG613	DH112 Sea Venom FAW21	Imperial War Museum, Duxford
	XG629	DH112 Sea Venom FAW22 <ff>	Privately owned, Stone, Staffs
	XG680	DH112 Sea Venom FAW22 [438]	North-East Aircraft Museum, Usworth
	XG691	DH112 Sea Venom FAW22 [93/J]	Jet Age Museum, Staverton
	XG692	DH112 Sea Venom FAW22 [668/LM]	Privately owned, Baxterley, Warwickshire
	XG730	DH112 Sea Venom FAW22 [499/A]	Mosquito Aircraft Museum, London Colney
	XG736	DH112 Sea Venom FAW22	Ulster Aviation Society, Newtownards
	XG737	DH112 Sea Venom FAW22 [220/Z]	Jet Avn Preservation Grp, stored Long Marston
	XG743	DH115 Sea Vampire T22 [597/LM]	Wymondham College, Norfolk
	XG775	DH115 Vampire T55 (U-1219/G-DHWW) [VL]	Source Classic Jet Flight, Bournemouth
	XG797	Fairey Gannet ECM6 [277]	Imperial War Museum, Duxford
	XG831	Fairey Gannet ECM6 [396]	Flambards Village Theme Park, Helston
	XG882	Fairey Gannet T5 (8754M) [771/LM]	Privately owned, Errol, Tayside
	XG883	Fairey Gannet T5 [773/BY]	FAA Museum, at Museum of Berkshire Aviation, Woodley
	XG900	Short SC1	Science Museum, at FAA Museum, RNAS Yeovilton
	XG905	Short SC1	Ulster Folk & Transpt Mus, Holywood, Co Down
	XH131	EE Canberra PR9 [AA]	RAF No 39(1 PRU) Sqn, Marham
	XH132	Short SC9 Canberra (8915M) <ff>	Privately owned, St Austell
	XH134	EE Canberra PR9 [AB]	RAF No 39(1 PRU) Sqn, Marham
	XH135	EE Canberra PR9 [AC]	RAF No 39(1 PRU) Sqn, Marham
	XH136	EE Canberra PR9 (8782M) <ff>	Phoenix Aviation, Bruntingthorpe
	XH165	EE Canberra PR9 <ff>	Blyth Valley Aviation Collection, Walpole
	XH168	EE Canberra PR9 [AD]	RAF No 39(1 PRU) Sqn, Marham
	XH169	EE Canberra PR9	RAF No 39(1 PRU) Sqn, Marham
	XH170	EE Canberra PR9 (8739M)	RAF Wyton, on display
	XH171	EE Canberra PR9 (8746M) [U]	RAF Cosford Aerospace Museum
	XH174	EE Canberra PR9 <ff>	RAF, stored Shawbury
	XH175	EE Canberra PR9 <ff>	Privately owned, Stock, Essex
	XH177	EE Canberra PR9 <ff>	Privately owned, Stock, Essex
	XH278	DH115 Vampire T11 (8595M/7866M)	Privately owned, Felton, Northumberland
	XH312	DH115 Vampire T11 [18]	Privately owned, Dodleston, Cheshire
	XH313	DH115 Vampire T11 [E]	Privately owned, Sandtoft
	XH328	DH115 Vampire T11	Jet Heritage Ltd, Bournemouth (dismantled)
	XH330	DH115 Vampire T11 [73]	Privately owned, Bridgnorth
	XH537	Avro 698 Vulcan B2MRR (8749M) <ff>	Privately owned, Bruntingthorpe
	XH558	Avro 698 Vulcan B2 (G-VLCN)	British Aviation Heritage, Bruntingthorpe
	XH560	Avro 698 Vulcan K2 <ff>	Privately owned, Foulness
	XH563	Avro 698 Vulcan B2MRR <ff>	Privately owned, Banchory, Fife
	XH567	EE Canberra B6(mod) (G-BXOD)	*Sold as N40UP, April 1998*
	XH568	EE Canberra B6(mod) (G-BVIC)	Classic Aviation Projects, Bruntingthorpe
	XH584	EE Canberra T4 (G-27-374) <ff>	South Yorkshire Avn Museum, Firbeck
	XH592	HP80 Victor K1A (8429M) <ff>	Phoenix Aviation, Bruntingthorpe
	XH648	HP80 Victor K1A	Imperial War Museum, Duxford
	XH669	HP80 Victor K2 (9092M) <ff>	Privately owned, Foulness
	XH670	HP80 Victor SR2 <ff>	Privately owned, Foulness
	XH672	HP80 Victor K2	RAF Cosford Aerospace Museum
	XH673	HP80 Victor K2 (8911M)	RAF Marham, on display
	XH767	Gloster Javelin FAW9 (7955M) [A]	City of Norwich Aviation Museum
	XH783	Gloster Javelin FAW7 (8719M) <ff>	Privately owned, Catford
	XH837	Gloster Javelin FAW7 (8032M) <ff>	Caernarfon Air World
	XH892	Gloster Javelin FAW9 (7982M) [J]	Norfolk & Suffolk Avn Museum, Flixton
	XH897	Gloster Javelin FAW9	Imperial War Museum, Duxford
	XH903	Gloster Javelin FAW9 (7938M)	Jet Age Museum, Staverton
	XH992	Gloster Javelin FAW8 (7829M) [P]	Newark Air Museum, Winthorpe
	XJ314	RR Thrust Measuring Rig	Science Museum, at FAA Museum, RNAS Yeovilton

Serial	Type (other identity) [code]	Owner/operator, location or fate	Notes
XJ380	Bristol 171 Sycamore HR14 (8628M)	Montrose Air Station Museum	
XJ389	Fairey Jet Gyrodyne (XD759/G-AJJP)	Museum of Berkshire Aviation, Woodley	
XJ393	WS55 Whirlwind HAR3 (XD763)	Scrapped	
XJ409	WS55 Whirlwind HAR10 (XD779)	Maes Artro Craft Village, Llanbedr	
XJ435 use	WS55 Whirlwind HAR10 (8671M) [V]	RAF Manston History Museum, spares	
XJ476	DH110 Sea Vixen FAW1 <ff>	No 424 Sqn ATC, Southampton Hall of Avn	
XJ481	DH110 Sea Vixen FAW1 [VL]	FAA Museum, at RNAY Fleetlands Museum	
XJ482	DH110 Sea Vixen FAW1 [713/VL]	Norfolk & Suffolk Avn Museum, Flixton	
XJ488	DH110 Sea Vixen FAW1 <ff>	Robertsbridge Aviation Society, Mayfield	
XJ494	DH110 Sea Vixen FAW2	Privately owned, Kings Langley, Herts	
XJ560	DH110 Sea Vixen FAW2 (8142M) [242]	Newark Air Museum, Winthorpe	
XJ565	DH110 Sea Vixen FAW2 [127/E]	Mosquito Aircraft Museum, London Colney	
XJ571	DH110 Sea Vixen FAW2 (8140M) [242/R]	Privately owned, Brooklands Museum, Weybridge	
XJ575	DH110 Sea Vixen FAW2 <ff> [SAH-13]	Wellesbourne Wartime Museum	
XJ579	DH110 Sea Vixen FAW2 <ff>	Midland Air Museum, Coventry	
XJ580	DH110 Sea Vixen FAW2 [131/E]	Sea Vixen Society, Christchurch	
XJ607	DH110 Sea Vixen FAW2 (8171M) <ff>	Privately owned, Horsell, Surrey	
XJ634	Hawker Hunter F6A (8684M) [29]	Privately owned, Sproughton	
XJ639	Hawker Hunter F6A (8687M) [H]	Privately owned, Sproughton	
XJ676	Hawker Hunter F6A (8844M) <ff>	Privately owned, Leavesden	
XJ714	Hawker Hunter FR10 (comp XG226)	Jet Avn Preservation Grp, Long Marston	
XJ723	WS55 Whirlwind HAR10	Montrose Air Station Museum	
XJ726	WS55 Whirlwind HAR10	Caernarfon Air World	
XJ727	WS55 Whirlwind HAR10 (8661M) [L]	RAF Manston History Museum	
XJ729	WS55 Whirlwind HAR10 (8732M/ G-BVGE)	Privately owned, Oaksey Park, Wilts	
XJ758	WS55 Whirlwind HAR10 (8464M) <ff>	Privately owned, Welshpool	
XJ763	WS55 Whirlwind HAR10 (G-BKHA) [P]	Privately owned, stored Thornicombe, Dorset	
XJ772	DH115 Vampire T11 [H]	Mosquito Aircraft Museum, London Colney	
XJ823	Avro 698 Vulcan B2A	Solway Aviation Society, Carlisle	
XJ824	Avro 698 Vulcan B2A	Imperial War Museum, Duxford	
XJ917	Bristol 171 Sycamore HR14 [H-S]	Bristol Aero Collection, stored Kemble	
XJ918	Bristol 171 Sycamore HR14 (8190M)	RAF Cosford Aerospace Museum	
XK149	Hawker Hunter F6A (8714M) [L]	Privately owned, Bruntingthorpe	
XK378	Auster AOP9 (TAD200/XS238)	Privately owned, Dale, Dyfed	
XK416	Auster AOP9 (7855M/G-AYUA)	De Havilland Aviation, Swansea	
XK417	Auster AOP9 (G-AVXY)	Privately owned, RAF Newton	
XK418	Auster AOP9 (7976M)	SWWAPS, Lasham	
XK421	Auster AOP9 (8365M) (frame)	South Yorkshire Avn Museum, Firbeck	
XK482	Saro Skeeter AOP12 (7840M/ G-BJWC) [C]	Privately owned, Sywell	
XK488	Blackburn NA39 Buccaneer S1	FAA Museum, RNAS Yeovilton	
XK526	Blackburn NA39 Buccaneer S2 (8648M)	RAF Honington, at main gate	
XK527	Blackburn NA39 Buccaneer S2D (8818M) <ff>	Jet Heritage Museum, Bournemouth	
XK532	Blackburn NA39 Buccaneer S1 (8867M) [632/LM]	The Fresson Trust, Inverness Airport	
XK533	Blackburn NA39 Buccaneer S1 <ff>	Royal Scottish Mus'm of Flight, E Fortune	
XK590	DH115 Vampire T11 [V]	Wellesbourne Wartime Museum	
XK623	DH115 Vampire T11 (G-VAMP) [56]	Caernarfon Air World	
XK624	DH115 Vampire T11 [32]	Norfolk & Suffolk Avn Museum, Flixton	
XK625	DH115 Vampire T11 [12]	Brenzett Aeronautical Museum	
XK627	DH115 Vampire T11	Privately owned, Barton	
XK632	DH115 Vampire T11 [67]	No 2370 Sqn ATC, Denham	
XK637	DH115 Vampire T11 [56]	RAF Millom Museum, Haverigg	

Notes	Serial	Type (other identity) [code]	Owner/operator, location or fate
	XK655	DH106 Comet C2(RC) <ff>	Gatwick Airport, on display (BOAC colours)
	XK659	DH106 Comet C2(RC) <ff>	Privately owned, Elland, West Yorkshire
	XK695	DH106 Comet C2(RC) (9164M) <ff>	Mosquito Aircraft Museum, London Colney
	XK699	DH106 Comet C2 (7971M)	RAF Lyneham on display
	XK724	Folland Gnat F1 (7715M)	RAF Cosford Aerospace Museum
	XK740	Folland Gnat F1 (8396M)	Southampton Hall of Aviation
	XK741	Folland Gnat F1 (fuselage)	Midland Air Museum, Coventry
	XK776	ML Utility 1	Museum of Army Flying, Middle Wallop
	XK788	Slingsby T38 Grasshopper TX1	Privately owned, Sproughton
	XK789	Slingsby T38 Grasshopper TX1	Warwick School, Warwick
	XK790	Slingsby T38 Grasshopper TX1	Privately owned, stored Husbands Bosworth
	XK819	Slingsby T38 Grasshopper TX1	Privately owned, Selby
	XK822	Slingsby T38 Grasshopper TX1	Privately owned, Kenley
	XK895	DH104 Sea Devon C20 (G-SDEV) [19/CU]	Privately owned, Shoreham
	XK896	DH104 Sea Devon C20 (G-RNAS)	Privately owned, Filton (for spares)
	XK907	WS55 Whirlwind HAS7 [U]	Midland Air Museum, Coventry
	XK911	WS55 Whirlwind HAS7 [519/PO]	Privately owned, Hixon, Staffs
	XK936	WS55 Whirlwind HAS7 [62]	Imperial War Museum, Duxford
	XK940	WS55 Whirlwind HAS7 (G-AYXT)	Privately owned, Tibenham, Norfolk
	XK944	WS55 Whirlwind HAS7	No 617 Sqn ATC, Malpas, Cheshire
	XK968	WS55 Whirlwind HAR10 (8445M) [E]	Burnt at Manston, 1996
	XK988	WS55 Whirlwind HAR10 [D]	AAC Middle Wallop Fire Section
	XL149	Blackburn B101 Beverley C1 (7988M) <ff>	Newark Air Museum, Winthorpe
	XL160	HP80 Victor K2 (8910M) <ff>	HP Victor Association, Walpole
	XL164	HP80 Victor K2 (9215M) <ff>	Vallance By-Ways, Charlwood, Surrey
	XL188	HP80 Victor K2 (9100M) (fuselage)	RAF Kinloss Fire Section
	XL190	HP80 Victor K2 (9216M)	Privately owned, St Mawgan
	XL231	HP80 Victor K2	Yorkshire Air Museum, Elvington
	XL318	Avro 698 Vulcan B2 (8733M)	RAF Museum, Hendon
	XL319	Avro 698 Vulcan B2	North-East Aircraft Museum, Usworth
	XL360	Avro 698 Vulcan B2A	Midland Air Museum, Coventry
	XL388	Avro 698 Vulcan B2 <ff>	Blyth Valley Aviation Collection, Walpole
	XL391	Avro 698 Vulcan B2	Privately owned, Blackpool
	XL426	Avro 698 Vulcan B2 (G-VJET)	Vulcan Restoration Trust, Southend
	XL445	Avro 698 Vulcan K2 (8811M) <ff>	Blyth Valley Aviation Collection, Walpole
	XL449	Fairey Gannet AEW3 <ff>	Privately owned, Booker
	XL472	Fairey Gannet AEW3 [044/R]	Vallance By-Ways, Charlwood, Surrey
	XL497	Fairey Gannet AEW3 [041/R]	RN, Prestwick, on display
	XL500	Fairey Gannet AEW3 [CU]	RNAS Culdrose, on display
	XL502	Fairey Gannet AEW3 (8610M/ G-BMYP)	Privately owned, Sandtoft
	XL503	Fairey Gannet AEW3 [070/E]	FAA Museum, RNAS Yeovilton
	XL563	Hawker Hunter T7 (9218M)	RAF No 1 Officers' Mess, Farnborough, on display
	XL564	Hawker Hunter T7 [4]	Crashed 6 August 1998, Boscombe Down
	XL565	Hawker Hunter T7 (parts of WT745)	Delta Engineering Aviation, Kemble
	XL567	Hawker Hunter T7 (8723M) [84]	Privately owned, Exeter
	XL568	Hawker Hunter T7A (9224M) [C]	AMIF, RAFC Cranwell
	XL569	Hawker Hunter T7 (8833M) [SC]	Privately owned, East Midlands Airport
	XL572	Hawker Hunter T7 (8834M/ G-HNTR) [83]	Yorkshire Air Museum, Elvington
	XL573	Hawker Hunter T7 (G-BVGH)	Classic Jet Aircraft Co, Exeter
	XL577	Hawker Hunter T7 (G-BXKF/ 8676M) [W]	Delta Engineering Aviation, Kemble
	XL578	Hawker Hunter T7 (fuselage)	Privately owned, Kemble
	XL580	Hawker Hunter T8M [723]	FAA Museum, stored RNAS Yeovilton
	XL586	Hawker Hunter T7 <rf>	Delta Engineering Aviation, Kemble
	XL587	Hawker Hunter T7 (8807M) [Z]	The Old Flying Machine Company, Duxford
	XL591	Hawker Hunter T7	Delta Engineering Aviation, Kemble
	XL592	Hawker Hunter T7 (8836M) [Y]	Classic Jet Aircraft Co, Exeter
	XL601	Hawker Hunter T7 [874/VL]	Classic Jet Aircraft Co, Exeter
	XL602	Hawker Hunter T8M (G-BWFT)	South West Aviation Heritage, Exeter
	XL603	Hawker Hunter T8M [724]	Privately owned, Bruntingthorpe
	XL612	Hawker Hunter T7 [2]	MoD(PE)/AFD/ETPS, DERA Boscombe Down
	XL613	Hawker Hunter T7 (G-BVMB)	Classic Jet Aircraft Co, Exeter
	XL616	Hawker Hunter T7 (9223M/ G-BWIE)	Sold as SE-DXH, July 1997
	XL618	Hawker Hunter T7 (8892M) [05]	Caernarfon Air World

Serial	Type (other identity) [code]	Owner/operator, location or fate	Notes
XL621	Hawker Hunter T7 (G-BNCX)	Privately owned, Brooklands Museum	
XL623	Hawker Hunter T7 (8770M)	The Planets Leisure Centre, Woking	
XL629	EE Lightning T4	DERA Boscombe Down, at main gate	
XL703	SAL Pioneer CC1 (8034M)	RAF Cosford Aerospace Museum, stored	
XL714	DH82A Tiger Moth II (T6099/ G-AOGR)	Privately owned, Swanton Morley	
XL735	Saro Skeeter AOP12	Privately owned, Tattershall Thorpe	
XL738	Saro Skeeter AOP12 (7860M)	Privately owned, Ivybridge, Devon	
XL739	Saro Skeeter AOP12	AAC Wattisham, instructional use	
XL762	Saro Skeeter AOP12 (8017M)	Royal Scottish Mus'm of Flight, E Fortune	
XL763	Saro Skeeter AOP12	Privately owned, Ivybridge, Devon	
XL764	Saro Skeeter AOP12 (7940M) [J]	Newark Air Museum, Winthorpe	
XL765	Saro Skeeter AOP12	Privately owned, Clapham, Beds	
XL770	Saro Skeeter AOP12 (8046M)	Southampton Hall of Aviation	
XL809	Saro Skeeter AOP12 (G-BLIX)	Privately owned, Wilden, Beds	
XL811	Saro Skeeter AOP12	The Helicopter Museum, Weston-super-Mare	
XL812	Saro Skeeter AOP12 (G-SARO)	Privately owned, Old Buckenham	
XL813	Saro Skeeter AOP12	Museum of Army Flying, Middle Wallop	
XL814	Saro Skeeter AOP12	AAC Historic Aircraft Flight, Middle Wallop	
XL824	Bristol 171 Sycamore HR14 (8021M)	Gr Manchester Mus of Science & Industry	
XL829	Bristol 171 Sycamore HR14	Bristol Industrial Museum	
XL836	WS55 Whirlwind HAS7 [65]	*Burnt at Predannack by April 1998*	
XL840	WS55 Whirlwind HAS7	Privately owned, Long Marston	
XL847	WS55 Whirlwind HAS7 [83]	AAC Middle Wallop Fire Section	
XL853	WS55 Whirlwind HAS7 [PO]	RNAY Fleetlands Museum, at RNAS Portland	
XL875	WS55 Whirlwind HAR9	Perth Technical College	
XL929	Percival P66 Pembroke C1 (G-BNPU)	D-Day Museum, Shoreham Airport	
XL954	Percival P66 Pembroke C1 (9042M/N4234C/G-BXES)	Air Atlantique Historic Flight, Coventry	
XL993	SAL Twin Pioneer CC1 (8388M)	RAF Cosford Aerospace Museum	
XM135	BAC Lightning F1 [B]	Imperial War Museum, Duxford	
XM144	BAC Lightning F1 (8417M) <ff>	South West Aviation Heritage, Eaglescott	
XM169	BAC Lightning F1A (8422M) <ff>	N Yorks Aircraft Recovery Centre, Chop Gate	
XM172	BAC Lightning F1A (8427M)	Privately owned, Farnborough	
XM173	BAC Lightning F1A (8414M) [A]	RAF Bentley Priory, at main gate	
XM191	BAC Lightning F1A (7854M/ 8590M) <ff>	RAF EPTT, St Athan	
XM192	BAC Lightning F1A (8413M) [K]	Bomber County Aviation Museum, Hemswell	
XM223	DH104 Devon C2 (G-BWWC) [J]	Privately owned, Cumbernauld	
XM279	EE Canberra B(I)8 <ff>	Privately owned, Flixton	
XM300	WS58 Wessex HAS1	Welsh Industrial & Maritime Mus'm, stored Cardiff	
XM327	WS58 Wessex HAS3 [401/KE]	*Scrapped*	
XM328	WS58 Wessex HAS3 [653/PO]	SFDO, RNAS Culdrose	
XM330	WS58 Wessex HAS1	The Helicopter Museum, Weston-super-Mare	
XM349	Hunting Jet Provost T3A (9046M) [T]	Global Aviation, Binbrook	
XM350	Hunting Jet Provost T3A (9036M) [89]	South Yorkshire Avn Museum, Firbeck	
XM351	Hunting Jet Provost T3 (8078M) [Y]	RAF Museum, Cosford	
XM355	Hunting Jet Provost T3 (8229M) [D]	Privately owned, Shobdon	
XM358	Hunting Jet Provost T3A (8987M) [53]	Privately owned, Twyford, Bucks	
XM362	Hunting Jet Provost T3 (8230M)	RAF No 1 SoTT, Cosford	
XM363	Hunting Jet Provost T3 <ff>	RAF Cranwell	
XM365	Hunting Jet Provost T3A (G-BXBH) [37]	Privately owned, Norwich	
XM369	Hunting Jet Provost T3 (8084M) [C]	Privately owned, Portsmouth	
XM370	Hunting Jet Provost T3A (G-BVSP) [10]	Privately owned, Norwich	
XM372	Hunting Jet Provost T3A (8917M) [55]	RAF Linton-on-Ouse Fire Section	

Notes	Serial	Type (other identity) [code]	Owner/operator, location or fate
	XM375	Hunting Jet Provost T3 (8231M) [B]	RAF Linton-on-Ouse Fire Section
	XM376	Hunting Jet Provost T3A (G-BWDR) [27]	Global Aviation, Binbrook
	XM378	Hunting Jet Provost T3A (G-BWZE) [34]	Privately owned, Norwich
	XM379	Hunting Jet Provost T3	
	XM383	Hunting Jet Provost T3A [90]	Newark Air Museum, Winthorpe
	XM401	Hunting Jet Provost T3A [17]	
	XM402	Hunting Jet Provost T3 (8055AM) [J]	Fenland & W Norfolk Aviation Museum, Wisbech
	XM403	Hunting Jet Provost T3A (9048M)	
	XM404	Hunting Jet Provost T3 (8055BM)	FETC, Moreton-in-Marsh, Glos
	XM405	Hunting Jet Provost T3A (G-TORE) [42]	Kennet Aviation, Cranfield
	XM409	Hunting Jet Provost T3 (8082M) <rf>	Air Scouts, Guernsey Airport
	XM410	Hunting Jet Provost T3 (8054AM) [B]	RAF North Luffenham Training Area
	XM412	Hunting Jet Provost T3A (9011M) [41]	Privately owned, Sproughton
	XM414	Hunting Jet Provost T3A (8996M)	Flight Experience Workshop, Belfast
	XM417	Hunting Jet Provost T3 (8054BM) [D] <ff>	Privately owned, Hednesford, Staffs
	XM419	Hunting Jet Provost T3A (8990M) [102]	RAF CTTS, St Athan
	XM424	Hunting Jet Provost T3A (G-BWDS)	Sold as N77506
	XM425	Hunting Jet Provost T3A (8995M) [88]	Privately owned, Longton
	XM455	Hunting Jet Provost T3A (8960M) [K]	Global Aviation, Binbrook
	XM459	Hunting Jet Provost T3A [F]	Global Aviation, Binbrook
	XM463	Hunting Jet Provost T3A [38] (fuselage)	RAF Museum, Hendon
	XM465	Hunting Jet Provost T3A [55]	Sold as N7075H, 1995
	XM468	Hunting Jet Provost T3 (8081M)	Privately owned, Terrington St Clement
	XM470	Hunting Jet Provost T3A (G-BWZZ) [12]	Privately owned, Blackpool
	XM471	Hunting Jet Provost T3A (8968M) [L,93]	
	XM473	Hunting Jet Provost T3A (8974M/ G-TINY)	KLM UK, Norwich, instructional use
	XM474	Hunting Jet Provost T3 (8121M)	Bryants Air Park, Stockport
	XM475	Hunting Jet Provost T3A (9112M) [44]	FSCTE, RAF Manston
	XM478	Hunting Jet Provost T3A (8983M/ G-BXDL) [33]	Transair(UK) Ltd, North Weald
	XM479	Hunting Jet Provost T3A (G-BVEZ) [54]	Privately owned, Newcastle
	XM480	Hunting Jet Provost T3 (8080M)	4x4 Car Centre, Chesterfield
	XM496	Bristol 253 Britannia C1 (EL-WXA)	Britannia Preservation Society, Kemble
	XM529	Saro Skeeter AOP12 (7979M/ G-BDNS)	Privately owned, Handforth
	XM553	Saro Skeeter AOP12 (G-AWSV)	Privately owned, Middle Wallop
	XM555	Saro Skeeter AOP12 (8027M)	RAF Cosford Aerospace Museum, stored
	XM561	Saro Skeeter AOP12 (7980M)	South Yorkshire Avn Museum, Firbeck
	XM564	Saro Skeeter AOP12	National Tank Museum, Bovington
	XM569	Avro 698 Vulcan B2 <ff>	Jet Age Museum, Staverton
	XM575	Avro 698 Vulcan B2A (G-BLMC)	Privately owned, East Midlands Airport
	XM594	Avro 698 Vulcan B2	Newark Air Museum, Winthorpe
	XM597	Avro 698 Vulcan B2	Royal Scottish Mus'm of Flight, E Fortune
	XM598	Avro 698 Vulcan B2 (8778M)	RAF Cosford Aerospace Museum
	XM602	Avro 698 Vulcan B2 (8771M) <ff>	Avro Aircraft Heritage Society, Woodford
	XM603	Avro 698 Vulcan B2	Avro Aircraft Heritage Society, Woodford
	XM607	Avro 698 Vulcan B2 (8779M)	RAF Waddington, on display
	XM612	Avro 698 Vulcan B2	City of Norwich Aviation Museum
	XM652	Avro 698 Vulcan B2 <ff>	Privately owned, Welshpool
	XM655	Avro 698 Vulcan B2 (G-VULC)	Privately owned, Wellesbourne Mountford
	XM660	WS55 Whirlwind HAS7 [78]	RAF Millom Museum, Haverigg
	XM685	WS55 Whirlwind HAS7 (G-AYZJ) [513/PO]	Newark Air Museum, Winthorpe
	XM692	HS Gnat T1 <ff>	Robertsbridge Aviation Society, Mayfield

Serial	Type (other identity) [code]	Owner/operator, location or fate	Notes
XM693	HS Gnat T1 (7891M)	BAe Hamble, on display	
XM693	HS Gnat T1 (8618M/XP504/ G-TIMM)	Kennet Aviation, Cranfield	
XM694	HS Gnat T1	*Sold to the USA, 1997*	
XM697	HS Gnat T1 (G-NAAT)	Privately owned, Dunsfold	
XM708	HS Gnat T1 (8573M)	Privately owned, Kings Langley, Herts	
XM709	HS Gnat T1 (8617M) [67]	Privately owned	
XM715	HP80 Victor K2	British Aviation Heritage, Bruntingthorpe	
XM717	HP80 Victor K2 <ff>	RAF Museum, Hendon	
XM819	Lancashire EP9 Prospector (G-APXW)	Museum of Army Flying, Middle Wallop	
XM833	WS58 Wessex HAS3	SWWAPS, Lasham	
XM868	WS58 Wessex HAS1 [517]	RN, Predannack Fire School	
XM870	WS58 Wessex HAS3 [PO]	RN, Predannack Fire School	
XM874	WS58 Wessex HAS1 [521/CU]	RN, Predannack Fire School	
XM927	WS58 Wessex HAS3 (8814M) [660/PO]	RAF Shawbury Fire Section	
XN126	WS55 Whirlwind HAR10 (8655M) [S]	Phoenix Aviation, Bruntingthorpe	
XN185	Slingsby T21B Sedbergh TX1 (8942M/BGA 4077)	RAFGSA, Syerston	
XN187	Slingsby T21B Sedbergh TX1 (BGA 3903)	Privately owned, Seighford	
XN198	Slingsby T31B Cadet TX3	Privately owned, Challock Lees	
XN238	Slingsby T31B Cadet TX3 <ff>	S Yorkshire Aviation Museum, Firbeck	
XN239	Slingsby T31B Cadet TX3 (8889M) [G]	Imperial War Museum, Duxford	
XN243	Slingsby T31B Cadet TX3 (BGA 3145)	Privately owned, Bicester	
XN246	Slingsby T31B Cadet TX3	Southampton Hall of Aviation	
XN258	WS55 Whirlwind HAR9 [589/CU]	North-East Aircraft Museum, Usworth	
XN259	WS55 Whirlwind HAS7	*Burnt at London City Airport*	
XN263	WS55 Whirlwind HAS7	Privately owned, Chichester	
XN297	WS55 Whirlwind HAR9 (XN311) [12]	Privately owned, Hull	
XN298	WS55 Whirlwind HAR9 [810/LS]	International Fire Training Centre, Chorley	
XN299	WS55 Whirlwind HAS7 [ZZ]	Tangmere Military Aviation Museum	
XN302	WS55 Whirlwind HAS7 (9037M)	Scrapped at Stockby April 1997	
XN304	WS55 Whirlwind HAS7 [64]	Norfolk & Suffolk Avn Museum, Flixton	
XN332	Saro P531 (G-APNV)	FAA Museum, stored Yeovilton	
XN334	Saro P531	FAA Museum, stored Wroughton	
XN341	Saro Skeeter AOP12 (8022M)	Stondon Transport Mus & Garden Centre, Beds	
XN344	Saro Skeeter AOP12 (8018M)	Science Museum, South Kensington	
XN351	Saro Skeeter AOP12 (G-BKSC)	Privately owned, Ipswich	
XN380	WS55 Whirlwind HAS7	Lashenden Air Warfare Museum, Headcorn	
XN385	WS55 Whirlwind HAS7 [T]	Botany Bay Village, Chorley, Lancs	
XN386	WS55 Whirlwind HAR9 [435/ED]		
XN412	Auster AOP9	Cotswold Aircraft Rest'n Grp, Innsworth	
XN435	Auster AOP9 (G-BGBU)	Privately owned, Egham	
XN437	Auster AOP9 (G-AXWA)	Privately owned, North Weald	
XN441	Auster AOP9 (G-BGKT)	Auster 9 Group, Melton Mowbray	
XN459	Hunting Jet Provost T3A (G-BWOT)	Transair(UK) Ltd, North Weald	
XN462	Hunting Jet Provost T3A [17]	FAA Museum, Yeovilton	
XN466	Hunting Jet Provost T3A [29] <ff>	No 1005 Sqn ATC, Radcliffe, Gtr Manchester	
XN470	Hunting Jet Provost T3A (G-BXBJ) [41]	Global Aviation, Binbrook	
XN473	Hunting Jet Provost T3A (8862M) [98] <ff>		
XN492	Hunting Jet Provost T3 (8079M) <ff>	No 1940 Sqn ATC, Levenshulme	
XN493	Hunting Jet Provost T3 (XN137) <ff>	Privately owned, Camberley	
XN494	Hunting Jet Provost T3A (9012M) [43]	Crawley Technical College	
XN495	Hunting Jet Provost T3A (8786M) [102]	RAF	
XN497	Hunting Jet Provost T3A [52]	RAF St Athan	
XN498	Hunting Jet Provost T3A (G-BWSH) [16]	Global Aviation, Binbrook	
XN500	Hunting Jet Provost T3A [48]	CSE Ltd, Oxford, ground instruction	

XN 501– XN928

Notes	Serial	Type (other identity) [code]	Owner/operator, location or fate
	XN501	Hunting Jet Provost T3A (8958M) [G]	Privately owned, Billockby, Norfolk
	XN503	Hunting Jet Provost T3 <ff>	No 1284 Sqn ATC, Milford Haven
	XN505	Hunting Jet Provost T3A (25)	Privately owned, Binbrook
	XN508	Hunting Jet Provost T3A (47)	RAF St Athan
	XN510	Hunting Jet Provost T3A (G-BXBI) [40]	Global Aviation, Binbrook
	XN511	Hunting Jet Provost T3 (*XM426*) [64] <ff>	South Yorkshire Avn Museum, Firbeck
	XN512	Hunting Jet Provost T3 (8435M)	*Sold to Belgium by March 1998*
	XN549	Hunting Jet Provost T3 (8235M) [32,P]	RAF Shawbury Fire Section
	XN551	Hunting Jet Provost T3A (8984M)	RAF CTTS, St Athan
	XN554	Hunting Jet Provost T3 (8436M) [K]	RAF North Luffenham Training Area
	XN573	Hunting Jet Provost T3 [E] <ff>	Newark Air Museum, Winthorpe
	XN577	Hunting Jet Provost T3A (8956M) [89,F]	Privately owned, Billockby, Norfolk
	XN579	Hunting Jet Provost T3A (9137M) [14]	RAF North Luffenham Training Area
	XN582	Hunting Jet Provost T3A (8957M) [95,H]	Arbury College, Cambridge
	XN584	Hunting Jet Provost T3A (9014M) [E]	Phoenix Aviation, Bruntingthorpe
	XN586	Hunting Jet Provost T3A (9039M) [91,S]	Brooklands Technical College
	XN589	Hunting Jet Provost T3A (9143M) [46]	RAF Linton-on-Ouse, on display
	XN592	Hunting Jet Provost T3 <ff>	No 1105 Sqn ATC, Winchester
	XN593	Hunting Jet Provost T3A (8988M) [97,Q]	Privately owned, Billockby, Norfolk
	XN594	Hunting Jet Provost T3 (8077M) [W]	Privately owned,
	XN594	Hunting Jet Provost T3 (8234M/ XN458)	Privately owned, Ashington, W Sussex
	XN597	Hunting Jet Provost T3 (7984M) <ff>	RAF Millom Museum, Haverigg
	XN602	Hunting Jet Provost T3 (8088M)	*Burnt at Manston, 1997*
	XN607	Hunting Jet Provost T3 <ff> Chop Gate	N Yorks Aircraft Recovery Centre,
	XN629	Hunting Jet Provost T3A (G-BVEG) [49]	Transair (UK) Ltd, North Weald
	XN632	Hunting Jet Provost T3 (8352M)	Privately owned, Birlingham, Worcs
	XN634	Hunting Jet Provost T3A <ff>	Privately owned, Sproughton
	XN634	Hunting Jet Provost T3A [53] <rf>	BAe Warton Fire Section
	XN636	Hunting Jet Provost T3A (9045M) [15]	Privately owned
	XN637	Hunting Jet Provost T3 (G-BKOU) [3]	Privately owned, North Weald
	XN647	DH110 Sea Vixen FAW2 [707/VL]	Flambards Village Theme Park, Helston
	XN649	DH110 Sea Vixen FAW2 [126]	MoD(PE), stored DERA Farnborough
	XN650	DH110 Sea Vixen FAW2 <ff>	Privately owned, Welshpool
	XN651	DH110 Sea Vixen FAW2 <ff>	Communications & Electronics Museum, Bletchley Park
	XN657	DH110 Sea Vixen D3 [TR-1]	Privately owned, Stock, Essex
	XN685	DH110 Sea Vixen FAW2 (8173M) [03/VL]	Midland Air Museum, Coventry
	XN688	DH110 Sea Vixen FAW2 (8141M) [511]	DERA Farnborough Fire Section
	XN691	DH110 Sea Vixen FAW2 (8143M) [247/H]	Privately owned, North Weald
	XN696	DH110 Sea Vixen FAW2 <ff>	Blyth Valley Aviation Collection, Walpole
	XN714	Hunting H126	RAF Cosford Aerospace Museum
	XN724	EE Lightning F2A (8513M) [F]	Privately owned, Newcastle-upon-Tyne
	XN726	EE Lightning F2A (8545M) <ff>	Privately owned, Foulness
	XN728	EE Lightning F2A (8546M) [V]	Privately owned, Balderton, Notts
	XN734	EE Lightning F3A (8346M/ G-BNCA) <ff>	Privately owned, Cranfield
	XN769	EE Lightning F2 (8402M) <ff>	Privately owned, Sidcup, Kent
	XN776	EE Lightning F2A (8535M) [C]	Royal Scottish Mus'm of Flight, E Fortune
	XN795	EE Lightning F2A <ff>	Privately owned, Foulness
	XN817	AW660 Argosy C1	DERA West Freugh Fire Section
	XN819	AW660 Argosy C1 (8205M) <ff>	Newark Air Museum, Winthorpe
	XN923	HS Buccaneer S1 [13]	Vallance By-Ways, Charlwood, Surrey
	XN928	HS Buccaneer S1 (8179M) <ff>	Phoenix Aviation, Bruntingthorpe

Serial	Type (other identity) [code]	Owner/operator, location or fate	Notes
XN929	HS Buccaneer S1 (8051M) <ff>		
XN934	HS Buccaneer S1 [631] (fuselage)	RN, Predannack Fire School	
XN953	HS Buccaneer S1 (8182M)	*Burnt at Predannack by April 1998*	
XN957	HS Buccaneer S1 [630/LM]	FAA Museum, RNAS Yeovilton	
XN964	HS Buccaneer S1 [613/LM]	Newark Air Museum, Winthorpe	
XN967	HS Buccaneer S1 <ff>	Muckleburgh Collection, Weybourne, Norfolk	
XN972	HS Buccaneer S1 (8183M/XN962) <ff>	RAF Cosford Aeropsace Museum	
XN974	HS Buccaneer S2A	Yorkshire Air Museum, Elvington	
XN983	HS Buccaneer S2B <ff>	Privately owned, Terrington St Clement	
XP110	WS58 Wessex HAS3 [55/FL]	RN AESS, *HMS Sultan*, Gosport, BDRT	
XP137	WS58 Wessex HAS3 [711/DD]	SFDO, RNAS Culdrose	
XP142	WS58 Wessex HAS3	FAA Museum, stored Wroughton	
XP150	WS58 Wessex HAS1 [LS]	FETC, Moreton-in-Marsh, Glos	
XP151	WS58 Wessex HAS1 [047/R]	*Burnt at Predannack by April 1998*	
XP157	WS58 Wessex HAS1 [AN]	RNAS Yeovilton Fire Section	
XP158	WS58 Wessex HAS1 [522]	*Burnt at Predannack by April 1998*	
XP159	WS58 Wessex HAS1 (8877M) [047/R]	Privately owned, Brands Hatch	
XP160	WS58 Wessex HAS1 [521/CU]	RN, Predannack Fire School	
XP165	WS Scout AH1	The Helicopter Museum, Weston-super-Mare	
XP166	WS Scout AH1 (G-APVL)	Privately owned, East Dereham, Norfolk	
XP190	WS Scout AH1	AAC Stockwell Hall, Middle Wallop, instructional use	
XP191	WS Scout AH1	Army, Bramley, Hants	
XP226	Fairey Gannet AEW3 [073/E]	Newark Air Museum, Winthorpe	
XP241	Auster AOP9	Privately owned, Andrewsfield	
XP242	Auster AOP9 (G-BUCI)	AAC Historic Aircraft Flight, Middle Wallop	
XP244	Auster AOP9 (7864M/*M7922*)	Army SEAE, Arborfield	
XP248	Auster AOP9 (7863M/WZ679)	Privately owned, Sandy, Beds	
XP254	Auster AOP11 (G-ASCC)	Privately owned, Tollerton	
XP279	Auster AOP9 (G-BWKK)	Privately owned, Popham	
XP280	Auster AOP9	Snibston Discovery Park, Coalville	
XP281	Auster AOP9	Imperial War Museum, Duxford	
XP283	Auster AOP9 (7859M) (frame)	Privately owned, Baxterley, Warwickshire	
XP299	WS55 Whirlwind HAR10 (8726M)	RAF Cosford Aerospace Museum	
XP329	WS55 Whirlwind HAR10 (8791M) [V]	Privately owned, Tattershall Thorpe	
XP330	WS55 Whirlwind HAR10	*Burnt at Tees-side Airport by 1997*	
XP344	WS55 Whirlwind HAR10 (8764M) [H723]	RAF North Luffenham Training Area	
XP345	WS55 Whirlwind HAR10 (8792M) [UN]	York Helicopter Preservation Group, Elvington	
XP346	WS55 Whirlwind HAR10 (8793M)	Privately owned, Long Marston	
XP350	WS55 Whirlwind HAR10	Flambards Village Theme Park, Helston	
XP351	WS55 Whirlwind HAR10 (8672M) [Z]	RAF Shawbury, on display	
XP353	WS55 Whirlwind HAR10 (8720M)	Privately owned, Brands Hatch	
XP354	WS55 Whirlwind HAR10 (8721M)	Privately owned, stored Cricklade, Wilts	
XP355	WS55 Whirlwind HAR10 (8463M/ G-BEBC)	City of Norwich Aviation Museum	
XP360	WS55 Whirlwind HAR10 [V]	Privately owned, Upper Hill, nr Leominster	
XP361	WS55 Whirlwind HAR10 (8731M)	*Scrapped at Bruntingthorpe, July 1997*	
XP395	WS55 Whirlwind HAR10 (8674M) [A]	Privately owned, Tattershall Thorpe	
XP398	WS55 Whirlwind HAR10 (8794M)	Vallance By-Ways, Charlwood, Surrey	
XP399	WS55 Whirlwind HAR10	Privately owned, Wickford, Essex	
XP404	WS55 Whirlwind HAR10 (8682M)	The Helicopter Museum, Weston-super-Mare	
XP405	WS55 Whirlwind HAR10 (8656M) [Y]		
XP411	AW660 Argosy C1 (8442M) [C]	RAF Cosford Aerospace Museum	
XP454	Slingsby T38 Grasshopper TX1	Wellingborough School, Wellingborough	
XP458	Slingsby T38 Grasshopper TX1	City of Norwich Aviation Museum	
XP488	Slingsby T38 Grasshopper TX1	Fenland & W Norfolk Aviation Museum, stored Wisbech	
XP490	Slingsby T38 Grasshopper TX1	*Repainted as BGA4552*	
XP493	Slingsby T38 Grasshopper TX1	Privately owned, stored Aston Down	
XP494	Slingsby T38 Grasshopper TX1	Privately owned, Rattlesden, Suffolk	

Notes	Serial	Type (other identity) [code]	Owner/operator, location or fate
	XP502	HS Gnat T1 (8576M)	RAF CTTS, stored St Athan
	XP503	HS Gnat T1 (8568M) [73]	Phoenix Aviation, Bruntingthorpe
	XP505	HS Gnat T1	Science Museum, Wroughton
	XP516	HS Gnat T1 (8580M) [16]	DERA Structures Dept, Farnborough
	XP540	HS Gnat T1 (8608M) [62]	Arbury College, Cambridge
	XP542	HS Gnat T1 (8575M) [42]	R. Military College of Science, Shrivenham
	XP556	Hunting Jet Provost T4 (9027M) [B]	RAF Cranwell Aviation Heritage Centre
	XP557	Hunting Jet Provost T4 (8494M) [23]	Bomber County Aviation Museum, Hemswell
	XP558	Hunting Jet Provost T4 (8627M) [20]	Privately owned,
	XP563	Hunting Jet Provost T4 (9028M) [C]	Privately owned, Bicester
	XP568	Hunting Jet Provost T4	Jet Avn Preservation Grp, Long Marston
	XP573	Hunting Jet Provost T4 (8236M) [19]	Jersey Airport Fire Section
	XP585	Hunting Jet Provost T4 (8407M) [24]	NE Wales Institute, Wrexham
	XP627	Hunting Jet Provost T4	North-East Aircraft Museum, Usworth
	XP629	Hunting Jet Provost T4 (9026M) [P]	RAF North Luffenham Training Area
	XP638	Hunting Jet Provost T4 (9034M) [A]	RAF Waddington, BDRT
	XP640	Hunting Jet Provost T4 (8501M) [27]	Yorkshire Air Museum, Elvington
	XP642	Hunting Jet Provost T4 (fuselage)	Privately owned, Luton
	XP672	Hunting Jet Provost T4 (8458M/ G-RAFI) [27]	Jet Heritage Ltd, Bournemouth
	XP677	Hunting Jet Provost T4 (8587M) <ff>	No 1343 Sqn ATC, East Grinstead
	XP680	Hunting Jet Provost T4 (8460M)	FETC, Moreton-in-Marsh, Glos
	XP686	Hunting Jet Provost T4 (8401M/ 8502M) [G]	RAF North Luffenham Training Area
	XP688	Hunting Jet Provost T4 (9031M) [E]	Botany Bay Village, Chorley, Lancs
	XP693	BAC Lightning F6 (G-FSIX)	To South Africa as ZU-BEY, 1998
	XP701	BAC Lightning F3 (8924M) <ff>	Robertsbridge Aviation Society, Mayfield
	XP703	BAC Lightning F3 <ff>	Lightning Preservation Grp, RAF Coltishall
	XP706	BAC Lightning F3 (8925M)	Lincs Lightning Pres'n Soc, Strubby
	XP745	BAC Lightning F3 (8453M) <ff>	Greenford Haulage, West London
	XP772	DHC2 Beaver AL1 (G-BUCJ)	AAC Historic Aircraft Flight, stored Duxford
	XP775	DHC2 Beaver AL1	Privately owned
	XP806	DHC2 Beaver AL1	Privately owned, Cumbernauld
	XP820	DHC2 Beaver AL1	AAC Historic Aircraft Flight, Middle Wallop
	XP821	DHC2 Beaver AL1 [MCO]	Museum of Army Flying, Middle Wallop
	XP822	DHC2 Beaver AL1	Museum of Army Flying, Middle Wallop
	XP831	Hawker P.1127 (8406M)	Science Museum, South Kensington
	XP841	Handley-Page HP115	FAA Museum, RNAS Yeovilton
	XP846	WS Scout AH1 [B,H] (fuselage)	RE 39 Regt, Waterbeach, instructional use
	XP847	WS Scout AH1	Museum of Army Flying, Middle Wallop
	XP848	WS Scout AH1	AAC Arborfield, on display
	XP849	WS Scout AH1	Privately owned, East Dereham, Norfolk
	XP853	WS Scout AH1	Yeovil Naval College
	XP854	WS Scout AH1 (7898M/TAD043)	AAC Wattisham, instructional use
	XP855	WS Scout AH1	Army SEAE, Arborfield
	XP856	WS Scout AH1	Army, Bramley, Hants
	XP857	WS Scout AH1	Scrapped
	XP883	WS Scout AH1	DERA Boscombe Down, Apprentice School
	XP884	WS Scout AH1	AAC Middle Wallop, instructional use
	XP886	WS Scout AH1	Scrapped, 1998
	XP888	WS Scout AH1	Army SEAE, Arborfield
	XP890	WS Scout AH1 [G] (fuselage)	Privately owned, Ipswich
	XP893	WS Scout AH1	AAC Middle Wallop, BDRT
	XP896	WS Scout AH1	AAC 70 Aircraft Workshops, Middle Wallop, BDRT
	XP899	WS Scout AH1 [D]	Army SEAE, Arborfield
	XP902	WS Scout AH1	To Otterburn Ranges by February 1998
	XP905	WS Scout AH1	Army SEAE, Arborfield
	XP907	WS Scout AH1 (G-SROE)	Privately owned, Wattisham
	XP910	WS Scout AH1	AAC Stockwell Hall, Middle Wallop, instructional use
	XP919	DH110 Sea Vixen FAW2 (8163M) [706/VL]	Blyth Valley Aviation Collection, Walpole
	XP924	DH110 Sea Vixen D3 (G-CVIX)	De Havilland Aviation, Swansea
	XP925	DH110 Sea Vixen FAW2 [752] <ff>	No 1268 Sqn ATC, Haslemere, Surrey

Serial	Type (other identity) [code]	Owner/operator, location or fate	Notes
XP956	DH110 Sea Vixen FAW2	Privately owned	
XP980	Hawker P.1127	FAA Museum, RNAS Yeovilton	
XP984	Hawker P.1127	BAe Dunsfold, at main gate	
XR220	BAC TSR2 (7933M)	RAF Cosford Aerospace Museum	
XR222	BAC TSR2	Imperial War Museum, Duxford	
XR232	Sud Alouette AH2 (F-WEIP)	Museum of Army Flying, Middle Wallop	
XR240	Auster AOP9 (G-BDFH)	Privately owned, Booker	
XR241	Auster AOP9 (G-AXRR)	The Aircraft Restoration Co, Duxford	
XR244	Auster AOP9	AAC Historic Aircraft Flight, Middle Wallop	
XR246	Auster AOP9 (7862M/G-AZBU)	Auster 9 Group, RAF Newton	
XR267	Auster AOP9 (G-BJXR)	Cotswold Aircraft Rest'n Grp, Innsworth	
XR271	Auster AOP9	Museum of Artillery, Woolwich	
XR371	SC5 Belfast C1	RAF Cosford Aerospace Museum	
XR379	Sud Alouette AH2	AAC Historic Aircraft Flight, Middle Wallop	
XR436	Saro Scout AH1	*Scrapped*	
XR453	WS55 Whirlwind HAR10 (8873M) [A]	RAF Odiham, on gate	
XR458	WS55 Whirlwind HAR10 (8662M) [H]	Museum of Army Flying, Middle Wallop	
XR485	WS55 Whirlwind HAR10 [Q]	Norfolk & Suffolk Avn Museum, Flixton	
XR486	WS55 Whirlwind HCC12 (8727M/ G-RWWW)	Privately owned, Redhill	
XR497	WS58 Wessex HC2 [F]	RAF No 72 Sqn, Aldergrove	
XR498	WS58 Wessex HC2 [X]	RAF No 72 Sqn, Aldergrove	
XR499	WS58 Wessex HC2 [W]	RAF, stored NARO Fleetlands	
XR501	WS58 Wessex HC2	RAF, stored Shawbury	
XR502	WS58 Wessex HC2 [Z]	RAF, stored NARO Fleetlands	
XR503	WS58 Wessex HC2	RN AESS, *HMS Sultan*, Gosport	
XR504	WS58 Wessex HC2 [*Joker*]	RAF No 84 Sqn, Akrotiri	
XR505	WS58 Wessex HC2 [WA]	*To Uruguayan Navy as 081, January 1998*	
XR506	WS58 Wessex HC2 [V]	RAF No 72 Sqn, Aldergrove	
XR507	WS58 Wessex HC2	RAF, stored Shawbury	
XR508	WS58 Wessex HC2 [B]	RAF, stored NARO Fleetlands	
XR511	WS58 Wessex HC2 [L]	RAF No 72 Sqn, Aldergrove	
XR516	WS58 Wessex HC2 [WB]	RAF, stored Shawbury	
XR517	WS58 Wessex HC2 [N]	Privately owned, Sproughton	
XR518	WS58 Wessex HC2 [O]	RAF, stored NARO Fleetlands	
XR520	WS58 Wessex HC2	RAF, stored Shawbury	
XR521	WS58 Wessex HC2 [WD]	*To Uruguayan Navy as 082, January 1998*	
XR523	WS58 Wessex HC2 [M]	RAF, stored NARO Fleetlands	
XR525	WS58 Wessex HC2 [G]	RAF No 72 Sqn, Aldergrove	
XR526	WS58 Wessex HC2 (8147M)	GKN Westland, Yeovil, instructional use	
XR527	WS58 Wessex HC2 [K]	*Sold to Germany, 1998*	
XR528	WS58 Wessex HC2	RAF St Mawgan, instructional use	
XR529	WS58 Wessex HC2 [E]	RAF No 72 Sqn, Aldergrove	
XR534	HS Gnat T1 (8578M) [65]	Privately owned, Newark	
XR535	HS Gnat T1 (8569M) [05]	*Sold as N8130N, 1986*	
XR537	HS Gnat T1 (8642M/G-NATY) [T]	Jet Heritage Ltd, Bournemouth	
XR538	HS Gnat T1 (8621M/G-RORI) [69]	*Repainted as G-RORI by April 1998*	
XR569	HS Gnat T1 (8560M) [08]	Phoenix Aviation, Bruntingthorpe	
XR571	HS Gnat T1 (8493M)	RAF *Red Arrows*, Cranwell, on display	
XR574	HS Gnat T1 (8631M) [72]	RAF No 1 SoTT, Cosford	
XR588	WS58 Wessex HC2 [*Hearts*]	RAF No 84 Sqn, Akrotiri	
XR595	WS Scout AH1 (G-BWHU) [M]	Privately owned, Plymouth	
XR597	WS Scout AH1	Army, Arborfield, BDRT	
XR600	WS Scout AH1 (fuselage)	*To Otterburn Ranges by February 1998*	
XR601	WS Scout AH1	Army SEAE, Arborfield	
XR625	WS Scout AH1 (XR633/*XR777*)	Privately owned, Ipswich	
XR627	WS Scout AH1 [X]	AAC Wattisham, BDRT	
XR628	WS Scout AH1	Privately owned, Ipswich	
XR629	WS Scout AH1 (fuselage)	Privately owned, Ipswich	
XR630	WS Scout AH1	AAC Middle Wallop, Fire Section	
XR635	WS Scout AH1	Army SEAE, Arborfield	
XR639	WS Scout AH1 [X] (fuselage)	*Scrapped*	
XR650	Hunting Jet Provost T4 (8459M) [28]	DERA Boscombe Down, Apprentice School	
XR651	Hunting Jet Provost T4 (8431M) [A]	*Scrapped*	
XR654	Hunting Jet Provost T4 <ff>	Privately owned	
XR658	Hunting Jet Provost T4 (8192M)	NE Wales Institute, Connah's Quay, Clwyd	
XR662	Hunting Jet Provost T4 (8410M) [25]	Privately owned, Bicester	

Notes	Serial	Type (other identity) [code]	Owner/operator, location or fate
	XR672	Hunting Jet Provost T4 (8495M) [50]	RAF Halton, Fire Section
	XR673	Hunting Jet Provost T4 (G-BXLO/ 9032M) [L]	McCarthy Aviation, North Weald
	XR681	Hunting Jet Provost T4 (8588M) <ff>	No 1216 Sqn ATC, Newhaven, E Sussex
	XR700	Hunting Jet Provost T4 (8589M) <ff>	RAF EPTT, Aldergrove
	XR713	BAC Lightning F3 (8935M) [C]	RAF Leuchars, on display
	XR718	BAC Lightning F6 (8932M) [DA]	Blyth Valley Aviation Collection, Walpole
	XR724	BAC Lightning F6 (G-BTSY)	The Lightning Association, Binbrook
	XR725	BAC Lightning F6	Privately owned, Binbrook
	XR726	BAC Lightning F6 <ff>	Privately owned, Harrogate
	XR728	BAC Lightning F6 [JS]	Lightning Preservation Grp, Bruntingthorpe
	XR747	BAC Lightning F6 <ff>	Lightning Flying Club, Plymouth
	XR749	BAC Lightning F3 (8934M) [DA]	Tees-side Airport, on display
	XR751	BAC Lightning F3	Privately owned, Tremar, Cornwall
	XR753	BAC Lightning F6 (8969M) [BP]	RAF Leeming on display
	XR754	BAC Lightning F6 (8972M) <ff>	South Yorkshire Avn Museum, Firbeck
	XR755	BAC Lightning F6	Privately owned, Callington, Cornwall
	XR757	BAC Lightning F6 <ff>	NATO Aircraft Museum, New Waltham, Humberside
	XR759	BAC Lightning F6 <ff>	Privately owned, Haxey, Lincs
	XR770	BAC Lightning F6 [AA]	NATO Aircraft Museum, New Waltham, Humberside
	XR771	BAC Lightning F6 [BM]	Midland Air Museum, Coventry
	XR773	BAC Lightning F6 (G-OPIB)	Sold to South Africa as ZU-BEW, June 1998
	XR806	BAC VC10 C1K	RAF Brize Norton, wfu
	XR807	BAC VC10 C1K	RAF, stored St Athan
	XR808	BAC VC10 C1K	RAF No 10 Sqn, Brize Norton
	XR810	BAC VC10 C1K	RAF No 10 Sqn, Brize Norton
	XR944	Wallis WA116 (G-ATTB)	RAF Museum, Hendon
	XR954	HS Gnat T1 (8570M) [30]	Privately owned, Bournemouth
	XR955	HS Gnat T1 [SAH-2]	Privately owned, Leavesden
	XR977	HS Gnat T1 (8640M) [3]	RAF Cosford Aerospace Museum
	XR985	HS Gnat T1 (7886M)	Vintage Aircraft Team, Bruntingthorpe
	XR991	HS Gnat T1 (8624M/XS102/ G-MOUR)	Intrepid Aviation Co, North Weald
	XR993	HS Gnat T1 (8620M/XP534/ G-BVPP)	Kennet Aviation, Cranfield
	XS100	HS Gnat T1 (8561M) [57]	Privately owned, Bournemouth
	XS101	HS Gnat T1 (8638M) (G-GNAT)	Privately owned, Cranfield
	XS122	WS58 Wessex HAS3 [655/PO]	RN AESS, HMS Sultan, Gosport
	XS128	WS58 Wessex HAS1 [37]	RNAS Yeovilton Fire Section
	XS149	WS58 Wessex HAS3 [661/GL]	The Helicopter Museum, Weston-super-Mare
	XS165	Hiller UH12E (G-ASAZ) [37]	Privately owned, North Weald
	XS176	Hunting Jet Provost T4 (8514M) [N]	University of Salford, Manchester
	XS177	Hunting Jet Provost T4 (9044M) [N]	RAF Valley Fire Section
	XS179	Hunting Jet Provost T4 (8237M) [20]	University of Salford, Manchester
	XS180	Hunting Jet Provost T4 (8238M) [21]	RAF Lyneham (dismantled)
	XS181	Hunting Jet Provost T4 (9033M) <ff>	Communications & Electronics Museum, Bletchley Park
	XS183	Hunting Jet Provost T4 <ff>	Privately owned, Plymouth
	XS186	Hunting Jet Provost T4 (8408M) [M]	RAF North Luffenham Training Area
	XS209	Hunting Jet Provost T4 (8409M) [29]	Privately owned, Kemble
	XS215	Hunting Jet Provost T4 (8507M) [17]	RAF Halton
	XS216	Hunting Jet Provost T4 <ff>	Privately owned
	XS217	Hunting Jet Provost T4 (9029M) [O]	Privately owned, Bruntingthorpe
	XS218	Hunting Jet Provost T4 (8508M) <ff>	No 447 Sqn ATC, Henley-on-Thames, Berks
	XS231	BAC Jet Provost T5 (G-ATAJ)	Phoenix Aviation, Bruntingthorpe
	XS235	DH106 Comet 4C	British Aviation Heritage, Bruntingthorpe
	XS416	BAC Lightning T5 <ff>	NATO Aircraft Museum, New Waltham, Humberside
	XS417	BAC Lightning T5 [DZ]	Newark Air Museum, Winthorpe
	XS420	BAC Lightning T5	Privately owned, Norfolk
	XS421	BAC Lightning T5 <ff>	Privately owned, Foulness
	XS451	BAC Lightning T5 (8503M/ G-LTNG)	Sold to South Africa as ZU-BEX, June 1998
	XS452	BAC Lightning T5 (G-BPFE/	Sold to South Africa as ZU-BBD, June 1998
	XS456	BAC Lightning T5 [DX]	Privately owned, Wainfleet

Serial	Type (other identity) [code]	Owner/operator, location or fate	Notes
XS457	BAC Lightning T5 <ff>	NATO Aircraft Museum, New Waltham, Humberside	
XS458	BAC Lightning T5	T5 Projects, Cranfield	
XS459	BAC Lightning T5 [AW]	Fenland & W Norfolk Aviation Museum, Wisbech	
XS463	WS Wasp HAS1 (XT431)	The Helicopter Museum, Weston-super-Mare	
XS463	WS Wasp HAS1	*Burnt at Predannack by April 1998*	
XS479	WS58 Wessex HU5 (8819M) [XF]	Privately owned, Stock, Essex	
XS481	WS58 Wessex HU5	South Yorkshire Avn Museum, Firbeck	
XS482	WS58 Wessex HU5 [A/D]	FSCTE, RAF Manston	
XS484	WS58 Wessex HU5 [821/CU]	*Scrapped at Stock by April 1997*	
XS485	WS58 Wessex HC5C [*Hearts*] (comp XR503)	RN AESS, *HMS Sultan*, Gosport	
XS486	WS58 Wessex HU5 [524/CU,F]	RN Recruiting Team, Wroughton	
XS488	WS58 Wessex HU5 (9056M) [XK]	AAC Wattisham, instructional use	
XS489	WS58 Wessex HU5 [R]		
XS491	WS58 Wessex HU5 [XM]	RAF No 16 MU Stafford Fire Section	
XS492	WS58 Wessex HU5 [623]	RN, stored NARO Fleetlands	
XS493	WS58 Wessex HU5	RN, stored NARO Fleetlands	
XS496	WS58 Wessex HU5 [625/PO]	RN AESS, *HMS Sultan*, Gosport	
XS498	WS58 Wessex HC5C (comp XS677) [WK]	RN AESS, *HMS Sultan*, Gosport	
XS507	WS58 Wessex HU5	RN AESS, *HMS Sultan*, Gosport	
XS508	WS58 Wessex HU5	FAA Museum, RNAS Yeovilton	
XS509	WS58 Wessex HU5	*To New Zealand, as ZK-HVK, Feb1998*	
XS510	WS58 Wessex HU5 [626/PO]	RN AESS, *HMS Sultan*, Gosport	
XS511	WS58 Wessex HU5 [M]	RN AESS, *HMS Sultan*, Gosport	
XS513	WS58 Wessex HU5 [419/CU]	RN AESS, *HMS Sultan*, Gosport	
XS514	WS58 Wessex HU5 [L]	RN AESS, *HMS Sultan*, Gosport	
XS515	WS58 Wessex HU5 [N]	RN AESS, *HMS Sultan*, Gosport	
XS516	WS58 Wessex HU5 [Q]	RN AESS, *HMS Sultan*, Gosport, BDRT	
XS517	WS58 Wessex HC5C (comp XS679) [*Diamonds*]	RN AESS, *HMS Sultan*, Gosport	
XS520	WS58 Wessex HU5 [F]	RN AESS, *HMS Sultan*, Gosport	
XS521	WS58 Wessex HU5	Army, Saighton, Cheshire	
XS522	WS58 Wessex HU5 [ZL]	RN AESS, *HMS Sultan*, Gosport, BDRT	
XS527	WS Wasp HAS1	FAA Museum, RNAS Yeovilton	
XS529	WS Wasp HAS1 [461]	*Burnt at Predannackby Novembe.1998l*	
XS539	WS Wasp HAS1 [435]	NARO Fleetlands Apprentice School	
XS567	WS Wasp HAS1 [434/E]	Imperial War Museum, Duxford	
XS568	WS Wasp HAS1 [441]	RN AESS, *HMS Sultan*, Gosport	
XS569	WS Wasp HAS1	NARO Fleetlands Apprentice School	
XS570	WS Wasp HAS1 [445/P]	Warship Preservation Trust, Birkenhead	
XS572	WS Wasp HAS1 (8845M) [414]	RAF No 16 MU Stafford Fire Section	
XS576	DH110 Sea Vixen FAW2 [125/E]	Imperial War Museum, Duxford	
XS577	DH110 Sea Vixen D3 <ff>	Phoenix Aviation, stored Bruntingthorpe	
XS587	DH110 Sea Vixen FAW(TT)2 (8828M/G-VIXN)	Vallance By-Ways, Charlwood, Surrey	
XS590	DH110 Sea Vixen FAW2 [131/E]	FAA Museum, RNAS Yeovilton	
XS596	HS Andover C1(PR)	MoD(PE)/AFD/*Open Skies*, DERA Boscombe Down	
XS598	HS Andover C1 (fuselage)	FETC, Moreton-in-Marsh, Glos	
XS605	HS Andover E3	*Scrapped at Northolt, 1997*	
XS606	HS Andover C1	MoD(PE)/AFD/ETPS, DERA Boscombe Down	
XS639	HS Andover E3A	RAF Cosford Aerospace Museum	
XS641	HS Andover C1(PR) (9198M) [Z]	RAF No 1 SoTT, Cosford	
XS643	HS Andover E3A	FSCTE, RAF Manston	
XS646	HS Andover C1(mod)	MoD(PE)/AFD, DERA Boscombe Down	
XS652	Slingsby T45 Swallow TX1 (BGA 1107)	Privately owned, Rufforth	
XS674	WS58 Wessex HC2 [R]	Privately owned, Sproughton	
XS675	WS58 Wessex HC2 [*Spades*]	RAF No 84 Sqn, Akrotiri	
XS676	WS58 Wessex HC2 [WJ]	*To Uruguayan Navy as 083, January 1998*	
XS677	WS58 Wessex HC2 [WK]	RAF, stored Shawbury	
XS679	WS58 Wessex HC2 [WG]	*To Uruguayan Navy as 084, January 1998*	
XS695	HS Kestrel FGA1	RAF Museum Restoration Centre, Cardington	
XS709	HS125 Dominie T2 [M]	RAF No 3 FTS/55(R) Sqn, Cranwell	
XS710	HS125 Dominie T1 (9295M) [O]	RAF No 1 SoTT, Cosford	
XS711	HS125 Dominie T2 [L]	RAF No 3 FTS/55(R) Sqn, Cranwell	
XS712	HS125 Dominie T2 [A]	RAF No 3 FTS/55(R) Sqn, Cranwell	

Notes	Serial	Type (other identity) [code]	Owner/operator, location or fate
	XS713	HS125 Dominie T2 [C]	RAF No 3 FTS/55(R) Sqn, Cranwell
	XS714	HS125 Dominie T1 (9246M) [P]	FSCTE, RAF Manston
	XS726	HS125 Dominie T1 [T]	RAF No 1 SoTT, Cosford
	XS727	HS125 Dominie T2 [D]	RAF No 3 FTS/55(R) Sqn, Cranwell
	XS728	HS125 Dominie T2 [E]	RAF No 3 FTS/55(R) Sqn, Cranwell
	XS729	HS125 Dominie T1 [G]	RAF No 1 SoTT, Cosford
	XS730	HS125 Dominie T2 [H]	RAF No 3 FTS/55(R) Sqn, Cranwell
	XS731	HS125 Dominie T2 [J]	RAF No 3 FTS/55(R) Sqn, Cranwell
	XS732	HS125 Dominie T1 [B] (fuselage)	DERA, Fort Halstead, Kent
	XS733	HS125 Dominie T1 [Q]	RAF No 1 SoTT, Cosford
	XS734	HS125 Dominie T1 (9260M) [N]	RAF No 1 SoTT, Cosford
	XS735	HS125 Dominie T1 [R]	RAF Cranwell, instructional use
	XS736	HS125 Dominie T2 [S]	RAF No 3 FTS/55(R) Sqn, Cranwell
	XS737	HS125 Dominie T2 [K]	RAF No 3 FTS/55(R) Sqn, Cranwell
	XS738	HS125 Dominie T1 [U]	RAF No 1 SoTT, Cosford
	XS739	HS125 Dominie T2 [F]	RAF No 3 FTS/55(R) Sqn, Cranwell
	XS743	Beagle B206Z Basset CC1	MoD(PE)/AFD/ETPS, DERA Boscombe Down
	XS765	Beagle B206Z Basset CC1 (G-BSET)	Privately owned, Cranfield
	XS770	Beagle B206Z Basset CC1 (G-HRHI)	Privately owned, Cranfield
	XS790	HS748 Andover CC2 <ff>	The Air Defence Collection, Salisbury
	XS791	HS748 Andover CC2	Phoenix Aviation, Bruntingthorpe
	XS862	WS58 Wessex HAS3	Defence NBC Centre, Winterbourne Gunner
	XS863	WS58 Wessex HAS1	Imperial War Museum, Duxford
	XS866	WS58 Wessex HAS1 [520/CU]	SFDO, RNAS Culdrose
	XS868	WS58 Wessex HAS1	RN AESS, HMS Sultan, Gosport
	XS870	WS58 Wessex HAS1 [PO]	RNAS Portland, BDRT
	XS871	WS58 Wessex HAS1 (8457M)	Privately owned, Chippenham, Wilts
	XS872	WS58 Wessex HAS1 [572/CU]	
	XS876	WS58 Wessex HAS1 [523]	SFDO, RNAS Culdrose
	XS877	WS58 Wessex HAS1 [516/PO]	Burnt at Predannack by June 1997
	XS881	WS58 Wessex HAS1 [046/CU]	RN, Predannack Fire School
	XS885	WS58 Wessex HAS1 [12/CU]	SFDO, RNAS Culdrose
	XS886	WS58 Wessex HAS1 [527/CU]	Sea Scouts, Evesham, Worcs
	XS887	WS58 Wessex HAS1 [403/Fl]	Flambards Village Theme Park, Helston
	XS888	WS58 Wessex HAS1 [521]	Guernsey Airport Fire Section
	XS897	BAC Lightning F6	South Yorkshire Avn Museum, Firbeck
	XS898	BAC Lightning F6 <ff>	Privately owned, Lavendon, Bucks
	XS899	BAC Lightning F6 <ff>	RAF Coltishall
	XS903	BAC Lightning F6 [BA]	Yorkshire Air Museum, Elvington
	XS904	BAC Lightning F6 [BQ]	Lightning Preservation Grp, Bruntingthorpe
	XS919	BAC Lightning F6	Privately owned, Torpoint, Devon
	XS922	BAC Lightning F6 (8973M) <ff>	The Air Defence Collection, Salisbury
	XS923	BAC Lightning F6 <ff>	Privately owned, Welshpool
	XS925	BAC Lightning F6 (8961M) [BA]	RAF Museum, Hendon
	XS928	BAC Lightning F6 [AD]	BAe Warton, stored
	XS932	BAC Lightning F6 <ff>	D-Day Museum, Shoreham
	XS933	BAC Lightning F6 <ff>	Privately owned, Terrington St Clement
	XS936	BAC Lightning F6	Castle Motors, Liskeard, Cornwall
	XT108	Agusta-Bell 47G-3 Sioux AH1 [U]	Museum of Army Flying, Middle Wallop
	XT123	WS Sioux AH1 (XT827) [D]	AAC Middle Wallop, at main gate
	XT131	Agusta-Bell 47G-3 Sioux AH1 [B]	AAC Historic Aircraft Flight, Middle Wallop
	XT133	Agusta-Bell 47G-3 Sioux AH1 (7923M)	Royal Engineers' Museum, Chatham, stored
	XT140	Agusta-Bell 47G-3 Sioux AH1	Perth Technical College
	XT148	Agusta-Bell 47G-3 Sioux AH1	The Helicopter Museum, stored Weston-super-Mare
	XT150	Agusta-Bell 47G-3 Sioux AH1 (7883M) [R]	AAC Netheravon, at main gate
	XT151	WS Sioux AH1 [W]	Museum of Army Flying, stored Middle Wallop
	XT175	WS Sioux AH1 (TAD175)	CSE Ltd, Oxford for ground instruction
	XT176	WS Sioux AH1 [U]	FAA Museum, stored Wroughton
	XT190	WS Sioux AH1	The Helicopter Museum, Weston-super-Mare
	XT200	WS Sioux AH1 [F]	Newark Air Museum, Winthorpe
	XT223	WS Sioux AH1 (G-BGZK)	Privately owned, North Weald
	XT236	WS Sioux AH1 (frame only)	North-East Aircraft Museum, stored Usworth

Serial	Type (other identity) [code]	Owner/operator, location or fate	Notes
XT242	WS Sioux AH1 (composite) [12]	South Yorkshire Avn Museum, Firbeck	
XT255	WS58 Wessex HAS3 (8751M)		
XT257	WS58 Wessex HAS3 (8719M)	Privately owned, East Grinstead	
XT277	HS Buccaneer S2A (8853M) <ff>	Privately owned, Welshpool	
XT280	HS Buccaneer S2A <ff>	Dundonald Aviation Centre, Strathclyde	
XT284	HS Buccaneer S2A (8855M) <ff>	Privately owned, Stock, Essex	
XT288	HS Buccaneer S2B (9134M)	Royal Scottish Museum of Flight, stored E Fortune	
XT420	WS Wasp HAS1 [606]	Privately owned, East Dereham, Norfolk	
XT422	WS Wasp HAS1 [324]	Privately owned, Burgess Hill	
XT427	WS Wasp HAS1 [606]	FAA Museum, at Flambards Village Theme Park, Helston	
XT434	WS Wasp HAS1 [455]	NARO Fleetlands Apprentice School	
XT439	WS Wasp HAS1 [605]	Privately owned, King's Lynn	
XT443	WS Wasp HAS1 [422/AU]	The Helicopter Museum, Weston-super-Mare	
XT449	WS58 Wessex HU5 [C]	*Burnt at Predannack by April 1998*	
XT450	WS58 Wessex HU5	*Burnt at Predannack by April 1998*	
XT453	WS58 Wessex HU5 [A/B]	RN AESS, *HMS Sultan*, Gosport	
XT455	WS58 Wessex HU5 [U]	RN AESS, *HMS Sultan*, Gosport	
XT456	WS58 Wessex HU5 (8941M) [XZ]	RAF Aldergrove, BDRT	
XT458	WS58 Wessex HU5 [622]	RN AESS, *HMS Sultan*, Gosport	
XT463	WS58 Wessex HC5C (comp XR508) [*Clubs*, PO]	RN AESS, *HMS Sultan*, Gosport	
XT466	WS58 Wessex HU5 (8921M) [XV]	RN AESS, *HMS Sultan*, Gosport	
XT467	WS58 Wessex HU5 (8922M) [BF]	RAF Odiham Fire Section	
XT468	WS58 Wessex HU5 (comp XT460) [628]	RN, Predannack Fire School	
XT469	WS58 Wessex HU5 (8920M)	RAF No 16 MU, Stafford, ground instruction	
XT471	WS58 Wessex HU5	*Burnt at Dishforth, 1998*	
XT472	WS58 Wessex HU5 [XC]	The Helicopter Museum, Weston-super-Mare	
XT475	WS58 Wessex HU5 (9108M) [624]	Burnt at Manston, 1997	
XT480	WS58 Wessex HU5 [468/RG]	NARO Fleetlands, on display	
XT481	WS58 Wessex HU5	*Burnt at Predannack by August 1995*	
XT482	WS58 Wessex HU5 [ZM/VL]	FAA Museum, RNAS Yeovilton	
XT484	WS58 Wessex HU5 [H]	RN AESS, *HMS Sultan*, Gosport	
XT485	WS58 Wessex HU5 [621]	RN AESS, *HMS Sultan*, Gosport	
XT486	WS58 Wessex HU5 (8919M) [XR]	*To Altcar Ranges, 1996*	
XT550	WS Sioux AH1 [D]	*To Australia, 1996*	
XT575	Vickers Viscount 837 <ff>	Brooklands Museum, Weybridge	
XT595	McD F-4K Phantom FG1 (8851M) <ff>	RAF EPTT, St Athan	
XT596	McD F-4K Phantom FG1	FAA Museum, RNAS Yeovilton	
XT597	McD F-4K Phantom FG1	DERA Boscombe Down, for lightning tests	
XT601	WS58 Wessex HC2	RAF Odiham, BDRT	
XT602	WS58 Wessex HC2	RAF, stored Shawbury	
XT603	WS58 Wessex HC2 [WF]	*To Uruguayan Navy as 085, January 1998*	
XT604	WS58 Wessex HC2	RAF, stored NARO Fleetlands	
XT606	WS58 Wessex HC2 [WL]	RAF, stored Shawbury	
XT607	WS58 Wessex HC2 [P]	RAF, stored NARO Fleetlands	
XT616	WS Scout AH1 (fuselage)	*Scrapped*	
XT617	WS Scout AH1	AAC Wattisham, on display	
XT620	WS Scout AH1	AAC Dishforth Fire Section	
XT621	WS Scout AH1	R. Military College of Science, Shrivenham	
XT623	WS Scout AH1	Army SEAE, Arborfield	
XT624	WS Scout AH1 (G-NOTY) [D]	*Repainted as G-NOTY by May 1998*	
XT626	WS Scout AH1 [Q]	AAC Historic Aircraft Flt, Middle Wallop	
XT630	WS Scout AH1 (G-BXRL) [X]	*Crashed July 1998, Hambleton Hall, Leics*	
XT631	WS Scout AH1 [D]	Privately owned, Ipswich	
XT632	WS Scout AH1	Privately owned, Hawarden	
XT633	WS Scout AH1	Army SEAE, Arborfield	
XT634	WS Scout AH1 [T]	Privately owned, Hawarden	
XT638	WS Scout AH1 [N]	AAC Middle Wallop, at gate	
XT639	WS Scout AH1 [Y] (fuselage)	*Scrapped*	
XT640	WS Scout AH1	Army SEAE, Arborfield	
XT642	WS Scout AH1 (fuselage)	*Scrapped*	
XT643	WS Scout AH1 [Z]	Army, Thorpe Camp, East Wretham	
XT645	WS Scout AH1 (fuselage)	Privately owned, Ipswich	
XT649	WS Scout AH1	*Sold to ZK-HUK, 1996*	
XT668	WS58 Wessex HC2 [S]	RAF No 72 Sqn, Aldergrove	
XT670	WS58 Wessex HC2	*Sold to Germany, 1998*	

Notes	Serial	Type (other identity) [code]	Owner/operator, location or fate
	XT671	WS58 Wessex HC2 [D]	Privately owned, Redhill
	XT672	WS58 Wessex HC2 [WE]	RAF, stored Shawbury
	XT676	WS58 Wessex HC2 [I]	RAF No 72 Sqn, Aldergrove
	XT677	WS58 Wessex HC2 (8016M)	Privately owned, Stock, Essex
	XT680	WS58 Wessex HC2 [Diamonds]	RAF No 84 Sqn, Akrotiri
	XT681	WS58 Wessex HC2 [U]	RAF Benson, BDRT
	XT759	WS58 Wessex HU5 [XY]	
	XT760	WS58 Wessex HU5 (comp XT604)	Royal Navy Diving School, Horsey Island
	XT761	WS58 Wessex HU5	RN AESS, HMS Sultan, Gosport
	XT762	WS58 Wessex HU5	SFDO, RNAS Culdrose
	XT765	WS58 Wessex HU5 [J]	RN AESS, HMS Sultan, Gosport
	XT766	WS58 Wessex HU5 (9054M) [822/CU]	RN AESS, HMS Sultan, Gosport
	XT769	WS58 Wessex HU5 [823]	FAA Museum, RNAS Yeovilton
	XT770	WS58 Wessex HU5 (9055M) [P]	Privately owned, Shawell, Leics
	XT771	WS58 Wessex HU5 [620/PO]	RN AESS, HMS Sultan, Gosport
	XT772	WS58 Wessex HU5 (8805M)	SARTU RAF Valley, ground instruction
	XT773	WS58 Wessex HU5 (9123M) [822/CU]	RAF St Athan, BDRT
	XT778	WS Wasp HAS1 [430]	RN Portland, at main gate
	XT780	WS Wasp HAS1 [636]	NARO Fleetlands Apprentice School
	XT788	WS Wasp HAS1 (G-BMIR) [316] (painted as XT78?)	Privately owned, Dunkeswell
	XT793	WS Wasp HAS1 [456]	Privately owned, East Dereham, Norfolk
	XT803	WS Sioux AH1 [Y]	Privately owned, Panshanger
	XT852	McD YF-4M Phantom FGR2	DERA West Freugh Fire Section
	XT863	McD F-4K Phantom FG1 <ff>	Privately owned, Cowes, IOW
	XT864	McD F-4K Phantom FG1 (8998M/XT684) [BJ]	RAF Leuchars on display
	XT867	McD F-4K Phantom FG1 (9064M) [BH]	RAF Leuchars BDRT
	XT891	McD F-4M Phantom FGR2 (9136M)	RAF Coningsby, on display
	XT903	McD F-4M Phantom FGR2 [X]	RAF Leuchars, BDRT
	XT905	McD F-4M Phantom FGR2 [P]	RAF Coningsby, stored
	XT907	McD F-4M Phantom FGR2 (9151M) [W]	DEODS, Chattenden, Kent
	XT914	McD F-4M Phantom FGR2	RAF Brampton, Cambs, on display
	XV101	BAC VC10 C1K	RAF No 10 Sqn, Brize Norton
	XV102	BAC VC10 C1K	RAF No 10 Sqn, Brize Norton
	XV103	BAC VC10 C1K	RAF No 10 Sqn, Brize Norton
	XV104	BAC VC10 C1K	RAF No 10 Sqn, Brize Norton
	XV105	BAC VC10 C1K	RAF No 10 Sqn, Brize Norton
	XV106	BAC VC10 C1K	RAF No 10 Sqn, Brize Norton
	XV107	BAC VC10 C1K	RAF No 10 Sqn, Brize Norton
	XV108	BAC VC10 C1K	RAF No 10 Sqn, Brize Norton
	XV109	BAC VC10 C1K	RAF No 10 Sqn, Brize Norton
	XV118	WS Scout AH1 (9141M)	RAF Air Movements School, Brize Norton
	XV119	WS Scout AH1 [T]	To Otterburn Ranges by February 1998
	XV121	WS Scout AH1	Privately owned, Oaksey Park, Wilts
	XV122	WS Scout AH1 [D]	R. Military College of Science, Shrivenham
	XV123	WS Scout AH1	The Helicopter Museum, Weston-super-Mare
	XV124	WS Scout AH1 [W]	AAC Stockwell Hall, Middle Wallop, instructional use
	XV126	WS Scout AH1 (G-SCTA) [X]	Privately owned, Hawarden
	XV127	WS Scout AH1	Museum of Army Flying, Middle Wallop
	XV128	WS Scout AH1	Sold as ZK-HUD, 1996
	XV129	WS Scout AH1 [V]	Sold to New Zealand, 1996
	XV130	WS Scout AH1 (G-BWJW) [R]	Privately owned, Redhill
	XV131	WS Scout AH1 [Y]	AAC 70 Aircraft Workshops, Middle Wallop, BDRT
	XV134	WS Scout AH1 (G-BWLX) [P]	Privately owned, East Dereham, Norfolk
	XV135	WS Scout AH1	Scrapped
	XV136	WS Scout AH1 [X]	AAC Netheravon, on display
	XV137	WS Scout AH1 (G-CRUM)	Privately owned, Edinburgh
	XV138	WS Scout AH1	Privately owned, East Dereham
	XV139	WS Scout AH1	
	XV140	WS Scout AH1 (G-KAXL) [K]	Kennet Aviation, Cranfield
	XV141	WS Scout AH1	Army SEAE, Arborfield
	XV147	HS Nimrod MR1(mod) (fuselage)	MoD(PE)/BAe, Warton
	XV148	HS Nimrod MR1(mod) (fuselage)	BAe, stored Woodford
	XV161	HS Buccaneer S2B (9117M) <ff>	Privately owned, Birtley, Tyne & Wear

Serial	Type (other identity) [code]	Owner/operator, location or fate	Notes
XV165	HS Buccaneer S2B <ff>	Jet Age Museum, Staverton	
XV168	HS Buccaneer S2B	BAe Brough, on display	
XV176	Lockheed C-130K Hercules C3	RAF Lyneham Transport Wing	
XV177	Lockheed C-130K Hercules C3	RAF Lyneham Transport Wing	
XV178	Lockheed C-130K Hercules C1	RAF Lyneham Transport Wing	
XV179	Lockheed C-130K Hercules C1	RAF Lyneham Transport Wing	
XV181	Lockheed C-130K Hercules C1	RAF Lyneham Transport Wing	
XV182	Lockheed C-130K Hercules C1	RAF Lyneham Transport Wing	
XV183	Lockheed C-130K Hercules C3	RAF Lyneham Transport Wing	
XV184	Lockheed C-130K Hercules C3	RAF Lyneham Transport Wing	
XV185	Lockheed C-130K Hercules C1	RAF Lyneham Transport Wing	
XV186	Lockheed C-130K Hercules C1	RAF Lyneham Transport Wing	
XV187	Lockheed C-130K Hercules C1	RAF Lyneham Transport Wing	
XV188	Lockheed C-130K Hercules C3	RAF Lyneham Transport Wing	
XV189	Lockheed C-130K Hercules C3	RAF Lyneham Transport Wing	
XV190	Lockheed C-130K Hercules C3	RAF Lyneham Transport Wing	
XV191	Lockheed C-130K Hercules C1	RAF Lyneham Transport Wing	
XV192	Lockheed C-130K Hercules C1	RAF Lyneham Transport Wing	
XV195	Lockheed C-130K Hercules C1	RAF Lyneham Transport Wing	
XV196	Lockheed C-130K Hercules C1	RAF Lyneham Transport Wing	
XV197	Lockheed C-130K Hercules C3	RAF Lyneham Transport Wing	
XV199	Lockheed C-130K Hercules C3	RAF Lyneham Transport Wing	
XV200	Lockheed C-130K Hercules C1	RAF Lyneham Transport Wing	
XV201	Lockheed C-130K Hercules C1K	RAF, stored Cambridge	
XV202	Lockheed C-130K Hercules C3	RAF Lyneham Transport Wing	
XV203	Lockheed C-130K Hercules C1K	RAF, stored Cambridge	
XV204	Lockheed C-130K Hercules C1K	*Broken up at Cambridge, August 1998*	
XV205	Lockheed C-130K Hercules C1	RAF Lyneham Transport Wing	
XV206	Lockheed C-130K Hercules C1	RAF Lyneham Transport Wing	
XV207	Lockheed C-130K Hercules C3	RAF Lyneham Transport Wing	
XV208	Lockheed C-130K Hercules W2	MoD(PE)/MRF, DERA Boscombe Down	
XV209	Lockheed C-130K Hercules C3	RAF Lyneham Transport Wing	
XV210	Lockheed C-130K Hercules C1	RAF Lyneham Transport Wing	
XV211	Lockheed C-130K Hercules C1	RAF Lyneham Transport Wing	
XV212	Lockheed C-130K Hercules C3	RAF Lyneham Transport Wing	
XV213	Lockheed C-130K Hercules C1K	RAF, stored Cambridge	
XV214	Lockheed C-130K Hercules C3	RAF Lyneham Transport Wing	
XV215	Lockheed C-130K Hercules C1	RAF Lyneham Transport Wing	
XV217	Lockheed C-130K Hercules C3	RAF Lyneham Transport Wing	
XV218	Lockheed C-130K Hercules C1	RAF No 1312 Flt, Mount Pleasant, FI	
XV219	Lockheed C-130K Hercules C3	RAF Lyneham Transport Wing	
XV220	Lockheed C-130K Hercules C3	RAF Lyneham Transport Wing	
XV221	Lockheed C-130K Hercules C3	RAF Lyneham Transport Wing	
XV222	Lockheed C-130K Hercules C3	RAF Lyneham Transport Wing	
XV223	Lockheed C-130K Hercules C3	RAF Lyneham Transport Wing	
XV226	HS Nimrod MR2	RAF Kinloss MR Wing	
XV227	HS Nimrod MR2	RAF Kinloss MR Wing	
XV228	HS Nimrod MR2	RAF No 42(R) Sqn, Kinloss	
XV229	HS Nimrod MR2	RAF Kinloss MR Wing	
XV230	HS Nimrod MR2	RAF Kinloss MR Wing	
XV231	HS Nimrod MR2	RAF Kinloss MR Wing	
XV232	HS Nimrod MR2	RAF Kinloss MR Wing	
XV233	HS Nimrod MR2	RAF No 42(R) Sqn, Kinloss	
XV234	BAe Nimrod MRA4 [PA-2]	*Conversion to Nimrod MRA4 ZJ515.*	
XV235	HS Nimrod MR2	RAF Kinloss MR Wing	
XV236	HS Nimrod MR2	RAF No 42(R) Sqn, Kinloss	
XV237	HS Nimrod MR2 <ff>	Privately owned, St Austell	
XV238	HS Nimrod <R> (parts of G-ALYW)	RAF EPTT, St Athan	
XV240	HS Nimrod MR2 [CXX]	RAF No 120 Sqn, Kinloss	
XV241	HS Nimrod MR2	RAF No 206 Sqn, Kinloss	
XV242	BAe Nimrod MRA4 [PA-3]	*Conversion to Nimrod MRA4 ZJ516.*	
XV243	HS Nimrod MR2	RAF No 120 Sqn, Kinloss	
XV244	HS Nimrod MR2	RAF Kinloss MR Wing	
XV245	HS Nimrod MR2	RAF No 201 Sqn, Kinloss	
XV246	HS Nimrod MR2	RAF Kinloss MR Wing	
XV247	BAe Nimrod MRA4 [PA-1]	*Conversion to Nimrod MRA4 ZJ514*	
XV248	HS Nimrod MR2	RAF Kinloss MR Wing	
XV249	HS Nimrod R1	RAF No 51 Sqn, Waddington	
XV250	HS Nimrod MR2	RAF Kinloss MR Wing	
XV251	BAe Nimrod MRA4 [PA-4]	*Conversion to Nimrod MRA4 ZJ517.*	
XV252	HS Nimrod MR2	RAF No 201 Sqn, Kinloss	
XV253	HS Nimrod MR2 (9118M)	RAF Kinloss (instructional use)	
XV254	HS Nimrod MR2	RAF Kinloss MR Wing	

Notes	Serial	Type (other identity) [code]	Owner/operator, location or fate
	XV255	HS Nimrod MR2	RAF Kinloss MR Wing
	XV258	HS Nimrod MR2	RAF Kinloss MR Wing
	XV259	BAe Nimrod AEW3 <ff>	Privately owned, Carlisle
	XV260	HS Nimrod MR2 [CXX]	RAF No 120 Sqn, Kinloss
	XV263	BAe Nimrod AEW3P (8967M) <ff>	BAe Warton (instruction)
	XV263	BAe Nimrod AEW3P (8967M) <rf>	FR Aviation, Bournemouth
	XV268	DHC2 Beaver AL1 (G-BVER)	Privately owned
	XV277	HS P.1127(RAF)	Privately owned, Sproughton
	XV279	HS P.1127(RAF) (8566M)	RAF Harrier Maintenance School, Wittering
	XV280	HS P.1127(RAF) <ff>	RNAS Yeovilton Fire Section
	XV281	HS Harrier GR3	Used in the rebuild of XW272
	XV290	Lockheed C-130K Hercules C3	RAF Lyneham Transport Wing
	XV291	Lockheed C-130K Hercules C1	RAF Lyneham Transport Wing
	XV292	Lockheed C-130K Hercules C1	RAF Lyneham Transport Wing
	XV293	Lockheed C-130K Hercules C1	RAF Lyneham Transport Wing
	XV294	Lockheed C-130K Hercules C3	RAF Lyneham Transport Wing
	XV295	Lockheed C-130K Hercules C1	RAF Lyneham Transport Wing
	XV296	Lockheed C-130K Hercules C1K	RAF, stored Cambridge
	XV297	Lockheed C-130K Hercules C1	RAF Lyneham Transport Wing
	XV298	Lockheed C-130K Hercules C1	RAF Lyneham Transport Wing
	XV299	Lockheed C-130K Hercules C3	RAF Lyneham Transport Wing
	XV300	Lockheed C-130K Hercules C1	RAF Lyneham Transport Wing
	XV301	Lockheed C-130K Hercules C3	RAF Lyneham Transport Wing
	XV302	Lockheed C-130K Hercules C3	RAF Lyneham Transport Wing
	XV303	Lockheed C-130K Hercules C3	RAF Lyneham Transport Wing
	XV304	Lockheed C-130K Hercules C3	RAF Lyneham Transport Wing
	XV305	Lockheed C-130K Hercules C3	RAF Lyneham Transport Wing
	XV306	Lockheed C-130K Hercules C1	RAF Lyneham Transport Wing
	XV307	Lockheed C-130K Hercules C3	RAF Lyneham Transport Wing
	XV328	BAC Lightning T5 <ff>	Phoenix Aviation, Bruntingthorpe
	XV332	HS Buccaneer S2B (9232M)	RAF Marham Fire Section
	XV333	HS Buccaneer S2B [234/H]	FAA Museum, RNAS Yeovilton
	XV337	HS Buccaneer S2C (8852M) <ff>	Privately owned, Stock, Essex
	XV344	HS Buccaneer S2C	DERA Farnborough, on display
	XV350	HS Buccaneer S2B	Privately owned, East Midlands Airport
	XV352	HS Buccaneer S2B <ff>	Privately owned, Stock, Essex
	XV353	HS Buccaneer S2B (9144M) <ff>	Privately owned,
	XV359	HS Buccaneer S2B [035/R]	RNAS Culdrose, on display
	XV361	HS Buccaneer S2B	Ulster Aviation Society, Langford Lodge
	XV370	Sikorsky SH-3D	RN AESS, *HMS Sultan*, Gosport
	XV371	WS61 Sea King HAS1(DB)	RN AESS, *HMS Sultan*, Gosport
	XV372	WS61 Sea King HAS1	RAF St Mawgan, instructional use
	XV399	McD F-4M Phantom FGR2 <ff>	Privately owned, Stock, Essex
	XV401	McD F-4M Phantom FGR2 [I]	DERA Boscombe Down, GI use
	XV406	McD F-4M Phantom FGR2 (9098M) [CK]	Solway Aviation Society, Carlisle Airport
	XV408	McD F-4M Phantom FGR2 (9165M) [Z]	RAF Halton
	XV411	McD F-4M Phantom FGR2 (9103M) [L]	FSCTE, RAF Manston
	XV415	McD F-4M Phantom FGR2 (9163M) [E]	RAF Boulmer, on display
	XV420	McD F-4M Phantom FGR2 (9247M) [BT]	RAF Neatishead, at main gate
	XV422	McD F-4M Phantom FGR2 (9157M) [T]	Scrapped at Stornoway, October 1998
	XV423	McD F-4M Phantom FGR2 [Y]	RAF Leeming, BDRT
	XV424	McD F-4M Phantom FGR2 (9152M) [I]	RAF Museum, Hendon
	XV426	McD F-4M Phantom FGR2 [P]	RAF Coningsby, BDRT
	XV435	McD F-4M Phantom FGR2 [R]	DERA Llanbedr Fire Section
	XV460	McD F-4M Phantom FGR2 [R]	RAF Coningsby, BDRT
	XV465	McD F-4M Phantom FGR2 [S]	RAF Leeming, decoy
	XV467	McD F-4M Phantom FGR2 (9158M) [F]	Benbecula Airport, on display
	XV468	McD F-4M Phantom FGR2 (9159M) [H]	RAF Woodvale, on display
	XV474	McD F-4M Phantom FGR2 [T]	The Old Flying Machine Company, Duxford
	XV489	McD F-4M Phantom FGR2 <ff>	Sold to Holland, 1997

Serial	Type (other identity) [code]	Owner/operator, location or fate	Notes
XV490	McD F-4M Phantom FGR2 <ff>	Privately owned, Bruntingthorpe	
XV497	McD F-4M Phantom FGR2	RAF Coningsby	
XV499	McD F-4M Phantom FGR2	RAF Leeming, WLT	
XV500	McD F-4M Phantom FGR2 (9113M)	RAF St Athan, on display	
XV577	McD F-4K Phantom FG1 (9065M) [AM]	RAF Leuchars, BDRT	
XV581	McD F-4K Phantom FG1 (9070M) [AE]	RAF Buchan, on display	
XV582	McD F-4K Phantom FG1 (9066M) [M]	RAF Leuchars on display	
XV586	McD F-4K Phantom FG1 (9067M) [AJ]	RAF Leuchars BDRT	
XV591	McD F-4K Phantom FG1 <ff>	RAF Cosford Aerospace Museum	
XV625	WS Wasp HAS1 [471]	RN AESS, HMS Sultan, Gosport	
XV629	WS Wasp HAS1	AAC Middle Wallop, BDRT	
XV631	WS Wasp HAS1 (fuselage)	DERA Acoustics Dept, Farnborough	
XV642	WS61 Sea King HAS2A	RN AESS, HMS Sultan, Gosport	
XV643	WS61 Sea King HAS6 [703]	RN No 819 Sqn, Prestwick	
XV647	WS61 Sea King HU5 [820/CU]	RN No 771 Sqn, Culdrose	
XV648	WS61 Sea King HU5 [827]	MoD(PE)/AFD, DERA Boscombe Down	
XV649	WS61 Sea King AEW2 [184/L]	RN No 849 Sqn, B Flt, Culdrose	
XV650	WS61 Sea King AEW2	RN AMG, Culdrose	
XV651	WS61 Sea King HU5 [599/CU]	RN, NARO Fleetlands	
XV653	WS61 Sea King HAS6 [513/CU]	RN No 810 Sqn, Culdrose	
XV654	WS61 Sea King HAS6 [705] (wreck)	RN AESS, HMS Sultan, Gosport	
XV655	WS61 Sea King HAS6 [267/PW]	RN AMG, Culdrose	
XV656	WS61 Sea King AEW2 [180/CU]	RN No 849 Sqn, HQ Flt, Culdrose	
XV659	WS61 Sea King HAS6 [510/CU]	RN No 810 Sqn, Culdrose	
XV660	WS61 Sea King HAS6 [708]	RN AMG, Culdrose	
XV661	WS61 Sea King HU5 [821]	RN No 771 Sqn, Culdrose	
XV663	WS61 Sea King HAS6 [706/PW]	RN No 819 Sqn, Prestwick	
XV664	WS61 Sea King AEW2 [186/N]	RN No 849 Sqn, A Flt, Culdrose	
XV665	WS61 Sea King HAS6	RN No 810 Sqn, Culdrose	
XV666	WS61 Sea King HU5 [823/CU]	RN No 771 Sqn, Culdrose	
XV669	WS61 Sea King HAS1 [10]	Privately owned, Portsmouth	
XV670	WS61 Sea King HU5 [588]	RN, NARO Fleetlands	
XV671	WS61 Sea King AEW2 [185/L]	RN No 849 Sqn, B Flt, Culdrose	
XV672	WS61 Sea King AEW2 [182/L]	MoD(PE)/AFD, DERA Boscombe Down	
XV673	WS61 Sea King HU5 [597]	RN, stored NARO Fleetlands	
XV674	WS61 Sea King HAS6 [705/PW]	RN No 819 Sqn, Prestwick	
XV675	WS61 Sea King HAS6 [701/PW]	RN No 819 Sqn, Prestwick	
XV676	WS61 Sea King HAS6	RN No 810 Sqn, Culdrose	
XV677	WS61 Sea King HAS6 [269]	RN, stored NARO Fleetlands	
XV696	WS61 Sea King HAS6	RN No 814 Sqn, Culdrose	
XV697	WS61 Sea King AEW2 [187/N]	RN No 849 Sqn, A Flt, Culdrose	
XV699	WS61 Sea King HU5 [826]	RN NARO, Fleetlands	
XV700	WS61 Sea King HAS6 [008]	RN No 810 Sqn, Culdrose	
XV701	WS61 Sea King HAS6 [268/N]	RN No 814 Sqn, Culdrose	
XV703	WS61 Sea King HAS6 [011/L]	RN No 820 Sqn, Culdrose	
XV704	WS61 Sea King AEW2 [181/CU]	RN No 849 Sqn, HQ Flt, Culdrose	
XV705	WS61 Sea King HU5 [821/CU]	RN, stored NARO Fleetlands	
XV706	WS61 Sea King HAS6 [504/CU]	RN AMG, Culdrose	
XV707	WS61 Sea King AEW2	MoD(PE)/AFD, DERA Boscombe Down	
XV708	WS61 Sea King HAS6 [501/CU]	RN No 810 Sqn, Culdrose	
XV709	WS61 Sea King HAS6 [505]	RN No 810 Sqn, Culdrose	
XV710	WS61 Sea King HAS6 [012/L]	RN No 820 Sqn, Culdrose	
XV711	WS61 Sea King HAS6 [515/CT]	RN No 810 Sqn/B Flt, Culdrose	
XV712	WS61 Sea King HAS6 [266]	RN No 814 Sqn, Culdrose	
XV713	WS61 Sea King HAS6 [018]	RN, NARO Fleetlands	
XV714	WS61 Sea King AEW2 [187]	RN, NARO Fleetlands	
XV720	WS58 Wessex HC2	RN AESS, HMS Sultan, Gosport	
XV721	WS58 Wessex HC2 [H]	RAF No 72 Sqn, Aldergrove	
XV722	WS58 Wessex HC2 [WH]	RAF, stored Shawbury	
XV723	WS58 Wessex HC2 [Q]	RAF No 72 Sqn, Aldergrove	
XV724	WS58 Wessex HC2	RAF, stored NARO Fleetlands	
XV725	WS58 Wessex HC2 [C]	RAF, stored Shawbury	
XV726	WS58 Wessex HC2 [J]	RAF No 72 Sqn, Aldergrove	
XV728	WS58 Wessex HC2 [A]	Newark Air Museum, Winthorpe	
XV729	WS58 Wessex HC2	Privately owned, Redhill	
XV730	WS58 Wessex HC2 [Clubs]	RAF No 84 Sqn, Akrotiri	
XV731	WS58 Wessex HC2 [Y]	RAF, stored NARO Fleetlands	
XV732	WS58 Wessex HCC4	RAF, stored Shawbury	

Notes	Serial	Type (other identity) [code]	Owner/operator, location or fate
	XV733	WS58 Wessex HCC4	RAF, stored Shawbury
	XV738	HS Harrier GR3 (9074M) [B]	*Sold as N4320W, February 1998*
	XV741	HS Harrier GR3 [1,5]	SFDO, RNAS Culdrose
	XV744	HS Harrier GR3 (9167M) [3K]	R. Military College of Science, Shrivenham
	XV747	HS Harrier GR3 (8979M) (fuselage)	No 1803 Sqn ATC, Hucknall
	XV748	HS Harrier GR3 [3D]	Cranfield University
	XV751	HS Harrier GR3	Vallance By-Ways, Charlwood, Surrey
	XV752	HS Harrier GR3 (9078M) [B,HF]	RAF No 1 SoTT, Cosford
	XV753	HS Harrier GR3 (9075M) [3F,4]	SFDO, RNAS Culdrose
	XV755	HS Harrier GR3 [M]	RNAS Yeovilton Fire Section
	XV759	HS Harrier GR3 [O] <ff>	Privately owned, South Molton, Devon
	XV779	HS Harrier GR3 (8931M) [01,A]	RAF Wittering on display
	XV783	HS Harrier GR3 [N]	SFDO, RNAS Culdrose
	XV784	HS Harrier GR3 (8909M) <ff>	DERA Boscombe Down, GI use
	XV786	HS Harrier GR3 <ff>	RNAS Culdrose
	XV786	HS Harrier GR3 [S] <rf>	RN, Predannack Fire School
	XV798	HS Harrier GR1(mod)	Bristol Aero Collection, stored Kemble
	XV804	HS Harrier GR3 [O]	RAF North Luffenham Training Area
	XV806	HS Harrier GR3 [E]	*Dismantled at Boscombe Down by October 1998*
	XV808	HS Harrier GR3 (9076M) [3J,6]	SFDO, RNAS Culdrose
	XV810	HS Harrier GR3 (9038M) [K]	Privately owned, Bruntingthorpe
	XV814	DH106 Comet 4 (G-APDF) <ff>	Privately owned, Chipping Campden
	XV863	HS Buccaneer S2B (9115M/ 9139M/9145M) [S]	RAF Lossiemouth, on display
	XV864	HS Buccaneer S2B (9234M)	FSCTE, RAF Manston
	XV865	HS Buccaneer S2B (9226M)	Imperial War Museum, Duxford
	XV867	HS Buccaneer S2B <ff>	N Yorks Aircraft Recovery Centre, Chop Gate
	XW175	HS Harrier T4(VAAC)	MoD(PE)/AFD, DERA Boscombe Down
	XW198	WS Puma HC1	RAF No 230 Sqn, Aldergrove
	XW199	WS Puma HC1 [AE]	RAF No 72 Sqn, Aldergrove
	XW200	WS Puma HC1 [NC]	RAF No 33 Sqn, Benson
	XW201	WS Puma HC1	RAF No 33 Sqn, Benson
	XW202	WS Puma HC1 [NE]	RAF No 33 Sqn, Benson
	XW204	WS Puma HC1	RAF No 72 Sqn, Aldergrove
	XW206	WS Puma HC1	RAF No 33 Sqn, Benson
	XW207	WS Puma HC1	RAF No 33 Sqn, Benson
	XW208	WS Puma HC1	MoD(PE)/AFD, DERA Boscombe Down
	XW209	WS Puma HC1	RAF No 230 Sqn, Aldergrove
	XW210	WS Puma HC1 (comp XW215)	GKN Westland, Weston-super-Mare (on rebuild)
	XW211	WS Puma HC1 [AC]	RAF No 72 Sqn, Aldergrove
	XW212	WS Puma HC1 [AA]	RAF No 72 Sqn, Aldergrove
	XW213	WS Puma HC1[NE]	RAF No 230 Sqn, Aldergrove
	XW214	WS Puma HC1	RAF No 230 Sqn, Aldergrove
	XW216	WS Puma HC1	MoD(PE) GKN Westland, Weston-super-Mare
	XW217	WS Puma HC1	RAF No 230 Sqn, Aldergrove
	XW218	WS Puma HC1	RAF No 33 Sqn, Benson
	XW219	WS Puma HC1	RAF No 230 Sqn, Aldergrove
	XW220	WS Puma HC1	RAF No 230 Sqn, Aldergrove
	XW221	WS Puma HC1	RAF No 230 Sqn, Aldergrove
	XW222	WS Puma HC1	RAF No 33 Sqn, Benson
	XW223	WS Puma HC1	RAF No 33 Sqn, Benson
	XW224	WS Puma HC1 [AD]	RAF No 72 Sqn, Aldergrove
	XW225	WS Puma HC1	RAF, Odiham (wreck)
	XW226	WS Puma HC1	RAF No 72 Sqn, Aldergrove
	XW227	WS Puma HC1 [NJ]	RAF No 33 Sqn, Benson
	XW229	WS Puma HC1	RAF No 230 Sqn, Aldergrove
	XW231	WS Puma HC1 [NM]	RAF No 230 Sqn, Aldergrove
	XW232	WS Puma HC1	RAF No 33 Sqn, Benson
	XW234	WS Puma HC1 [AB]	RAF No 72 Sqn, Aldergrove
	XW235	WS Puma HC1	RAF No 33 Sqn, Benson
	XW236	WS Puma HC1	RAF No 230 Sqn, Aldergrove
	XW237	WS Puma HC1	RAF No 33 Sqn, Benson
	XW241	Sud SA330E Puma	DERA Avionics & Sensors Dept, Farnborough
	XW264	HS Harrier T2 <ff>	Jet Age Museum, Staverton
	XW265	HS Harrier T4A [W]	RAF No 1 SoTT, Cosford
	XW266	HS Harrier T4N	
	XW267	HS Harrier T4 [SA]	Territorial Army, Chetwynd Barracks, Notts

Serial	Type (other identity) [code]	Owner/operator, location or fate	Notes
XW269	HS Harrier T4 [BD]	RAF, stored DERA Boscombe Down	
XW270	HS Harrier T4 (fuselage)	Phoenix Aviation, Bruntingthorpe	
XW271	HS Harrier T4 [X,1]	SFDO, RNAS Culdrose	
XW272	HS Harrier T4 (8783M) (fuselage) (comp XV281)	BAe Dunsfold, Apprentice School	
XW276	Aérospatiale SA341 Gazelle (F-ZWRI)	North-East Aircraft Museum, Usworth	
XW281	WS Scout AH1 [U]	Privately owned, Oaksey Park, Wilts	
XW282	WS Scout AH1 [W]	Sold as ZK-HUC, 1996	
XW283	WS Scout AH1 [U]	RM, stored Yeovilton	
XW284	WS Scout AH1 [A] (fuselage)	Privately owned, Ipswich	
XW289	BAC Jet Provost T5A (G-BVXT/ G-JPVA) [73]	Kennet Aviation, Cranfield	
XW290	BAC Jet Provost T5A (9199M) [41,MA]	RAF No 1 SoTT, Cosford	
XW291	BAC Jet Provost T5 (G-BWOF) [N]	Privately owned, Bournemouth	
XW292	BAC Jet Provost T5A (9128M) [32]	RAF No 1 SoTT, Cosford	
XW293	BAC Jet Provost T5 (G-BWCS) [Z]	Privately owned, Liverpool	
XW294	BAC Jet Provost T5A (9129M) [45]	RAF No 1 SoTT, Cosford	
XW299	BAC Jet Provost T5A (9146M) [60,MB]	RAF No 1 SoTT, Cosford	
XW301	BAC Jet Provost T5A (9147M) [63,MC]	RAF No 1 SoTT, Cosford	
XW302	BAC Jet Provost T5B (N166A/ G-BYED]	Privately owned, Sandtoft	
XW303	BAC Jet Provost T5A (9119M) [127]	RAF No 1 SoTT, Cosford	
XW304	BAC Jet Provost T5 (9172M) [MD]	RAF No 1 SoTT, Cosford	
XW309	BAC Jet Provost T5 (9179M) [V,ME]	RAF No 1 SoTT, Cosford	
XW311	BAC Jet Provost T5 (9180M) [W,MF]	RAF No 1 SoTT, Cosford	
XW312	BAC Jet Provost T5A (9109M) [64]	RAF No 1 SoTT, Cosford	
XW315	BAC Jet Provost T5A <ff>	Privately owned, Long Marston	
XW318	BAC Jet Provost T5A (9190M) [78,MG]	RAF No 1 SoTT, Cosford	
XW320	BAC Jet Provost T5A (9015M) [71]	RAF No 1 SoTT, Cosford	
XW321	BAC Jet Provost T5A (9154M) [62,MH]	RAF No 1 SoTT, Cosford	
XW323	BAC Jet Provost T5A (9166M) [86]	RAF Museum, Hendon	
XW324	BAC Jet Provost T5 (G-BWSG)	Privately owned, Southend	
XW325	BAC Jet Provost T5B (G-BWGF) [E]	Privately owned, Woodford	
XW327	BAC Jet Provost T5A (9130M) [62]	RAF No 1 SoTT, Cosford	
XW328	BAC Jet Provost T5A (9177M) [75,MI]	RAF No 1 SoTT, Cosford	
XW330	BAC Jet Provost T5A (9195M) [82,MJ]	RAF No 1 SoTT, Cosford	
XW333	BAC Jet Provost T5A (G-BVTC)	Global Aviation, Binbrook	
XW335	BAC Jet Provost T5A (9061M) [74]	RAF No 1 SoTT, Cosford	
XW351	BAC Jet Provost T5A (9062M) [31]	RAF No 1 SoTT, Cosford	
XW352	BAC Jet Provost T5 [R]	Sold to the USA, May 1998	
XW353	BAC Jet Provost T5A (9090M) [3]	RAF Cranwell, on display	
XW355	BAC Jet Provost T5A (G-JPTV) [20]	Privately owned, Rugby	
XW358	BAC Jet Provost T5A (9181M) [59,MK]	RAF No 1 SoTT, Cosford	
XW360	BAC Jet Provost T5A (9153M) [61,ML]	RAF No 1 SoTT, Cosford	
XW361	BAC Jet Provost T5A (9192M) [81,MM]	RAF No 1 SoTT, Cosford	
XW363	BAC Jet Provost T5A [36]	Royal Ordnance. Chorley, Lancs	
XW364	BAC Jet Provost T5A (9188M) [35,MN]	RAF No 1 SoTT, Cosford	
XW365	BAC Jet Provost T5A (9018M) [73]	RAF No 1 SoTT, Cosford	
XW366	BAC Jet Provost T5A (9097M) [75]	RAF No 1 SoTT, Cosford	
XW367	BAC Jet Provost T5A (9193M) [64,MO]	RAF No 1 SoTT, Cosford	
XW370	BAC Jet Provost T5A (9196M) [72,MP]	RAF No 1 SoTT, Cosford	
XW375	BAC Jet Provost T5A (9149M) [52]	RAF No 1 SoTT, Cosford	
XW404	BAC Jet Provost T5A (9049M)	RAF CTTS, St Athan	
XW405	BAC Jet Provost T5A (9187M) [J,MQ]	RAF No 1 SoTT, Cosford	

Notes	Serial	Type (other identity) [code]	Owner/operator, location or fate
	XW409	BAC Jet Provost T5A (9047M)	RAF CTTS, St Athan
	XW410	BAC Jet Provost T5A (9125M) [80,MR]	RAF No 1 SoTT, Cosford
	XW413	BAC Jet Provost T5A (9126M) [69]	RAF No 1 SoTT, Cosford
	XW416	BAC Jet Provost T5A (9191M) [84,MS]	RAF No 1 SoTT, Cosford
	XW418	BAC Jet Provost T5A (9173M) [MT]	RAF No 1 SoTT, Cosford
	XW419	BAC Jet Provost T5A (9120M) [125]	RAF No 1 SoTT, Cosford
	XW420	BAC Jet Provost T5A (9194M) [83,MU]	RAF No 1 SoTT, Cosford
	XW421	BAC Jet Provost T5A (9111M) [60]	RAF No 1 SoTT, Cosford
	XW423	BAC Jet Provost T5A (G-BWUW) [14]	Privately owned, North Weald
	XW425	BAC Jet Provost T5A (9200M) [H,MV]	RAF No 1 SoTT, Cosford
	XW427	BAC Jet Provost T5A (9124M) [67]	RAF No 1 SoTT, Cosford
XW428	Hunting Jet Provost T4 (XR674/ G-TOMG/9030M)	Privately owned, Lydd
	XW430	BAC Jet Provost T5A (9176M) [77,MW]	RAF No 1 SoTT, Cosford
	XW431	BAC Jet Provost T5B (G-BWBS) [A]	Crashed 24 Dec 1998, Thames Estuary
	XW432	BAC Jet Provost T5A (9127M) [76,MX]	RAF No 1 SoTT, Cosford
	XW433	BAC Jet Provost T5A (G-JPRO) [63]	Global Aviation, Binbrook
	XW434	BAC Jet Provost T5A (9091M) [78,MY]	RAF No 1 SoTT, Cosford
	XW436	BAC Jet Provost T5A (9148M) [68]	RAF No 1 SoTT, Cosford
	XW527	HS Buccaneer S2B <ff>	Privately owned, Wittering
	XW528	HS Buccaneer S2B (8861M) [C]	RAF Coningsby Fire Section
	XW530	HS Buccaneer S2B	Buccaneer Service Station, Elgin
	XW544	HS Buccaneer S2B (8857M) [Y]	Privately owned, Shawbury
	XW547	HS Buccaneer S2B (9095M/ 9169M) [R]	RAF Cosford Aerospace Museum
	XW549	HS Buccaneer S2B (8860M) (fuselage)	RAF Kinloss, BDRT
	XW550	HS Buccaneer S2B <ff>	Privately owned, West Horndon, Essex
	XW566	SEPECAT Jaguar T2	DERA Avionics & Sensors Dept, Farnborough
	XW612	WS Scout AH1 (G-BXRR) [A]	Privately owned, Thruxton
	XW613	WS Scout AH1 (G-BXRS) [W]	Privately owned, Thruxton
	XW614	WS Scout AH1	Crashed 2 December 1978
	XW616	WS Scout AH1	AAC Dishforth, instructional use
	XW630	HS Harrier GR3	RN AESS, *HMS Sultan*, Gosport, on display
	XW635	Beagle D5/180 (G-AWSW)	Privately owned, Spanhoe Lodge
	XW664	HS Nimrod R1	RAF No 51 Sqn, Waddington
	XW665	HS Nimrod R1	RAF No 51 Sqn, Waddington
	XW666	HS Nimrod R1 (fuselage)	BAe Woodford, spares use
	XW750	HS748 Series 107	MoD(PE)/AFD, DERA Boscombe Down
	XW763	HS Harrier GR3 (9002M/9041M) <ff>	Privately owned, Wigston, Leics
	XW768	HS Harrier GR3 (9072M) [N]	RAF No 1 SoTT, Cosford
	XW784	Mitchell-Procter Kittiwake I (G-BBRN) [VL]	Privately owned, Compton Abbas
	XW795	WS Scout AH1	Blessingbourne Museum, Fivemiletown, Co Tyrone, NI
	XW796	WS Scout AH1	AAC Wattisham, BDRT
	XW798	WS Scout AH1 (G-BXOE/G-ONEB)	*Repainted as G-ONEB by May 1998*
	XW799	WS Scout AH1 (G-BXSL)	Privately owned, Thruxton
	XW835	WS Lynx	AAC Wattisham, instructional use
	XW836	WS Lynx	*Scrapped*
	XW837	WS Lynx (fuselage)	RNAS Yeovilton Fire Section
	XW838	WS Lynx (TAD 009)	Army SEAE, Arborfield
	XW839	WS Lynx	The Helicopter Museum, Weston-super-Mare
	XW843	WS Gazelle AH1	
	XW844	WS Gazelle AH1	AAC No 661 Sqn/1 Regt, Gütersloh
	XW845	WS Gazelle HT2 [47/CU]	RN, stored Shawbury
	XW846	WS Gazelle AH1 [M]	AAC No 671 Sqn/2 Regt, Middle Wallop
	XW847	WS Gazelle AH1	AAC No 665 Sqn/5 Regt, Aldergrove
	XW848	WS Gazelle AH1 [D]	AAC No 671 Sqn/2 Regt, Middle Wallop
	XW849	WS Gazelle AH1 [G]	RM No 847 Sqn, Yeovilton

Serial	Type (other identity) [code]	Owner/operator, location or fate	Notes
XW851	WS Gazelle AH1 [H]	RM No 847 Sqn, Yeovilton	
XW852	WS Gazelle HCC4	RAF, stored NARO Fleetlands	
XW853	WS Gazelle HT2 [53/CU]	RN, stored Shawbury	
XW854	WS Gazelle HT2 [46/CU]	RN, stored Shawbury	
XW855	WS Gazelle HCC4	RAF, stored NARO Fleetlands	
XW856	WS Gazelle HT2 [49/CU]	RN, stored Shawbury	
XW857	WS Gazelle HT2 [55/CU]	RN, stored Shawbury	
XW858	WS Gazelle HT3 [C]	RAF, stored Shawbury	
XW860	WS Gazelle HT2 (TAD021)	Army SEAE, Arborfield	
XW861	WS Gazelle HT2 [52/CU]	RN, stored Shawbury	
XW862	WS Gazelle HT3 [D]	RAF, stored Shawbury	
XW863	WS Gazelle HT2 (TAD022) [42/CU]	Army SEAE, Arborfield	
XW864	WS Gazelle HT2 [54/CU]	RN, stored Shawbury	
XW865	WS Gazelle AH1 [C]	AAC No 671 Sqn/2 Regt, Middle Wallop	
XW866	WS Gazelle HT3 (G-BXTH) [E]	Flightline Ltd, Southend	
XW868	WS Gazelle HT2 [50/CU]	RN, stored Shawbury	
XW870	WS Gazelle HT3 [F]	RAF, stored Shawbury (damaged)	
XW871	WS Gazelle HT2 [44/CU]	RN, stored Shawbury	
XW884	WS Gazelle HT2 [41/CU]	RN, stored Shawbury	
XW885	WS Gazelle AH1	AAC, stored Shawbury	
XW887	WS Gazelle HT2 [FL]	RN, stored Shawbury	
XW888	WS Gazelle AH1 (TAD017)	Army SEAE, Arborfield	
XW889	WS Gazelle AH1 (TAD018)	Army SEAE, Arborfield	
XW890	WS Gazelle HT2	RNAS Yeovilton, on display	
XW892	WS Gazelle AH1 [C]	AAC, stored Shawbury	
XW893	WS Gazelle AH1	AAC 70 Aircraft Workshops, Middle Wallop	
XW894	WS Gazelle HT2 [37/CU]	RN, stored Shawbury	
XW895	WS Gazelle HT2 (G-BXZD) [51/CU]	Privately owned, Culdrose	
XW897	WS Gazelle AH1	AAC No 658 Sqn/7 Regt, Netheravon	
XW898	WS Gazelle HT3 [G]	RAF, stored Shawbury	
XW899	WS Gazelle AH1 [Z]	AAC No 658 Sqn/7 Regt, Netheravon	
XW900	WS Gazelle AH1 (TAD 900)	AAC Stockwell Hall, Middle Wallop, instructional use	
XW902	WS Gazelle HT3 [H]	RAF, stored Shawbury	
XW903	WS Gazelle AH1	AAC, stored Shawbury	
XW904	WS Gazelle AH1 [H]	AAC No 666(V) Sqn/7 Regt, Netheravon	
XW906	WS Gazelle HT3 [J]	RAF, stored Shawbury	
XW907	WS Gazelle HT2 [48/CU]	RN, stored Shawbury	
XW908	WS Gazelle AH1 [A]	AAC No 666(V) Sqn/7 Regt, Netheravon	
XW909	WS Gazelle AH1	AAC No 656 Sqn/9 Regt, Dishforth	
XW910	WS Gazelle HT3 (G-BXZE) [K]	Privately owned, Culdrose	
XW911	WS Gazelle AH1 [H]	AAC, stored Shawbury	
XW912	WS Gazelle AH1 (TAD019)	Army SEAE, Arborfield	
XW913	WS Gazelle AH1	AAC, NARO Fleetlands	
XW916	HS Harrier GR3 [W]	Scrapped at Wittering by 1998	
XW919	HS Harrier GR3 [W]	R. Military College of Science, Shrivenham	
XW922	HS Harrier GR3 (8885M)	FSCTE, RAF Manston	
XW923	HS Harrier GR3 (8724M) <ff>	RAF Wittering for rescue training	
XW934	HS Harrier T4 [Y]	MoD(PE), DERA Farnborough	
XW986	HS Buccaneer S2B	Delta Engineering Aviation, Kemble	
XX105	BAC 1-11/201AC (G-ASJD)	MoD(PE)/AFD, DERA Boscombe Down	
XX108	SEPECAT Jaguar GR1A	MoD(PE)/AFD, DERA Boscombe Down	
XX109	SEPECAT Jaguar GR1 (8918M) [US]	RAF Coltishall, ground instruction	
XX110	SEPECAT Jaguar GR1 (8955M) [EP]	RAF No 1 SoTT, Cosford	
XX110	SEPECAT Jaguar GR1 <R> (BAPC 169)	RAF No 1 SoTT, Cosford	
XX112	SEPECAT Jaguar GR1A (Jag 96(A)) [EA]	RAF No 6 Sqn, Coltishall	
XX115	SEPECAT Jaguar GR1 (8821M) (fuselage)	RAF No 1 SoTT, Cosford	
XX116	SEPECAT Jaguar GR1A (Jag 97)	RAF AWC/SAOEU, DERA Boscombe Down	
XX117	SEPECAT Jaguar GR1A (Jag 96) [EB]	RAF No 6 Sqn, Coltishall	
XX119	SEPECAT Jaguar GR1A (Jag 96(T)) (8898M) [GD]	RAF No 54 Sqn, Coltishall	
XX121	SEPECAT Jaguar GR1 (92..M) [EQ]	Privately owned, Charlwood	
XX139	SEPECAT Jaguar T4 [T]	MoD(PE)/AFD, DERA Boscombe Down	

Notes	Serial	Type (other identity) [code]	Owner/operator, location or fate
	XX140	SEPECAT Jaguar T2 (9008M) [D,JJ]	RAF No 1 SoTT, Cosford
	XX141	SEPECAT Jaguar T2A [EV]	RAF No 6 Sqn, Coltishall
	XX143	SEPECAT Jaguar T2A [X] (wreck)	Privately owned, Charlwood
	XX144	SEPECAT Jaguar T2A [U]	RAF No 16(R) Sqn, Lossiemouth
	XX145	SEPECAT Jaguar T2	MoD(PE)/AFD/ETPS, DERA Boscombe Down
	XX146	SEPECAT Jaguar T2B [GT]	RAF No 54 Sqn, Coltishall
	XX150	SEPECAT Jaguar T4 [W]	MoD(PE)/AFD, DERA Boscombe Down
	XX153	WS Lynx AH1	AAC,
	XX154	HS Hawk T1	MoD(PE), DERA Llanbedr
	XX156	HS Hawk T1	RAF No 4 FTS/208(R) Sqn, Valley
	XX157	HS Hawk T1A	RN FRADU, Culdrose
	XX158	HS Hawk T1A	RAF No 4 FTS/208(R) Sqn, Valley
	XX159	HS Hawk T1A	RAF No 4 FTS/208(R) Sqn, Valley
	XX160	HS Hawk T1	RAF No 4 FTS/208(R) Sqn, Valley
	XX161	HS Hawk T1	MoD(PE)/AFD, DERA Boscombe Down
	XX162	HS Hawk T1	MoD(PE)/SAM, DERA Boscombe Down
	XX163	HS Hawk T1 (9243M) [PH] (wreck)	Privately owned,
	XX165	HS Hawk T1	RAF, St Athan
	XX167	HS Hawk T1	RAF No 4 FTS/19(R) Sqn, Valley
	XX168	HS Hawk T1 [CA]	RAF, stored Shawbury
	XX169	HS Hawk T1	RAF, stored St Athan
	XX170	HS Hawk T1	RAF No 4 FTS/208(R) Sqn, Valley
	XX171	HS Hawk T1	RAF No 4 FTS/208(R) Sqn, Valley
	XX172	HS Hawk T1	RAF No 4 FTS/19(R) Sqn, Valley
	XX173	HS Hawk T1	RAF, stored Shawbury
	XX174	HS Hawk T1	RAF No 4 FTS/19(R) Sqn, Valley
	XX175	HS Hawk T1	RAF No 4 FTS/208(R) Sqn, Valley
	XX176	HS Hawk T1]	RAF No 4 FTS/208(R) Sqn, Valley
	XX177	HS Hawk T1	RAF No 4 FTS/208(R) Sqn, Valley
	XX178	HS Hawk T1 [PQ]	RAF No 4 FTS/19(R) Sqn, Valley
	XX179	HS Hawk T1	RAF No 4 FTS/19(R) Sqn, Valley
	XX181	HS Hawk T1	RAF, St Athan
	XX183	HS Hawk T1	RAF No 4 FTS/208(R) Sqn, Valley
	XX184	HS Hawk T1	RAF, stored Shawbury
	XX185	HS Hawk T1 [TM]	RAF, St Athan
	XX186	HS Hawk T1A	Crashed 30 April 1998, Irish Sea
	XX187	HS Hawk T1A	RN FRADU, Culdrose
	XX188	HS Hawk T1A [TI]	RAF No 4 FTS/74(R) Sqn, Valley
	XX189	HS Hawk T1A	RAF No 4 FTS/74(R) Sqn, Valley
	XX190	HS Hawk T1A	RAF No 4 FTS/208(R) Sqn, Valley
	XX191	HS Hawk T1A	RAF No 4 FTS/208(R) Sqn, Valley
	XX193	HS Hawk T1A [CB]	RAF No 100 Sqn, Leeming
	XX194	HS Hawk T1A [CO]	RAF No 100 Sqn/JFACSTU, Leeming
	XX195	HS Hawk T1A	RAF No 4 FTS/19(R) Sqn, Valley
	XX196	HS Hawk T1A	MoD(PE)/BAe, Warton
	XX198	HS Hawk T1A	RAF No 4 FTS/19(R) Sqn, Valley
	XX199	HS Hawk T1A	RAF No 4 FTS/208(R) Sqn, Valley
	XX200	HS Hawk T1A [CF]	RAF No 100 Sqn, Leeming
	XX201	HS Hawk T1A [N]	RN FRADU, Culdrose
	XX202	HS Hawk T1A	RAF No 4 FTS/19(R) Sqn, Valley
	XX203	HS Hawk T1A	RAF No 4 FTS/74(R) Sqn, Valley
	XX204	HS Hawk T1A	RAF No 4 FTS/208(R) Sqn, Valley
	XX205	HS Hawk T1A	RN FRADU, Culdrose
	XX217	HS Hawk T1A	RAF No 4 FTS/19(R) Sqn, Valley
	XX218	HS Hawk T1A	RAF No 4 FTS/19(R) Sqn, Valley
	XX219	HS Hawk T1A [CT]	RAF No 100 Sqn, Leeming
	XX220	HS Hawk T1A	RN FRADU, Culdrose
	XX221	HS Hawk T1A	RAF No 4 FTS/74(R) Sqn, Valley
	XX222	HS Hawk T1A	RAF No 4 FTS/208(R) Sqn, Valley
	XX223	HS Hawk T1 (fuselage)	Privately owned, Charlwood, Surrey
	XX224	HS Hawk T1	RAF No 4 FTS/19(R) Sqn, Valley
	XX225	HS Hawk T1	RAF No 4 FTS/208(R) Sqn, Valley
	XX226	HS Hawk T1 [74]	RAF, stored St Athan
	XX226	HS Hawk T1 <R> (BAPC 152)	RAF EPTT, St Athan
	XX227	HS Hawk T1A	RAF *Red Arrows*, Cranwell
	XX228	HS Hawk T1A	RAF No 4 FTS/208(R) Sqn, Valley
	XX230	HS Hawk T1A	RAF No 4 FTS/74(R) Sqn, Valley
	XX231	HS Hawk T1W	RAF No 4 FTS/74(R) Sqn, Valley
	XX232	HS Hawk T1	RAF No 4 FTS/19(R) Sqn, Valley
	XX233 .	HS Hawk T1	RAF *Red Arrows*, Cranwell
	XX234	HS Hawk T1]	RAF St Athan

Serial	Type (other identity) [code]	Owner/operator, location or fate	Notes
XX235	HS Hawk T1	RAF No 4 FTS/19(R) Sqn, Valley	
XX236	HS Hawk T1	RAF No 4 FTS/19(R) Sqn, Valley	
XX237	HS Hawk T1	RAF *Red Arrows*, Cranwell	
XX238	HS Hawk T1	RAF No 4 FTS/19(R) Sqn, Valley	
XX239	HS Hawk T1 [DZ]	RAF No 4 FTS/74(R) Sqn, Valley	
XX240	HS Hawk T1	RAF No 4 FTS/19(R) Sqn, Valley	
XX242	HS Hawk T1	RN, stored Shawbury	
XX244	HS Hawk T1	RAF No 4 FTS/208(R) Sqn, Valley	
XX245	HS Hawk T1	RAF St Athan	
XX246	HS Hawk T1A	RAF No 4 FTS/74(R) Sqn, Valley	
XX247	HS Hawk T1A [CM]	RAF No 100 Sqn, Leeming	
XX248	HS Hawk T1A [CJ]	RAF No 100 Sqn, Leeming	
XX249	HS Hawk T1W	RAF No 4 FTS/74(R) Sqn, Valley	
XX250	HS Hawk T1	RAF No 4 FTS/208(R) Sqn, Valley	
XX252	HS Hawk T1A	*Crashed 17 November 1998, Cranwell*	
XX253	HS Hawk T1A	RAF *Red Arrows*, Cranwell	
XX253	HS Hawk T1 <R> (BAPC 171)	RAF EPTT, St Athan	
XX254	HS Hawk T1A	BAe Brough, fatigue test rig	
XX254	HS Hawk T1A <R>	Privately owned, Marlow, Bucks	
XX255	HS Hawk T1A [TE]	RN FRADU, Culdrose	
XX256	HS Hawk T1A	RAF No 4 FTS/74(R) Sqn, Valley	
XX258	HS Hawk T1A	RAF No 4 FTS/74(R) Sqn, Valley	
XX260	HS Hawk T1A	RAF *Red Arrows*, Cranwell	
XX261	HS Hawk T1A	RAF No 4 FTS/208(R) Sqn, Valley	
XX263	HS Hawk T1A	RN FRADU, Culdrose	
XX264	HS Hawk T1A	RAF *Red Arrows*, Cranwell	
XX265	HS Hawk T1A [CN]	RAF No 100 Sqn, Leeming	
XX266	HS Hawk T1A	RAF *Red Arrows*, Cranwell	
XX278	HS Hawk T1A	RAF No 4 FTS/19(R) Sqn, Valley	
XX280	HS Hawk T1A	RAF No 4 FTS/19(R) Sqn, Valley	
XX281	HS Hawk T1A	RAF No 4 FTS/74(R) Sqn, Valley	
XX282	HS Hawk T1A [CQ]	RAF No 100 Sqn, Leeming	
XX283	HS Hawk T1	RAF No 4 FTS/208(R) Sqn, Valley	
XX284	HS Hawk T1A [CL]	RAF No 100 Sqn, Leeming	
XX285	HS Hawk T1A	RAF,No 100 Sqn, Leeming	
XX286	HS Hawk T1A	RN FRADU, Culdrose	
XX287	HS Hawk T1A	RAF No 4 FTS/208(R) Sqn, Valley	
XX289	HS Hawk T1A	RAF No 100 Sqn, Leeming	
XX290	HS Hawk T1 [DV]	MoD(PE)/BAe, Warton	
XX292	HS Hawk T1W	RAF *Red Arrows*, Cranwell	
XX294	HS Hawk T1	RAF *Red Arrows*, Cranwell	
XX295	HS Hawk T1 [DA]	MoD(PE)/BAe, Warton	
XX296	HS Hawk T1 [DR]	RAF, stored Shawbury	
XX299	HS Hawk T1W	RAF No 4 FTS/19(R) Sqn, Valley	
XX301	HS Hawk T1A	RN FRADU, Culdrose	
XX303	HS Hawk T1A	RAF No 4 FTS/74(R) Sqn, Valley	
XX304	HS Hawk T1A (fuselage)	RAF, stored Shawbury	
XX306	HS Hawk T1A	RAF *Red Arrows*, Cranwell	
XX307	HS Hawk T1	RAF *Red Arrows*, Cranwell	
XX308	HS Hawk T1	RAF *Red Arrows*, Cranwell	
XX309	HS Hawk T1	RAF No 4 FTS/19(R) Sqn, Valley	
XX310	HS Hawk T1W	RAF No 4 FTS/208(R) Sqn, Valley	
XX311	HS Hawk T1	RN FRADU, Culdrose	
XX312	HS Hawk T1	RAF No 4 FTS/74(R) Sqn, Valley	
XX313	HS Hawk T1	RAF No 4 FTS/208(R) Sqn, Valley	
XX314	HS Hawk T1 [DU]	RAF No 4 FTS/208(R) Sqn, Valley	
XX315	HS Hawk T1A	RN FRADU, Culdrose	
XX316	HS Hawk T1A	RAF No 4 FTS/74(R) Sqn, Valley	
XX317	HS Hawk T1A	RAF No 4 FTS/74(R) Sqn, Valley	
XX318	HS Hawk T1A	RAF No 4 FTS/74(R) Sqn, Valley	
XX319	HS Hawk T1A	RAF No 4 FTS/208(R) Sqn, Valley	
XX320	HS Hawk T1A [CS]	RAF No 100 Sqn, Leeming	
XX321	HS Hawk T1A	RAF No 4 FTS/19(R) Sqn, Valley	
XX322	HS Hawk T1A [W]	RN FRADU, Culdrose	
XX323	HS Hawk T1A	RAF No 4 FTS/74(R) Sqn, Valley	
XX324	HS Hawk T1A	RAF No 4 FTS/19(R) Sqn, Valley	
XX325	HS Hawk T1A [CE]	RAF No 100 Sqn, Leeming	
XX326	HS Hawk T1A	MoD(PE)/BAe, Brough (on rebuild)	
XX327	HS Hawk T1	MoD(PE)/SAM, DERA Boscombe Down	
XX329	HS Hawk T1A	RAF No 4 FTS/74(R) Sqn, Valley	
XX330	HS Hawk T1A	RAF No 4 FTS/19(R) Sqn, Valley	
XX331	HS Hawk T1A [CK]	RAF No 100 Sqn, Leeming	
XX332	HS Hawk T1A	RAF No 4 FTS/74(R) Sqn, Valley	

Notes	Serial	Type (other identity) [code]	Owner/operator, location or fate
	XX335	HS Hawk T1A [CD]	RAF No 100 Sqn, Leeming
	XX337	HS Hawk T1A	RN FRADU, Culdrose
	XX338	HS Hawk T1W	RAF No 4 FTS/19(R) Sqn, Valley
	XX339	HS Hawk T1A	RAF No 4 FTS/208(R) Sqn, Valley
	XX341	HS Hawk T1 ASTRA [1]	MoD(PE)/AFD/ETPS, DERA Boscombe Down
	XX342	HS Hawk T1 [2]	MoD(PE)/AFD/ETPS, DERA Boscombe Down
	XX344	HS Hawk T1 (8847M) (fuselage)	DERA Farnborough Fire Section
	XX345	HS Hawk T1A	RAF No 4 FTS/74(R) Sqn, Valley
	XX346	HS Hawk T1A	RN FRADU, Culdrose
	XX348	HS Hawk T1A	RAF No 4 FTS/74(R) Sqn, Valley
	XX349	HS Hawk T1W	RAF No 4 FTS/208(R) Sqn, Valley
	XX350	HS Hawk T1A	RAF No 4 FTS/74(R) Sqn, Valley
	XX351	HS Hawk T1A	MoD(PE)/BAe, Warton
	XX352	HS Hawk T1A [CP]	RAF No 100 Sqn/JFACSTU, Leeming
	XX370	WS Gazelle AH1	AAC No 665 Sqn/5 Regt, Aldergrove
	XX371	WS Gazelle AH1	AAC No 12 Flt, Brüggen
	XX372	WS Gazelle AH1	AAC No 657 Sqn/9 Regt, Dishforth
	XX375	WS Gazelle AH1 [E1]	RN, NARO Fleetlands
	XX378	WS Gazelle AH1 [Q]	AAC No 671 Sqn/2 Regt, Middle Wallop
	XX379	WS Gazelle AH1	AAC No 8 Flt, Middle Wallop
	XX380	WS Gazelle AH1 [A]	RM No 847 Sqn, Yeovilton
	XX381	WS Gazelle AH1	AAC No 662 Sqn/3 Regt, Wattisham
	XX382	WS Gazelle HT3 [M]	RAF, stored Shawbury
	XX383	WS Gazelle AH1	AAC, No 666(V) Sqn/7 Regt, Netheravon
	XX384	WS Gazelle AH1	AAC No 661 Sqn/1 Regt, Gütersloh
	XX385	WS Gazelle AH1	AAC No 654 Sqn/4 Regt, Wattisham
	XX386	WS Gazelle AH1	AAC No 12 Flt, Brüggen
	XX387	WS Gazelle AH1 (TAD 014)	Army SEAE, Arborfield
	XX388	WS Gazelle AH1	AAC, stored Shawbury
	XX389	WS Gazelle AH1	AAC No 656 Sqn/9 Regt, Dishforth
	XX391	WS Gazelle HT2 [56/CU]	RN, stored Shawbury
	XX392	WS Gazelle AH1	AAC No 3(V) Flt/7 Regt, Leuchars
	XX393	WS Gazelle AH1 [W]	AAC No 669 Sqn/4 Regt, Wattisham
	XX394	WS Gazelle AH1	AAC No 669 Sqn/4 Regt, Wattisham
	XX395	WS Gazelle AH1	*Crashed, 12 February 1998, Nanyuki, Kenya*
	XX396	WS Gazelle HT3 (8718M) [N]	RAF EPTT, Henlow
	XX398	WS Gazelle AH1	AAC No 9 Regt, Dishforth
	XX399	WS Gazelle AH1	AAC No 664 Sqn/9 Regt, Dishforth
	XX403	WS Gazelle AH1	AAC No 671 Sqn/2 Regt, Middle Wallop
	XX405	WS Gazelle AH1 [C1]	AAC, stored NARO Fleetlands
	XX406	WS Gazelle HT3 [P]	RAF No 7 Sqn, Odiham
	XX409	WS Gazelle AH1 [O]	AAC No 654 Sqn/4 Regt, Wattisham
	XX410	WS Gazelle HT2 [58/CU]	*Scrapped*
	XX411	WS Gazelle AH1 <rf>	FAA Museum, RNAS Yeovilton
	XX412	WS Gazelle AH1 [B]	RM No 847 Sqn, Yeovilton
	XX413	WS Gazelle AH1 [C]	RM, stored Shawbury
	XX414	WS Gazelle AH1	AAC No 651 Sqn/1 Regt, Gütersloh
	XX416	WS Gazelle AH1	AAC No 652 Sqn/1 Regt, Gütersloh
	XX417	WS Gazelle AH1	AAC No 667 Sqn/2 Regt, Middle Wallop
	XX418	WS Gazelle AH1	AAC, stored NARO Fleetlands
	XX419	WS Gazelle AH1	AAC No 651 Sqn/1 Regt, Gütersloh
	XX431	WS Gazelle HT2 [43/CU]	RN, stored Shawbury
	XX432	WS Gazelle AH1	AAC No 665 Sqn/5 Regt, Aldergrove
	XX433	WS Gazelle AH1 [F]	AAC, stored Shawbury
	XX435	WS Gazelle AH1 [W]	AAC No 671 Sqn/2 Regt, Middle Wallop
	XX436	WS Gazelle HT2 [39/CU]	RN, stored Shawbury
	XX437	WS Gazelle AH1	AAC No 651 Sqn/1 Regt, Gütersloh
	XX438	WS Gazelle AH1	AAC No 657 Sqn/9 Regt, Dishforth
	XX439	WS Gazelle AH1	AAC No 652 Sqn/1 Regt, Gütersloh
	XX440	WS Gazelle AH1 (G-BCHN)	NARO Fleetlands Apprentice School
	XX441	WS Gazelle HT2 [38/CU]	RN, stored Shawbury
	XX442	WS Gazelle AH1 [E]	AAC No 666(V) Sqn/7 Regt, Netheravon
	XX443	WS Gazelle AH1 [Y]	AAC Stockwell Hall, Middle Wallop, instructional use
	XX444	WS Gazelle AH1	AAC No 663 Sqn/3 Regt, Wattisham
	XX445	WS Gazelle AH1 [T]	AAC No 658 Sqn/7 Regt, Netheravon
	XX446	WS Gazelle HT2 [57/CU]	RN, stored Shawbury
	XX447	WS Gazelle AH1 [D1]	AAC No 671 Sqn/2 Regt, Middle Wallop
	XX448	WS Gazelle AH1	AAC No 664 Sqn/9 Regt, Dishforth
	XX449	WS Gazelle AH1	AAC No 669 Sqn/4 Regt, Wattisham
	XX450	WS Gazelle AH1 [D]	RM No 847 Sqn, Yeovilton

Serial	Type (other identity) [code]	Owner/operator, location or fate	Notes
XX453	WS Gazelle AH1	AAC No 652 Sqn/1 Regt, Gütersloh	
XX454	WS Gazelle AH1 [W]	AAC No 662 Sqn/3 Regt, Wattisham	
XX455	WS Gazelle AH1	AAC No 652 Sqn/1 Regt, Gütersloh	
XX456	WS Gazelle AH1	AAC No 3(V) Flt/7 Regt, Leuchars	
XX457	WS Gazelle AH1 <ff>	Army SEAE, Arborfield	
XX460	WS Gazelle AH1	AAC No 662 Sqn/3 Regt, Wattisham	
XX462	WS Gazelle AH1 [W]	AAC No 658 Sqn/7 Regt, Netheravon	
XX466	HS Hunter T66B/T7 (XL620) [830/DD]	*Burnt at Predannack by April 1998*	
XX467	HS Hunter T66B/T7 (XL605/ G-TVII) [86]	Privately owned, Kemble	
XX469	WS Lynx HAS2 (G-BNCL)		
XX475	HP137 Jetstream T2 (N1036S)	MoD(PE), DERA West Freugh	
XX476	HP137 Jetstream T2 (N1037S) [561/CU]	RN No 750 Sqn, Culdrose	
XX477	HP137 Jetstream T1 (G-AXXS/ 8462M) <ff>	RAF Cranwell, instructional use	
XX478	HP137 Jetstream T2 (G-AXXT) [564/CU]	RN No 750 Sqn, Culdrose	
XX479	HP137 Jetstream T2 (G-AXUR) [563/CU]	RN, Predannack Fire School	
XX480	HP137 Jetstream T2 (G-AXXU) [565/CU]	RN, stored Shawbury	
XX481	HP137 Jetstream T2 (G-AXUP) [560/CU]	RN, stored Culdrose	
XX482	SA Jetstream T1 [J]	RAF No 3 FTS/45(R) Sqn, Cranwell	
XX483	SA Jetstream T2 [562/CU]	RN, stored Shawbury	
XX484	SA Jetstream T2 [566/CU]	RN No 750 Sqn, Culdrose	
XX485	SA Jetstream T2 [567/CU]	*Sold to Uruguayan Navy as 875; Nov 1998*	
XX486	SA Jetstream T2 [569/CU]	RN No 750 Sqn, Culdrose	
XX487	SA Jetstream T2 [568/CU]	RN No 750 Sqn, Culdrose	
XX488	SA Jetstream T2 [562/CU]	RN No 750 Sqn, Culdrose	
XX490	SA Jetstream T2 [570/CU]	*Sold to Uruguayan Navy as 876; Nov 1998*	
XX491	SA Jetstream T1 [K]	RAF No 3 FTS/45(R) Sqn, Cranwell	
XX492	SA Jetstream T1 [A]	RAF No 3 FTS/45(R) Sqn, Cranwell	
XX493	SA Jetstream T1 [L]	RAF No 3 FTS/45(R) Sqn, Cranwell	
XX494	SA Jetstream T1 [B]	RAF No 3 FTS/45(R) Sqn, Cranwell	
XX495	SA Jetstream T1 [C]	RAF No 3 FTS/45(R) Sqn, Cranwell	
XX496	SA Jetstream T1 [D]	RAF No 3 FTS/45(R) Sqn, Cranwell	
XX497	SA Jetstream T1 [E]	RAF No 3 FTS/45(R) Sqn, Cranwell	
XX498	SA Jetstream T1 [F]	RAF No 3 FTS/45(R) Sqn, Cranwell	
XX499	SA Jetstream T1 [G]	RAF No 3 FTS/45(R) Sqn, Cranwell	
XX500	SA Jetstream T1 [H]	RAF No 3 FTS/45(R) Sqn, Cranwell	
XX507	HS125 CC2	*Sold as N606CC, November 1998*	
XX508	HS125 CC2	*Sold as N256WJ, September 1998*	
XX510	WS Lynx HAS2 [69/LS]	RN AESS, *HMS Sultan*, Gosport	
XX513	SA Bulldog T1 [10]	RAF CFS, Cranwell	
XX515	SA Bulldog T1 [4]	RAF Manchester & Salford Universities AS/No 10 AEF, Woodvale	
XX516	SA Bulldog T1 [C]	RAF Cambridge UAS/No 5 AEF, Cambridge	
XX518	SA Bulldog T1 [B]	RAF Cambridge UAS/No 5 AEF, Cambridge	
XX519	SA Bulldog T1 [14]	RAF CFS, Cranwell	
XX520	SA Bulldog T1 [A]	RAF East Midlands UAS/No 7 AEF, Newton	
XX521	SA Bulldog T1 [G]	RAF University of Birmingham AS/ No 8 AEF, Cosford	
XX522	SA Bulldog T1 [06]	RAF Aberdeen, Dundee & St Andrews UAS/No 12 AEF, Leuchars	
XX523	SA Bulldog T1 [X]	RAF Liverpool UAS, Woodvale	
XX524	SA Bulldog T1 [04]	RAF University of London AS/No 6 AEF, Benson	
XX525	SA Bulldog T1 (*bl*)	RAF Universities of Glasgow & Strathclyde AS, Glasgow	
XX526	SA Bulldog T1 [C]	RAF Oxford UAS, Benson	
XX527	SA Bulldog T1 [05]	RAF Aberdeen, Dundee & St Andrews UAS/No 12 AEF, Leuchars	
XX528	SA Bulldog T1 [D]	RAF Oxford UAS, Benson	
XX529	SA Bulldog T1 [F]	RAF Cambridge UAS/No 5 AEF, Cambridge	
XX530	SA Bulldog T1 (XX637/9197M) [F]	SERCO, RAF St Athan	
XX531	SA Bulldog T1 [S,04]	RAF University of Wales AS, St Athan	

Notes	Serial	Type (other identity) [code]	Owner/operator, location or fate
	XX532	SA Bulldog T1 [E]	RAF Cambridge UAS/No 5 AEF, Cambridge
	XX533	SA Bulldog T1 [U]	RAF Northumbrian Universities AS/No 11 AEF, Leeming
	XX534	SA Bulldog T1 [B]	RAF University of Birmingham AS/No 8 AEF, Cosford
	XX535	SA Bulldog T1 [S]	RAF East Midlands UAS/No 7 AEF, Newton
	XX536	SA Bulldog T1 [6]	RAF Manchester & Salford Universities AS/No 10 AEF, Woodvale
	XX537	SA Bulldog T1 [02]	RAF East Lowlands UAS, Leuchars
	XX538	SA Bulldog T1 [03]	RAF East Lowlands UAS, Leuchars
	XX539	SA Bulldog T1 [L]	RAF Liverpool UAS, Woodvale
	XX540	SA Bulldog T1 [15]	RAF CFS, Cranwell
	XX541	SA Bulldog T1 [F]	RAF Bristol UAS/No 3 AEF, Colerne
	XX543	SA Bulldog T1 [F]	RAF Yorkshire Universities AS/No 9 AEF, Church Fenton
	XX544	SA Bulldog T1 [01]	RAF University of London AS/No 6 AEF, Benson
	XX545	SA Bulldog T1 [02]	RAF East Lowlands UAS, Leuchars, GI use
	XX546	SA Bulldog T1 [03]	RAF University of London AS/No 6 AEF, Benson
	XX547	SA Bulldog T1 [05]	RAF University of London AS/No 6 AEF, Benson
	XX548	SA Bulldog T1 [06]	RAF University of London AS/No 6 AEF, Benson
	XX549	SA Bulldog T1 [6]	RAF Southampton UAS/No 2 AEF, DERA Boscombe Down
	XX550	SA Bulldog T1 [Z]	RAF Northumbrian Universities AS/No 11 AEF, Leeming
	XX551	SA Bulldog T1 [E]	RAF Oxford UAS, Benson
	XX552	SA Bulldog T1 [08]	RAF University of London AS/No 6 AEF, Benson
	XX553	SA Bulldog T1 [07]	RAF University of London AS/No 6 AEF, Benson
	XX554	SA Bulldog T1 [09]	RAF University of London AS/No 6 AEF, Benson
	XX555	SA Bulldog T1 [U]	RAF Liverpool UAS, Woodvale
	XX556	SA Bulldog T1 [M]	RAF East Midlands UAS/No 7 AEF, Newton
	XX558	SA Bulldog T1 [A]	RAF University of Birmingham AS/No 8 AEF, Cosford
	XX559	SA Bulldog T1	RAF Universities of Glasgow & Strathclyde AS, Glasgow
	XX560	SA Bulldog T1	RAF Universities of Glasgow & Strathclyde AS, Glasgow
	XX561	SA Bulldog T1 [7]	RAF CFS, Cranwell
	XX562	SA Bulldog T1 [18]	RAF CFS, Cranwell
	XX611	SA Bulldog T1	RAF Universities of Glasgow & Strathclyde AS, Glasgow
	XX612	SA Bulldog T1 [A,03]	RAF University of Wales AS, St Athan
	XX614	SA Bulldog T1 [B]	RAF Oxford UAS, Benson
	XX615	SA Bulldog T1 [2]	RAF Manchester & Salford Universities AS/No 10 AEF, Woodvale
	XX616	SA Bulldog T1 [3]	RAF Cambridge UAS/No 5 AEF, Cambridge
	XX617	SA Bulldog T1 [2]	RAF CFS, Cranwell
	XX619	SA Bulldog T1 [T]	RAF Northumbrian Universities AS/No 11 AEF, Leeming
	XX620	SA Bulldog T1 [C]	RAF Yorkshire Universities AS/No 9 AEF, Church Fenton
	XX621	SA Bulldog T1 [G]	RAF Yorkshire Universities AS/No 9 AEF, Church Fenton
	XX622	SA Bulldog T1 [B]	RAF Yorkshire Universities AS/No 9 AEF, Church Fenton
	XX623	SA Bulldog T1 [M]	RAF, stored Newton
	XX624	SA Bulldog T1 [D]	RAF Cambridge UAS/No 5 AEF, Cambridge
	XX625	SA Bulldog T1 [U,01]	RAF University of Wales AS, St Athan
	XX626	SA Bulldog T1 [W,02]	RAF University of Wales AS, St Athan
	XX627	SA Bulldog T1 [07]	RAF Southampton UAS/No 2 AEF, DERA Boscombe Down

Serial	Type (other identity) [code]	Owner/operator, location or fate	Notes
XX628	SA Bulldog T1 [J]	RAF Bristol UAS/No 3 AEF, Colerne	
XX629	SA Bulldog T1 [V]	RAF Manchester & Salford Universities AS/No 10 AEF, Woodvale	
XX630	SA Bulldog T1 [5]	RAF CFS, Cranwell	
XX631	SA Bulldog T1 [W]	RAF Northumbrian Universities AS/ No 11 AEF, Leeming	
XX632	SA Bulldog T1 [A]	RAF Yorkshire Universities AS/ No 9 AEF, Church Fenton	
XX633	SA Bulldog T1 [X]	RAF Northumbrian Universities AS/ No 11 AEF, Leeming	
XX634	SA Bulldog T1 [1]	RAF CFS, Cranwell	
XX635	SA Bulldog T1 (8767M)	RAF CTTS, St Athan	
XX636	SA Bulldog T1 [Y]	RAF Northumbrian Universities AS/ No 11 AEF, Leeming	
XX637	SA Bulldog T1 (9197M) [U]	Repainted as XX530 by August 1998	
XX638	SA Bulldog T1	RAF CFS, Cranwell	
XX639	SA Bulldog T1 [02]	RAF University of London AS/No 6 AEF, Benson	
XX640	SA Bulldog T1 [K]	RAF Bristol UAS/No 3 AEF, Colerne	
XX653	SA Bulldog T1 [E]	RAF Bristol UAS/No 3 AEF, Colerne	
XX654	SA Bulldog T1 [3]	RAF CFS, Cranwell	
XX655	SA Bulldog T1 [B]	RAF Bristol UAS/No 3 AEF, Colerne	
XX656	SA Bulldog T1 [C]	RAF Bristol UAS/No 3 AEF, Colerne	
XX657	SA Bulldog T1 [U]	RAF, stored Newton	
XX658	SA Bulldog T1 [A]	RAF Cambridge UAS/No 5 AEF, Cambridge	
XX659	SA Bulldog T1 [S]	RAF Cambridge UAS/No 5 AEF, Cambridge	
XX661	SA Bulldog T1 [6]	RAF CFS, Cranwell	
XX663	SA Bulldog T1 [01]	RAF East Lowlands UAS, Leuchars	
XX664	SA Bulldog T1 [04]	RAF East Lowlands UAS, Leuchars	
XX665	SA Bulldog T1	RAF, stored Newton	
XX666	SA Bulldog T1 [08]	RAF East Lowlands UAS, Leuchars	
XX667	SA Bulldog T1 [16]	RAF CFS, Cranwell	
XX668	SA Bulldog T1 [1]	RAF Manchester & Salford Universities AS/ No 10 AEF, Woodvale	
XX669	SA Bulldog T1 (8997M) [B]	Privately owned, Cardiff	
XX670	SA Bulldog T1 [C]	RAF University of Birmingham AS/ No 8 AEF, Cosford	
XX671	SA Bulldog T1 [D]	RAF University of Birmingham AS/ No 8 AEF, Cosford	
XX672	SA Bulldog T1 [E]	RAF University of Birmingham AS/ No 8 AEF, Cosford	
XX685	SA Bulldog T1 [11]	RAF CFS, Cranwell	
XX686	SA Bulldog T1 [4]	RAF CFS, Cranwell	
XX687	SA Bulldog T1 [13]	RAF CFS, Cranwell	
XX688	SA Bulldog T1 [8]	RAF CFS, Cranwell	
XX689	SA Bulldog T1 [D]	RAF Bristol UAS/No 3 AEF, Colerne	
XX690	SA Bulldog T1 [A]	RAF Liverpool UAS, Woodvale	
XX691	SA Bulldog T1 [10]	RAF University of London AS/No 6 AEF, Benson	
XX692	SA Bulldog T1 [A]	RAF Bristol UAS/No 3 AEF, Colerne	
XX693	SA Bulldog T1 [07]	RAF Aberdeen, Dundee & St Andrews UAS/No 12 AEF, Leuchars	
XX694	SA Bulldog T1 [E]	RAF East Midlands UAS/No 7 AEF, Newton	
XX695	SA Bulldog T1 [A]	RAF Oxford UAS, Benson	
XX696	SA Bulldog T1 [S]	RAF Liverpool UAS, Woodvale	
XX697	SA Bulldog T1 [H]	RAF Bristol UAS/No 3 AEF, Colerne	
XX698	SA Bulldog T1 [9]	RAF CFS, Cranwell	
XX699	SA Bulldog T1 [F]	RAF University of Birmingham AS/ No 8 AEF, Cosford	
XX700	SA Bulldog T1 [17]	RAF CFS, Cranwell	
XX701	SA Bulldog T1 [2]	RAF Southampton UAS/No 2 AEF, DERA Boscombe Down	
XX702	SA Bulldog T1 [π]	RAF East Midlands UAS/No 7 AEF, Newton	
XX704	SA Bulldog T1 [U]	RAF East Midlands UAS/No 7 AEF, Newton	
XX705	SA Bulldog T1 [5]	RAF Southampton UAS/No 2 AEF, DERA Boscombe Down	
XX706	SA Bulldog T1 [1]	RAF Southampton UAS/No 2 AEF, DERA Boscombe Down	

Notes	Serial	Type (other identity) [code]	Owner/operator, location or fate
	XX707	SA Bulldog T1 [4]	RAF Southampton UAS/No 2 AEF, DERA Boscombe Down
	XX708	SA Bulldog T1 [3]	RAF Southampton UAS/No 2 AEF, DERA Boscombe Down
	XX709	SA Bulldog T1 [E]	RAF Yorkshire Universities AS/No 9 AEF, Church Fenton
	XX711	SA Bulldog T1 [S]	RAF Oxford UAS, Benson
	XX713	SA Bulldog T1 [G]	RAF Bristol UAS/No 3 AEF, Colerne
	XX714	SA Bulldog T1 [D]	RAF Yorkshire Universities AS/No 9 AEF, Church Fenton
	XX719	SEPECAT Jaguar GR1A [EE]	*RAF St Athan, for Royal Air Force of Oman as 226*
	XX720	SEPECAT Jaguar GR1A (Jag 96(A)) [GB]	RAF No 54 Sqn, Coltishall
	XX722	SEPECAT Jaguar GR1 [EF]	RAF, stored St Athan
	XX723	SEPECAT Jaguar GR1A (Jag 96(A))	RAF AWC/SAOEU, DERA Boscombe Down
	XX724	SEPECAT Jaguar GR1A [GA]	RAF, stored Shawbury
	XX725	SEPECAT Jaguar GR1B [GU]	RAF No 54 Sqn, Coltishall
	XX725	SEPECAT Jaguar GR1 <R> (BAPC 150/*XX718*) [GU]	RAF EPTT, St Athan
	XX726	SEPECAT Jaguar GR1A (8947M) [EB]	RAF No 1 SoTT, Cosford
	XX727	SEPECAT Jaguar GR1A (8951M) [ER]	RAF No 1 SoTT, Cosford
	XX729	SEPECAT Jaguar GR1A (Jag 96(T)) [EL]	RAF No 6 Sqn, Coltishall
	XX730	SEPECAT Jaguar GR1 (8952M) [EC]	RAF No 1 SoTT, Cosford
	XX733	SEPECAT Jaguar GR1B [ER]	RAF, stored Coltishall (wreck)
	XX736	SEPECAT Jaguar GR1 (9110M) <ff>	BAe Brough
	XX737	SEPECAT Jaguar GR1A (Jag 96(A)) [EE]	RAF No 6 Sqn, Coltishall
	XX738	SEPECAT Jaguar GR1A (Jag 96(T)) [GG]	MoD(PE)/AFD, DERA Boscombe Down
	XX739	SEPECAT Jaguar GR1 (8902M) [I]	RAF No 1 SoTT, Cosford
	XX741	SEPECAT Jaguar GR1A [04]	RAF, stored Shawbury
	XX743	SEPECAT Jaguar GR1 (8949M) [EG]	RAF No 1 SoTT, Cosford
	XX744	SEPECAT Jaguar GR1	RAF Coltishall, instructional use
	XX745	SEPECAT Jaguar GR1A [D]	RAF No 16(R) Sqn, Lossiemouth
	XX746	SEPECAT Jaguar GR1A (8895M) [09]	RAF No 1 SoTT, Cosford
	XX747	SEPECAT Jaguar GR1 (8903M)	
	XX748	SEPECAT Jaguar GR1A (Jag 96(A)) [GK]	RAF No 54 Sqn, Coltishall
	XX751	SEPECAT Jaguar GR1 (8937M) [10]	RAF No 1 SoTT, Cosford
	XX752	SEPECAT Jaguar GR1A [B]	RAF No 16(R) Sqn, Lossiemouth
	XX753	SEPECAT Jaguar GR1 (9087M) <ff>	RAF EPTT, St Athan
	XX756	SEPECAT Jaguar GR1 (8899M) [AM]	RAF No 1 SoTT, Cosford
	XX757	SEPECAT Jaguar GR1 (8948M) [CU]	RAF No 1 SoTT, Cosford
	XX761	SEPECAT Jaguar GR1 (8600M) <ff>	BAe Warton, instructional use
	XX763	SEPECAT Jaguar GR1 (9009M)	RAF CTTS, St Athan
	XX764	SEPECAT Jaguar GR1 (9010M)	RAF CTTS, St Athan
	XX765	SEPECAT Jaguar ACT	RAF Cosford Aerospace Museum
	XX766	SEPECAT Jaguar GR1A [EA]	RAF, stored St Athan
	XX767	SEPECAT Jaguar GR1A (Jag 96(T)) [GE]	RAF No 54 Sqn, Coltishall
	XX818	SEPECAT Jaguar GR1 (8945M) [DE]	RAF No 1 SoTT, Cosford
	XX819	SEPECAT Jaguar GR1 (8923M) [CE]	RAF No 1 SoTT, Cosford
	XX821	SEPECAT Jaguar GR1 (8896M) [P]	AMIF, RAFC Cranwell
	XX824	SEPECAT Jaguar GR1 (9019M) [AD]	RAF No 1 SoTT, Cosford
	XX825	SEPECAT Jaguar GR1 (9020M) [BN]	RAF No 1 SoTT, Cosford

Serial	Type (other identity) [code]	Owner/operator, location or fate	Notes
XX826	SEPECAT Jaguar GR1 (9021M) [34,JH]	RAF No 1 SoTT, Cosford	
XX829	SEPECAT Jaguar T2A [Y]	MoD(PE)/AFD, DERA Boscombe Down	
XX830	SEPECAT Jaguar T2	MoD(PE) stored, Shawbury	
XX832	SEPECAT Jaguar T2A [Z]	RAF No 16(R) Sqn, Lossiemouth	
XX833	SEPECAT Jaguar T2B	RAF AWC/SAOEU, DERA Boscombe Down	
XX835	SEPECAT Jaguar T2B [FY]	RAF No 41 Sqn, Coltishall	
XX836	SEPECAT Jaguar T2A	RAF, stored Shawbury	
XX837	SEPECAT Jaguar T2 (8978M) [Z]	RAF No 1 SoTT, Cosford	
XX838	SEPECAT Jaguar T4 [X]	RAF, St Athan (conversion)	
XX839	SEPECAT Jaguar T2A (9256M)	RAF CTTS, St Athan	
XX840	SEPECAT Jaguar T4 [X]	RAF, St Athan (conversion)	
XX841	SEPECAT Jaguar T4 [ES]	RAF, St Athan (conversion)	
XX842	SEPECAT Jaguar T2A [X]	RAF No 16(R) Sqn, Lossiemouth	
XX844	SEPECAT Jaguar T2 (9023M) [F,JF]	*Scrapped at St Athan, 1997*	
XX845	SEPECAT Jaguar T2A [ET]	RAF No 6 Sqn, Coltishall	
XX846	SEPECAT Jaguar T2A [V]	RAF No 16(R) Sqn, Lossiemouth	
XX847	SEPECAT Jaguar T2A	RAF, stored St Athan	
XX885	HS Buccaneer S2B (9225M)	RAF Lossiemouth, BDRT	
XX888	HS Buccaneer S2B <ff>	Dundonald Aviation Centre, Strathclyde	
XX889	HS Buccaneer S2B	Jet Age Museum, Staverton	
XX892	HS Buccaneer S2B <ff>	Christies Garden Centre, Forres, Grampian	
XX893	HS Buccaneer S2B <ff>	Privately owned, Birtley, Tyne & Wear	
XX894	HS Buccaneer S2B [020/R]	Buccaneer Preservation Society, Kemble	
XX895	HS Buccaneer S2B	The Planets Leisure Centre, Woking	
XX897	HS Buccaneer S2B(mod)	Privately owned, Bournemouth	
XX899	HS Buccaneer S2B <ff>	Midland Air Museum, Coventry	
XX900	HS Buccaneer S2B	British Aviation Heritage, Bruntingthorpe	
XX901	HS Buccaneer S2B	Yorkshire Air Museum, Elvington	
XX907	WS Lynx AH1	DERA Structures Dept, Farnborough	
XX910	WS Lynx HAS2	DERA Structures Dept, Farnborough	
XX914	BAC VC10/1103 (8777M) <rf>	RAF AMS, Brize Norton	
XX919	BAC 1-11/402AP (PI-C1121)	MoD(PE)/AFD, DERA Boscombe Down	
XX946	Panavia Tornado (P02) (8883M)	RAF Museum, Hendon	
XX947	Panavia Tornado (P03) (8797M)	RAF Cosford, WLT	
XX948	Panavia Tornado (P06) (8879M) [P]	RAF No 1 SoTT, Cosford	
XX955	SEPECAT Jaguar GR1A [GK]	RAF, stored Shawbury	
XX956	SEPECAT Jaguar GR1 (8950M) [BE]	RAF No 1 SoTT, Cosford	
XX958	SEPECAT Jaguar GR1 (9022M) [BK,JG]	RAF No 1 SoTT, Cosford	
XX959	SEPECAT Jaguar GR1 (8953M) [CJ]	RAF No 1 SoTT, Cosford	
XX962	SEPECAT Jaguar GR1B [E]	AMIF, RAFC Cranwell	
XX965	SEPECAT Jaguar GR1A [C]	AMIF, RAFC Cranwell	
XX966	SEPECAT Jaguar GR1A (8904M) [EL]	RAF No 1 SoTT, Cosford	
XX967	SEPECAT Jaguar GR1 (9006M) [AC,JD]	RAF No 1 SoTT, Cosford	
XX968	SEPECAT Jaguar GR1 (9007M) [AJ,JE]	RAF No 1 SoTT, Cosford	
XX969	SEPECAT Jaguar GR1A (8897M) [01]	RAF No 1 SoTT, Cosford	
XX970	SEPECAT Jaguar GR1B [EH]	RAF No 6 Sqn, Coltishall	
XX974	SEPECAT Jaguar GR1A (Jag 96(A)) [GH]	RAF No 54 Sqn, Coltishall	
XX975	SEPECAT Jaguar GR1 (8905M) [07]	RAF No 1 SoTT, Cosford	
XX976	SEPECAT Jaguar GR1 (8906M) [BD]	RAF No 1 SoTT, Cosford	
XX977	SEPECAT Jaguar GR1 (9132M) [DL,05]	RAF St Athan, BDRT	
XX979	SEPECAT Jaguar GR1A (Jag 96)	RAF, St Athan (conversion)	
XZ101	SEPECAT Jaguar GR1A [D]	RAF, St Athan	
XZ103	SEPECAT Jaguar GR1A (Jag 96(R)) [FP]	RAF Coltishall	
XZ104	SEPECAT Jaguar GR1A (Jag 96(R)) [FM]	RAF, St Athan (conversion)	

Notes	Serial	Type (other identity) [code]	Owner/operator, location or fate
	XZ106	SEPECAT Jaguar GR1A (Jag 96(R)) [FR]	RAF No 41 Sqn, Coltishall
	XZ107	SEPECAT Jaguar GR1A (Jag 96(R)) [FH]	RAF No 41 Sqn, Coltishall
	XZ108	SEPECAT Jaguar GR1A (Jag 96(R)) [GL]	Crashed 3 September 1998, North Sea
	XZ109	SEPECAT Jaguar GR1A (Jag 96(R)) [EN]	RAF, St Athan (conversion)
	XZ111	SEPECAT Jaguar GR1A [GO]	RAF No 54 Sqn, Coltishall
	XZ112	SEPECAT Jaguar GR1A (Jag 96(R)) [GA]	RAF No 54 Sqn, Coltishall
	XZ113	SEPECAT Jaguar GR1A (Jag 96(R)) [FD]	RAF No 41 Sqn, Coltishall
	XZ114	SEPECAT Jaguar GR1A [FB]	RAF, stored Shawbury
	XZ115	SEPECAT Jaguar GR1A (Jag 96(R)) [FC]	RAF No 41 Sqn, Coltishall
	XZ117	SEPECAT Jaguar GR1A (Jag 96(R)) [EP]	RAF, St Athan (conversion)
	XZ118	SEPECAT Jaguar GR1A (Jag 96(R)) [FF]	RAF No 41 Sqn, Coltishall
	XZ119	SEPECAT Jaguar GR1A [F]	AMIF, RAFC Cranwell
	XZ129	HS Harrier GR3 [ETS]	RN ETS, Yeovilton
	XZ130	HS Harrier GR3 (9079M) [A,HE]	RAF No 1 SoTT, Cosford
	XZ131	HS Harrier GR3 (9174M) <ff>	No 2156 Sqn ATC, Brierley Hill, W Mids
	XZ132	HS Harrier GR3 (9168M) [C]	ATF, RAFC Cranwell
	XZ133	HS Harrier GR3 [10]	Imperial War Museum, Duxford
	XZ135	HS Harrier GR3 (8848M) <ff>	RAF EPTT, St Athan
	XZ138	HS Harrier GR3 (9040M) <ff>	RAFC Cranwell, Trenchard Hall
	XZ145	HS Harrier T4 [T]	SFDO, RNAS Culdrose
	XZ146	HS Harrier T4 [S]	RAF North Luffenham Training Area
	XZ170	WS Lynx AH9	MoD(PE)/GKN Westland, Yeovil
	XZ171	WS Lynx AH7	AAC NARO Fleetlands
	XZ172	WS Lynx AH7	AAC No 655 Sqn/5 Regt, Aldergrove
	XZ173	WS Lynx AH7	AAC NARO Fleetlands
	XZ174	WS Lynx AH7	AAC No 655 Sqn/5 Regt, Aldergrove
	XZ175	WS Lynx AH7	AAC No 661 Sqn/1 Regt, Gütersloh
	XZ176	WS Lynx AH7	AAC No 661 Sqn/1 Regt, Gütersloh
	XZ177	WS Lynx AH7	AAC No 669 Sqn/4 Regt, Wattisham
	XZ178	WS Lynx AH7 [1]	AAC No 662 Sqn/3 Regt, Wattisham
	XZ179	WS Lynx AH7	AAC No 652 Sqn/1 Regt, Gütersloh
	XZ180	WS Lynx AH7 [R]	RM No 847 Sqn, Yeovilton
	XZ181	WS Lynx AH1	MoD(PE)/GKN Westland, Yeovil
	XZ182	WS Lynx AH7 [M]	MoD(PE)/GKN Westland, Weston-super-Mare (on repair)
	XZ183	WS Lynx AH7	AAC No 661 Sqn/1 Regt, Gütersloh
	XZ184	WS Lynx AH7	AAC No 671 Sqn/2 Regt, Middle Wallop
	XZ185	WS Lynx AH7	AAC No 669 Sqn/4 Regt, Wattisham
	XZ186	WS Lynx AH7 (wreckage)	AAC, NARO Fleetlands
	XZ187	WS Lynx AH7	AAC No 667 Sqn/2 Regt, Middle Wallop
	XZ188	WS Lynx AH7	Army SEAE, Arborfield
	XZ190	WS Lynx AH7	AAC No 663 Sqn/3 Regt, Wattisham
	XZ191	WS Lynx AH7 [X]	AAC, stored NARO Fleetlands
	XZ192	WS Lynx AH7	AAC, NARO Fleetlands (on rebuild)
	XZ193	WS Lynx AH7 [I]	AAC No 671 Sqn/2 Regt, Middle Wallop
	XZ194	WS Lynx AH7	AAC No 9 Regt, Dishforth
	XZ195	WS Lynx AH7	AAC No 655 Sqn/5 Regt, Aldergrove
	XZ196	WS Lynx AH7	AAC No 657 Sqn/9 Regt, Dishforth
	XZ197	WS Lynx AH7	AAC No 661 Sqn/1 Regt, Gütersloh
	XZ198	WS Lynx AH7	AAC No 655 Sqn/5 Regt, Aldergrove
	XZ199	WS Lynx AH7	AAC No 657 Sqn/9 Regt, Dishforth
	XZ203	WS Lynx AH7 [L]	AAC No 671 Sqn/2 Regt, Middle Wallop
	XZ205	WS Lynx AH7	AAC No 655 Sqn/5 Regt, Aldergrove
	XZ206	WS Lynx AH7	AAC No 25 Flt, Belize
	XZ207	WS Lynx AH7	AAC No 652 Sqn/1 Regt, Gütersloh
	XZ208	WS Lynx AH7	AAC No 9 Regt, Dishforth
	XZ209	WS Lynx AH7 [T]	AAC, NARO Fleetlands (conversion)
	XZ210	WS Lynx AH7	AAC No 9 Regt, Dishforth
	XZ211	WS Lynx AH7	AAC No 651 Sqn/1 Regt, Gütersloh
	XZ212	WS Lynx AH7	AAC No 664 Sqn/9 Regt, Dishforth
	XZ213	WS Lynx AH1 (TAD 213)	NARO Fleetlands Apprentice School
	XZ214	WS Lynx AH7	AAC No 657 Sqn/9 Regt, Dishforth
	XZ215	WS Lynx AH7 [4]	AAC No 655 Sqn/5 Regt, Aldergrove
	XZ216	WS Lynx AH7	AAC No 654 Sqn/4 Regt, Wattisham

Serial	Type (other identity) [code]	Owner/operator, location or fate	Notes
XZ217	WS Lynx AH7	AAC, NARO Fleetlands	
XZ218	WS Lynx AH7	AAC No 655 Sqn/5 Regt, Aldergrove	
XZ219	WS Lynx AH7	AAC No 9 Regt, Dishforth	
XZ220	WS Lynx AH7	AAC No 651 Sqn/1 Regt, Gütersloh	
XZ221	WS Lynx AH7	AAC No 9 Regt, Dishforth	
XZ222	WS Lynx AH7	AAC No 657 Sqn/9 Regt, Dishforth	
XZ228	WS Lynx HAS3S [407/YK]	RN No 815 Sqn, *York* Flt, Yeovilton	
XZ229	WS Lynx HAS3S [304]	RN No 815 Sqn, HQ Flt, Yeovilton	
XZ230	WS Lynx HAS3S [305]	RN No 815 Sqn, HQ Flt, Yeovilton	
XZ232	WS Lynx HAS3S [355/SM]	RN AMG, Yeovilton	
XZ233	WS Lynx HAS3ICE [435/ED]	RN AMG, Yeovilton	
XZ234	WS Lynx HAS3S [335/CF]	RN No 815 Sqn, *Cardiff* Flt, Yeovilton	
XZ235	WS Lynx HAS3S [635]	RN, NARO Fleetlands	
XZ236	WS Lynx HMA8	MoD(PE) AFD/DERA Boscombe Down	
XZ237	WS Lynx HAS3S [630]	RN No 702 Sqn, Yeovilton	
XZ238	WS Lynx HAS3S(ICE) [435/EE]	RN No 815 Sqn, *Endurance* Flt, Yeovilton	
XZ239	WS Lynx HAS3S [437]	RN No 815 Sqn, *Grafton* Flt, Yeovilton	
XZ241	WS Lynx HAS3S(ICE) [434/EE]	RN No 815 Sqn, *Endurance* Flt, Yeovilton	
XZ243	WS Lynx HAS3 <f>	RN AESS, *HMS Sultan*, Gosport, BDRT	
XZ245	WS Lynx HAS3S [306]	RN AMG, Yeovilton	
XZ246	WS Lynx HAS3ICE [435/EE]	RN AMG, Yeovilton	
XZ248	WS Lynx HAS3S [634]	RN No 702 Sqn, Yeovilton	
XZ250	WS Lynx HAS3S [360/MC]	RN No 815 Sqn, *Manchester* Flt, Yeovilton	
XZ252	WS Lynx HAS3S	RN, stored NARO Fleetlands	
XZ254	WS Lynx HAS3S [302]	RN No 815 Sqn, HQ Flt, Yeovilton	
XZ255	WS Lynx HMA8 [462/WM]	RN No 815 Sqn, *Westminster* Flt, Yeovilton	
XZ256	WS Lynx HMA8 [352/SD]	RN No 815 Sqn, *Sheffield* Flt, Yeovilton	
XZ257	WS Lynx HAS3S [644]	RN No 702 Sqn, Yeovilton	
XZ284	HS Nimrod MR2	RAF No 206 Sqn, Kinloss	
XZ286	BAe Nimrod AEW3 (rf)	RAF Kinloss Fire Section	
XZ287	BAe Nimrod AEW3 (9140M) (fuselage)	RAF TSW, Stafford	
XZ290	WS Gazelle AH1 [F01]	RN, NARO Fleetlands Station Flight	
XZ291	WS Gazelle AH1	AAC No 12 Flt, Brüggen	
XZ292	WS Gazelle AH1	AAC No 656 Sqn/9 Regt, Dishforth	
XZ294	WS Gazelle AH1 [X]	AAC No 658 Sqn/7 Regt, Netheravon	
XZ295	WS Gazelle AH1	AAC No 12 Flt, Brüggen	
XZ296	WS Gazelle AH1	AAC No 669 Sqn/4 Regt, Wattisham	
XZ298	WS Gazelle AH1	AAC No 656 Sqn/9 Regt, Dishforth	
XZ299	WS Gazelle AH1	AAC No 665 Sqn/5 Regt, Aldergrove	
XZ300	WS Gazelle AH1 [L] (wreck)	Army, Bramley, Hants	
XZ301	WS Gazelle AH1 [U]	AAC No 654 Sqn/4 Regt, Wattisham	
XZ302	WS Gazelle AH1 (fuselage)	AAC, stored NARO Fleetlands	
XZ303	WS Gazelle AH1 [4]	AAC No 3 Regt, Wattisham	
XZ304	WS Gazelle AH1	AAC No 6(V) Flt/7 Regt, Shawbury	
XZ305	WS Gazelle AH1 (TAD020)	Army SEAE, Arborfield	
XZ307	WS Gazelle AH1	NARO Fleetlands Apprentice School	
XZ308	WS Gazelle AH1 [V]	AAC No 657 Sqn/9 Regt, Dishforth	
XZ309	WS Gazelle AH1	AAC No 6(V) Flt/7 Regt, Shawbury	
XZ311	WS Gazelle AH1	AAC No 6(V) Flt/7 Regt, Shawbury	
XZ312	WS Gazelle AH1	AAC No 664 Sqn/9 Regt, Dishforth	
XZ313	WS Gazelle AH1	AAC No 667 Sqn/2 Regt, Middle Wallop	
XZ314	WS Gazelle AH1	AAC No 8 Flt, Middle Wallop	
XZ315	WS Gazelle AH1	AAC No 665 Sqn/5 Regt, Aldergrove	
XZ316	WS Gazelle AH1 [B]	AAC No 666(V) Sqn/7 Regt, Netheravon	
XZ317	WS Gazelle AH1 [R]	AAC, stored Shawbury	
XZ318	WS Gazelle AH1	AAC, stored NARO Fleetlands	
XZ320	WS Gazelle AH1	AAC No 654 Sqn/4 Regt, Wattisham	
XZ321	WS Gazelle AH1	AAC No 665 Sqn/5 Regt, Aldergrove	
XZ322	WS Gazelle AH1 [N]	RAF St Athan, BDRT	
XZ323	WS Gazelle AH1	AAC, NARO Fleetlands	
XZ324	WS Gazelle AH1	AAC No 3(V) Flt/7 Regt, Leuchars	
XZ325	WS Gazelle AH1 [T]	Army SEAE, Arborfield	
XZ326	WS Gazelle AH1	AAC No 3 Regt, Wattisham	
XZ327	WS Gazelle AH1	AAC No 661 Sqn/1 Regt, Gütersloh	
XZ328	WS Gazelle AH1	AAC No 3 Regt, Wattisham	
XZ329	WS Gazelle AH1 [J]	AAC, stored Shawbury	
XZ330	WS Gazelle AH1 [Y]	AAC No 671 Sqn/2 Regt, Middle Wallop	
XZ331	WS Gazelle AH1	AAC No 669 Sqn/4 Regt, Wattisham	
XZ332	WS Gazelle AH1	Army SEAE, Arborfield	
XZ333	WS Gazelle AH1 [A]	Army SEAE, Arborfield	
XZ334	WS Gazelle AH1 [S]	AAC No 671 Sqn/2 Regt, Middle Wallop	

Notes	Serial	Type (other identity) [code]	Owner/operator, location or fate
	XZ335	WS Gazelle AH1	AAC No 6(V) Flt/7 Regt, Shawbury
	XZ337	WS Gazelle AH1	AAC No 663 Sqn/3 Regt, Wattisham
	XZ338	WS Gazelle AH1	AAC No 652 Sqn/1 Regt, Gütersloh
	XZ339	WS Gazelle AH1	AAC No 667 Sqn/2 Regt, Middle Wallop
	XZ340	WS Gazelle AH1 [5A]	AAC No 29 Flt, BATUS, Suffield, Canada
	XZ341	WS Gazelle AH1	AAC No 3(V) Flt/7 Regt, Leuchars
	XZ342	WS Gazelle AH1	AAC NARO Fleetlands
	XZ343	WS Gazelle AH1	AAC No 661 Sqn/1 Regt, Gütersloh
	XZ344	WS Gazelle AH1 [I]	AAC No 9 Regt, Dishforth
	XZ345	WS Gazelle AH1	AAC No 657 Sqn/9 Regt, Dishforth
	XZ346	WS Gazelle AH1	AAC No 665 Sqn/5 Regt, Aldergrove
	XZ347	WS Gazelle AH1	AAC No 3 Regt, Wattisham
	XZ348	WS Gazelle AH1 (wreck)	AAC, stored NARO Fleetlands
	XZ349	WS Gazelle AH1 [G1]	AAC No 671 Sqn/2 Regt, Middle Wallop
	XZ355	SEPECAT Jaguar GR1A (Jag 96(R)) [FJ]	RAF, No 41 Sqn, Coltishall
	XZ356	SEPECAT Jaguar GR1A [EP]	RAF, stored Shawbury
	XZ357	SEPECAT Jaguar GR1A (Jag 96(R)) [FK]	RAF, St Athan (conversion)
	XZ358	SEPECAT Jaguar GR1A [L]	AMIF, RAFC Cranwell
	XZ360	SEPECAT Jaguar GR1A (Jag 96(R))	RAF No 41 Sqn, Coltishall
	XZ361	SEPECAT Jaguar GR1A [FT]	RAF No 41 Sqn, Coltishall
	XZ363	SEPECAT Jaguar GR1A (Jag 96(R)) [FO]	RAF No 41 Sqn, Coltishall
	XZ363	SEPECAT Jaguar GR1A <R> (BAPC 151) [A]	RAF EPTT, St Athan
	XZ364	SEPECAT Jaguar GR1A (Jag 96(R)) [GJ]	RAF No 54 Sqn, Coltishall
	XZ366	SEPECAT Jaguar GR1A (Jag 96(R)) [FS]	RAF St Athan (conversion)l
	XZ367	SEPECAT Jaguar GR1A (Jag 96(R)) [GP]	RAF No 54 Sqn, Coltishall
	XZ368	SEPECAT Jaguar GR1 [8900M] [AG]	RAF No 1 SoTT, Cosford
	XZ369	SEPECAT Jaguar GR1A (Jag 96(T)) [EF]	RAF No 6 Sqn, Coltishall
	XZ370	SEPECAT Jaguar GR1 (9004M) [JB]	RAF No 1 SoTT, Cosford
	XZ371	SEPECAT Jaguar GR1 (8907M) [AP]	RAF No 1 SoTT, Cosford
	XZ372	SEPECAT Jaguar GR1A (Jag 96) [ED]	RAF, St Athan (conversion)
	XZ374	SEPECAT Jaguar GR1 (9005M) [JC]	RAF No 1 SoTT, Cosford
	XZ375	SEPECAT Jaguar GR1A (9255M)	
	XZ377	SEPECAT Jaguar GR1A (Jag 96(A)) [EG]	RAF No 6 Sqn, Coltishall
	XZ378	SEPECAT Jaguar GR1A [EP]	RAF, stored Shawbury
	XZ381	SEPECAT Jaguar GR1A (Jag 96) [EC]	RAF, St Athan (conversion)
	XZ382	SEPECAT Jaguar GR1 (8908M)	Privately owned, RAF Coltishall
	XZ383	SEPECAT Jaguar GR1 (8901M) [AF]	RAF No 1 SoTT, Cosford
	XZ384	SEPECAT Jaguar GR1 (8954M) [BC]	RAF No 1 SoTT, Cosford
	XZ385	SEPECAT Jaguar GR1A [C]	RAF No 16(R) Sqn, Lossiemouth
	XZ389	SEPECAT Jaguar GR1 (8946M) [BL]	RAF No 1 SoTT, Cosford
	XZ390	SEPECAT Jaguar GR1A (9003M) [35,JA]	RAF No 1 SoTT, Cosford
	XZ391	SEPECAT Jaguar GR1A [A]	RAF No 16(R) Sqn, Lossiemouth
	XZ392	SEPECAT Jaguar GR1A [GQ]	RAF, stored Shawbury
	XZ394	SEPECAT Jaguar GR1A (Jag 96(A)) [GN]	RAF No 54 Sqn, Coltishall
	XZ396	SEPECAT Jaguar GR1A	RAF No 6 Sqn, Coltishall
	XZ398	SEPECAT Jaguar GR1A (Jag 96(R)) [FA]	RAF, St Athan (conversion)
	XZ399	SEPECAT Jaguar GR1A (Jag 97) [EJ]	MoD(PE)/AFD, DERA Boscombe Down
	XZ400	SEPECAT Jaguar GR1A (Jag 96(A)) [GR]	RAF No 54 Sqn, Coltishall
	XZ431	HS Buccaneer S2B (9233M)	RAF Marham Fire Section

Serial	Type (other identity) [code]	Owner/operator, location or fate	Notes
XZ439	BAe Sea Harrier FA2	MoD(PE)/BAe, Dunsfold	
XZ440	BAe Sea Harrier FA2 [126/N]	MoD(PE)/BAe, Dunsfold (conversion)	
XZ445	BAe Harrier T4A [721] (wreck)	RN FSAIU, Yeovilton	
XZ455	BAe Sea Harrier FA2 [001] (wreck)	RN FSAIU, Yeovilton	
XZ457	BAe Sea Harrier FA2 [714] (wreck)	RN FSAIU, Yeovilton	
XZ459	BAe Sea Harrier FA2 [003]	RN No 801 Sqn, Yeovilton	
XZ492	BAe Sea Harrier FA2 [127] (wreck)	RN FSAIU, Yeovilton	
XZ493	BAe Sea Harrier FRS1 (comp XV760) [126]	FAA Museum, at BAe Dunsfold (restoration)	
XZ493	BAe Sea Harrier FRS1 <ff>	RN Yeovilton, Fire Section	
XZ494	BAe Sea Harrier FA2 [128]	RN No 800 Sqn, Yeovilton	
XZ497	BAe Sea Harrier FA2 [712/R]	MoD(PE)/BAe, Dunsfold	
XZ499	BAe Sea Harrier FA2	MoD(PE)/BAe, Dunsfold (conversion)	
XZ559	Slingsby T61F Venture T2 (G-BUEK)	Privately owned, Tibenham	
XZ570	WS61 Sea King HAS5(mod)	MoD(PE)/GKN Westland, Yeovil	
XZ571	WS61 Sea King HAS6 [016/L]	RN No 820 Sqn, Culdrose	
XZ574	WS61 Sea King HAS6 [015/L]	RN No 820 Sqn, Culdrose	
XZ575	WS61 Sea King HU5	RN, NARO Fleetlands (conversion)	
XZ576	WS61 Sea King HAS6	MoD(PE)/AFD, DERA Boscombe Down	
XZ578	WS61 Sea King HU5 [188/CU]	RN No 819 Sqn, Prestwick	
XZ579	WS61 Sea King HAS6	RN No 819 Sqn, Prestwick	
XZ580	WS61 Sea King HAS6 [704/PW]	RN No 819 Sqn, Prestwick	
XZ581	WS61 Sea King HAS6 [269/N]	RN No 814 Sqn, Culdrose	
XZ585	WS61 Sea King HAR3	RAF No 22 Sqn, C Flt, Valley	
XZ586	WS61 Sea King HAR3 [S]	MoD(PE)/GKN Westland, Yeovil	
XZ587	WS61 Sea King HAR3	RAF HMF, St Mawgan	
XZ588	WS61 Sea King HAR3	RAF No 202 Sqn, A Flt, Boulmer	
XZ589	WS61 Sea King HAR3	RAF No 22 Sqn, C Flt, Valley	
XZ590	WS61 Sea King HAR3	RAF No 202 Sqn, E Flt, Leconfield	
XZ591	WS61 Sea King HAR3 [S]	RAF No 78 Sqn, Mount Pleasant, FI	
XZ592	WS61 Sea King HAR3 [S]	RAF No 202 Sqn, D Flt, Lossiemouth	
XZ593	WS61 Sea King HAR3	RAF, NARO Fleetlandsr	
XZ594	WS61 Sea King HAR3	RAF HMF, St Mawgan	
XZ595	WS61 Sea King HAR3	RAF No 202 Sqn, D Flt, Lossiemouth	
XZ596	WS61 Sea King HAR3	RAF No 202 Sqn, A Flt, Boulmer	
XZ597	WS61 Sea King HAR3	RAF No 203(R) Sqn, St Mawgan	
XZ598	WS61 Sea King HAR3	MoD(PE)/GKN Westland, Weston-super-Mare	
XZ599	WS61 Sea King HAR3 [S]	RAF No 78 Sqn, Mount Pleasant, FI	
XZ605	WS Lynx AH7 [Y]	RM No 847 Sqn, Yeovilton	
XZ606	WS Lynx AH7	AAC No 667 Sqn/2 Regt, Middle Wallop	
XZ607	WS Lynx AH7	AAC No 9 Regt, Dishforth	
XZ608	WS Lynx AH7	AAC No 657 Sqn/9 Regt, Dishforth	
XZ609	WS Lynx AH7	AAC No 652 Sqn/1 Regt, Gütersloh	
XZ610	WS Lynx AH7	Crashed 22 December 1998, Bosnia	
XZ611	WS Lynx AH7 [Y]	AAC, No 661 Sqn/1 Regt, Gütersloh	
XZ612	WS Lynx AH7	RM No 847 Sqn, Yeovilton	
XZ613	WS Lynx AH7 [F]	Army SEAE, Arborfield	
XZ614	WS Lynx AH7 [X]	RM No 847 Sqn, Yeovilton	
XZ615	WS Lynx AH7	AAC No 655 Sqn/5 Regt, Aldergrove	
XZ616	WS Lynx AH7	AAC No 657 Sqn/9 Regt, Dishforth	
XZ617	WS Lynx AH7	AAC No 661 Sqn/1 Regt, Gütersloh	
XZ630	Panavia Tornado GR1 (8976M)	RAF St Athan, BDRT	
XZ631	Panavia Tornado GR1	MoD(PE)/BAe, Warton	
XZ641	WS Lynx AH7	AAC No 25 Flt, Belize	
XZ642	WS Lynx AH7	AAC No 662 Sqn/3 Regt, Wattisham	
XZ643	WS Lynx AH7 [3]	AAC, NARO Fleetlands	
XZ645	WS Lynx AH7	AAC No 9 Regt, Dishforth	
XZ646	WS Lynx AH7	AAC No 651 Sqn/1 Regt, Gütersloh	
XZ647	WS Lynx AH7	AAC No 655 Sqn/5 Regt, Aldergrove	
XZ648	WS Lynx AH7	AAC No 661 Sqn/1 Regt, Gütersloh	
XZ649	WS Lynx AH7	AAC No 655 Sqn/5 Regt, Aldergrove	
XZ651	WS Lynx AH7	AAC No 657 Sqn/9 Regt, Dishforth	
XZ652	WS Lynx AH7 [T]	AAC No 671 Sqn/2 Regt, Middle Wallop	
XZ653	WS Lynx AH7	AAC No 661 Sqn/1 Regt, Gütersloh	
XZ654	WS Lynx AH7	AAC, stored NARO Fleetlands	
XZ655	WS Lynx AH7	AAC No 655 Sqn/5 Regt, Aldergrove	
XZ661	WS Lynx AH1	AAC, stored NARO Fleetlands	
XZ662	WS Lynx AH7	AAC No 655 Sqn/5 Regt, Aldergrove	
XZ663	WS Lynx AH7	AAC No 655 Sqn/5 Regt, Aldergrove	
XZ664	WS Lynx AH7	AAC, NARO Fleetlands	
XZ665	WS Lynx AH7	AAC, NARO Fleetlands	

Notes	Serial	Type (other identity) [code]	Owner/operator, location or fate
	XZ666	WS Lynx AH7	Army SEAE, Arborfield
	XZ667	WS Lynx AH7	*Crashed 10 April 1994, Portadown*
	XZ668	WS Lynx AH7 [UN] (wreckage)	AAC Middle Wallop, instructional use
	XZ669	WS Lynx AH7	AAC No 669 Sqn/4 Regt, Wattisham
	XZ670	WS Lynx AH7	RM No 847 Sqn, Yeovilton
	XZ671	WS Lynx AH7 <ff>	GKN Westland, Yeovil, instructional use
	XZ672	WS Lynx AH7	AAC No 655 Sqn/5 Regt, Aldergrove
	XZ673	WS Lynx AH7	AAC No 655 Sqn/5 Regt, Aldergrove
	XZ674	WS Lynx AH7	AAC No 9 Regt, Dishforth
	XZ675	WS Lynx AH7 [E]	AAC No 671 Sqn/2 Regt, Middle Wallop
	XZ676	WS Lynx AH7 [N]	AAC No 671 Sqn/2 Regt, Middle Wallop
	XZ677	WS Lynx AH7	AAC, stored NARO Fleetlands
	XZ678	WS Lynx AH7	AAC No 9 Regt, Dishforth
	XZ679	WS Lynx AH7	AAC No 663 Sqn/3 Regt, Wattisham
	XZ680	WS Lynx AH7	AAC No 9 Regt, Dishforth
	XZ681	WS Lynx AH1	AAC Middle Wallop, BDRT
	XZ689	WS Lynx HMA8	RN No 702 Sqn, Yeovilton
	XZ690	WS Lynx HMA8	RN, NARO Fleetlands (conversion)
	XZ691	WS Lynx HMA8 [474/RM]	RN No 815 Sqn, *Richmond* Flt, Yeovilton
	XZ692	WS Lynx HMA8 [457/LA]	RN No 815 Sqn, *Lancaster* Flt, Yeovilton
	XZ693	WS Lynx HAS3S [301]	RN No 815 Sqn, HQ Flt, Yeovilton
	XZ694	WS Lynx HAS3S [417]	RN No 815 Sqn, *Nottingham* Flt, Yeovilton
	XZ695	WS Lynx HAS3S [345/NC]	RN No 815 Sqn, *Newcastle* Flt, Yeovilton
	XZ696	WS Lynx HAS3S [479]	RN No 815 Sqn, Lynx Support Flt, Yeovilton
	XZ697	WS Lynx HMA8 [308]	RN No 815 Sqn, HQ Flt, Yeovilton
	XZ698	WS Lynx HMA8 [308]	RN, NARO Fleetlands (conversion)
	XZ699	WS Lynx HAS3S [303]	RN No 815 Sqn, HQ Flt, Yeovilton
	XZ719	WS Lynx HMA8 [644]	RN NARO Fleetlands (conversion)
	XZ720	WS Lynx HAS3S [411/EB]	RN No 815 Sqn, *Edinburgh* Flt, Yeovilton
	XZ721	WS Lynx HMA8 [350/CL]	RN No 815 Sqn, *Cumberland* Flt, Yeovilton
	XZ722	WS Lynx HMA8 [372/NL]	RN No 815 Sqn, *Northumberland* Flt, Yeovilton
	XZ723	WS Lynx HMA8	RN, Yeovilton
	XZ724	WS Lynx HAS3S [336/CV]	RN AMG, Yeovilton
	XZ725	WS Lynx HAS3S [633]	RN No 702 Sqn, Yeovilton
	XZ726	WS Lynx HMA8	RN, NARO Fleetlands (conversion)
	XZ727	WS Lynx HAS3S [332/LP]	RN No 815 Sqn, *Liverpool* Flt, Yeovilton
	XZ728	WS Lynx HMA8 [415/MM]	RN, stored NARO Fleetlands
	XZ729	WS Lynx HAS3S [632]	RN No 702 Sqn, Yeovilton
	XZ730	WS Lynx HAS3CTS [302]	RN No 815 Sqn, HQ Flt, Yeovilton
	XZ731	WS Lynx HMA8 [363/MA]	RN No 815 Sqn, *Marlborough* Flt, Yeovilton
	XZ732	WS Lynx HMA8 [318]	RN No 815 Sqn OEU, Yeovilton
	XZ733	WS Lynx HAS3S [361]	RN No 815 Sqn, *Norfolk* Flt, Yeovilton
	XZ735	WS Lynx HAS3S [360/MC]	RN AMG, Yeovilton
	XZ736	WS Lynx HMA8 [350/CL]	RN NARO Fleetlands (conversion)
	XZ920	WS61 Sea King HU5 [822/CU]	RN No 771 Sqn, Culdrose
	XZ921	WS61 Sea King HAS6 [507/CU]	RN No 810 Sqn, Culdrose
	XZ922	WS61 Sea King HAS6 [503/CU]	RN No 810 Sqn, Culdrose
	XZ930	WS Gazelle HT3 [Q]	RAF, stored Shawbury
	XZ931	WS Gazelle HT3 [R]	RAF, stored Shawbury
	XZ932	WS Gazelle HT3 [S]	RAF, stored Shawbury
	XZ933	WS Gazelle HT3 [T]	RAF, stored Shawbury
	XZ934	WS Gazelle HT3 [U]	RAF, stored Shawbury
	XZ935	WS Gazelle HCC4	RAF, stored NARO Fleetlands
	XZ936	WS Gazelle HT2 [6]	MoD(PE)/AFD/ETPS, DERA Boscombe Down
	XZ937	WS Gazelle HT2 [Y]	RAF, stored Shawbury
	XZ938	WS Gazelle HT2 [45/CU]	RN, stored Shawbury
	XZ939	WS Gazelle HT2 [9]	MoD(PE)/AFD/ETPS, DERA Boscombe Down
	XZ940	WS Gazelle HT2 [O]	RAF, stored Shawbury
	XZ941	WS Gazelle HT2 [B]	RAF, stored Shawbury
	XZ942	WS Gazelle HT2 [42/CU]	RN, stored Shawbury
	XZ964	BAe Harrier GR3 [D]	Royal Engineers Museum, Chatham
	XZ966	BAe Harrier GR3 (9221M) [G]	FSCTE, RAF Manston
	XZ967	BAe Harrier GR3 (9077M) [F]	*Sold to the USA, July 1998*
	XZ968	BAe Harrier GR3 (9222M) [3G]	Muckleborough Collection, Weybourne
	XZ969	BAe Harrier GR3 [D]	SFDO, RNAS Culdrose
	XZ971	BAe Harrier GR3 (9219M) [G]	RAF, stored Shawbury
	XZ987	BAe Harrier GR3 (9185M) [C]	RAF Stafford, at main gate
	XZ990	BAe Harrier GR3 <ff>	No 1220 Sqn ATC, March, Cambs

Serial	Type (other identity) [code]	Owner/operator, location or fate	Notes
XZ990	BAe Harrier GR3 <rf>	RAF Wittering, derelict	
XZ991	BAe Harrier GR3 (9162M) [3A]	RAF St Athan, BDRT	
XZ993	BAe Harrier GR3 (9240M) (fuselage)	RAF St Athan, BDRT	
XZ994	BAe Harrier GR3 (9170M) [U]	RAF Air Movements School, Brize Norton	
XZ995	BAe Harrier GR3 (9220M) [3G]	RAF St Mawgan, BDRT	
XZ996	BAe Harrier GR3 [2,3]	SFDO, RNAS Culdrose	
XZ997	BAe Harrier GR3 (9122M) [V]	RAF Museum, Hendon	
ZA101	BAe Hawk 100 (G-HAWK)	MoD(PE)/BAe, Warton	
ZA105	WS61 Sea King HAR3 [S]	RAF No 203(R) Sqn, St Mawgan	
ZA110	BAe Jetstream T2 (F-BTMI) [563/CU]	RN, Culdrose (damaged)	
ZA111	BAe Jetstream T2 (9Q-CTC) [565/CU]	RN No 750 Sqn, Culdrose	
ZA126	WS61 Sea King HAS6 [500]	RN No 810 Sqn, Culdrose	
ZA127	WS61 Sea King HAS6 [509/CU]	RN No 810 Sqn, Culdrose	
ZA128	WS61 Sea King HAS6 [013/L]	RN No 820 Sqn, Culdrose	
ZA129	WS61 Sea King HAS6 [502/CU]	RN No 810 Sqn, Culdrose	
ZA130	WS61 Sea King HU5 [587/CU]	RN, NARO Fleetlands	
ZA131	WS61 Sea King HAS6 [271/N]	RN No 814 Sqn, Culdrose	
ZA133	WS61 Sea King HAS6 [500]	RN No 810 Sqn, Culdrose	
ZA134	WS61 Sea King HU5 [824/CU]	RN No 771 Sqn, Culdrose	
ZA135	WS61 Sea King HAS6 [010/L]	RN AMG, Culdrose	
ZA135	WS61 Sea King HAS5 (XV657) [132]	RN ETS, Culdrose	
ZA136	WS61 Sea King HAS6 [018/L]	RN AMG, Culdrose (damaged)	
ZA137	WS61 Sea King HU5 [597]	RN, NARO Fleetlands	
ZA140	BAe VC10 K2 (G-ARVL)	RAF No 101 Sqn, Brize Norton	
ZA141	BAe VC10 K2 (G-ARVG) [B]	RAF No 101 Sqn, Brize Norton	
ZA142	BAe VC10 K2 (G-ARVI) [C]	RAF No 101 Sqn, Brize Norton	
ZA143	BAe VC10 K2 (G-ARVK) [D]	RAF, stored St Athan	
ZA144	BAe VC10 K2 (G-ARVC) [E]	RAF No 101 Sqn, Brize Norton	
ZA147	BAe VC10 K3 (5H-MMT) [F]	RAF No 101 Sqn, Brize Norton	
ZA148	BAe VC10 K3 (5Y-ADA) [G]	RAF No 101 Sqn, Brize Norton	
ZA149	BAe VC10 K3 (5X-UVJ) [H]	RAF No 101 Sqn, Brize Norton	
ZA150	BAe VC10 K3 (5H-MOG) [J]	RAF No 101 Sqn, Brize Norton	
ZA166	WS61 Sea King HU5 [511]	RN AMG, Culdrose	
ZA167	WS61 Sea King HU5 [825/CU]	RN AMG, Culdrose	
ZA168	WS61 Sea King HAS6 [512/CU]	RN No 810 Sqn, Culdrose	
ZA169	WS61 Sea King HAS6 [265/N]	RN, NARO Fleetlands	
ZA170	WS61 Sea King HU5	RN, NARO Fleetlands	
ZA175	BAe Sea Harrier FA2 [126]	RN No 800 Sqn, Yeovilton	
ZA176	BAe Sea Harrier FA2	RN No 800 Sqn, Yeovilton	
ZA195	BAe Sea Harrier FA2	MoD(PE)/BAe, Dunsfold	
ZA250	BAe Harrier T52 (G-VTOL)	Brooklands Museum, Weybridge	
ZA254	Panavia Tornado F2 (fuselage)	RAF Coningsby, instructional use	
ZA267	Panavia Tornado F2	RAF Marham, instructional use	
ZA283	Panavia Tornado F2	MoD(PE)/BAe, Warton	
ZA291	WS61 Sea King HC4 [ZX]	RN No 846 Sqn, Yeovilton	
ZA292	WS61 Sea King HC4 [ZR]	MoD(PE)/GKN Westland, Weston-super-Mare	
ZA293	WS61 Sea King HC4 [ZO]	RN No 848 Sqn, Yeovilton	
ZA295	WS61 Sea King HC4 [ZR]	RN No 848 Sqn, Yeovilton	
ZA296	WS61 Sea King HC4 [VO]	RN No 846 Sqn, Yeovilton	
ZA297	WS61 Sea King HC4 [C]	RN No 845 Sqn, Yeovilton	
ZA298	WS61 Sea King HC4 [G]	RN No 845 Sqn, Yeovilton	
ZA299	WS61 Sea King HC4 [ZT]	RN No 848 Sqn, Yeovilton	
ZA310	WS61 Sea King HC4 [ZY]	RN No 848 Sqn, Yeovilton	
ZA312	WS61 Sea King HC4 [ZS]	RN No 848 Sqn, Yeovilton	
ZA313	WS61 Sea King HC4 [M]	RN No 845 Sqn, Yeovilton	
ZA314	WS61 Sea King HC4 [F]	RN No 845 Sqn, Yeovilton	
ZA319	Panavia Tornado GR1 [B-11]	RAF TTTE, Cottesmore	
ZA320	Panavia Tornado GR1 [B-01]	RAF TTTE, Cottesmore	
ZA321	Panavia Tornado GR1 [B-58]	RAF TTTE, Cottesmore	
ZA322	Panavia Tornado GR1 [B-50]	RAF TTTE, Cottesmore	
ZA323	Panavia Tornado GR1 [TAZ]	RAF No 15(R) Sqn, Lossiemouth	
ZA324	Panavia Tornado GR1 [B-02]	RAF TTTE, Cottesmore	
ZA325	Panavia Tornado GR1 [B-03]	RAF TTTE, Cottesmore	
ZA326	Panavia Tornado GR1P	MoD(PE)/AFD, DERA Boscombe Down	
ZA327	Panavia Tornado GR1	MoD(PE)/BAe, Warton	
ZA328	Panavia Tornado GR1	MoD(PE)/BAe, Warton	
ZA330	Panavia Tornado GR1 [B-08]	Crashed 21 January 1999, Everton, Notts	
ZA352	Panavia Tornado GR1 [B-04]	RAF TTTE, Cottesmore	

Notes	Serial	Type (other identity) [code]	Owner/operator, location or fate
	ZA353	Panavia Tornado GR1 [B-53]	MoD(PE)/AFD, DERA Boscombe Down
	ZA354	Panavia Tornado GR1	MoD(PE)/BAe, Warton
	ZA355	Panavia Tornado GR1 [TAA]	RAF No 15(R) Sqn, Lossiemouth
	ZA356	Panavia Tornado GR1 [B-07]	RAF TTTE, Cottesmore
	ZA357	Panavia Tornado GR1 [B-05]	RAF TTTE, Cottesmore
	ZA358	Panavia Tornado GR1	MoD(PE)/BAe, Warton
	ZA359	Panavia Tornado GR1	BAe Warton, Overseas Customer Training Centre
	ZA360	Panavia Tornado GR1 [B-56]	RAF TTTE, Cottesmore
	ZA361	Panavia Tornado GR1 [B-57]	RAF TTTE, Cottesmore
	ZA362	Panavia Tornado GR1 [B-09]	RAF TTTE, Cottesmore
	ZA365	Panavia Tornado GR1B [AJ-T]	RAF St Athan
	ZA367	Panavia Tornado GR1 [II]	RAF No 2 Sqn, Marham
	ZA368	*Panavia Tornado GR1 <R> (BAPC 155) [AJ-P]*	*Repainted as ZA556 by June 1998*
	ZA369	Panavia Tornado GR4A	RAF No 13 Sqn, Marham
	ZA370	Panavia Tornado GR1A [A]	RAF No 2 Sqn, Marham
	ZA371	Panavia Tornado GR4A	MoD(PE)/AFD, DERA Boscombe Down
	ZA372	Panavia Tornado GR1A [E]	RAF No 2 Sqn, Marham
	ZA373	Panavia Tornado GR1A [H]	RAF No 2 Sqn, Marham
	ZA374	Panavia Tornado GR1B [AJ-L]	RAF No 617 Sqn, Lossiemouth
	ZA375	Panavia Tornado GR1B [AJ-W]	RAF No 617 Sqn, Lossiemouth
	ZA393	Panavia Tornado GR1 [BE]	RAF No 14 Sqn, Brüggen
	ZA395	Panavia Tornado GR1A [N]	RAF No 2 Sqn, Marham
	ZA398	Panavia Tornado GR1A [S]	RAF No 2 Sqn, Marham
	ZA399	Panavia Tornado GR1B [AJ-C]	RAF No 617 Sqn, Lossiemouth
	ZA400	Panavia Tornado GR1A [T]	RAF No 2 Sqn, Marham
	ZA401	Panavia Tornado GR1A [R]	RAF No 2 Sqn, Marham
	ZA402	Panavia Tornado GR1	MoD(PE)/AFD, DERA Boscombe Down
	ZA404	Panavia Tornado GR4A [W]	MoD(PE)/BAe, Warton (conversion)
	ZA405	Panavia Tornado GR1A [Y]	RAF No 2 Sqn, Marham
	ZA406	Panavia Tornado GR1 [CI]	RAF No 17 Sqn, Brüggen
	ZA407	Panavia Tornado GR1B [AJ-G]	RAF No 617 Sqn, Lossiemouth
	ZA409	Panavia Tornado GR1B [FQ]	RAF No 12 Sqn, Lossiemouth
	ZA410	Panavia Tornado GR1 [FZ]	RAF No 12 Sqn, Lossiemouth
	ZA411	Panavia Tornado GR1B [AJ-S]	RAF No 617 Sqn, Lossiemouth
	ZA412	Panavia Tornado GR1 [FX]	RAF, stored St Athan
	ZA446	Panavia Tornado GR1B [E]	RAF AWC/SAOEU, DERA Boscombe Down
	ZA447	Panavia Tornado GR1B [FA]	RAF No 12 Sqn, Lossiemouth
	ZA449	Panavia Tornado GR1	MoD(PE)/AFD, DERA Boscombe Down
	ZA450	Panavia Tornado GR1B [FB]	RAF No 12 Sqn, Lossiemouth
	ZA452	Panavia Tornado GR1B [FC]	RAF No 12 Sqn, Lossiemouth
	ZA453	Panavia Tornado GR1B [AJ-M]	RAF No 617 Sqn, Lossiemouth
	ZA455	Panavia Tornado GR1B [FE]	RAF No 12 Sqn, Lossiemouth
	ZA456	Panavia Tornado GR1B [AJ-Q]	RAF No 617 Sqn, Lossiemouth
	ZA457	Panavia Tornado GR1B [AJ-J]	RAF No 617 Sqn, Lossiemouth
	ZA458	Panavia Tornado GR1 [JA]	RAF No 17 Sqn, Brüggen
	ZA459	Panavia Tornado GR1B [AJ-B]	RAF No 617 Sqn, Lossiemouth
	ZA460	Panavia Tornado GR1B [AJ-A]	RAF No 617 Sqn, Lossiemouth
	ZA461	Panavia Tornado GR1B [FD]	RAF No 12 Sqn, Lossiemouth
	ZA462	Panavia Tornado GR1 [CG]	RAF No 17 Sqn, Brüggen
	ZA463	Panavia Tornado GR1 [CR]	RAF No 17 Sqn, Brüggen
	ZA465	Panavia Tornado GR1B [FF]	RAF No 12 Sqn, Lossiemouth
	ZA466	Panavia Tornado GR1 <ff>	RAF St Athan, BDRT
	ZA469	Panavia Tornado GR1B [AJ-O]	RAF, stored St Athan
	ZA470	Panavia Tornado GR1 [BQ]	RAF No 14 Sqn, Brüggen
	ZA471	Panavia Tornado GR1B [AJ-K]	RAF No 617 Sqn, Lossiemouth
	ZA472	Panavia Tornado GR1 [CT]	RAF No 17 Sqn, Brüggen
	ZA473	Panavia Tornado GR1B [FG]	RAF No 12 Sqn, Lossiemouth
	ZA474	Panavia Tornado GR1B [AJ-F]	RAF No 617 Sqn, Lossiemouth
	ZA475	Panavia Tornado GR1B [FH]	RAF No 12 Sqn, Lossiemouth
	ZA490	Panavia Tornado GR1B [FJ]	RAF No 12 Sqn, Lossiemouth
	ZA491	Panavia Tornado GR1B [FK]	RAF No 12 Sqn, Lossiemouth
	ZA492	Panavia Tornado GR1B [FL]	RAF No 12 Sqn, Lossiemouth
	ZA541	Panavia Tornado GR4	MoD(PE)/BAe, Warton (conversion)
	ZA542	Panavia Tornado GR4	MoD(PE)/BAe, Warton (conversion)
	ZA543	Panavia Tornado GR4	MoD(PE)/BAe, Warton (conversion)
	ZA544	Panavia Tornado GR4	MoD(PE)/BAe, Warton (conversion)
	ZA546	Panavia Tornado GR1 [AJ-C]	RAF St Athan, instructional use
	ZA547	Panavia Tornado GR4	RAF St Athan
	ZA548	Panavia Tornado GR1 [TQ]	RAF No 15(R) Sqn, Lossiemouth
	ZA549	Panavia Tornado GR4	RAF, No 13 Sqn, Marham

Serial	Type (other identity) [code]	Owner/operator, location or fate	Notes
ZA550	Panavia Tornado GR4	RAF, St Athan	
ZA551	Panavia Tornado GR4 [IV]	MoD(PE)/BAe, Warton (conversion)	
ZA552	Panavia Tornado GR4	MoD(PE)/BAe, Warton (conversion)	
ZA553	Panavia Tornado GR4	MoD(PE)/BAe, Warton (conversion)	
ZA554	Panavia Tornado GR4	RAF St Athan)	
ZA556	Panavia Tornado GR4	RAF St Athan	
ZA556	Panavia Tornado GR1 <R> (*ZA368*/BAPC 155) [F]	RAF EPTT, St Athan	
ZA557	Panavia Tornado GR4	MoD(PE)/BAe Warton	
ZA559	Panavia Tornado GR4 [AD]	RAF No 9 Sqn, Brüggen	
ZA560	Panavia Tornado GR4	RAF AWC/SAOEU, DERA Boscombe Down	
ZA562	Panavia Tornado GR1 [TT]	RAF No 15(R) Sqn, Lossiemouth	
ZA563	Panavia Tornado GR4	RAF,No 9 Sqn, Brüggen	
ZA564	Panavia Tornado GR1 [CK]	RAF No 17 Sqn, Brüggen	
ZA585	Panavia Tornado GR4	RAF, St Athan	
ZA587	Panavia Tornado GR4 [F]	RAF No 15(R) Sqn, Lossiemouth	
ZA588	Panavia Tornado GR1 [TM]	RAF No 15(R) Sqn, Lossiemouth	
ZA589	Panavia Tornado GR4 [TE]	MoD(PE)/BAe, Warton (conversion)	
ZA590	Panavia Tornado GR1	RAF, stored St Athan	
ZA591	Panavia Tornado GR4	MoD(PE)/BAe, Warton (conversion)	
ZA592	Panavia Tornado GR1 [C]	RAF No 2 Sqn, Marham	
ZA594	Panavia Tornado GR4	RAF, St Athan	
ZA595	Panavia Tornado GR4	MoD(PE)/BAe, Warton (conversion)	
ZA596	Panavia Tornado GR1	RAF, stored St Athan	
ZA597	Panavia Tornado GR1 [TA]	RAF No 15(R) Sqn, Lossiemouth	
ZA598	Panavia Tornado GR1B [TN]	RAF No 15(R) Sqn, Lossiemouth	
ZA599	Panavia Tornado GR4 [TX]	RAF No 15(R) Sqn, Lossiemouth	
ZA600	Panavia Tornado GR1 [TH]	RAF No 15(R) Sqn, Lossiemouth	
ZA601	Panavia Tornado GR1 [TI]	RAF No 15(R) Sqn, Lossiemouth	
ZA602	Panavia Tornado GR4	MoD(PE)/BAe, Warton (conversion)	
ZA604	Panavia Tornado GR1 [TY]	RAF No 15(R) Sqn, Lossiemouth	
ZA606	Panavia Tornado GR4	MoD(PE)/BAe, Warton (conversion)n	
ZA607	Panavia Tornado GR4 [AB]	RAF No 9 Sqn, Brüggen	
ZA608	Panavia Tornado GR1 [TK]	RAF No 15(R) Sqn, Lossiemouth	
ZA609	Panavia Tornado GR1 [Z]	RAF No 13 Sqn, Marham	
ZA611	Panavia Tornado GR1 [TG]	RAF No 15(R) Sqn, Lossiemouth	
ZA612	Panavia Tornado GR1 [TZ]	RAF No 15(R) Sqn, Lossiemouth	
ZA613	Panavia Tornado GR1 [TL]	RAF No 15(R) Sqn, Lossiemouth	
ZA614	Panavia Tornado GR1 [TB]	RAF No 15(R) Sqn, Lossiemouth	
ZA634	Slingsby T61F Venture T2 (G-BUHA) [C]	Privately owned, Rufforth	
ZA663	Slingsby T61F Venture T2 (G-BUFP)	Privately owned, Currock Hill	
ZA612	Panavia Tornado GR1 [TZ]	RAF No 15(R) Sqn, Lossiemouth	
ZA670	B-V Chinook HC2 (N37010) [BF]	RAF No 18 Sqn, Odiham	
ZA671	B-V Chinook HC2 (N37011) [J]	RAF No 78 Sqn, Mount Pleasant, FI	
ZA673	B-V Chinook HC2 (N37016)	RAF No 27 Sqn, Odiham	
ZA674	B-V Chinook HC2 (N37019) [EF]	RAF No 7 Sqn, Odiham	
ZA675	B-V Chinook HC2 (N37020) [EB]	RAF No 18 Sqn, Odiham	
ZA676	B-V Chinook HC1 (N37021/9230M) [FG] (wreck)	FSCTE, RAF Manston	
ZA677	B-V Chinook HC2 (N37022) [EG]	RAF No 7 Sqn, Odiham	
ZA678	B-V Chinook HC1 (N37023/9229M) [EZ] (wreck)	RAF Odiham, BDRT	
ZA679	B-V Chinook HC2 (N37025) [C]	RAF, NARO Fleetlands	
ZA680	B-V Chinook HC2 (N37026) [NX]	RAF No 27 Sqn, Odiham	
ZA681	B-V Chinook HC2 (N37027) [ED]	RAF No 7 Sqn, Odiham	
ZA682	B-V Chinook HC2 (N37029) [BG]	RAF No 18 Sqn, Odiham	
ZA683	B-V Chinook HC2 (N37030) [D]	RAF, NARO Fleetlands	
ZA684	B-V Chinook HC2 (N37031) [EL]	RAF No 7 Sqn, Odiham	
ZA704	B-V Chinook HC2 (N37033) [EJ]	RAF No 7 Sqn, Odiham	
ZA705	B-V Chinook HC2 (N37035) [BE]	RAF No 18 Sqn, Odiham	
ZA707	B-V Chinook HC2 (N37040) [EV]	RAF No 7 Sqn, Odiham	
ZA708	B-V Chinook HC2 (N37042) [BC]	RAF No 18 Sqn, Odiham	
ZA709	B-V Chinook HC2 (N37043) [EQ]	RAF No 7 Sqn, Odiham	
ZA710	B-V Chinook HC2 (N37044) [EC]	RAF No 7 Sqn, Odiham	
ZA711	B-V Chinook HC2 (N37046) [ET]	RAF No 7 Sqn, Odiham	
ZA712	B-V Chinook HC2 (N37047) [ER]	RAF No 7 Sqn, Odiham	
ZA713	B-V Chinook HC2 (N37048) [EM]	RAF No 7 Sqn, Odiham	
ZA714	B-V Chinook HC2 (N37051)	RAF, NARO Fleetlands	
ZA717	B-V Chinook HC1 (N37056/9238M) (wreck)	RAF Cranwell, BDRT	

Notes	Serial	Type (other identity) [code]	Owner/operator, location or fate
	ZA718	B-V Chinook HC2 (N37058) [BN]	RAF No 18 Sqn, Odiham
	ZA720	B-V Chinook HC2 (N37060) [EP]	RAF No 7 Sqn, Odiham
	ZA726	WS Gazelle AH1 [F1]	AAC No 671 Sqn/2 Regt, Middle Wallop
	ZA728	WS Gazelle AH1 [E]	RM No 847 Sqn, Yeovilton
	ZA729	WS Gazelle AH1 [V]	AAC No 658 Sqn/7 Regt, Netheravon
	ZA730	WS Gazelle AH1	AAC No 665 Sqn/5 Regt, Aldergrove
	ZA731	WS Gazelle AH1 [A]	AAC No 29 Flt, BATUS, Suffield, Canada
	ZA733	WS Gazelle AH1	NARO Fleetlands Apprentice School
	ZA734	WS Gazelle AH1	AAC No 25 Flt, Belize
	ZA735	WS Gazelle AH1	AAC No 25 Flt, Belize
	ZA736	WS Gazelle AH1	AAC, No 29 Flt, BATUS, Suffield, Canada
	ZA737	WS Gazelle AH1	AAC No 1 Regt, Gütersloh
	ZA765	WS Gazelle AH1	AAC, NARO Fleetlands (damaged)
	ZA766	WS Gazelle AH1	AAC No 651 Sqn/1 Regt, Gütersloh
	ZA767	WS Gazelle AH1	AAC No 25 Flt, Belize
	ZA768	WS Gazelle AH1 [F] (wreck)	AAC, stored NARO Fleetlands
	ZA769	WS Gazelle AH1 [K]	Army SEAE, Arborfield
	ZA771	WS Gazelle AH1	AAC No 663 Sqn/3 Regt, Wattisham
	ZA772	WS Gazelle AH1	AAC No 665 Sqn/5 Regt, Aldergrove
	ZA773	WS Gazelle AH1 [F]	AAC No 666(V) Sqn/7 Regt, Netheravon
	ZA774	WS Gazelle AH1	AAC No 665 Sqn/5 Regt, Aldergrove
	ZA775	WS Gazelle AH1	AAC No 665 Sqn/5 Regt, Aldergrove
	ZA776	WS Gazelle AH1 [F]	RM No 847 Sqn, Yeovilton
	ZA777	WS Gazelle AH1 [B]	AAC No 671 Sqn/2 Regt, Middle Wallop
	ZA802	WS Gazelle HT3 [W]	RAF, stored Shawbury
	ZA803	WS Gazelle HT3 [X]	RAF, stored Shawbury
	ZA804	WS Gazelle HT3 [I]	RAF, stored Shawbury
	ZA934	WS Puma HC1 [BZ]	RAF No 33 Sqn, Benson
	ZA935	WS Puma HC1	RAF No 230 Sqn, Aldergrove
	ZA936	WS Puma HC1	RAF No 230 Sqn, Aldergrove
	ZA937	WS Puma HC1	RAF No 230 Sqn, Aldergrove
	ZA938	WS Puma HC1	RAF No 230 Sqn, Aldergrove
	ZA939	WS Puma HC1	RAF No 230 Sqn, Aldergrove
	ZA940	WS Puma HC1	RAF No 230 Sqn, Aldergrove
	ZA947	Douglas Dakota C3 [YS-H]	RAF BBMF, Coningsby
	ZB500	WS Lynx 800 (G-LYNX/ZA500)	The Helicopter Museum, Weston-super-Mare
	ZB506	WS61 Sea King Mk 4X	MoD(PE)/AFD, DERA Boscombe Down
	ZB507	WS61 Sea King HC4 [ZN]	RN No 848 Sqn, Yeovilton
	ZB600	BAe Harrier T4	BAe Dunsfold, for Indian Navy
	ZB601	BAe Harrier T4 (fuselage)	Privately owned, Charlwood, Surrey
	ZB602	BAe Harrier T4	BAe Dunsfold, for Indian Navy
	ZB603	BAe Harrier T8 [722/VL]	MoD(PE)/BAe, Dunsfold (conversion)
	ZB604	BAe Harrier T8 [722]	MoD(PE)/BAe, Dunsfold (conversion)
	ZB605	BAe Harrier T8 [720/VL]	RN No 899 Sqn, Yeovilton
	ZB615	SEPECAT Jaguar T2	MoD(PE)/AFD, DERA Boscombe Down
	ZB625	WS Gazelle HT3 [N]	MoD(PE)/AFD, DERA Boscombe Down
	ZB626	WS Gazelle HT3 [L]	RAF, stored Shawbury
	ZB627	WS Gazelle HT3 [A]	RAF, stored Shawbury
	ZB629	WS Gazelle HCC4	RAF, stored NARO Fleetlands
	ZB646	WS Gazelle HT2 [59/CU]	RN, stored Shawbury
	ZB647	WS Gazelle HT2 [40/CU]	RN, stored Shawbury
	ZB648	WS Gazelle HT2 <ff>	RN, Predannack Fire School
	ZB649	WS Gazelle HT2 [VL]	RN, stored Shawbury
	ZB665	WS Gazelle AH1	AAC No 665 Sqn/5 Regt, Aldergrove
	ZB666	WS Gazelle AH1 [G]	RN, NARO Fleetlands
	ZB667	WS Gazelle AH1	AAC, NARO Fleetlands
	ZB668	WS Gazelle AH1 (TAD 015)	Army SEAE, Arborfield
	ZB669	WS Gazelle AH1	AAC No 654 Sqn/4 Regt, Wattisham
	ZB670	WS Gazelle AH1	AAC No 665 Sqn/5 Regt, Aldergrove
	ZB671	WS Gazelle AH1 [2]	AAC No 29 Flt, BATUS, Suffield, Canada
	ZB672	WS Gazelle AH1	AAC No 661 Sqn/1 Regt, Gütersloh
	ZB673	WS Gazelle AH1 [P]	AAC No 671 Sqn/2 Regt, Middle Wallop
	ZB674	WS Gazelle AH1	AAC No 665 Sqn/5 Regt, Aldergrove
	ZB676	WS Gazelle AH1 [C]	RM No 847 Sqn, Yeovilton
	ZB677	WS Gazelle AH1 [3]	AAC No 29 Flt, BATUS, Suffield, Canada
	ZB678	WS Gazelle AH1	Army SEAE, Arborfield
	ZB679	WS Gazelle AH1	AAC No 16 Flt, Dhekelia, Cyprus
	ZB682	WS Gazelle AH1	AAC No 665 Sqn/5 Regt, Aldergrove
	ZB683	WS Gazelle AH1	AAC No 665 Sqn/5 Regt, Aldergrove
	ZB684	WS Gazelle AH1	AAC No 665 Sqn/5 Regt, Aldergrove
	ZB685	WS Gazelle AH1	AAC No 665 Sqn/5 Regt, Aldergrove

Serial	Type (other identity) [code]	Owner/operator, location or fate	Notes
ZB686	WS Gazelle AH1	AAC No 665 Sqn/5 Regt, Aldergrove	
ZB688	WS Gazelle AH1 [H]	AAC No 671 Sqn/2 Regt, Middle Wallop	
ZB689	WS Gazelle AH1	AAC No 665 Sqn/5 Regt, Aldergrove	
ZB690	WS Gazelle AH1	AAC No 16 Flt, Dhekelia, Cyprus	
ZB691	WS Gazelle AH1	AAC No 9 Regt, Dishforth	
ZB692	WS Gazelle AH1	AAC No 9 Regt, Dishforth	
ZB693	WS Gazelle AH1 [4]	AAC No 29 Flt, BATUS, Suffield, Canada	
ZD230	BAC Super VC10 K4 (G-ASGA) [K]	RAF No 101 Sqn, Brize Norton	
ZD234	BAC Super VC10 (G-ASGF/8700M)	RAF Brize Norton, tanker simulator	
ZD235	BAC Super VC10 K4 (G-ASGG) [L]	RAF No 101 Sqn, Brize Norton	
ZD239	BAC Super VC10 (G-ASGK)	FSCTE, RAF Manston	
ZD240	BAC Super VC10 K4 (G-ASGL) [M]	RAF No 101 Sqn, Brize Norton	
ZD241	BAC Super VC10 K4 (G-ASGM) [N]	RAF No 101 Sqn, Brize Norton	
ZD242	BAC Super VC10 K4 (G-ASGP) [P]	RAF No 101 Sqn, Brize Norton	
ZD249	WS Lynx HAS3S [642]	RN No 702 Sqn, Yeovilton	
ZD250	WS Lynx HAS3S [631]	RN No 702 Sqn, Yeovilton	
ZD251	WS Lynx HAS3S	RN No 702 Sqn, Yeovilton	
ZD252	WS Lynx HMA8 [671]	RN No 702 Sqn, Yeovilton	
ZD253	WS Lynx HAS3S [410]	RN No 815 Sqn, Lynx Support Flt, Yeovilton	
ZD254	WS Lynx HAS3S [645]	RN No 702 Sqn, Yeovilton	
ZD255	WS Lynx HAS3S [344/GW]	RN No 815 Sqn, *Glasgow* Flt, Yeovilton	
ZD256	WS Lynx HAS3S [437/GT]	Crashed 23 September 1998, South China Sea	
ZD257	WS Lynx HMA8	RN, AMG, Yeovilton	
ZD258	WS Lynx HMA8 (*XZ258*) [633]	RN, NARO Fleetlands (conversion)	
ZD259	WS Lynx HAS3S [635]	RN No 702 Sqn, Yeovilton	
ZD260	WS Lynx HMA8 [444]	RN No 815 Sqn, *Montrose* Flt, Yeovilton	
ZD261	WS Lynx HMA8 [672]	RN AMG, Yeovilton	
ZD262	WS Lynx HMA8 [415/MM]	RN No 815 Sqn, *Monmouth* Flt, Yeovilton	
ZD263	WS Lynx HAS3S	RN AMG, Yeovilton	
ZD264	WS Lynx HAS3S [333/BM]	RN No 815 Sqn, *Birmingham* Flt, Yeovilton	
ZD265	WS Lynx HMA8 [376/XB]	RN No 815 Sqn, *Boxer* Flt, Yeovilton	
ZD266	WS Lynx HMA8	MoD(PE)/GKN Westland, Yeovil	
ZD267	WS Lynx HMA8	MoD(PE)/GKN Westland, Yeovil	
ZD268	WS Lynx HMA8 [670]	RN No 702 Sqn, Yeovilton	
ZD272	WS Lynx AH7 [H]	AAC No 671 Sqn/2 Regt, Middle Wallop	
ZD273	WS Lynx AH7	AAC No 655 Sqn/5 Regt, Aldergrove	
ZD274	WS Lynx AH7	AAC No 656 Sqn/9 Regt, Dishforth	
ZD276	WS Lynx AH7	AAC No 663 Sqn/3 Regt, Wattisham	
ZD277	WS Lynx AH7	AAC No 651 Sqn/1 Regt, Gütersloh	
ZD278	WS Lynx AH7 [A]	AAC No 671 Sqn/2 Regt, Middle Wallop	
ZD279	WS Lynx AH7 [C]	AAC No 671 Sqn/2 Regt, Middle Wallop	
ZD280	WS Lynx AH7	AAC No 654 Sqn/4 Regt, Wattisham	
ZD281	WS Lynx AH7 [K]	AAC No 671 Sqn/2 Regt, Middle Wallop	
ZD282	WS Lynx AH7 [L]	RM No 847 Sqn, Yeovilton	
ZD283	WS Lynx AH7 [P]	AAC No 671 Sqn/2 Regt, Middle Wallop	
ZD284	WS Lynx AH7	AAC No 669 Sqn/4 Regt, Wattisham	
ZD285	WS Lynx AH7	MoD(PE)/AFD, DERA Boscombe Down	
ZD318	BAe Harrier GR7	MoD(PE)/BAe, Dunsfold	
ZD319	BAe Harrier GR7	MoD(PE)/AFD, DERA Boscombe Down	
ZD320	BAe Harrier GR7	MoD(PE)/BAe, Dunsfold	
ZD321	BAe Harrier GR7 [02]	RAF No 1 Sqn, Wittering	
ZD322	BAe Harrier GR7 [03]	RAF, St Athan	
ZD323	BAe Harrier GR7 [04]	RAF, St Athan	
ZD326	BAe Harrier GR7 [07]	RAF No 3 Sqn, Laarbruch	
ZD327	BAe Harrier GR7 [08]	RAF, St Athan	
ZD328	BAe Harrier GR7 [09]	RAF AWC/SAOEU, DERA Boscombe Down	
ZD329	BAe Harrier GR7 [10]	RAF, No 3 Sqn, Laarbruch	
ZD330	BAe Harrier GR7 [11]	RAF No 4 Sqn, Laarbruch	
ZD345	BAe Harrier GR7 [12]	RAF HOCU/No 20(R) Sqn, Wittering	
ZD346	BAe Harrier GR7 [13]	RAF No 3 Sqn, Laarbruch	
ZD347	BAe Harrier GR7 [14]	RAF HOCU/No 20(R) Sqn, Wittering	
ZD348	BAe Harrier GR7 [15]	RAF St Athan	
ZD350	BAe Harrier GR5 (9189M) <ff>	RAF St Athan, BDRT	
ZD351	BAe Harrier GR7 [18]	RAF, St Athan (damaged)	
ZD352	BAe Harrier GR7 [19]	RAF No 4 Sqn, Laarbruch	
ZD353	BAe Harrier GR5 (fuselage)	BAe Brough	
ZD354	BAe Harrier GR7 [21]	RAF HOCU/No 20(R) Sqn, Wittering	
ZD375	BAe Harrier GR7 [23]	RAF No 3 Sqn, Laarbruch	
ZD376	BAe Harrier GR7 [24]	RAF No 3 Sqn, Laarbruch	

Notes	Serial	Type (other identity) [code]	Owner/operator, location or fate
	ZD378	BAe Harrier GR7 [26]	RAF No 3 Sqn, Laarbruch
	ZD379	BAe Harrier GR7 [27]	RAF No 3 Sqn, Laarbruch
	ZD380	BAe Harrier GR7 [28]	RAF, St Athan
	ZD401	BAe Harrier GR7 [30]	RAF No 1 Sqn, Wittering
	ZD402	BAe Harrier GR7 [31]	RAF HOCU/No 20(R) Sqn, Wittering
	ZD403	BAe Harrier GR7 [32]	RAF No 1 Sqn, Wittering
	ZD404	BAe Harrier GR7 [33]	RAF HOCU/No 20(R) Sqn, Wittering
	ZD405	BAe Harrier GR7 [34]	RAF No 4 Sqn, Laarbruch
	ZD406	BAe Harrier GR7 [35]	RAF HOCU/No 20(R) Sqn, Wittering
	ZD407	BAe Harrier GR7 [36]	RAF HOCU/No 20(R) Sqn, Wittering
	ZD408	BAe Harrier GR7	RAF AWC/SAOEU, DERA Boscombe Down
	ZD409	BAe Harrier GR7 [38]	RAF No 3 Sqn, Laarbruch
	ZD410	BAe Harrier GR7 [39]	RAF No 3 Sqn, Laarbruch
	ZD411	BAe Harrier GR7 [U]	RAF AWC/SAOEU, DERA Boscombe Down
	ZD412	BAe Harrier GR5 (fuselage)	BAe Brough
	ZD431	BAe Harrier GR7 [43]	RAF HOCU/No 20(R) Sqn, Wittering
	ZD433	BAe Harrier GR7 [45]	RAF HOCU/No 20(R) Sqn, Wittering
	ZD434	BAe Harrier GR7 [46]	Crashed 18 December 1998, Barnard Castle, Co Durham
	ZD435	BAe Harrier GR7 [47]	RAF No 1 Sqn, Wittering
	ZD436	BAe Harrier GR7 [48]	RAF No 1 Sqn, Wittering
	ZD437	BAe Harrier GR7 [49]	RAF HOCU/No 20(R) Sqn, Wittering
	ZD438	BAe Harrier GR7 [50]	RAF No 1 Sqn, Wittering
	ZD461	BAe Harrier GR7 [51]	RAF No 1 Sqn, Wittering
	ZD462	BAe Harrier GR7 [52]	RAF St Athan (damaged)
	ZD463	BAe Harrier GR7 [53]	RAF HOCU/No 20(R) Sqn, Wittering
	ZD464	BAe Harrier GR7 [54]	RAF No 4 Sqn, Laarbruch
	ZD465	BAe Harrier GR7 [55]	RAF No 1 Sqn, Wittering
	ZD466	BAe Harrier GR7 [56]	RAF No 4 Sqn, Laarbruch
	ZD467	BAe Harrier GR7 [57]	RAF HOCU/No 20(R) Sqn, Wittering
	ZD468	BAe Harrier GR7 [58]	RAF No 1 Sqn, Wittering
	ZD469	BAe Harrier GR7 [59]	RAF No 4 Sqn, Laarbruch
	ZD470	BAe Harrier GR7 [60]	RAF No 1 Sqn, Wittering
	ZD476	WS61 Sea King HC4 [ZU]	RN, NARO Fleetlands
	ZD477	WS61 Sea King HC4 [H]	RN No 845 Sqn, Yeovilton
	ZD478	WS61 Sea King HC4 [VG]	RN No 846 Sqn, Yeovilton
	ZD479	WS61 Sea King HC4 [ZV]	RN No 848 Sqn, Yeovilton
	ZD480	WS61 Sea King HC4 [E]	RN No 845 Sqn, Yeovilton
	ZD559	WS Lynx AH5X	MoD(PE)/AFD, DERA Boscombe Down
	ZD560	WS Lynx AH7	MoD(PE)/AFD/ETPS, DERA Boscombe Down
	ZD565	WS Lynx HMA8	RN, NARO Fleetlands (conversion)
	ZD566	WS Lynx HMA8 [422/SU]	RN No 815 Sqn, *Sutherland* Flt, Yeovilton
	ZD574	B-V Chinook HC2 (N37077) [EH]	RAF No 7 Sqn, Odiham
	ZD575	B-V Chinook HC2 (N37078) [NZ]	RAF No 27 Sqn, Odiham
	ZD578	BAe Sea Harrier FA2 [001/L]	RN No 801 Sqn, Yeovilton
	ZD579	BAe Sea Harrier FA2 [004/L]	RN No 801 Sqn, Yeovilton
	ZD580	BAe Sea Harrier FA2	RN, stored St Athan
	ZD581	BAe Sea Harrier FA2	RN, St Athan
	ZD582	BAe Sea Harrier FA2 [712]	RN No 899 Sqn, Yeovilton
	ZD607	BAe Sea Harrier FA2 [125]	RN No 800 Sqn, Yeovilton
	ZD608	BAe Sea Harrier FA2 [717/VL]	RN St Athan
	ZD610	BAe Sea Harrier FA2 [000/L]	RN St Athan
	ZD611	BAe Sea Harrier FA2 [123]	RN St Athan
	ZD612	BAe Sea Harrier FA2 [711]	RN No 899 Sqn, Yeovilton
	ZD613	BAe Sea Harrier FA2 [002]	RN No 801 Sqn, Yeovilton
	ZD614	BAe Sea Harrier FA2 [124]	RN No 800 Sqn, Yeovilton
	ZD615	BAe Sea Harrier FA2 [005/L]	RN No 801 Sqn, Yeovilton
	ZD620	BAe 125 CC3	RAF No 32(The Royal) Sqn, Northolt
	ZD621	BAe 125 CC3	RAF No 32(The Royal) Sqn, Northolt
	ZD625	WS61 Sea King HC4 [VF]	RN No 846 Sqn, Yeovilton
	ZD626	WS61 Sea King HC4 [ZZ]	RN AMG, Yeovilton
	ZD627	WS61 Sea King HC4 [VL]	RN No 846 Sqn, Yeovilton
	ZD630	WS61 Sea King HAS6 [271/N]	RN, stored NARO Fleetlands
	ZD631	WS61 Sea King HAS6 [66] (fuselage)	RN AESS, *HMS Sultan*, Gosport, BDRT
	ZD633	WS61 Sea King HAS6 [014/L]	RN No 820 Sqn, Culdrose
	ZD634	WS61 Sea King HAS6 [506/CU]	RN AMG, Culdrose
	ZD636	WS61 Sea King AEW2 [188]	RN No 849 Sqn, A Flt, Culdrose
	ZD637	WS61 Sea King HAS6 [700/PW]	RN No 819 Sqn, Prestwick

Serial	Type (other identity) [code]	Owner/operator, location or fate	Notes
ZD657	Schleicher ASW-19B Valiant TX1 [YW]	RAF No 615 VGS, Kenley	
ZD658	Schleicher ASW-19B Valiant TX1 [YX]	RAF No 661 VGS, Kirknewton	
ZD659	Schleicher ASW-19B Valiant TX1 [YY]	RAF ACCGS, Syerston	
ZD660	Schleicher ASW-19B Valiant TX1 [YZ]	RAF No 621 VGS, Hullavington	
ZD667	BAe Harrier GR3 (9201M) [3,2]	SFDO, RNAS Culdrose	
ZD668	BAe Harrier GR3 [3E]	Phoenix Aviation, Bruntingthorpe	
ZD670	BAe Harrier GR3 [3A]	Trocadero, Leicester Square,London	
ZD703	BAe 125 CC3	RAF No 32(The Royal) Sqn, Northolt	
ZD704	BAe 125 CC3	RAF No 32(The Royal) Sqn, Northolt	
ZD707	Panavia Tornado GR1 [CH]	RAF No 17 Sqn, Brüggen	
ZD708	Panavia Tornado GR4	MoD(PE)/BAe, Warton	
ZD709	Panavia Tornado GR1 [DG]	RAF No 31 Sqn, Brüggen	
ZD710	Panavia Tornado GR1 <ff>	Robertsbridge Aviation Society, Mayfield	
ZD711	Panavia Tornado GR 4	MoD(PE)/BAe, Warton (conversion)	
ZD712	Panavia Tornado GR1 [BY]	RAF No 14 Sqn, Brüggen	
ZD713	Panavia Tornado GR1 [TW]	RAF No 15(R) Sqn, Lossiemouth	
ZD714	Panavia Tornado GR4	MoD(PE)/BAe, Warton (conversion)	
ZD715	Panavia Tornado GR1 [JC]	RAF No 17 Sqn, Brüggen	
ZD716	Panavia Tornado GR1 [JM]	RAF No 17 Sqn, Brüggen	
ZD719	Panavia Tornado GR1 [DE]	RAF No 31 Sqn, Brüggen	
ZD720	Panavia Tornado GR4 [AG]	MoD(PE)/BAe, Warton (conversion)	
ZD739	Panavia Tornado GR1 [AC]	RAF No 9 Sqn, Brüggen	
ZD740	Panavia Tornado GR4 [AF]	RAF No 9 Sqn, Brüggen	
ZD741	Panavia Tornado GR4	MoD(PE)/BAe, Warton (conversion)	
ZD742	Panavia Tornado GR4	MoD(PE)/BAe, Warton (conversion)	
ZD743	Panavia Tornado GR1 [CX]	RAF No 17 Sqn, Brüggen	
ZD744	Panavia Tornado GR1 [BD]	RAF No 14 Sqn, Brüggen	
ZD745	Panavia Tornado GR4 [BM]	MoD(PE)/BAe, Warton (conversion)	
ZD746	Panavia Tornado GR1 [AB]	RAF St Athan	
ZD747	Panavia Tornado GR4 [AL]	RAF No 9 Sqn, Brüggen	
ZD748	Panavia Tornado GR1 [AK]	RAF No 9 Sqn, Brüggen	
ZD749	Panavia Tornado GR1 [BG]	RAF No 14 Sqn, Brüggen	
ZD788	Panavia Tornado GR1 [CB]	RAF No 17 Sqn, Brüggen	
ZD789	Panavia Tornado GR1	RAF No 31 Sqn, Brüggen	
ZD790	Panavia Tornado GR1 [JF]	RAF No 14 Sqn, Brüggen	
ZD792	Panavia Tornado GR1 [JG]	RAF No 31 Sqn, Brüggen	
ZD793	Panavia Tornado GR1 [JH]	RAF No 17 Sqn, Brüggen	
ZD809	Panavia Tornado GR1 [BA]	RAF No 14 Sqn, Brüggen	
ZD810	Panavia Tornado GR1 [DB]	RAF No 31 Sqn, Brüggen	
ZD811	Panavia Tornado GR1 [JJ]	RAF No 14 Sqn, Brüggen	
ZD812	Panavia Tornado GR1 [BW]	RAF No 14 Sqn, Brüggen	
ZD842	Panavia Tornado GR1 [DX]	RAF No 31 Sqn, Brüggen	
ZD843	Panavia Tornado GR1 [CJ]	RAF No 17 Sqn, Brüggen	
ZD844	Panavia Tornado GR1 [DE]	RAF TMF, Marham	
ZD847	Panavia Tornado GR4 [AA]	RAF No 9 Sqn, Brüggen	
ZD848	Panavia Tornado GR1	RAF No 17 Sqn, Brüggen	
ZD849	Panavia Tornado GR1 [JL]	RAF No 14 Sqn, Brüggen	
ZD850	Panavia Tornado GR1 [DR]	RAF No 31 Sqn, Brüggen	
ZD851	Panavia Tornado GR1 [AJ]	RAF No 9 Sqn, Brüggen	
ZD890	Panavia Tornado GR1 [AE]	RAF No 9 Sqn, Brüggen	
ZD892	Panavia Tornado GR1 [BJ]	RAF No 14 Sqn, Brüggen	
ZD895	Panavia Tornado GR1 [BF]	RAF No 14 Sqn, Brüggen	
ZD899	Panavia Tornado F2	MoD(PE)/BAe, Warton	
ZD900	Panavia Tornado F2 (comp ZE343)	RAF, stored St Athan	
ZD901	Panavia Tornado F2 (comp ZE154)	RAF, stored St Athan	
ZD902	Panavia Tornado F2A(TIARA)	MoD(PE)/AFD, DERA Boscombe Down	
ZD903	Panavia Tornado F2 (comp ZE728)	RAF, stored St Athan	
ZD904	Panavia Tornado F2 (comp ZE759)	RAF, stored St Athan	
ZD905	Panavia Tornado F2 (comp ZE258)	RAF, stored St Athan	
ZD906	Panavia Tornado F2 (comp ZE294)	RAF, stored St Athan	
ZD932	Panavia Tornado F2 (comp ZE255)	RAF, stored St Athan	
ZD933	Panavia Tornado F2 (comp ZE729)	RAF, stored St Athan	
ZD934	Panavia Tornado F2 (comp ZE786) [AD]	RAF, stored St Athan	
ZD935	Panavia Tornado F2 (comp ZE793)	RAF, stored St Athan	
ZD936	Panavia Tornado F2 (comp ZE251)	RAF, stored St Athan	
ZD937	Panavia Tornado F2 (comp ZE736)	RAF St Athan, BDRT	
ZD938	Panavia Tornado F2 (comp ZE295)	RAF, stored St Athan	
ZD939	Panavia Tornado F2 (comp ZE292)	RAF, stored St Athan	

ZD940 – ZE339

ZD940 – ZE339

Notes	Serial	Type (other identity) [code]	Owner/operator, location or fate
	ZD940	Panavia Tornado F2 (comp ZE288)	RAF, stored St Athan
	ZD941	Panavia Tornado F2 (comp ZE254)	RAF, stored St Athan
	ZD948	Lockheed TriStar KC1 (G-BFCA)	RAF No 216 Sqn, Brize Norton
	ZD949	Lockheed TriStar K1 (G-BFCB)	RAF No 216 Sqn, Brize Norton
	ZD950	Lockheed TriStar KC1 (G-BFCC)	RAF No 216 Sqn, Brize Norton
	ZD951	Lockheed TriStar K1 (G-BFCD)	RAF No 216 Sqn, Brize Norton
	ZD952	Lockheed TriStar KC1 (G-BFCE)	RAF No 216 Sqn, Brize Norton
	ZD953	Lockheed TriStar KC1 (G-BFCF)	RAF No 216 Sqn, Brize Norton
	ZD974	Schempp-Hirth Kestrel TX1 [SY]	RAF No 662 VGS, Arbroath
	ZD975	Schempp-Hirth Kestrel TX1 [SZ]	RAF ACCGS, Syerston
	ZD980	B-V Chinook HC2 (N37082) [EA]	RAF No 7 Sqn, Odiham
	ZD981	B-V Chinook HC2 (N37083)	RAF No 18 Sqn, Odiham
	ZD982	B-V Chinook HC2 (N37085) [EK]	RAF No 7 Sqn, Odiham
	ZD983	B-V Chinook HC2 (N37086) [EI]	RAF No 7 Sqn, Odiham
	ZD984	B-V Chinook HC2 (N37088)	RAF, NARO Fleetlands
	ZD990	BAe Harrier T8 [721/VL]	RN No 899 Sqn, Yeovilton
	ZD991	BAe Harrier T8 (9228M) [722/VL]	RN, St Athan (on repair)
	ZD992	BAe Harrier T8 [724/VL]	RN No 899 Sqn, Yeovilton
	ZD993	BAe Harrier T8 [723/VL]	RN No 899 Sqn, Yeovilton
	ZD996	Panavia Tornado GR1A [I]	RAF No 2 Sqn, Marham
	ZE116	Panavia Tornado GR4A [X]	RAF No 13 Sqn, Marham
	ZE154	Panavia Tornado F3 (comp ZD901) [AN]	RAF F3 OCU/No 56(R) Sqn, Coningsby
	ZE155	Panavia Tornado F3	MoD(PE)/BAe, Warton
	ZE156	Panavia Tornado F3 [HE]	RAF No 111 Sqn, Leuchars
	ZE157	Panavia Tornado F3 [GK]	RAF No 43 Sqn, Leuchars
	ZE158	Panavia Tornado F3 [Z]	RAF No 111 Sqn, Leuchars
	ZE159	Panavia Tornado F3 [R]	RAF No 111 Sqn, Leuchars
	ZE160	Panavia Tornado F3 [DV]	RAF 11 Sqn, Leeming
	ZE161	Panavia Tornado F3	RAF No 11 Sqn, Leeming
	ZE162	Panavia Tornado F3 [FK]	RAF No 25 Sqn, Leeming
	ZE163	Panavia Tornado F3	RAF, St Athan (damaged)
	ZE164	Panavia Tornado F3 [DA]	RAF No 11 Sqn, Leeming
	ZE165	Panavia Tornado F3 [Q]	RAF No 111 Sqn, Leuchars
	ZE168	Panavia Tornado F3 [FN]	RAF No 25 Sqn, Leeming
	ZE199	Panavia Tornado F3 [FL]	RAF No 25 Sqn, Leeming
	ZE200	Panavia Tornado F3 [DB]	RAF No 11 Sqn, Leeming
	ZE201	Panavia Tornado F3	RAF No 43 Sqn, Leuchars
	ZE203	Panavia Tornado F3 [FI]	RAF No 25 Sqn, Leeming
	ZE204	Panavia Tornado F3 [DD]	RAF No 11 Sqn, Leeming
	ZE206	Panavia Tornado F3 [FH]	RAF No 25 Sqn, Leeming
	ZE207	Panavia Tornado F3 [GC]	RAF No 43 Sqn, Leuchars
	ZE209	Panavia Tornado F3 [AP]	RAF F3 OCU/No 56(R) Sqn, Coningsby
	ZE210	Panavia Tornado F3 [GA]	RAF No 43 Sqn, Leuchars
	ZE250	Panavia Tornado F3 [HZ]	RAF F3 OCU/No 56(R) Sqn, Coningsby
	ZE251	Panavia Tornado F3 (comp ZD936) [GA]	RAF No 43 Sqn, Leuchars
	ZE253	Panavia Tornado F3 [AC]	RAF F3 OCU/No 56(R) Sqn, Coningsby
	ZE254	Panavia Tornado F3 (comp ZD941) [AW]	RAF F3 OCU/No 56(R) Sqn, Coningsby
	ZE255	Panavia Tornado F3 (comp ZD932) [AY]	RAF F3 OCU/No 56(R) Sqn, Coningsby
	ZE256	Panavia Tornado F3	RAF F3 OCU/No 56(R) Sqn, Coningsby
	ZE257	Panavia Tornado F3 [DC]	RAF No 11 Sqn, Leeming
	ZE258	Panavia Tornado F3 (comp ZD905) [AQ]	RAF F3 OCU/No 56(R) Sqn, Coningsby
	ZE287	Panavia Tornado F3	RAF, St Athan
	ZE288	Panavia Tornado F3 (comp ZD940) [AT]	RAF F3 OCU/No 56(R) Sqn, Coningsby
	ZE289	Panavia Tornado F3 [C]	RAF No 1435 Flt, Mount Pleasant, FI
	ZE290	Panavia Tornado F3 [CJ]	RAF No 5 Sqn, Coningsby
	ZE291	Panavia Tornado F3 [GQ]	RAF No 43 Sqn, Leuchars
	ZE292	Panavia Tornado F3 (comp ZD939) [AZ]	RAF F3 OCU/No 56(R) Sqn, Coningsby
	ZE293	Panavia Tornado F3 [HT]	MoD(PE)/AFD, DERA Boscombe Down
	ZE294	Panavia Tornado F3 (comp ZD906) [AS]	RAF F3 OCU/No 56(R) Sqn, Coningsby
	ZE295	Panavia Tornado F3 (comp ZD938) [BC]	RAF, St Athan
	ZE296	Panavia Tornado F3 [AD]	RAF F3 OCU/No 56(R) Sqn, Coningsby
	ZE338	Panavia Tornado F3 [G]	RAF No 111 Sqn, Leuchars
	ZE339	Panavia Tornado F3	RAF F3OCU/No 56(R) Sqn, Coningsby

Serial	Type (other identity) [code]	Owner/operator, location or fate	Notes
ZE340	Panavia Tornado F3 [AE]	RAF F3OCU/No 56(R) Sqn, Coningsby	
ZE341	Panavia Tornado F3 [J]	RAF No 111 Sqn, Leuchars	
ZE342	Panavia Tornado F3 [W]	RAF No 111 Sqn, Leuchars	
ZE343	Panavia Tornado F3 (comp ZD900) [AA]	RAF F3 OCU/No 56(R) Sqn, Coningsby	
ZE353	McD F-4J(UK) Phantom (9083M) [E]	FSCTE, RAF Manston	
ZE354	McD F-4J(UK) Phantom (9084M) [R]	RAF Coningsby Fire Section	
ZE356	McD F-4J(UK) Phantom (9060M) [Q]	RAF Waddington BDRT	
ZE360	McD F-4J(UK) Phantom (9059M) [O]	FSCTE, RAF Manston	
ZE361	McD F-4J(UK) Phantom (9057M) [P]	RAF Honington Fire Section	
ZE368	WS61 Sea King HAR3	RAF HMF, St Mawgan	
ZE369	WS61 Sea King HAR3	RAF No 203(R) Sqn, St Mawgan	
ZE370	WS61 Sea King HAR3	RAF HMF, St Mawgan	
ZE375	WS Lynx AH9 [2,9]	AAC No 659 Sqn/4 Regt, Wattisham	
ZE376	WS Lynx AH9	AAC No 659 Sqn/4 Regt, Wattisham	
ZE378	WS Lynx AH7	AAC No 9 Regt, Dishforth	
ZE379	WS Lynx AH7	AAC No 655 Sqn/5 Regt, Aldergrove	
ZE380	WS Lynx AH9 [3]	AAC No 659 Sqn/4 Regt, Wattisham	
ZE381	WS Lynx AH7	AAC NARO Fleetlands	
ZE382	WS Lynx AH9 [1,3]	AAC No 659 Sqn/4 Regt, Wattisham	
ZE395	BAe 125 CC3	RAF No 32(The Royal) Sqn, Northolt	
ZE396	BAe 125 CC3	RAF No 32(The Royal) Sqn, Northolt	
ZE410	Agusta A109A (AE-334)	AAC No 8 Flt, Netheravon	
ZE411	Agusta A109A (AE-331)	AAC No 8 Flt, Netheravon	
ZE412	Agusta A109A	AAC No 8 Flt, Netheravon	
ZE413	Agusta A109A	AAC No 8 Flt, Netheravon	
ZE418	WS61 Sea King AEW2 [182/CU]	RN No 849 Sqn, HQ Flt, Culdrose	
ZE419	WS61 Sea King HAS6 (fuselage)	*Burnt at Predannack by April 1998*	
ZE420	WS61 Sea King AEW2 [183/L]	RN No 849 Sqn, B Flt, Culdrose	
ZE422	WS61 Sea King HAS6 [270]	RN No 814 Sqn, Culdrose	
ZE425	WS61 Sea King HC4 [J]	RN No 845 Sqn, Yeovilton	
ZE426	WS61 Sea King HC4 [ZW]	RN No 848 Sqn, Yeovilton	
ZE427	WS61 Sea King HC4 [B]	RN No 845 Sqn, Yeovilton	
ZE428	WS61 Sea King HC4 [VK]	RN No 846 Sqn, Yeovilton	
ZE432	BAC 1-11/479FU (DQ-FBV)	MoD(PE)/AFD/ETPS, DERA Boscombe Down	
ZE433	BAC 1-11/479FU (DQ-FBQ)	MoD(PE)/GEC-Ferranti, Edinburgh	
ZE438	BAe Jetstream T3 [76]	RN FONA/Heron Flight, Yeovilton	
ZE439	BAe Jetstream T3 [77]	RN FONA/Heron Flight, Yeovilton	
ZE440	BAe Jetstream T3 [78]	RN FONA/Heron Flight, Yeovilton	
ZE441	BAe Jetstream T3 [79]	RN FONA/Heron Flight, Yeovilton	
ZE449	SA330L Puma HC1 (9017M/PA-12)	RAF Odiham	
ZE477	WS Lynx 3	The Helicopter Museum, Weston-super-Mare	
ZE495	Grob G103 Viking T1 (BGA3000) [VA]	RAF No 622 VGS, Upavon	
ZE496	Grob G103 Viking T1 (BGA3001) [VB]	RAF No 634 VGS, St Athan	
ZE498	Grob G103 Viking T1 (BGA3003) [VC]	RAF No 614 VGS, Wethersfield	
ZE499	Grob G103 Viking T1 (BGA3004) [VD]	RAF No 615 VGS, Kenley	
ZE501	Grob G103 Viking T1 (BGA3006) [VE]	RAF No 636 VGS, Aberporth	
ZE502	Grob G103 Viking T1 (BGA3007) [VF]	RAF No 645 VGS, Catterick	
ZE503	Grob G103 Viking T1 (BGA3008) [VG]	RAF No 645 VGS, Catterick	
ZE504	Grob G103 Viking T1 (BGA3009) [VH]	RAF ACCGS Engineering Flt, Syerston	
ZE520	Grob G103 Viking T1 (BGA3010) [VJ]	RAF No 614 VGS, Wethersfield	
ZE521	Grob G103 Viking T1 (BGA3011) [VK]	RAF No 626 VGS, Predannack	
ZE522	Grob G103 Viking T1 (BGA3012) [VL]	RAF No 634 VGS, St Athan	
ZE524	Grob G103 Viking T1 (BGA3014) [VM]	RAF No 645 VGS, Catterick	

Notes	Serial	Type (other identity) [code]	Owner/operator, location or fate
	ZE526	Grob G103 Viking T1 (BGA3016) [VN]	RAF ACCGS , Syerston
	ZE527	Grob G103 Viking T1 (BGA3017) [VP]	RAF No 611 VGS, Watton
	ZE528	Grob G103 Viking T1 (BGA3018) [VQ]	RAF No 645 VGS, Catterick
	ZE529	Grob G103 Viking T1 (BGA3019) (comp ZE655) [VR]	RAF ACCGS, Syerston
	ZE530	Grob G103 Viking T1 (BGA3020) [VS]	RAF No 611 VGS, Watton
	ZE531	Grob G103 Viking T1 (BGA3021) [VS]	RAF No 617 VGS, Manston
	ZE532	Grob G103 Viking T1 (BGA3022) [VU]	RAF No 614 VGS, Wethersfield
	ZE533	Grob G103 Viking T1 (BGA3023) [VV]	RAF No 622 VGS, Upavon
	ZE534	Grob G103 Viking T1 (BGA3024) [VW]	RAF No 614 VGS, Wethersfield
	ZE550	Grob G103 Viking T1 (BGA3025) [VX]	RAF ACCGS, Syerston
	ZE551	Grob G103 Viking T1 (BGA3026) [VY]	RAF No 614 VGS, Wethersfield
	ZE552	Grob G103 Viking T1 (BGA3027) [VZ]	RAF ACCGS Engineering Flt, Syerston
	ZE553	Grob G103 Viking T1 (BGA3028) [WA]	RAF No 611 VGS, Watton
	ZE554	Grob G103 Viking T1 (BGA3029) [WB]	RAF No 615 VGS, Kenley
	ZE555	Grob G103 Viking T1 (BGA3030) [WC]	RAF No 645 VGS, Catterick
	ZE556	Grob G103 Viking T1 (BGA3031) [WD]	RAF No 662 VGS, Arbroath
	ZE557	Grob G103 Viking T1 (BGA3032) [WE]	RAF No 622 VGS, Upavon
	ZE558	Grob G103 Viking T1 (BGA3033)] [WF	RAF No 615 VGS, Kenley
	ZE559	Grob G103 Viking T1 (BGA3034) [WG]	RAF No 631 VGS, Sealand
	ZE560	Grob G103 Viking T1 (BGA3035) [WH]	RAF No 661 VGS, Kirknewton
	ZE561	Grob G103 Viking T1 (BGA3036) [WJ]	RAF No 621 VGS, Hullavington
	ZE562	Grob G103 Viking T1 (BGA3037) [WK]	RAF No 661 VGS, Kirknewton
	ZE563	Grob G103 Viking T1 (BGA3038) [WL]	RAF No 631 VGS, Sealand
	ZE564	Grob G103 Viking T1 (BGA3039) [WN]	RAF No 625 VGS, Hullavington
	ZE584	Grob G103 Viking T1 (BGA3040) [WP]	RAF No 631 VGS, Sealand
	ZE585	Grob G103 Viking T1 (BGA3041) [WQ]	RAF ACCGS, Syerston
	ZE586	Grob G103 Viking T1 (BGA3042) [WR]	RAF No 631 VGS, Sealand
	ZE587	Grob G103 Viking T1 (BGA3043) [WS]	RAF ACCGS Engineering Flt, Syerston
	ZE590	Grob G103 Viking T1 (BGA3046) [WT]	RAF No 615 VGS, Kenley
	ZE591	Grob G103 Viking T1 (BGA3047) [WU]	RAF No 631 VGS, Sealand
	ZE592	Grob G103 Viking T1 (BGA3048) [WV]	RAF No 626 VGS, Predannack
	ZE593	Grob G103 Viking T1 (BGA3049) [WW]	RAF No 661 VGS, Kirknewton
	ZE594	Grob G103 Viking T1 (BGA3050) [WX]	RAF No 615 VGS, Kenley
	ZE595	Grob G103 Viking T1 (BGA3051) [WY]	RAF No 622 VGS, Upavon
	ZE600	Grob G103 Viking T1 (BGA3052) [WZ]	RAF No 622 VGS, Upavon
	ZE601	Grob G103 Viking T1 (BGA3053) [XA]	RAF ACCGS Engineering Flt, Syerston

Serial	Type (other identity) [code]	Owner/operator, location or fate	Notes
ZE602	Grob G103 Viking T1 (BGA3054) [XB]	RAF ACCGS Engineering Flt, Syerston	
ZE603	Grob G103 Viking T1 (BGA3055) [XC]	RAF ACCGS Engineering Flt, Syerston	
ZE604	Grob G103 Viking T1 (BGA3056) [XD]	RAF No 617 VGS, Manston	
ZE605	Grob G103 Viking T1 (BGA3057) [XE]	RAF No 662 VGS, Arbroath	
ZE606	Grob G103 Viking T1 (BGA3058) [XF]	RAF No 625 VGS, Hullavington	
ZE607	Grob G103 Viking T1 (BGA3059) [XG]	RAF No 625 VGS, Hullavington	
ZE608	Grob G103 Viking T1 (BGA3060) [XH]	RAF No 621 VGS, Hullavington	
ZE609	Grob G103 Viking T1 (BGA3061) [XJ]	RAF ACCGS, Syerston	
ZE610	Grob G103 Viking T1 (BGA3062) [XK]	RAF No 626 VGS, Predannack	
ZE611	Grob G103 Viking T1 (BGA3063) [XL]	RAF ACCGS Engineering Flt, Syerston	
ZE613	Grob G103 Viking T1 (BGA3065) [XM]	RAF No 625 VGS, Hullavington	
ZE614	Grob G103 Viking T1 (BGA3066) [XN]	RAF No 631 VGS, Sealand	
ZE625	Grob G103 Viking T1 (BGA3067) [XP]	RAF No 625 VGS, Hullavington	
ZE626	Grob G103 Viking T1 (BGA3068) [XQ]	RAF No 626 VGS, Predannack	
ZE627	Grob G103 Viking T1 (BGA3069) [XR]	RAF No 634 VGS, St Athan	
ZE628	Grob G103 Viking T1 (BGA3070) [XS]	RAF ACCGS Engineering Flt, Syerston	
ZE629	Grob G103 Viking T1 (BGA3071) [XT]	RAF No 662 VGS, Arbroath	
ZE630	Grob G103 Viking T1 (BGA3072) [XU]	RAF No 662 VGS, Arbroath	
ZE631	Grob G103 Viking T1 (BGA3073) [XV]	RAF No 662 VGS, Arbroath	
ZE632	Grob G103 Viking T1 (BGA3074) [XW]	RAF No 617 VGS, Manston	
ZE633	Grob G103 Viking T1 (BGA3075) [XX]	RAF No 614 VGS, Wethersfield	
ZE635	Grob G103 Viking T1 (BGA3077) [XY]	RAF No 662 VGS, Arbroath	
ZE636	Grob G103 Viking T1 (BGA3078) [XZ]	RAF ACCGS Engineering Flt, Syerston	
ZE637	Grob G103 Viking T1 (BGA3079) [YA]	RAF No 622 VGS, Upavon	
ZE650	Grob G103 Viking T1 (BGA3080) [YB]	RAF ACCGS, Syerston	
ZE651	Grob G103 Viking T1 (BGA3081) [YC]	RAF ACCGS, Syerston	
ZE652	Grob G103 Viking T1 (BGA3082)	RAF, stored St Athan	
ZE653	Grob G103 Viking T1 (BGA3083) [YE]	RAF No 661 VGS, Kirknewton	
ZE655	Grob G103 Viking T1 (BGA3085) (wreck)	*Used in the rebuild of ZE529, 1998*	
ZE656	Grob G103 Viking T1 (BGA3086) [YH]	RAF No 617 VGS, Manston	
ZE657	Grob G103 Viking T1 (BGA3087) [YJ]	RAF No 617 VGS, Manston	
ZE658	Grob G103 Viking T1 (BGA3088) [YK]	RAF No 621 VGS, Hullavington	
ZE659	Grob G103 Viking T1 (BGA3089) [YL]	RAF No 636 VGS, Aberporth	
ZE677	Grob G103 Viking T1 (BGA3090) [YM]	RAF, stored St Athan	
ZE678	Grob G103 Viking T1 (BGA3091) [YN]	RAF No 621 VGS, Hullavington	
ZE679	Grob G103 Viking T1 (BGA3092) [YP]	RAF No 661 VGS, Kirknewton	
ZE680	Grob G103 Viking T1 (BGA3093) [YQ]	RAF ACCGS Engineering Flt, Syerston	

Notes	Serial	Type (other identity) [code]	Owner/operator, location or fate
	ZE681	Grob G103 Viking T1 (BGA3094) [YR]	RAF No 615 VGS, Kenley
	ZE682	Grob G103 Viking T1 (BGA3095) [YS]	RAF ACCGS Engineering Flt, Syerston (damaged)
	ZE683	Grob G103 Viking T1 (BGA3096) [YT]	RAF No 645 VGS, Catterick
	ZE684	Grob G103 Viking T1 (BGA3097) [YU]	RAF No 621 VGS, Hullavington
	ZE685	Grob G103 Viking T1 (BGA3098) [YV]	RAF ACCGS Engineering Flt, Syerston
	ZE686	Grob G103 Viking T1 (BGA3099)	MoD(PE)/Slingsby Kirkbymoorside
	ZE690	BAe Sea Harrier FA2 [123]	RN AMG, Yeovilton
	ZE691	BAe Sea Harrier FA2 [710/VL]	RN, St Athan
	ZE692	BAe Sea Harrier FA2	RN No 801 Sqn, Yeovilton
	ZE693	BAe Sea Harrier FA2 [127]	RN No 800 Sqn, Yeovilton
	ZE694	BAe Sea Harrier FA2 [006/L]	RN No 801 Sqn, Yeovilton
	ZE695	BAe Sea Harrier FA2 [718/VL]	RN No 899 Sqn, Yeovilton
	ZE696	BAe Sea Harrier FA2 [126]	RN, St Athan
	ZE697	BAe Sea Harrier FA2 [710]	RN No 899 Sqn, Yeovilton
	ZE698	BAe Sea Harrier FA2 [127]	RN, St Athan
	ZE700	BAe 146 CC2 (G-6-021)	RAF No 32(The Royal) Sqn, Northolt
	ZE701	BAe 146 CC2 (G-6-029)	RAF No 32(The Royal) Sqn, Northolt
	ZE702	BAe 146 CC2 (G-6-124)	RAF No 32(The Royal) Sqn, Northolt
	ZE704	Lockheed TriStar C2 (N508PA)	RAF 216 Sqn, Brize Norton
	ZE705	Lockheed TriStar C2 (N509PA)	RAF 216 Sqn, Brize Norton
	ZE706	Lockheed TriStar C2A (N503PA)	RAF 216 Sqn, Brize Norton
	ZE728	Panavia Tornado F3 (comp ZD903) [AH]	RAF F3 OCU/No 56(R) Sqn, Coningsby
	ZE729	Panavia Tornado F3 (comp ZD933) [CF]	RAF AMF, Coningsby (on repair)
	ZE731	Panavia Tornado F3 [GF]	RAF No 43 Sqn, Leuchars
	ZE732	Panavia Tornado F3 [BB]	Crashed 15 June 1998, North Sea
	ZE734	Panavia Tornado F3 [GB]	RAF No 43 Sqn, Leuchars
	ZE735	Panavia Tornado F3 [AL]	RAF F3 OCU/No 56(R) Sqn, Coningsby
	ZE736	Panavia Tornado F3 (comp ZD937) [AX]	RAF F3 OCU/No 56(R) Sqn, Coningsby
	ZE737	Panavia Tornado F3 [FF]	RAF No 25 Sqn, Leeming
	ZE755	Panavia Tornado F3 [GJ]	RAF No 43 Sqn, Leuchars
	ZE756	Panavia Tornado F3	RAF AWC/F3 OEU, Coningsby
	ZE757	Panavia Tornado F3 [GK]	RAF F3 OCU/No 56(R) Sqn, Coningsby
	ZE758	Panavia Tornado F3 [CH]	RAF No 43 Sqn, Leuchars
	ZE763	Panavia Tornado F3 [DG]	RAF No 25 Sqn, Leeming
	ZE764	Panavia Tornado F3 [DH]	RAF No 11 Sqn, Leeming
	ZE785	Panavia Tornado F3	RAF No 111 Sqn, Leuchars
	ZE786	Panavia Tornado F3 (comp ZD934) [AG]	RAF F3 OCU/No 56(R) Sqn, Coningsby
	ZE788	Panavia Tornado F3	RAF No 11 Sqn, Leeming
	ZE790	Panavia Tornado F3 [GD]	RAF No 43 Sqn, Leuchars
	ZE791	Panavia Tornado F3	RAF No 111 Sqn, Leuchars
	ZE793	Panavia Tornado F3 (comp ZD935) [AI]	RAF F3 OCU/No 56(R) Sqn, Coningsby
	ZE794	Panavia Tornado F3	RAF AWC/F3 OEU, Coningsby
	ZE808	Panavia Tornado F3 [FA]	RAF No 25 Sqn, Leeming
	ZE810	Panavia Tornado F3 [P]	RAF No 111 Sqn, Leuchars
	ZE812	Panavia Tornado F3	RAF No 25 Sqn, Leeming
	ZE830	Panavia Tornado F3	RAF AWC/F3 OEU, Coningsby
	ZE831	Panavia Tornado F3 [GG]	RAF No 43 Sqn, Leuchars
	ZE834	Panavia Tornado F3 [CX]	RAF No 5 Sqn, Coningsby
	ZE838	Panavia Tornado F3 [GH]	RAF No 43 Sqn, Leuchars
	ZE839	Panavia Tornado F3 [B]	RAF No 111 Sqn, Leuchars
	ZE887	Panavia Tornado F3 [DJ]	RAF No 11 Sqn, Leeming
	ZE888	Panavia Tornado F3 [T]	RAF No 111 Sqn, Leuchars
	ZE889	Panavia Tornado F3	RAF No 1435 Flt, Mount Pleasant, FI
	ZE907	Panavia Tornado F3 [FM]	RAF No 25 Sqn, Leeming
	ZE908	Panavia Tornado F3 [HV]	RAF No 111 Sqn, Leuchars
	ZE934	Panavia Tornado F3 [HS]	RAF No 111 Sqn, Leuchars
	ZE936	Panavia Tornado F3 [DL]	RAF No 11 Sqn, Leeming
	ZE941	Panavia Tornado F3 [FE]	RAF No 25 Sqn, Leeming
	ZE942	Panavia Tornado F3	RAF AWC/F3 OEU, Coningsby
	ZE961	Panavia Tornado F3	RAF No 11 Sqn, Leeming
	ZE962	Panavia Tornado F3	RAF No 25 Sqn, Leeming
	ZE963	Panavia Tornado F3 [GE]	RAF No 43 Sqn, Leuchars
	ZE964	Panavia Tornado F3 [DY]	RAF No 11 Sqn, Leeming

Serial	Type (other identity) [code]	Owner/operator, location or fate	Notes
ZE965	Panavia Tornado F3 [GM]	RAF No 43 Sqn, Leuchars	
ZE966	Panavia Tornado F3 [DXI]	RAF No 11 Sqn, Leeming	
ZE967	Panavia Tornado F3 [FU]	RAF No 25 Sqn, Leeming	
ZE968	Panavia Tornado F3 [GN]	RAF St Athan	
ZE969	Panavia Tornado F3	RAF No 11 Sqn, Leeming	
ZE982	Panavia Tornado F3	RAF AWC/F3 OEU, Coningsby	
ZE983	Panavia Tornado F3 [DN]	RAF No 11 Sqn, Leeming	
ZF115	WS61 Sea King HC4	MoD(PE)/AFD, DERA Boscombe Down	
ZF116	WS61 Sea King HC4 [ZP]	RN No 848 Sqn, Yeovilton	
ZF117	WS61 Sea King HC4 [VQ]	RN No 846 Sqn, Yeovilton	
ZF118	WS61 Sea King HC4 [VP]	RN No 846 Sqn, Yeovilton	
ZF119	WS61 Sea King HC4 [VH]	RN No 846 Sqn, Yeovilton	
ZF120	WS61 Sea King HC4 [K]	RN No 845 Sqn, Yeovilton	
ZF121	WS61 Sea King HC4 [VJ]	RN No 846 Sqn, Yeovilton	
ZF122	WS61 Sea King HC4 [VI]	RN No 846 Sqn, Yeovilton	
ZF123	WS61 Sea King HC4 [ZQ]	RN No 848 Sqn, Yeovilton	
ZF124	WS61 Sea King HC4 [L]	RN No 845 Sqn, Yeovilton	
ZF130	BAe 125-600B (G-BLUW)	MoD(PE), stored BAe Dunsfold	
ZF135	Shorts Tucano T1	RAF No 1 FTS, Linton-on-Ouse	
ZF136	Shorts Tucano T1	RAF No 1 FTS, Linton-on-Ouse	
ZF137	Shorts Tucano T1	RAF No 1 FTS, Linton-on-Ouse	
ZF138	Shorts Tucano T1	RAF No 1 FTS, Linton-on-Ouse	
ZF139	Shorts Tucano T1	RAF, stored Shawbury	
ZF140	Shorts Tucano T1	RAF No 1 FTS, Linton-on-Ouse	
ZF141	Shorts Tucano T1	RAF, stored Shawbury	
ZF142	Shorts Tucano T1	RAF No 1 FTS, Linton-on-Ouse	
ZF143	Shorts Tucano T1	RAF No 1 FTS, Linton-on-Ouse	
ZF144	Shorts Tucano T1	RAF No 1 FTS, Linton-on-Ouse	
ZF145	Shorts Tucano T1	RAF, stored Shawbury	
ZF160	Shorts Tucano T1	RAF No 1 FTS, Linton-on-Ouse	
ZF161	Shorts Tucano T1	RAF No 1 FTS, Linton-on-Ouse	
ZF162	Shorts Tucano T1	RAF No 1 FTS, Linton-on-Ouse	
ZF163	Shorts Tucano T1	RAF No 1 FTS, Linton-on-Ouse	
ZF164	Shorts Tucano T1	RAF, stored Shawbury	
ZF165	Shorts Tucano T1	RAF, stored Shawbury	
ZF166	Shorts Tucano T1	RAF No 1 FTS, Linton-on-Ouse	
ZF167	Shorts Tucano T1	RAF, stored Shawbury	
ZF168	Shorts Tucano T1	RAF No 1 FTS, Linton-on-Ouse	
ZF169	Shorts Tucano T1	RAF No 1 FTS, Linton-on-Ouse	
ZF170	Shorts Tucano T1	RAF No 1 FTS, Linton-on-Ouse	
ZF171	Shorts Tucano T1	RAF, stored Shawbury	
ZF172	Shorts Tucano T1	RAF, stored Shawbury	
ZF200	Shorts Tucano T1	RAF, stored Shawbury	
ZF201	Shorts Tucano T1	RAF, stored Shawbury	
ZF202	Shorts Tucano T1	RAF, stored Shawbury	
ZF203	Shorts Tucano T1	RAF No 1 FTS, Linton-on-Ouse	
ZF204	Shorts Tucano T1	RAF, stored Shawbury	
ZF205	Shorts Tucano T1	RAF, stored Shawbury	
ZF206	Shorts Tucano T1	RAF No 1 FTS, Linton-on-Ouse	
ZF207	Shorts Tucano T1	RAF No 1 FTS, Linton-on-Ouse	
ZF208	Shorts Tucano T1	RAF, stored Shawbury	
ZF209	Shorts Tucano T1	RAF, stored Shawbury	
ZF210	Shorts Tucano T1	RAF, stored Shawbury	
ZF211	Shorts Tucano T1	RAF No 1 FTS, Linton-on-Ouse	
ZF212	Shorts Tucano T1	RAF No 1 FTS, Linton-on-Ouse	
ZF238	Shorts Tucano T1	RAF No 1 FTS, Linton-on-Ouse	
ZF239	Shorts Tucano T1	RAF, stored Shawbury	
ZF240	Shorts Tucano T1	RAF, stored Shawbury	
ZF241	Shorts Tucano T1	RAF No 1 FTS, Linton-on-Ouse	
ZF242	Shorts Tucano T1	RAF No 1 FTS, Linton-on-Ouse	
ZF243	Shorts Tucano T1	RAF, stored Shawbury	
ZF244	Shorts Tucano T1	RAF, stored Shawbury	
ZF245	Shorts Tucano T1	RAF, stored Shawbury	
ZF263	Shorts Tucano T1	RAF No 1 FTS, Linton-on-Ouse	
ZF264	Shorts Tucano T1	RAF, stored Shawbury	
ZF265	Shorts Tucano T1	RAF, stored Shawbury	
ZF266	Shorts Tucano T1	RAF No 1 FTS, Linton-on-Ouse	
ZF267	Shorts Tucano T1	RAF, stored Shawbury	
ZF268	Shorts Tucano T1	RAF No 1 FTS, Linton-on-Ouse	
ZF269	Shorts Tucano T1	RAF, stored Shawbury	
ZF284	Shorts Tucano T1	RAF, stored Shawbury	
ZF285	Shorts Tucano T1	RAF, stored Shawbury	

Notes	Serial	Type (other identity) [code]	Owner/operator, location or fate
	ZF286	Shorts Tucano T1	RAF No 1 FTS, Linton-on-Ouse
	ZF287	Shorts Tucano T1	RAF, stored Shawbury
	ZF288	Shorts Tucano T1	RAF No 1 FTS, Linton-on-Ouse
	ZF289	Shorts Tucano T1	RAF, stored Shawbury
	ZF290	Shorts Tucano T1	RAF No 1 FTS, Linton-on-Ouse
	ZF291	Shorts Tucano T1	RAF, stored Shawbury
	ZF292	Shorts Tucano T1	RAF No 1 FTS, Linton-on-Ouse
	ZF293	Shorts Tucano T1	RAF, stored Shawbury
	ZF294	Shorts Tucano T1	RAF No 1 FTS, Linton-on-Ouse
	ZF295	Shorts Tucano T1	RAF No 1 FTS, Linton-on-Ouse
	ZF315	Shorts Tucano T1	RAF No 1 FTS, Linton-on-Ouse
	ZF317	Shorts Tucano T1	RAF, stored Shawbury
	ZF318	Shorts Tucano T1	RAF No 1 FTS, Linton-on-Ouse
	ZF319	Shorts Tucano T1	RAF No 1 FTS, Linton-on-Ouse
	ZF320	Shorts Tucano T1	RAF No 1 FTS, Linton-on-Ouse
	ZF338	Shorts Tucano T1	RAF, stored Shawbury
	ZF339	Shorts Tucano T1	RAF St Athan Station Flight
	ZF340	Shorts Tucano T1	RAF, stored Shawbury
	ZF341	Shorts Tucano T1	RAF No 1 FTS, Linton-on-Ouse
	ZF342	Shorts Tucano T1	RAF No 1 FTS, Linton-on-Ouse
	ZF343	Shorts Tucano T1	RAF, stored Shawbury
	ZF344	Shorts Tucano T1	RAF, stored Shawbury
	ZF345	Shorts Tucano T1	RAF No 1 FTS, Linton-on-Ouse
	ZF346	Shorts Tucano T1	RAF No 1 FTS, Linton-on-Ouse
	ZF347	Shorts Tucano T1	RAF St Athan Station Flight
	ZF348	Shorts Tucano T1	RAF No 1 FTS, Linton-on-Ouse
	ZF349	Shorts Tucano T1	RAF, stored Shawbury
	ZF350	Shorts Tucano T1	RAF No 1 FTS, Linton-on-Ouse
	ZF372	Shorts Tucano T1	RAF No 1 FTS, Linton-on-Ouse
	ZF373	Shorts Tucano T1	RAF, stored Shawbury
	ZF374	Shorts Tucano T1	RAF, stored Shawbury
	ZF375	Shorts Tucano T1	RAF No 1 FTS, Linton-on-Ouse
	ZF376	Shorts Tucano T1	RAF No 1 FTS, Linton-on-Ouse
	ZF377	Shorts Tucano T1	RAF, stored Shawbury
	ZF378	Shorts Tucano T1	RAF, stored Shawbury
	ZF379	Shorts Tucano T1	RAF No 1 FTS, Linton-on-Ouse
	ZF380	Shorts Tucano T1	RAF No 1 FTS, Linton-on-Ouse
	ZF405	Shorts Tucano T1	RAF No 1 FTS, Linton-on-Ouse
	ZF406	Shorts Tucano T1	RAF No 1 FTS, Linton-on-Ouse
	ZF407	Shorts Tucano T1	RAF, stored Shawbury
	ZF408	Shorts Tucano T1	RAF No 1 FTS, Linton-on-Ouse
	ZF409	Shorts Tucano T1	RAF, stored Shawbury
	ZF410	Shorts Tucano T1	RAF No 1 FTS, Linton-on-Ouse
	ZF411	Shorts Tucano T1	RAF, stored Shawbury
	ZF412	Shorts Tucano T1	RAF No 1 FTS, Linton-on-Ouse
	ZF413	Shorts Tucano T1	RAF No 1 FTS, Linton-on-Ouse
	ZF414	Shorts Tucano T1	RAF No 1 FTS, Linton-on-Ouse
	ZF415	Shorts Tucano T1	RAF, stored Shawbury
	ZF416	Shorts Tucano T1	RAF No 1 FTS, Linton-on-Ouse
	ZF417	Shorts Tucano T1	RAF No 1 FTS, Linton-on-Ouse
	ZF418	Shorts Tucano T1	RAF No 1 FTS, Linton-on-Ouse
	ZF445	Shorts Tucano T1	RAF No 1 FTS, Linton-on-Ouse
	ZF446	Shorts Tucano T1	RAF No 1 FTS, Linton-on-Ouse
	ZF447	Shorts Tucano T1	RAF, stored Shawbury
	ZF448	Shorts Tucano T1	RAF No 1 FTS, Linton-on-Ouse
	ZF449	Shorts Tucano T1	RAF No 1 FTS, Linton-on-Ouse
	ZF450	Shorts Tucano T1	RAF, stored Shawbury
	ZF483	Shorts Tucano T1	RAF No 1 FTS, Linton-on-Ouse
	ZF484	Shorts Tucano T1	RAF No 1 FTS, Linton-on-Ouse
	ZF485	Shorts Tucano T1 (G-BULU)	RAF No 1 FTS, Linton-on-Ouse
	ZF486	Shorts Tucano T1	RAF No 1 FTS, Linton-on-Ouse
	ZF487	Shorts Tucano T1	RAF No 1 FTS, Linton-on-Ouse
	ZF488	Shorts Tucano T1	RAF No 1 FTS, Linton-on-Ouse
	ZF489	Shorts Tucano T1	RAF No 1 FTS, Linton-on-Ouse
	ZF490	Shorts Tucano T1	RAF No 1 FTS, Linton-on-Ouse
	ZF491	Shorts Tucano T1	RAF, stored Shawbury
	ZF492	Shorts Tucano T1	RAF No 1 FTS, Linton-on-Ouse
	ZF510	Shorts Tucano T1	MoD(PE)/AFD, DERA Boscombe Down
	ZF511	Shorts Tucano T1	MoD(PE)/AFD, DERA Boscombe Down
	ZF512	Shorts Tucano T1	RAF No 1 FTS, Linton-on-Ouse
	ZF513	Shorts Tucano T1	RAF No 1 FTS, Linton-on-Ouse
	ZF514	Shorts Tucano T1	RAF No 1 FTS, Linton-on-Ouse
	ZF515	Shorts Tucano T1	RAF No 1 FTS, Linton-on-Ouse

Serial	Type (other identity) [code]	Owner/operator, location or fate	Notes
ZF516	Shorts Tucano T1	RAF No 1 FTS, Linton-on-Ouse	
ZF521	Piper PA-31 Navajo Chieftain 350 (N27509)	*Sold as N4409S, April 1998*	
ZF534	BAe EAP	Loughborough University	
ZF537	WS Lynx AH9	AAC No 659 Sqn/4 Regt, Wattisham	
ZF538	WS Lynx AH9	AAC No 653 Sqn/3 Regt, Wattisham	
ZF539	WS Lynx AH9 [5]	AAC No 659 Sqn/4 Regt, Wattisham	
ZF540	WS Lynx AH9 [6]	AAC No 659 Sqn/4 Regt, Wattisham	
ZF557	WS Lynx HMA8	RN AMG, Yeovilton	
ZF558	WS Lynx HMA8 [319]	RN AMG, Yeovilton	
ZF560	WS Lynx HMA8 [307]	RN No 815 Sqn, HQ Flt, Yeovilton	
ZF562	WS Lynx HMA8 [328]	RN No 815 Sqn, *Brave* Flt, Yeovilton	
ZF563	WS Lynx HMA8 [328/BA]	RN AMG, Yeovilton	
ZF573	PBN 2T Islander CC2A (G-SRAY)	RAF Northolt Station Flight	
ZF577	BAC Lightning F53	*Sold to Japan, 1998*	
ZF578	BAC Lightning F53	Privately owned, Quedgeley, Glos	
ZF579	BAC Lightning F53	*Sold to Japan, 1998*	
ZF580	BAC Lightning F53	BAe Samlesbury, at main gate	
ZF581	BAC Lightning F53	*Sold to Japan, 1998*	
ZF582	BAC Lightning F53 <ff>	Privately owned, Desborough, Hants	
ZF583	BAC Lightning F53	Solway Aviation Society, Carlisle	
ZF584	BAC Lightning F53	Ferranti Ltd, South Gyle, Edinburgh	
ZF585	BAC Lightning F53	*Sold to Japan, 1998*	
ZF586	BAC Lightning F55	*Sold to Japan, 1998*	
ZF587	BAC Lightning F53	*Sold to Japan, 1998*	
ZF588	BAC Lightning F53 [L]	Privately owned, East Midlands Airport	
ZF589	BAC Lightning F53	*Sold to Japan, 1998*	
ZF590	BAC Lightning F53	*Sold to Japan, 1998*	
ZF591	BAC Lightning F53	*Sold to Japan, 1998*	
ZF592	BAC Lightning F53	*Sold to Japan, 1998*	
ZF594	BAC Lightning F53	North-East Aircraft Museum, Usworth	
ZF595	BAC Lightning T55 <ff>	Privately owned, Bruntingthorpe	
ZF596	BAC Lightning T55 <ff>	BAe North-West Heritage Group, Warton	
ZF598	BAC Lightning T55	Midland Air Museum, Coventry	
ZF622	Piper PA-31 Navajo Chieftain 350 (N35487)	MoD(PE)/AFD, DERA Boscombe Down	
ZF641	WS/Agusta EH-101 [PP1]	RNAS Culdrose, instructional use	
ZF649	WS/Agusta EH-101 Merlin [PP5]	MoD(PE)/GKN Westland, Yeovil	
ZG101	WS/Agusta EH-101 (mock-up) [GB]	GKN Westland/Agusta, Yeovil	
ZG468	WS70 Blackhawk	*Sold to Bahrain, 1996*	
ZG471	BAe Harrier GR7 [61]	RAF No 1 Sqn, Wittering	
ZG472	BAe Harrier GR7 [O]	RAF AWC/SAOEU, DERA Boscombe Down	
ZG474	BAe Harrier GR7 [64]	RAF No 3 Sqn, Laarbruch	
ZG477	BAe Harrier GR7 [67]	RAF No 3 Sqn, Laarbruch	
ZG478	BAe Harrier GR7 [68]	RAF No 4 Sqn, Laarbruch	
ZG479	BAe Harrier GR7 [69]	MoD(PE)/BAe, Dunsfold	
ZG480	BAe Harrier GR7 [70]	RAF No 1 Sqn, Wittering	
ZG500	BAe Harrier GR7 [71]	RAF No 3 Sqn, Laarbruch	
ZG501	BAe Harrier GR7 [E]	MoD(PE)/BAe, Dunsfold	
ZG502	BAe Harrier GR7 [73]	RAF No 1 Sqn, Wittering	
ZG503	BAe Harrier GR7 [74]	RAF No 3 Sqn, Laarbruch	
ZG504	BAe Harrier GR7 [75]	RAF No 3 Sqn, Laarbruch	
ZG505	BAe Harrier GR7 [76]	RAF No 1 Sqn, Wittering	
ZG506	BAe Harrier GR7 [77]	RAF No 3 Sqn, Laarbruch	
ZG507	BAe Harrier GR7 [78]	RAF No 4 Sqn, Laarbruch	
ZG508	BAe Harrier GR7 [79]	RAF No 1 Sqn, Wittering	
ZG509	BAe Harrier GR7 [80]	RAF No 4 Sqn, Laarbruch	
ZG510	BAe Harrier GR7 [81]	RAF No 4 Sqn, Laarbruch	
ZG511	BAe Harrier GR7 [82]	RAF No 3 Sqn, Laarbruch	
ZG512	BAe Harrier GR7 [83]	RAF No 4 Sqn, Laarbruch	
ZG530	BAe Harrier GR7 [84]	RAF No 4 Sqn, Laarbruch	
ZG531	BAe Harrier GR7 [85]	RAF No 3 Sqn, Laarbruch	
ZG532	BAe Harrier GR7 [86]	RAF No 3 Sqn, Laarbruch	
ZG533	BAe Harrier GR7 [87]	*Crashed 7 July 1998, Laarbruch*	
ZG705	Panavia Tornado GR1A [J]	RAF No 13 Sqn, Marham	
ZG706	Panavia Tornado GR1A [E]	RAF AWC/SAOEU, DERA Boscombe Down	
ZG707	Panavia Tornado GR4A [B]	RAF No 13 Sqn, Marham	
ZG709	Panavia Tornado GR1A [V]	RAF No 13 Sqn, Marham	
ZG710	Panavia Tornado GR4A [O]	RAF No 2 Sqn, Marham	
ZG711	Panavia Tornado GR1A [P]	RAF No 13 Sqn, Marham	

Notes	Serial	Type (other identity) [code]	Owner/operator, location or fate
	ZG712	Panavia Tornado GR4A	MoD(PE)/BAe, Warton (conversion)
	ZG713	Panavia Tornado GR1A [G]	RAF No 13 Sqn, Marham
	ZG714	Panavia Tornado GR4A [Q]	MoD(PE)/BAe, Warton (conversion)
	ZG726	Panavia Tornado GR4A [K]	MoD(PE)/BAe, Warton (conversion)
	ZG727	Panavia Tornado GR1A [L]	RAF No 13 Sqn, Marham
	ZG729	Panavia Tornado GR1A [M]	RAF St Athan
	ZG731	Panavia Tornado F3 [HH]	RAF No 111 Sqn, Leuchars
	ZG750	Panavia Tornado GR4	MoD(PE)/AFD, DERA Boscombe Down
	ZG751	Panavia Tornado F3 [AV]	RAF F3 OCU/No 56(R) Sqn, Coningsby
	ZG752	Panavia Tornado GR1 [XIII]	RAF No 13 Sqn, Marham
	ZG753	Panavia Tornado F3 [F]	RAF, St Athan (on repair)
	ZG754	Panavia Tornado GR1 [VI]	RAF No 13 Sqn, Marham
	ZG755	Panavia Tornado F3 [CD]	RAF No 5 Sqn, Coningsby
	ZG756	Panavia Tornado GR1 [AX]	RAF No 9 Sqn, Brüggen
	ZG757	Panavia Tornado F3	RAF No 43 Sqn, Leuchars
	ZG769	Panavia Tornado GR1 [AY]	RAF No 9 Sqn, Brüggen
	ZG770	Panavia Tornado F3 [CC]	RAF No 5 Sqn, Coningsby
	ZG771	Panavia Tornado GR4 [AZ]	RAF No 9 Sqn, Brüggen
	ZG772	Panavia Tornado F3 [CO]	RAF St Athan
	ZG773	Panavia Tornado GR4	MoD(PE)/BAe, Warton
	ZG774	Panavia Tornado F3 [CG]	RAF No 5 Sqn, Coningsby
	ZG775	Panavia Tornado GR1 [DN]	RAF No 31 Sqn, Brüggen
	ZG776	Panavia Tornado F3	RAF No 1435 Flt, Mount Pleasant, FI
	ZG777	Panavia Tornado GR1 [BS]	RAF No 14 Sqn, Brüggen
	ZG778	Panavia Tornado F3 [BG]	RAF No 5 Sqn, Coningsby
	ZG779	Panavia Tornado GR1 [DK]	RAF No 31 Sqn, Brüggen
	ZG780	Panavia Tornado F3 [AU]	RAF F3 OCU/No 56(R) Sqn, Coningsby
	ZG791	Panavia Tornado GR1 [DC]	RAF No 31 Sqn, Brüggen
	ZG792	Panavia Tornado GR1 [DD]	RAF No 31 Sqn, Brüggen
	ZG793	Panavia Tornado F3 [CY]	RAF No 5 Sqn, Coningsby
	ZG794	Panavia Tornado GR1 [BP]	RAF No 14 Sqn, Brüggen
	ZG795	Panavia Tornado F3 [CB]	RAF No 5 Sqn, Coningsby
	ZG796	Panavia Tornado F3 [D]	RAF No 1435 Flt, Mount Pleasant, FI
	ZG797	Panavia Tornado F3 [GI]	RAF No 43 Sqn, Leuchars
	ZG798	Panavia Tornado F3 [F]	RAF, St Athan
	ZG799	Panavia Tornado F3 [D]	RAF, St Athan
	ZG816	WS61 Sea King HAS6	RN No 814 Sqn, Culdrose
	ZG817	WS61 Sea King HAS6 [702/PW]	RN No 819 Sqn, Prestwick
	ZG818	WS61 Sea King HAS6	RN No 814 Sqn, Culdrose
	ZG819	WS61 Sea King HAS6 [270/N]	RN No 814 Sqn, Culdrose
	ZG820	WS61 Sea King HC4 [A]	RN No 845 Sqn, Yeovilton
	ZG821	WS61 Sea King HC4 [D]	RN No 845 Sqn, Yeovilton
	ZG822	WS61 Sea King HC4 [VN]	RN No 846 Sqn, Yeovilton
	ZG844	PBN 2T Islander AL1 (G-BLNE)	AAC No 1 Flt, Aldergrove
	ZG845	PBN 2T Islander AL1 (G-BLNT)	AAC AFWF, Middle Wallop
	ZG846	PBN 2T Islander AL1 (G-BLNU)	AAC No 1 Flt, Aldergrove
	ZG847	PBN 2T Islander AL1 (G-BLNV)	AAC No 1 Flt, Aldergrove
	ZG848	PBN 2T Islander AL1 (G-BLNY)	AAC No 1 Flt, Aldergrove
	ZG856	BAe Harrier GR7 [89]	*Crashed Nellis Ranges USA, 29 Jan 1999*
	ZG857	BAe Harrier GR7 [89]	RAF No 4 Sqn, Laarbruch
	ZG858	BAe Harrier GR7 [90]	RAF No 4 Sqn, Laarbruch
	ZG859	BAe Harrier GR7 [91]	RAF No 4 Sqn, Laarbruch
	ZG860	BAe Harrier GR7 [92]	RAF No 1 Sqn, Wittering
	ZG862	BAe Harrier GR7 [94]	RAF, St Athan
	ZG875	WS61 Sea King HAS6 [013/L]	RN No 820 Sqn, Culdrose
	ZG879	Powerchute Raider Mk 1	MoD(PE)/Powerchute, Hereford
	ZG884	WS Lynx AH9	MoD(PE)/GKN Westland, Yeovil
	ZG885	WS Lynx AH9	AAC No 659 Sqn/4 Regt, Wattisham
	ZG886	WS Lynx AH9	AAC No 653 Sqn/3 Regt, Wattisham
	ZG887	WS Lynx AH9	AAC No 653 Sqn/3 Regt, Wattisham
	ZG888	WS Lynx AH9	AAC No 653 Sqn/3 Regt, Wattisham
	ZG889	WS Lynx AH9	AAC No 653 Sqn/3 Regt, Wattisham
	ZG914	WS Lynx AH9	AAC No 653 Sqn/3 Regt, Wattisham
	ZG915	WS Lynx AH9 [7]	AAC No 653 Sqn/3 Regt, Wattisham
	ZG916	WS Lynx AH9 [8]	AAC No 659 Sqn/4 Regt, Wattisham
	ZG917	WS Lynx AH9 [2,9]	AAC No 659 Sqn/4 Regt, Wattisham
	ZG918	WS Lynx AH9	AAC No 659 Sqn/4 Regt, Wattisham
	ZG919	WS Lynx AH9	AAC No 653 Sqn/3 Regt, Wattisham
	ZG920	WS Lynx AH9	AAC No 653 Sqn/3 Regt, Wattisham
	ZG921	WS Lynx AH9	AAC No 659 Sqn/4 Regt, Wattisham
	ZG922	WS Lynx AH9	AAC No 653 Sqn/3 Regt, Wattisham
	ZG923	WS Lynx AH9	AAC No 653 Sqn/3 Regt, Wattisham
	ZG969	Pilatus PC-9 (HB-HQE)	BAe Warton

Serial	Type (other identity) [code]	Owner/operator, location or fate	Notes
ZG989	PBN 2T Islander ASTOR (G-DLRA)	MoD(PE)/PBN, Bembridge	
ZG993	PBN 2T Islander AL1 (G-BOMD)	AAC No 1 Flight, Aldergrove	
ZG994	PBN 2T Islander AL1 (G-BPLN)	AAC No 1 Flight, Aldergrove	
ZH101	Boeing E-3D Sentry AEW1	RAF No 8 Sqn/No 23 Sqn, Waddington	
ZH102	Boeing E-3D Sentry AEW1	RAF No 8 Sqn/No 23 Sqn, Waddington	
ZH103	Boeing E-3D Sentry AEW1	RAF No 8 Sqn/No 23 Sqn, Waddington	
ZH104	Boeing E-3D Sentry AEW1	RAF No 8 Sqn/No 23 Sqn, Waddington	
ZH105	Boeing E-3D Sentry AEW1	RAF No 8 Sqn/No 23 Sqn, Waddington	
ZH106	Boeing E-3D Sentry AEW1	RAF No 8 Sqn/No 23 Sqn, Waddington	
ZH107	Boeing E-3D Sentry AEW1	RAF No 8 Sqn/No 23 Sqn, Waddington	
ZH115	Grob G109B Vigilant T1 [TA]	RAF ACCGS, Syerston	
ZH116	Grob G109B Vigilant T1 [TB]	RAF No 664 VGS, Belfast City Airport	
ZH117	Grob G109B Vigilant T1 [TC]	RAF No 642 VGS, Linton-on-Ouse	
ZH118	Grob G109B Vigilant T1 [TD]	RAF No 612 VGS, Abingdon	
ZH119	Grob G109B Vigilant T1 [TE]	RAF No 635 VGS, Samlesbury	
ZH120	Grob G109B Vigilant T1 [TF]	RAF No 663 VGS, Kinloss	
ZH121	Grob G109B Vigilant T1 [TG]	RAF No 633 VGS, Cosford	
ZH122	Grob G109B Vigilant T1 [TH]	RAF No 616 VGS, Henlow	
ZH123	Grob G109B Vigilant T1 [TJ]	RAF No 663 VGS, Kinloss	
ZH124	Grob G109B Vigilant T1 [TK]	RAF No 642 VGS, Linton-on-Ouse	
ZH125	Grob G109B Vigilant T1 [TL]	RAF No 633 VGS, Cosford	
ZH126	Grob G109B Vigilant T1 [TM]	RAF No 637 VGS, Little Rissington	
ZH127	Grob G109B Vigilant T1 [TN]	RAF No 642 VGS, Linton-on-Ouse	
ZH128	Grob G109B Vigilant T1 [TP]	RAF No 624 VGS, Chivenor RMB	
ZH129	Grob G109B Vigilant T1 [TQ]	RAF No 613 VGS, Halton	
ZH139	BAe Harrier GR7 <R> (BAPC 191/ ZD472)	RAF EPTT, St Athan	
ZH144	Grob G109B Vigilant T1 [TR]	RAF No 616 VGS, Henlow	
ZH145	Grob G109B Vigilant T1 [TS]	RAF No 624 VGS, Chivenor RMB	
ZH146	Grob G109B Vigilant T1 [TT]	RAF ACCGS Engineering Flt, Syerston (damaged)	
ZH147	Grob G109B Vigilant T1 [TU]	RAF No 632 VGS, Ternhill	
ZH148	Grob G109B Vigilant T1 [TV]	RAF ACCGS, Syerston	
ZH184	Grob G109B Vigilant T1 [TW]	RAF, stored Syerston	
ZH185	Grob G109B Vigilant T1 [TX]	RAF No 642 VGS, Linton-on-Ouse	
ZH186	Grob G109B Vigilant T1 [TY]	RAF No 635 VGS, Samlesbury	
ZH187	Grob G109B Vigilant T1 [TZ]	RAF No 633 VGS, Cosford	
ZH188	Grob G109B Vigilant T1 [UA]	RAF No 635 VGS, Samlesbury	
ZH189	Grob G109B Vigilant T1 [UB]	RAF No 612 VGS, Abingdon	
ZH190	Grob G109B Vigilant T1 [UC]	RAF No 632 VGS, Ternhill	
ZH191	Grob G109B Vigilant T1 [UD]	RAF No 616 VGS, Henlow	
ZH192	Grob G109B Vigilant T1 [UE]	RAF No 635 VGS, Samlesbury	
ZH193	Grob G109B Vigilant T1 [UF]	RAF No 637 VGS, Little Rissington	
ZH194	Grob G109B Vigilant T1 [UG]	RAF No 613 VGS, Halton	
ZH195	Grob G109B Vigilant T1 [UH]	RAF ACCGS, Syerston	
ZH196	Grob G109B Vigilant T1 [UJ]	RAF No 612 VGS, Abingdon	
ZH197	Grob G109B Vigilant T1 [UK]	RAF No 633 VGS, Cosford	
ZH200	BAe Hawk 200	MoD(PE), stored BAe Warton	
ZH205	Grob G109B Vigilant T1 [UL]	RAF No 613 VGS, Halton	
ZH206	Grob G109B Vigilant T1 [UM]	RAF No 633 VGS, Cosford	
ZH207	Grob G109B Vigilant T1 [UN]	RAF No 632 VGS, Ternhill	
ZH208	Grob G109B Vigilant T1 [UP]	RAF No 663 VGS, Kinloss	
ZH209	Grob G109B Vigilant T1 [UQ]	RAF No 664 VGS, Belfast City Airport	
ZH211	Grob G109B Vigilant T1 [UR]	RAF ACCGS, Syerston	
ZH247	Grob G109B Vigilant T1 [US]	RAF No 613 VGS, Halton	
ZH248	Grob G109B Vigilant T1 [UT]	RAF No 663 VGS, Kinloss	
ZH249	Grob G109B Vigilant T1 [UU]	RAF ACCGS , Syerston	
ZH257	B-V CH-47C Chinook (AE-520/ 9217M)	AAC Wattisham, instructional use	
ZH263	Grob G109B Vigilant T1 [UV]	RAF No 632 VGS, Ternhill	
ZH264	Grob G109B Vigilant T1 [UW]	RAF No 616 VGS, Henlow	
ZH265	Grob G109B Vigilant T1 [UX]	RAF ACCGS Engineering Flt, Syerston	
ZH266	Grob G109B Vigilant T1 [UY]	RAF No 635 VGS, Samlesbury	
ZH267	Grob G109B Vigilant T1 [UZ]	RAF No 637 VGS, Little Rissington	
ZH268	Grob G109B Vigilant T1 [SA]	RAF No 612 VGS, Abingdon	
ZH269	Grob G109B Vigilant T1 [SB]	RAF No 642 VGS, Linton-on-Ouse	
ZH270	Grob G109B Vigilant T1 [SC]	RAF No 616 VGS, Henlow	
ZH271	Grob G109B Vigilant T1	RAF No 613 VGS, Halton	
ZH536	PBN 2T Islander CC2 (G-BSAH)	RAF Northolt Station Flight	
ZH540	WS61 Sea King HAR3A	RAF No 22 Sqn, A Flt, Chivenor RMB	
ZH541	WS61 Sea King HAR3A	RAF HMF, St Mawgan	
ZH542	WS61 Sea King HAR3A	RAF No 203(R) Sqn, St Mawgan	

Notes	Serial	Type (other identity) [code]	Owner/operator, location or fate
	ZH543	WS61 Sea King HAR3A	RAF No 22 Sqn, B Flt, Wattisham
	ZH544	WS61 Sea King HAR3A	RAF No 22 Sqn, A Flt, Chivenor RMB
	ZH545	WS61 Sea King HAR3A	RAF No 22 Sqn, B Flt, Wattisham
	ZH552	Panavia Tornado F3 [CH]	RAF No 5 Sqn, Coningsby
	ZH553	Panavia Tornado F3 [AB]	RAF F3 OCU/No 56(R) Sqn, Coningsby
	ZH554	Panavia Tornado F3 [AO]	RAF F3 OCU/No 56(R) Sqn, Coningsby
	ZH555	Panavia Tornado F3 [CV]	RAF No 5 Sqn, Coningsby
	ZH556	Panavia Tornado F3 [AK]	RAF F3 OCU/No 56(R) Sqn, Coningsby
	ZH557	Panavia Tornado F3 [LF]	RAF No 111 Sqn, Leuchars
	ZH559	Panavia Tornado F3 [AJ]	RAF F3 OCU/No 56(R) Sqn, Coningsby
	ZH588	Eurofighter Typhoon (DA2)	MoD(PE)/BAe, Warton
	ZH590	Eurofighter Typhoon (DA4)	MoD(PE)/BAe, Warton
	ZH647	WS/Agusta EH-101 (G-EHIL)	Marks not taken up
	ZH653	BAe Harrier T10	MoD(PE)/BAe, Dunsfold
	ZH654	BAe Harrier T10	MoD(PE)/BAe, Dunsfold
	ZH655	BAe Harrier T10	RAF, stored St Athan (damaged)
	ZH656	BAe Harrier T10 [104]	RAF No 3 Sqn, Laarbruch
	ZH657	BAe Harrier T10 [XX]	RAF HOCU/No 20(R) Sqn, Wittering
	ZH658	BAe Harrier T10 [106]	RAF No 1 Sqn, Wittering
	ZH659	BAe Harrier T10 [O]	RAF HOCU/No 20(R) Sqn, Wittering
	ZH660	BAe Harrier T10 [P]	RAF HOCU/No 20(R) Sqn, Wittering
	ZH661	BAe Harrier T10 [Z]	RAF HOCU/No 20(R) Sqn, Wittering
	ZH662	BAe Harrier T10 [R]	RAF HOCU/No 20(R) Sqn, Wittering
	ZH663	BAe Harrier T10 [Q]	RAF HOCU/No 20(R) Sqn, Wittering
	ZH664	BAe Harrier T10 [112]	RAF No 4 Sqn, Laarbruch
	ZH665	BAe Harrier T10 [S]	RAF HOCU/No 20(R) Sqn, Wittering
	ZH762	Westinghouse Skyship 500 (G-SKSC)	Westinghouse, stored Cardington
	ZH763	BAC 1-11/539GL (G-BGKE)	MoD(PE)/AFD, DERA Boscombe Down
	ZH775	B-V Chinook HC2 (N7424J) [NS]	RAF No 27 Sqn, Odiham
	ZH776	B-V Chinook HC2 (N7424L) [NU]	RAF No 27 Sqn, Odiham
	ZH777	B-V Chinook HC2 (N7424M) [NY]	RAF No 27 Sqn, Odiham
	ZH796	BAe Sea Harrier FA2 [716/VL]	RN No 899 Sqn, Yeovilton
	ZH797	BAe Sea Harrier FA2 [714]	RN No 899 Sqn, Yeovilton
	ZH798	BAe Sea Harrier FA2 [730]	RN, St Athan
	ZH799	BAe Sea Harrier FA2 [711]	RN AMG, Yeovilton
	ZH800	BAe Sea Harrier FA2 [714/VL]	RNAMG, Yeovilton
	ZH801	BAe Sea Harrier FA2 [731]	RN No 899 Sqn, Yeovilton
	ZH802	BAe Sea Harrier FA2 [730/VL]	RN No 899 Sqn, Yeovilton
	ZH803	BAe Sea Harrier FA2	RN, stored St Athan
	ZH804	BAe Sea Harrier FA2	RN, stored St Athan
	ZH805	BAe Sea Harrier FA2 [715/VL]	RN No 899 Sqn, Yeovilton
	ZH806	BAe Sea Harrier FA2 [717]	RN No 899 Sqn, Yeovilton
	ZH807	BAe Sea Harrier FA2 [719/VL]	RN No 899 Sqn, Yeovilton
	ZH808	BAe Sea Harrier FA2	RN, stored St Athan
	ZH809	BAe Sea Harrier FA2	RN, stored St Athan
	ZH810	BAe Sea Harrier FA2	RN, stored St Athan
	ZH811	BAe Sea Harrier FA2	RN, stored St Athan
	ZH812	BAe Sea Harrier FA2	RN, stored St Athan
	ZH813	BAe Sea Harrier FA2	RN, stored St Athan
	ZH814	Bell 212 (G-BGMH)	AAC No 7 Flt, Brunei
	ZH815	Bell 212 (G-BGCZ)	AAC No 7 Flt, Brunei
	ZH816	Bell 212 (G-BGMG)	AAC No 7 Flt, Brunei
	ZH821	EHI-101 Merlin HM1	MoD(PE)/GKN Westland, Yeovil
	ZH822	EHI-101 Merlin HM1	MoD(PE)/GKN Westland, Yeovil
	ZH823	EHI-101 Merlin HM1	MoD(PE)/GKN Westland, Yeovil
	ZH824	EHI-101 Merlin HM1	MoD(PE)/GKN Westland, Yeovil
	ZH825	EHI-101 Merlin HM1 [535/CU]	RN No 700M Sqn, Culdrose
	ZH826	EHI-101 Merlin HM1 [536/CU]	RN No 700M Sqn, Culdrose
	ZH827	EHI-101 Merlin HM1 [537/CU]	RN No 700M Sqn, Culdrose
	ZH828	EHI-101 Merlin HM1 [538/CU]	RN No 700M Sqn, Culdrosel
	ZH829	EHI-101 Merlin HM1	MoD(PE)/GKN Westland, Yeovil
	ZH830	EHI-101 Merlin HM1	MoD(PE)/GKN Westland, Yeovil
	ZH831	EHI-101 Merlin HM1	GKN Westland, Yeovil, for RN
	ZH832	EHI-101 Merlin HM1	GKN Westland, Yeovil, for RN
	ZH833	EHI-101 Merlin HM1	GKN Westland, Yeovil, for RN
	ZH834	EHI-101 Merlin HM1	GKN Westland, Yeovil, for RN
	ZH835	EHI-101 Merlin HM1	GKN Westland, Yeovil, for RN
	ZH836	EHI-101 Merlin HM1	GKN Westland, Yeovil, for RN
	ZH837	EHI-101 Merlin HM1	GKN Westland, Yeovil, for RN
	ZH838	EHI-101 Merlin HM1	GKN Westland, Yeovil, for RN
	ZH839	EHI-101 Merlin HM1	GKN Westland, Yeovil, for RN
	ZH840	EHI-101 Merlin HM1	GKN Westland, Yeovil, for RN

Serial	Type (other identity) [code]	Owner/operator, location or fate	Notes
ZH841	EHI-101 Merlin HM1	GKN Westland, Yeovil, for RN	
ZH842	EHI-101 Merlin HM1	GKN Westland, Yeovil, for RN	
ZH843	EHI-101 Merlin HM1	GKN Westland, Yeovil, for RN	
ZH844	EHI-101 Merlin HM1	GKN Westland, Yeovil, for RN	
ZH845	EHI-101 Merlin HM1	GKN Westland, Yeovil, for RN	
ZH846	EHI-101 Merlin HM1	GKN Westland, Yeovil, for RN	
ZH847	EHI-101 Merlin HM1	GKN Westland, Yeovil, for RN	
ZH848	EHI-101 Merlin HM1	GKN Westland, Yeovil, for RN	
ZH849	EHI-101 Merlin HM1	GKN Westland, Yeovil, for RN	
ZH850	EHI-101 Merlin HM1	GKN Westland, Yeovil, for RN	
ZH851	EHI-101 Merlin HM1	GKN Westland, Yeovil, for RN	
ZH852	EHI-101 Merlin HM1	GKN Westland, Yeovil, for RN	
ZH853	EHI-101 Merlin HM1	GKN Westland, Yeovil, for RN	
ZH854	EHI-101 Merlin HM1	GKN Westland, Yeovil, for RN	
ZH855	EHI-101 Merlin HM1	GKN Westland, Yeovil, for RN	
ZH856	EHI-101 Merlin HM1	GKN Westland, Yeovil, for RN	
ZH857	EHI-101 Merlin HM1	GKN Westland, Yeovil, for RN	
ZH858	EHI-101 Merlin HM1	GKN Westland, Yeovil, for RN	
ZH859	EHI-101 Merlin HM1	GKN Westland, Yeovil, for RN	
ZH860	EHI-101 Merlin HM1	GKN Westland, Yeovil, for RN	
ZH861	EHI-101 Merlin HM1	GKN Westland, Yeovil, for RN	
ZH862	EHI-101 Merlin HM1	GKN Westland, Yeovil, for RN	
ZH863	EHI-101 Merlin HM1	GKN Westland, Yeovil, for RN	
ZH864	EHI-101 Merlin HM1	GKN Westland, Yeovil, for RN	
ZH865	Lockheed C-130J-30 Hercules C4 (N130JA)	MoD(PE)/AFD, DERA Boscombe Down	
ZH866	Lockheed C-130J-30 Hercules C4 (N130JE)	Lockheed-Martin, Marietta	
ZH867	Lockheed C-130J-30 Hercules C4 (N130JJ)	Lockheed-Martin, Marietta	
ZH868	Lockheed C-130J-30 Hercules C4 (N130JN)	Lockheed-Martin, Marietta	
ZH869	Lockheed C-130J-30 Hercules C4 (N130JV)	LMASC/Marshall Aerospace, Cambridge	
ZH870	Lockheed C-130J-30 Hercules C4 (N73235/N78235)	LMASC/Marshall Aerospace, Cambridge	
ZH871	Lockheed C-130J-30 Hercules C4 (N73238)	MoD(PE)/AFD, DERA Boscombe Down	
ZH872	Lockheed C-130J-30 Hercules C4 (N4249Y)	LMASC/Marshall Aerospace, Cambridge	
ZH873	Lockheed C-130J-30 Hercules C4 (N4242N)	LMASC/Marshall Aerospace, Cambridge	
ZH874	Lockheed C-130J-30 Hercules C4 (N41030)	LMASC/Marshall Aerospace, Cambridge	
ZH875	Lockheed C-130J-30 Hercules C4 (N4099R)	LMASC/Marshall Aerospace, Cambridge	
ZH876	Lockheed C-130J-30 Hercules C4 (N4080M)	LMASC/Marshall Aerospace, Cambridge	
ZH877	Lockheed C-130J-30 Hercules C4 (N4081M)	LMASC/Marshall Aerospace, Cambridge	
ZH878	Lockheed C-130J-30 Hercules C4 (N73232)	LMASC/Marshall Aerospace, Cambridge	
ZH879	Lockheed C-130J-30 Hercules C4 (N4080M)	LMASC/Marshall Aerospace, Cambridge	
ZH880	Lockheed C-130J Hercules C5	Lockheed-Martin, for RAF	
ZH881	Lockheed C-130J Hercules C5	Lockheed-Martin, for RAF	
ZH882	Lockheed C-130J Hercules C5	Lockheed-Martin, for RAF	
ZH883	Lockheed C-130J Hercules C5	Lockheed-Martin, for RAF	
ZH884	Lockheed C-130J Hercules C5	Lockheed-Martin, for RAF	
ZH885	Lockheed C-130J Hercules C5	Lockheed-Martin, for RAF	
ZH886	Lockheed C-130J Hercules C5	Lockheed-Martin, for RAF	
ZH887	Lockheed C-130J Hercules C5	Lockheed-Martin, for RAF	
ZH888	Lockheed C-130J Hercules C5	Lockheed-Martin, for RAF	
ZH889	Lockheed C-130J Hercules C5	Lockheed-Martin, for RAF	
ZH890	Grob G109B Vigilant T1 [SE]	RAF ACCGS, Syerston	
ZH891	B-V Chinook HC2A (N20075)	MoD(PE)/AFD, DERA Boscombe Down	
ZH892	B-V Chinook HC2A (N2019V)	MoD(PE)/GKN Westland, Yeovil	
ZH893	B-V Chinook HC2A (N2025L)	MoD(PE)/AFD, DERA Boscombe Down	
ZH894	B-V Chinook HC2A (N2026E)	RAF, NARO Fleetlands	
ZH895	B-V Chinook HC2A (N2034K)	RAF, NARO Fleetlands	
ZH896	B-V Chinook HC2A (N2038G)	RAF Odiham	
ZH897	B-V Chinook HC3 [N2045G]	Boeing, Philadelphia, for RAF	
ZH898	B-V Chinook HC3	Boeing, Philadelphia, for RAF	

Notes	Serial	Type (other identity) [code]	Owner/operator, location or fate
	ZH899	B-V Chinook HC3	Boeing, Philadelphia, for RAF
	ZH900	B-V Chinook HC3	Boeing, Philadelphia, for RAF
	ZH901	B-V Chinook HC3	Boeing, Philadelphia, for RAF
	ZH902	B-V Chinook HC3	Boeing, Philadelphia, for RAF
	ZH903	B-V Chinook HC3	Boeing, Philadelphia, for RAF
	ZH904	B-V Chinook HC3	Boeing, Philadelphia, for RAF
	ZH935	Panavia Tornado IDS	To R Saudi AF as 7518, 18 December 1997
	ZH936	Panavia Tornado IDS	To R Saudi AF as 7519, 18 December 1997
	ZH937	Panavia Tornado IDS	To R Saudi AF as 8304, 12 March 1998
	ZH938	Panavia Tornado IDS	To R Saudi AF as 8305, 12 March 1998
	ZH939	Panavia Tornado IDS	To R Saudi AF as 8306, 26 February 1998
	ZH940	Panavia Tornado IDS	To R Saudi AF as 8307, 26 February 1998
	ZH941	Panavia Tornado IDS	To R Saudi AF as 8308, 17 April 1998
	ZH942	Panavia Tornado IDS	To R Saudi AF as 8309, 8 May 1998
	ZH943	Panavia Tornado IDS	To R Saudi AF as 8310, 8 May 1998
	ZH944	Panavia Tornado IDS	To R Saudi AF as 8311, 18 April 1998
	ZH945	Panavia Tornado IDS	To R Saudi AF as 8312, 30 May 1998
	ZH946	Panavia Tornado IDS	To R Saudi AF as 8313, 2 July 1998
	ZH947	Panavia Tornado IDS	To R Saudi AF as 8314, 30 May 1998
	ZH948	Panavia Tornado IDS	To R Saudi AF as 8315, 2 July 1998
	ZH949	Panavia Tornado IDS	To R Saudi AF as 8316, 30 July 1998
	ZH950	Panavia Tornado IDS	To R Saudi AF as 8317, 30 July 1998
	ZH951	Panavia Tornado IDS	To R Saudi AF as 8318, 28 September 1998
	ZH952	Panavia Tornado IDS	To R Saudi AF as 8319, 28 September 1998
	ZH971	WS Super Lynx Mk 21A	To Brazilian Navy as N-4011, 15 December 1997
	ZH972	WS Super Lynx Mk 21A	To Brazilian Navy as N-4011, 15 December 1997
	ZH973	WS Super Lynx Mk 21A	To Brazilian Navy as N-4013, 27 April 1998
	ZH974	WS Super Lynx Mk 21A	To Brazilian Navy as N-4014, 27 April 1998
	ZJ100	BAe Hawk 102D	BAe Warton
	ZJ114	BAe Hawk T65A	To R Saudi AF as 7919, 18 December 1997
	ZJ115	BAe Hawk T65A	To R Saudi AF as 7920, 18 December 1997
	ZJ116	EHI-101 (G-OIOI) (PP8)	MoD(PE)/GKN Westland, Yeovil
	ZJ117	EHI-101 Merlin HC3	MoD(PE)/GKN Westland, Yeovil
	ZJ118	EHI-101 Merlin HC3	GKN Westland, Yeovil, for RAF
	ZJ119	EHI-101 Merlin HC3	GKN Westland, Yeovil, for RAF
	ZJ120	EHI-101 Merlin HC3	GKN Westland, Yeovil, for RAF
	ZJ121	EHI-101 Merlin HC3	GKN Westland, Yeovil, for RAF
	ZJ122	EHI-101 Merlin HC3	GKN Westland, Yeovil, for RAF
	ZJ123	EHI-101 Merlin HC3	GKN Westland, Yeovil, for RAF
	ZJ124	EHI-101 Merlin HC3	GKN Westland, Yeovil, for RAF
	ZJ125	EHI-101 Merlin HC3	GKN Westland, Yeovil, for RAF
	ZJ126	EHI-101 Merlin HC3	GKN Westland, Yeovil, for RAF
	ZJ127	EHI-101 Merlin HC3	GKN Westland, Yeovil, for RAF
	ZJ128	EHI-101 Merlin HC3	GKN Westland, Yeovil, for RAF
	ZJ129	EHI-101 Merlin HC3	GKN Westland, Yeovil, for RAF
	ZJ130	EHI-101 Merlin HC3	GKN Westland, Yeovil, for RAF
	ZJ131	EHI-101 Merlin HC3	GKN Westland, Yeovil, for RAF
	ZJ132	EHI-101 Merlin HC3	GKN Westland, Yeovil, for RAF
	ZJ133	EHI-101 Merlin HC3	GKN Westland, Yeovil, for RAF
	ZJ134	EHI-101 Merlin HC3	GKN Westland, Yeovil, for RAF
	ZJ135	EHI-101 Merlin HC3	GKN Westland, Yeovil, for RAF
	ZJ136	EHI-101 Merlin HC3	GKN Westland, Yeovil, for RAF
	ZJ137	EHI-101 Merlin HC3	GKN Westland, Yeovil, for RAF
	ZJ138	EHI-101 Merlin HC3	GKN Westland, Yeovil, for RAF
	ZJ139	AS355F-1 Twin Squirrel HCC1 (G-NUTZ)	RAF No 32(The Royal) Sqn, Northolt
	ZJ140	AS355F-1 Twin Squirrel HCC1 (G-FFHI)	RAF No 32(The Royal) Sqn, Northolt
	ZJ157	Lockheed C-130J <Sim>	MoD(PE)/LMASC for RAF
	ZJ158	Lockheed C-130J <Sim>	MoD(PE)/LMASC for RAF
	ZJ159	Lockheed C-130J <Sim>	MoD(PE)/LMASC for RAF
	ZJ160	Lockheed C-130J <Sim>	MoD(PE)/LMASC for RAF
	ZJ161	Lockheed C-130J <Sim>	MoD(PE)/LMASC for RAF
	ZJ164	AS365N-2 Dauphin 2 (G-BTLC)	RN/Bond Helicopters, Plymouth
	ZJ165	AS365N-2 Dauphin 2 (G-NTOO)	RN/Bond Helicopters, Plymouth
	ZJ166	WS WAH-64D Apache AH1 (N9219G)	Boeing Helicopters, Mesa, for AAC
	ZJ167	WS WAH-64D Apache AH1	GKN Westland, for AAC
	ZJ168	WS WAH-64D Apache AH1	GKN Westland, for AAC
	ZJ169	WS WAH-64D Apache AH1	GKN Westland, for AAC

Serial	Type (other identity) [code]	Owner/operator, location or fate	Notes
ZJ170	WS WAH-64D Apache AH1	GKN Westland, for AAC	
ZJ171	WS WAH-64D Apache AH1	GKN Westland, for AAC	
ZJ172	WS WAH-64D Apache AH1	GKN Westland, for AAC	
ZJ173	WS WAH-64D Apache AH1	GKN Westland, for AAC	
ZJ174	WS WAH-64D Apache AH1	GKN Westland, for AAC	
ZJ175	WS WAH-64D Apache AH1	GKN Westland, for AAC	
ZJ176	WS WAH-64D Apache AH1	GKN Westland, for AAC	
ZJ177	WS WAH-64D Apache AH1	GKN Westland, for AAC	
ZJ178	WS WAH-64D Apache AH1	GKN Westland, for AAC	
ZJ179	WS WAH-64D Apache AH1	GKN Westland, for AAC	
ZJ180	WS WAH-64D Apache AH1	GKN Westland, for AAC	
ZJ181	WS WAH-64D Apache AH1	GKN Westland, for AAC	
ZJ182	WS WAH-64D Apache AH1	GKN Westland, for AAC	
ZJ183	WS WAH-64D Apache AH1	GKN Westland, for AAC	
ZJ184	WS WAH-64D Apache AH1	GKN Westland, for AAC	
ZJ185	WS WAH-64D Apache AH1	GKN Westland, for AAC	
ZJ186	WS WAH-64D Apache AH1	GKN Westland, for AAC	
ZJ187	WS WAH-64D Apache AH1	GKN Westland, for AAC	
ZJ188	WS WAH-64D Apache AH1	GKN Westland, for AAC	
ZJ189	WS WAH-64D Apache AH1	GKN Westland, for AAC	
ZJ190	WS WAH-64D Apache AH1	GKN Westland, for AAC	
ZJ191	WS WAH-64D Apache AH1	GKN Westland, for AAC	
ZJ192	WS WAH-64D Apache AH1	GKN Westland, for AAC	
ZJ193	WS WAH-64D Apache AH1	GKN Westland, for AAC	
ZJ194	WS WAH-64D Apache AH1	GKN Westland, for AAC	
ZJ195	WS WAH-64D Apache AH1	GKN Westland, for AAC	
ZJ196	WS WAH-64D Apache AH1	GKN Westland, for AAC	
ZJ197	WS WAH-64D Apache AH1	GKN Westland, for AAC	
ZJ198	WS WAH-64D Apache AH1	GKN Westland, for AAC	
ZJ199	WS WAH-64D Apache AH1	GKN Westland, for AAC	
ZJ200	WS WAH-64D Apache AH1	GKN Westland, for AAC	
ZJ201	BAe Hawk 200RDA	BAe Warton	
ZJ202	WS WAH-64D Apache AH1	GKN Westland, for AAC	
ZJ203	WS WAH-64D Apache AH1	GKN Westland, for AAC	
ZJ204	WS WAH-64D Apache AH1	GKN Westland, for AAC	
ZJ205	WS WAH-64D Apache AH1	GKN Westland, for AAC	
ZJ206	WS WAH-64D Apache AH1	GKN Westland, for AAC	
ZJ207	WS WAH-64D Apache AH1	GKN Westland, for AAC	
ZJ208	WS WAH-64D Apache AH1	GKN Westland, for AAC	
ZJ209	WS WAH-64D Apache AH1	GKN Westland, for AAC	
ZJ210	WS WAH-64D Apache AH1	GKN Westland, for AAC	
ZJ211	WS WAH-64D Apache AH1	GKN Westland, for AAC	
ZJ212	WS WAH-64D Apache AH1	GKN Westland, for AAC	
ZJ213	WS WAH-64D Apache AH1	GKN Westland, for AAC	
ZJ214	WS WAH-64D Apache AH1	GKN Westland, for AAC	
ZJ215	WS WAH-64D Apache AH1	GKN Westland, for AAC	
ZJ216	WS WAH-64D Apache AH1	GKN Westland, for AAC	
ZJ217	WS WAH-64D Apache AH1	GKN Westland, for AAC	
ZJ218	WS WAH-64D Apache AH1	GKN Westland, for AAC	
ZJ219	WS WAH-64D Apache AH1	GKN Westland, for AAC	
ZJ220	WS WAH-64D Apache AH1	GKN Westland, for AAC	
ZJ221	WS WAH-64D Apache AH1	GKN Westland, for AAC	
ZJ222	WS WAH-64D Apache AH1	GKN Westland, for AAC	
ZJ223	WS WAH-64D Apache AH1	GKN Westland, for AAC	
ZJ224	WS WAH-64D Apache AH1	GKN Westland, for AAC	
ZJ225	WS WAH-64D Apache AH1	GKN Westland, for AAC	
ZJ226	WS WAH-64D Apache AH1	GKN Westland, for AAC	
ZJ227	WS WAH-64D Apache AH1	GKN Westland, for AAC	
ZJ228	WS WAH-64D Apache AH1	GKN Westland, for AAC	
ZJ229	WS WAH-64D Apache AH1	GKN Westland, for AAC	
ZJ230	WS WAH-64D Apache AH1	GKN Westland, for AAC	
ZJ231	WS WAH-64D Apache AH1	GKN Westland, for AAC	
ZJ232	WS WAH-64D Apache AH1	GKN Westland, for AAC	
ZJ233	WS WAH-64D Apache AH1	GKN Westland, for AAC	
ZJ234	Bell 412EP Griffin HT1 (C-FZLM/ G-BWZR) [S]	DHFS No 60(R) Sqn, RAF Shawbury	
ZJ235	Bell 412EP Griffin HT1 (C-FZNF/ G-BXBF) [I]	DHFS No 60(R) Sqn, RAF Shawbury	
ZJ236	Bell 412EP Griffin HT1 (C-FZLN/ G-BXBE) [X]	DHFS No 60(R) Sqn, RAF Shawbury	
ZJ237	Bell 412EP Griffin HT1 (C-FZVV/ G-BXFF) [T]	DHFS No 60(R) Sqn, RAF Shawbury	

Notes	Serial	Type (other identity) [code]	Owner/operator, location or fate
	ZJ238	Bell 412EP Griffin HT1 (C-FZXD/ G-BXFH) [Y]	DHFS No 60(R) Sqn, RAF Shawbury
	ZJ239	Bell 412EP Griffin HT1 (C-GAFF/ G-BXHC) [R]	DHFS No 60(R) Sqn, RAF Shawbury
	ZJ240	Bell 412EP Griffin HT1 (C-GAIE/ G-BXIR) [U]	DHFS No 60(R) Sqn/SARTU, RAF Valley
	ZJ241	Bell 412EP Griffin HT1 (C-GAIG/ G-BXIS) [L]	DHFS No 60(R) Sqn/SARTU, RAF Valley
	ZJ242	Bell 412EP Griffin HT1 (N2291Q/ G-BXDK) [E]	DHFS No 60(R) Sqn/SARTU, RAF Valley
	ZJ243	AS350BA Squirrel HT2 (G-BWZS)	School of Army Aviation/No 670 Sqn, Middle Wallop
	ZJ244	AS350BA Squirrel HT2 (G-BXMD)	School of Army Aviation/No 670 Sqn, Middle Wallop
	ZJ245	AS350BA Squirrel HT2 (G-BXME)	School of Army Aviation/No 670 Sqn, Middle Wallop
	ZJ246	AS350BA Squirrel HT2 (G-BXMJ)	School of Army Aviation/No 670 Sqn, Middle Wallop
	ZJ247	AS350BA Squirrel HT2 (G-BXNB)	School of Army Aviation/No 670 Sqn, Middle Wallop
	ZJ248	AS350BA Squirrel HT2 (G-BXNE)	School of Army Aviation/No 670 Sqn, Middle Wallop
	ZJ249	AS350BA Squirrel HT2 (G-BXNJ)	School of Army Aviation/No 670 Sqn, Middle Wallop
	ZJ250	AS350BA Squirrel HT2 (G-BXOG)	School of Army Aviation/No 670 Sqn, Middle Wallop
	ZJ251	AS350BA Squirrel HT2 (G-BXNY)	School of Army Aviation/No 670 Sqn, Middle Wallop
	ZJ252	AS350BA Squirrel HT2 (G-BXOK)	School of Army Aviation/No 670 Sqn, Middle Wallop
	ZJ253	AS350BA Squirrel HT2 (G-BXPG)	School of Army Aviation/No 670 Sqn, Middle Wallop
	ZJ254	AS350BA Squirrel HT2 (G-BXPJ)	School of Army Aviation/No 670 Sqn, Middle Wallop
	ZJ255	AS350BB Squirrel HT1 (G-BXAG)	DHFS, RAF Shawbury
	ZJ256	AS350BB Squirrel HT1 (G-BXCE)	DHFS, RAF Shawbury
	ZJ257	AS350BB Squirrel HT1 (G-BXDJ)	DHFS, RAF Shawbury
	ZJ258	AS350BB Squirrel HT1 (G-BXEO)	DHFS, RAF Shawbury
	ZJ259	AS350BB Squirrel HT1 (G-BXFJ)	DHFS, RAF Shawbury
	ZJ260	AS350BB Squirrel HT1 (G-BXGB)	DHFS, RAF Shawbury
	ZJ261	AS350BB Squirrel HT1 (G-BXGJ)	DHFS, RAF Shawbury
	ZJ262	AS350BB Squirrel HT1 (G-BXHB)	DHFS, RAF Shawbury
	ZJ263	AS350BB Squirrel HT1 (G-BXHK)	DHFS, RAF Shawbury
	ZJ264	AS350BB Squirrel HT1 (G-BXHW)	DHFS, RAF Shawbury
	ZJ265	AS350BB Squirrel HT1 (G-BXHX)	DHFS, RAF Shawbury
	ZJ266	AS350BB Squirrel HT1 (G-BXIL)	DHFS, RAF Shawbury
	ZJ267	AS350BB Squirrel HT1 (G-BXIP)	DHFS, RAF Shawbury
	ZJ268	AS350BB Squirrel HT1 (G-BXJE)	DHFS, RAF Shawbury
	ZJ269	AS350BB Squirrel HT1 (G-BXJN)	DHFS, RAF Shawbury
	ZJ270	AS350BB Squirrel HT1 (G-BXJR)	DHFS, RAF Shawbury
	ZJ271	AS350BB Squirrel HT1 (G-BXKE)	DHFS, RAF Shawbury
	ZJ272	AS350BB Squirrel HT1 (G-BXKN)	DHFS, RAF Shawbury
	ZJ273	AS350BB Squirrel HT1 (G-BXKP)	DHFS, RAF Shawbury
	ZJ274	AS350BB Squirrel HT1 (G-BXKR)	DHFS, RAF Shawbury
	ZJ275	AS350BB Squirrel HT1 (G-BXLB)	DHFS, RAF Shawbury
	ZJ276	AS350BB Squirrel HT1 (G-BXLE)	DHFS, RAF Shawbury
	ZJ277	AS350BB Squirrel HT1 (G-BXLH)	DHFS, RAF Shawbury
	ZJ278	AS350BB Squirrel HT1 (G-BXMB)	DHFS, RAF Shawbury
	ZJ279	AS350BB Squirrel HT1 (G-BXMC)	DHFS, RAF Shawbury
	ZJ280	AS350BB Squirrel HT1 (G-BXMI)	DHFS, RAF Shawbury
	ZJ514	BAe Nimrod MRA4 (XV247) [PA-1]	MoD(PE)/FRA, Bournemouth (conversion)
	ZJ514	BAe Nimrod MRA4 (XV234) [PA-2]	MoD(PE)/FRA, Bournemouth (conversion)
	ZJ514	BAe Nimrod MRA4 (XV242) [PA-3]	MoD(PE)/FRA, Bournemouth (conversion)
	ZJ514	BAe Nimrod MRA4 (XV251) [PA-4]	MoD(PE)/FRA, Bournemouth (conversion)
	ZJ518	Bae Nimrod MRA4	FRA/BAe, for RAF
	ZJ519	Bae Nimrod MRA4	FRA/BAe, for RAF
	ZJ520	Bae Nimrod MRA4	FRA/BAe, for RAF
	ZJ521	Bae Nimrod MRA4	FRA/BAe, for RAF
	ZJ522	Bae Nimrod MRA4	FRA/BAe, for RAF
	ZJ523	Bae Nimrod MRA4	FRA/BAe, for RAF
	ZJ524	Bae Nimrod MRA4	FRA/BAe, for RAF
	ZJ525	Bae Nimrod MRA4	FRA/BAe, for RAF
	ZJ526	Bae Nimrod MRA4	FRA/BAe, for RAF

Serial	Type (other identity) [code]	Owner/operator, location or fate	Notes
ZJ527	Bae Nimrod MRA4	FRA/BAe, for RAF	
ZJ528	Bae Nimrod MRA4	FRA/BAe, for RAF	
ZJ529	Bae Nimrod MRA4	FRA/BAe, for RAF	
ZJ530	Bae Nimrod MRA4	FRA/BAe, for RAF	
ZJ531	Bae Nimrod MRA4	FRA/BAe, for RAF	
ZJ532	Bae Nimrod MRA4	FRA/BAe, for RAF	
ZJ533	Bae Nimrod MRA4	FRA/BAe, for RAF	
ZJ534	Bae Nimrod MRA4	FRA/BAe, for RAF	
ZJ535	WS Super Lynx Mk 88A	GKN Westland, Yeovil, for German Navy as 83+20	
ZJ536	WS Super Lynx Mk 88A	GKN Westland, Yeovil, for German Navy as 83+21	
ZJ537	WS Super Lynx Mk 88A	GKN Westland, Yeovil, for German Navy as 83+22	
ZJ555	BAe Hawk 209	BAe Warton, for Indonesian AF	
ZJ556	BAe Hawk 209	BAe Warton, for Indonesian AF	
ZJ557	BAe Hawk 209	BAe Warton, for Indonesian AF	
ZJ558	BAe Hawk 209	BAe Warton, for Indonesian AF	
ZJ559	BAe Hawk 209	BAe Warton, for Indonesian AF	
ZJ560	BAe Hawk 209	BAe Warton, for Indonesian AF	
ZJ561	BAe Hawk 209	BAe Warton, for Indonesian AF	
ZJ562	BAe Hawk 209	BAe Warton, for Indonesian AF	
ZJ563	BAe Hawk 209	BAe Warton, for Indonesian AF	
ZJ564	BAe Hawk 209	BAe Warton, for Indonesian AF	
ZJ565	BAe Hawk 209	BAe Warton, for Indonesian AF	
ZJ566	BAe Hawk 209	BAe Warton, for Indonesian AF	
ZJ567	BAe Hawk 209	BAe Warton, for Indonesian AF	
ZJ568	BAe Hawk 209	BAe Warton, for Indonesian AF	
ZJ569	BAe Hawk 209	BAe Warton, for Indonesian AF	
ZJ570	BAe Hawk 209	BAe Warton, for Indonesian AF	

Two-seat Harrier T10 ZH657 coded XX of No 20 Squadron, the Harrier OCU at Wittering. *PRM*

No 216 Squadron operates Tristar KC1 ZD948 from Brize Norton. *PRM*

1764M/K4972	7532M/WT651	7851M/WZ706	8018M/XN344
2015M/K5600	7533M/WT680	7852M/XG506	8019M/WZ869
2292M/K8203	7544M/WN904	7854M/XM191	8021M/XL824
2361M/K6035	7548M/PS915	7855M/XK416	8022M/XN341
3118M/H5199/BK892	7554M/FS890	7859M/XP283	8023M/XD463
3858M/X7688	7555M/AR614	7860M/XL738	8027M/XM555
4354M/BL614	7556M/WK584	7862M/XR246	8032M/XH837
4552M/T5298	7564M/XE982	7863M/*XP248*	8033M/XD382
5377M/EP120	7570M/XD674	7864M/XP244	8034M/XL703
5378M/AR614	7582M/WP190	7865M/TX226	8041M/XF690
5405M/LF738	7583M/WP185	7866M/XH278	8043M/XF836
5466M/*BN230*/(LF751)	7602M/WE600	7868M/WZ736	8046M/XL770
5690M/MK356	7605M/WS692	7869M/WK935	8049M/WE168
5718M/BM597	7606M/WV562	7872M/*WZ826*/(XD826)	8050M/XG329
5758M/DG202	7607M/TJ138	7881M/WD413	8051M/XN929
6457M/ML427	7615M/WV679	7882M/XD525	8052M/WH166
6490M/LA255	7616M/WW388	7883M/XT150	8054AM/XM410
6640M/RM694	7618M/WW442	7886M/XR985	8054BM/XM417
6850M/TE184	7622M/WV606	7887M/XD375	8055AM/XM402
6946M/RW388	7625M/WD356	7891M/XM693	8055BM/XM404
6948M/DE673	7631M/VX185	7894M/XD818	8056M/XG337
6960M/MT847	7641M/XA634	7895M/WF784	8057M/XR243
7008M/EE549	7645M/WD293	7898M/XP854	8063M/WT536
7014M/N6720	7646M/VX461	7899M/XG540	8070M/EP120
7015M/NL985	7648M/XF785	7900M/WA576	8072M/PK624
7035M/*K2567*/(DE306)	7673M/WV332	7906M/WH132	8073M/TB252
7060M/VF301	7688M/WW421	7917M/WA591	8077M/XN594
7090M/EE531	7693M/WV483	7920M/WL360	8078M/XM351
7118M/LA198	7696M/WV493	7923M/XT133	8079M/XN492
7119M/LA226	7698M/WV499	7925M/WV666	8080M/XM480
7150M/PK683	7703M/WG725	7928M/XE849	8081M/XM468
7154M/WB188	7704M/TW536	7930M/WH301	8082M/XM409
7174M/VX272	7705M/WL505	7931M/RD253	8086M/TB752
7175M/VV106	7706M/WB584	7932M/WZ744	8092M/WK654
7200M/VT812	7709M/WT933	7933M/XR220	8094M/WT520
7241M/*MK178*/(TE311)	7711M/PS915	7937M/WS843	8101M/WH984
7243M/TE462	7712M/WK281	7938M/XH903	8102M/WT486
7244M/*MK673*/(TB382)	7715M/XK724	7939M/XD596	8103M/WR985
7246M/TD248	7716M/WS776	7940M/XL764	8106M/WR982
7256M/TB752	7718M/WA577	7955M/XH767	8108M/WV703
7257M/TB252	7719M/WK277	7957M/XF545	8114M/WL798
7279M/TB752	7728M/WZ458	7959M/WS774	8117M/WR974
7281M/TB252	7729M/WB758	7960M/WS726	8118M/WZ549
7288M/PK724	7734M/XD536	7961M/WS739	8119M/WR971
7293M/RW393	7737M/XD602	7964M/WS760	8121M/XM474
7323M/VV217	7741M/VZ477	7965M/WS792	8124M/XD614
7325M/R5868	7750M/*WK864*/(WL168)	7967M/WS788	8128M/WH775
7326M/VN485	7751M/WL131	7970M/WP907	8131M/WT507
7362M/475081/(VP546)	7755M/WG760	7971M/XK699	8140M/XJ571
7416M/WN907	7758M/PM651	7973M/WS807	8141M/XN688
7421M/WT660	7759M/PK664	7976M/XK418	8142M/XJ560
7422M/WT684	7761M/XH318	7979M/XM529	8143M/XN691
7428M/WK198	7762M/XE670	7980M/XM561	8147M/XR526
7432M/WZ724	7770M/WT746	7982M/XH892	8151M/WV795
7438M/*18671*/(WP905)	7793M/XG523	7983M/XD506	8153M/WV903
7443M/WX853	7796M/WJ676	7984M/XN597	8154M/WV908
7458M/WX905	7798M/XH783	7986M/WG777	8155M/WV797
7464M/XA564	7806M/TA639	7988M/XL149	8156M/XE339
7467M/WP978	7809M/XA699	7990M/XD452	8158M/XE369
7470M/XA553	7816M/WG763	7997M/XG452	8159M/XD528
7473M/XE946	7817M/TX214	7998M/*XM515*/(XD515)	8160M/XD622
7491M/WT569	7825M/WK991	8005M/WG768	8161M/XE993
7496M/WT612	7827M/XA917	8009M/XG518	8162M/WM913
7499M/WT555	7829M/XH992	8010M/XG547	8163M/XP919
7510M/WT694	7839M/WV781	8012M/VS562	8164M/*WN105*/(WF299)
7525M/WT619	7840M/XK482	8016M/XT677	8165M/WH791
7530M/WT648	7841M/WV783	8017M/XL762	8169M/WH364

8173M/XN685	8402M/XN769	8578M/XR534	8724M/XW923
8176M/WH791	8406M/XP831	8581M/WJ775	8726M/XP299
8177M/*WM311*/(WM224)	8407M/XP585	8582M/XE874	8727M/XR486
8179M/XN928	8408M/XS186	8583M/BAPC 94	8728M/WT532
8183M/*XN972*/(XN962)	8409M/XS209	8584M/WH903	8729M/WJ815
8184M/WT520	8410M/XR662	8585M/XE670	8732M/XJ729
8185M/WH946	8413M/XM192	8586M/XE643	8733M/XL318
8186M/WR977	8414M/XM173	8587M/XP677	8736M/XF375
8187M/WH791	8417M/XM144	8588M/XR681	8738M/*XF519*/(XJ695)
8189M/WD646	8422M/XM169	8589M/XR700	8739M/XH170
8190M/XJ918	8427M/XM172	8590M/XM191	8740M/WE173
8192M/XR658	8429M/XH592	8595M/XH278	8741M/XW329
8196M/XE920	8436M/XN554	8598M/WP270	8743M/WD790
8198M/WT339	8437M/*WX643*/(WG362)	8600M/XX761	8746M/XH171
8203M/XD377	8439M/WZ846	8602M/*PF179*/(XR541)	8749M/XH537
8205M/XN819	8440M/WD935	8606M/XP530	8751M/XT255
8206M/WG419	8442M/XP411	8608M/XP540	8753M/WL795
8207M/WD318	8453M/XP745	8610M/XL502	8762M/WH740
8208M/WG303	8457M/XS871	8611M/WF128	8763M/WH665
8209M/WG418	8458M/XP672	8617M/XM709	8764M/XP344
8210M/WG471	8460M/XR650	8618M/*XM693*/(XP504)	8767M/XX635
8211M/WK570	8462M/XX477	8620M/XR534	8768M/A-522
8213M/WK626	8463M/XP355	8624M/*XR991*/(XS102)	8769M/A-528
8214M/WP864	8464M/XJ758	8627M/XP558	8770M/XL623
8216M/WP927	8465M/W1048	8628M/XJ380	8771M/XM602
8217M/WZ866	8466M/L-866	8630M/*WX643*/(WG362)	8772M/WR960
8218M/WB645	8467M/WP912	8631M/XR574	8777M/XX914
8229M/XM355	8468M/MM5701/(BT474)	8633M/MK732	8778M/XM598
8230M/XM362	8470M/584219	8634M/WP314	8779M/XM607
8231M/XM375	8471M/701152	8638M/XS101	8780M/WK102
8234M/XN458	8472M/120227//(VN679)	8640M/XR977	8781M/WE982
8235M/XN549	8473M/WP190	8642M/XR537	8782M/XH136
8236M/XP573	8474M/494083	8645M/XD163	8783M/XW272
8237M/XS179	8475M/360043/(PJ876)	8648M/XK526	8785M/XS642
8238M/XS180	8476M/24	8653M/XS120	8786M/XN495
8344M/WH960	8477M/4101/(DG200)	8655M/XN126	8791M/XP329
8345M/XG540	8478M/10639	8656M/XP405	8792M/XP345
8350M/WH840	8479M/730301	8657M/VZ634	8793M/XP346
8352M/XN632	8481M/191614	8661M/XJ727	8794M/XP398
8355M/*KG374*/(KN645)	8482M/112372/(VK893)	8662M/XR458	8796M/XK943
8357M/WK576	8483M/420430	8664M/WJ603	8797M/XX947
8359M/WF825	8484M/5439	8666M/XE793	8799M/WV787
8360M/WP863	8485M/997	8668M/WJ821	8800M/XG226
8361M/WB670	8486M/BAPC 99	8671M/XJ435	8805M/XT772
8362M/WG477	8487M/J-1172	8672M/XP351	8807M/XL587
8364M/WG464	8488M/WL627	8673M/XD165	8810M/XJ825
8365M/XK421	8491M/WJ880	8674M/XP395	8814M/XM927
8366M/XG454	8492M/WJ872	8676M/XL577	8818M/XK527
8367M/XG474	8493M/XR571	8677M/*XF519*/(XJ695)	8819M/XS479
8368M/XF926	8494M/XP557	8679M/XP526	8820M/VP952
8369M/WE139	8495M/XR672	8680M/XF527	8821M/XX115
8370M/N1671	8501M/XP640	8681M/XG164	8822M/WP957
8371M/XA847	8502M/XP686	8682M/XP404	8828M/XS587
8372M/K8042	8507M/XS215	8684M/XJ634	8830M/XF515
8373M/P2617	8508M/XS218	8685M/XF516	8831M/XG160
8375M/NX611	8509M/XT141	8687M/XJ639	8832M/XG172
8376M/RF398	8513M/XN724	8693M/WH863	8833M/XL569
8377M/R9125	8514M/XS176	8696M/WH773	8834M/XL522
8378M/*T9707*	8535M/XN776	8700M/ZD234	8836M/XL592
8379M/DG590	8538M/XN781	8702M/XG196	8838M/*34037*/(429356)
8380M/Z7197	8545M/XN726	8703M/VW453	8839M/*69*/(XG194)
8382M/VR930	8546M/XN728	8706M/XF383	8840M/XG252
8383M/K9942	8548M/WT507	8708M/XF509	8844M/XJ676
8384M/X4590	8549M/WT534	8709M/XG209	8845M/XS572
8385M/N5912	8554M/TG511	8710M/XG274	8847M/XX344
8386M/NV778	8560M/XR569	8711M/XG290	8848M/XZ135
8387M/T6296	8561M/XS100	8713M/XG225	8851M/XT595
8388M/XL993	8565M/*WT720*/(E-408)	8714M/XK149	8852M/XV337
8389M/VX573	8566M/XV279	8718M/XX396	8853M/XT277
8392M/SL674	8568M/XP503	8719M/XT257	8855M/XT284
8394M/WG422	8570M/XR954	8720M/XP353	8857M/XW544
8395M/WF408	8573M/XM708	8721M/XP354	8860M/XW549
8396M/XK740	8575M/XP542	8722M/WJ640	8861M/XW528
8399M/WR539	8576M/XP502	8723M/XL567	8862M/XN473
8401M/XP686			8863M/XG154

RAF Maintenance Cross-reference

8867M/XK532	8969M/XR753	9075M/XV753	9179M/XW309
8868M/WH775	8972M/XR754	9076M/XV808	9180M/XW311
8869M/WH957	8973M/XS922	9078M/XV752	9181M/XW358
8870M/WH964	8974M/XM473	9079M/XZ130	9183M/*XF519*/(XJ695)
8871M/WJ565	8976M/XZ630	9083M/ZE353	9185M/XZ987
8873M/XR453	8978M/XX837	9084M/ZE354	9186M/XF967
8874M/XE597	8979M/XV747	9087M/XX753	9187M/XW405
8875M/XE624	8983M/XM478	9090M/XW353	9188M/XW364
8876M/*VM791*/(XA312)	8984M/XN551	9091M/XW434	9189M/ZD350
8877M/XP159	8985M/WK127	9092M/XH669	9190M/XW318
8879M/XX948	8986M/XV261	9093M/WK124	9191M/XW416
8880M/XF435	8987M/XM358	9095M/XW547	9192M/XW361
8881M/XG254	8988M/XN593	9096M/WV322	9193M/XW367
8883M/XX946	8990M/XM419	9097M/XW366	9194M/XW420
8884M/VX275	8995M/XM425	9098M/XV406	9195M/XW330
8885M/XW922	8996M/XM414	9100M/XL188	9196M/XW370
8886M/XA243	8997M/XX669	9101M/WL756	9197M/*XX530*/(XX637)
8888M/XA231	8998M/XT864	9103M/XV411	9198M/XS641
8889M/XN239	9002M/XW763	9109M/XW312	9199M/XW290
8890M/WT532	9003M/XZ390	9110M/XX736	9200M/XW425
8892M/XL618	9004M/XZ370	9111M/XW421	9201M/ZD667
8895M/XX746	9005M/XZ374	9112M/XM475	9202M/*433*
8896M/XX821	9006M/XX967	9113M/XV500	9203M/*3066*
8897M/XX969	9007M/XX968	9115M/XV863	9205M/*E449*
8898M/XX119	9008M/XX140	9117M/XV161	9206M/F6314
8899M/XX756	9009M/XX763	9118M/XV253	9207M/8417/18
8900M/XZ368	9010M/XX764	9119M/XW303	9208M/F938
8901M/XZ383	9011M/XM412	9120M/XW419	9209M/164
8902M/XX739	9012M/XN494	9122M/XZ997	9210M/MF628
8903M/XX747	9014M/XN584	9123M/XT773	9211M/733682
8904M/XX966	9015M/XW320	9124M/XW427	9212M/*KL216*/(45-49295)
8905M/XX975	9017M/ZE449	9125M/XW410	9213M/N5182
8906M/XX976	9018M/XW365	9126M/XW413	9215M/XL164
8907M/XZ371	9019M/XX824	9127M/XW432	9216M/XL190
8908M/XZ382	9020M/XX825	9128M/XW292	9217M/ZH257
8909M/XV784	9021M/XX826	9129M/XW294	9218M/XL563
8910M/XL160	9022M/XX958	9130M/XW327	9219M/XZ971
8911M/XH673	9026M/XP629	9131M/*DD931*	9220M/XZ995
8915M/XH132	9027M/XP556	9132M/XX977	9221M/XZ966
8917M/XM372	9028M/XP563	9133M/*413573*	9222M/XZ968
8918M/XX109	9029M/XS217	9134M/XT288	9224M/XL568
8920M/XT469	9030M/XR674	9136M/XT891	9225M/XX885
8921M/XT466	9031M/XP688	9137M/XN579	9226M/XV865
8922M/XT467	9032M/XR673	9139M/XV863	9227M/XB812
8923M/XX819	9033M/XS181	9140M/XZ287	9228M/ZD991
8924M/XP701	9034M/XP638	9141M/XV118	9229M/ZA678
8925M/XP706	9036M/XM350	9143M/XN589	9230M/ZA676
8931M/XV779	9038M/XV810	9144M/XV353	9231M
8932M/XR718	9039M/XN586	9145M/XV863	9232M/XV332
8934M/XR749	9040M/XZ138	9146M/XW299	9233M/XZ431
8935M/XR713	9041M/XW763	9147M/XW301	9234M/XV864
8937M/XX751	9042M/XL954	9148M/XW436	9236M
8938M/WV746	9044M/XS177	9149M/XW375	9237M/XF995
8941M/XT456	9045M/XN636	9150M/*FX760*	9238M/ZA717
8942M/XN185	9046M/XM349	9151M/XT907	9239M
8943M/XE799	9047M/XW409	9152M/XV424	9241M
8944M/WZ791	9048M/XM403	9153M/XW360	9242M
8945M/XX818	9049M/XW404	9154M/XW321	9243M/XX163
8946M/XZ389	9050M/XG577	9155M/WL679	9244M
8947M/XX726	9052M/WJ717	9158M/XV467	9245M
8948M/XX757	9054M/XT766	9159M/XV468	9246M/XS714
8949M/XX743	9055M/XT770	9162M/XZ991	9247M/XV420
8950M/XX956	9056M/XS488	9163M/XV415	9248M/WB627
8951M/XX727	9057M/ZE361	9165M/XV408	9249M/WV396
8952M/XX730	9059M/ZE360	9166M/XW323	9250M/162068
8953M/XX959	9060M/ZE356	9167M/XV744	9251M
8954M/XZ384	9061M/XW335	9168M/XZ132	9252M
8955M/XX110	9062M/XW351	9169M/XW547	9253M
8956M/XN577	9064M/XT867	9170M/XZ994	9254M
8957M/XN582	9065M/XV577	9172M/XW304	9255M/XZ375
8958M/XN501	9066M/XV582	9173M/XW418	9256M/XX839
8960M/XM455	9067M/XV586	9174M/XZ131	9257M
8961M/XS925	9070M/XV581	9175M/P1344	9258M
8967M/XV263	9072M/XW768	9176M/XW430	9259M/XS710
8968M/XM471	9073M/XW924	9177M/XW328	9260M/XS734

RN Landing Platform and Shore Station Code-letters

Code	Deck Letters	Vessel Name & Pennant No	Vessel Type & Unit
—	AS	RFA Argus (A135)	Aviation Training ship
365/6	AY	HMS Argyll (F231)	Type 23 (815 Sqn)
328/9	BA	HMS Brave (F94)	Type 22 (815 Sqn)
—	BD	RFA Sir Bedivere [L3004]	Landing ship
333	BM	HMS Birmingham (D86)	Type 42 (815 Sqn)
—	BV	RFA Black Rover (A273)	Fleet tanker
335	CF	HMS Cardiff (D108)	Type 42 (815 Sqn)
350/1	CL	HMS Cumberland (F85)	Type 22 (815 Sqn)
515	CM	HMS Chatham (F87)	Type 22 (810 Sqn)
338/9	CT	HMS Campbeltown (F86)	Type 22 (815 Sqn)
—	CU	RNAS Culdrose (HMS Seahawk)	
336/7	CV	HMS Coventry (F98)	Type 22 (815 Sqn)
412/3	CW	HMS Cornwall (F99)	Type 22 (815 Sqn)
—	DC	HMS Dumbarton Castle (P265)	Fishery protection
—	DG	RFA Diligence (A132)	Maintenance
411	EB	HMS Edinburgh (D97)	Type 42 (815 Sqn)
434/5	EE	HMS Endurance (A171)	Ice Patrol (815 Sqn)
420	EX	HMS Exeter (D89)	Type 42 (815 Sqn)
—	FA	RFA Fort Austin (A386)	Support ship
—	FG	RFA Fort Grange (A385)	Support ship
—	FL	RNAY Fleetlands	
—	FS	HMS Fearless (L10)	Assault
410	GC	HMS Gloucester (D96)	Type 42 (815 Sqn)
—	GD	RFA Sir Galahad (L3005)	Landing ship
—	GR	RFA Sir Geraint (L3027)	Landing ship
437	GT	HMS Grafton (F80)	Type 23 (815 Sqn)
—	GV	RFA Gold Rover (A271)	Fleet tanker
344	GW	HMS Glasgow (D88)	Type 42 (815 Sqn)
—	GY	RFA Grey Rover (A269)	Fleet tanker
—	HR	HMS Herald (H138)	Survey ship
—	ID	HMS Intrepid (L11)	Assault
404	IR	HMS Iron Duke (F234)	Type 23 (815 Sqn)
—	L	HMS Illustrious (R06)	Carrier
457	LA	HMS Lancaster (F229)	Type 23 (815 Sqn)
—	LC	HMS Leeds Castle (P258)	Fishery protection
405/6	LO	HMS London (F95)*	Type 22 (815 Sqn)
332	LP	HMS Liverpool (D92)	Type 42 (815 Sqn)
363/4	MA	HMS Marlborough (F233)	Type 23 (815 Sqn)
360	MC	HMS Manchester (D95)	Type 42 (815 Sqn)
415	MM	HMS Monmouth (F235)	Type 23 (815 Sqn)
444	MR	HMS Montrose (F236)	Type 23 (815 Sqn)
—	N	HMS Invincible (R05)	Carrier
345	NC	HMS Newcastle (D87)	Type 42 (815 Sqn)
361/2	NF	HMS Norfolk (F230)	Type 23 (815 Sqn)
372	NL	HMS Northumberland (F238)	Type 23 (815 Sqn)
417	NM	HMS Nottingham (D91)	Type 42 (815 Sqn)
—	O	HMS Ocean (L12)	Helicopter carrier
—	ON	RFA Olna (A123)	Fleet tanker
—	OW	RFA Olwen (A122)	Fleet tanker
—	PV	RFA Sir Percivale (L3036)	Landing ship
—	PW	Prestwick Airport (HMS Gannet)	
—	R	HMS Ark Royal (R07)	Carrier
474	RM	HMS Richmond (F239)	Type 23 (815 Sqn)
352/3	SD	HMS Sheffield (F96)	Type 22 (815 Sqn)
355	SM	HMS Somerset (F82)	Type 23 (815 Sqn)
334	SN	HMS Southampton (D90)	Type 42 (815 Sqn)
422	SU	HMS Sutherland (F81)	Type 23 (815 Sqn)
—	TM	RFA Sir Tristram (L3505)	Landing ship
374/5	VB	HMS Beaver (F93)*	Type 22 (815 Sqn)
—	VL	RNAS Yeovilton (HMS Heron)	
462	WM	HMS Westminster (F237)	Type 23 (815 Sqn)
376	XB	HMS Boxer (F92)*	Type 22 (815 Sqn)
407	YK	HMS York (D98)	Type 42 (815 Sqn)
—	—	HMS Albion	Assault
—	—	HMS Bulwark	Assault
—	—	RFA Fort Victoria (A387)	Auxiliary Oiler
—	—	RFA Fort George (A388)	Auxiliary Oiler

RN Landing Platforms

Code	Deck Letters	Vessel Name & Pennant No	Vessel Type & Unit
—	—	HMS *Kent* (F78)	Type 23
—	—	HMS *Portland* (F79)	Type 23
—	—	HMS *St Albans* (F83)	Type 23
—	—	RFA *Sir Bedivere* (L3004)	Landing ship
—	—	RFA *Wave Knight* [A389]	Fleet tanker
—	—	RFA *Wave Ruler*	Fleet tanker

* Planned to decommission during 1999.

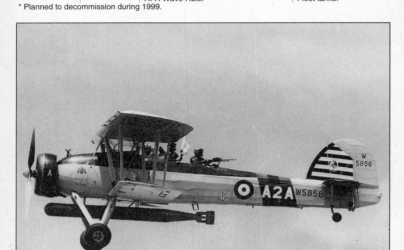

One of the RN Historic Flight's Swordfish, W5856. *PRM*

Jaguar GR1A XZ396 was painted in special anniversary colours at the end of 1998.
Daniel J. March

Ships' Numeric Code – Deck Letters Analysis

	0	1	2	3	4	5	6	7	8	9
32									BA	BA
33			LP	BM	SN	CF	CV	CV		
34					GW	NC				
35	CL	CL	SD	SD		SM				
36	MC	NF	NF	MA	MA	AY	AY			
37			NL		VB	VB	XB			
40					IR	LO	LO	YK		
41	GC	EB	CW	CW		MM		NM		
42	EX		SU							
43					EE	EE		GT		
44					MR					
45								LA		
46			WM							
47					RM					

RN Code – Squadron – Base – Aircraft Cross-check

Deck/Base Code Numbers	Letters	Unit	Location	Aircraft Type(s)
000 — 005	L	801 Sqn	Yeovilton	Sea Harrier FA2
010 — 020	L	820 Sqn	Culdrose	Sea King HAS6
122 — 129	N	800 Sqn	Yeovilton	Sea Harrier FA2
180 — 182	CU	849 Sqn HQ Flt	Culdrose	Sea King AEW2
183 — 185	L	849 Sqn B Flt	Culdrose	Sea King AEW2
186 — 188	R	849 Sqn A Flt	Culdrose	Sea King AEW2
264 — 274	N	814 Sqn	Culdrose	Sea King HAS6
300 — 308	VL	815 Sqn	Yeovilton	Lynx HAS3/HMA8
318 — 319	VL	815 Sqn OEU	Yeovilton	Lynx HMA8
328 — 479	*	815 Sqn	Yeovilton	Lynx HAS3/HMA8
500 — 515	CM/CU/CW	810 Sqn	Culdrose	Sea King HAS6
535 — 538	CU	700M Sqn	Culdrose	Merlin HM1
560 — 573	CU	750 Sqn	Culdrose	Jetstream T2
576 — 579	-	FONA	Yeovilton	Jetstream T3
580 — 599	CU	706 Sqn	Culdrose	Sea King HU5/HAS6
630 — 638	VL	702 Sqn	Yeovilton	Lynx HAS3
640 — 648	VL	702 Sqn	Yeovilton	Lynx HAS3
700 — 709	PW	819 Sqn	Prestwick	Sea King HAS6
710 — 719	VL	899 Sqn	Yeovilton	Sea Harrier FA2
720 — 724	VL	899 Sqn	Yeovilton	Harrier T8
730 — 731	VL	899 Sqn	Yeovilton	Sea Harrier FA2
820 — 827	CU	771 Sqn	Culdrose	Sea King HU5

*See foregoing separate ships' Deck Letter Analysis

Note that only the 'last two' digits of the Code are worn by some aircraft types, especially helicopters.

British-based Historic Aircraft in Overseas Markings

Some *historic, classic and warbird* aircraft carry the markings of overseas air arms and can be seen in the UK, mainly preserved in museums and collections or taking part in air shows.

Notes	Serial	Type (other identity)	Owner/operator, location
ARGENTINA			
	0729	Beech T-34C Turbo Mentor	FAA Museum, stored Wroughton
	0767	Aermacchi MB339AA	Rolls-Royce Heritage Trust, Filton
	A-515	FMA IA58 Pucara (ZD485)	RAF Cosford Aerospace Museum
	A-517	FMA IA58 Pucara (G-BLRP)	Privately owned, Channel Islands
	A-522	FMA IA58 Pucara (8768M)	FAA Museum, at NE Aircraft Museum, Usworth
	A-528	FMA IA58 Pucara (8769M)	Norfolk & Suffolk Avn Museum, Flixton
	A-533	FMA IA58 Pucara (ZD486)	The Air Defence Collection, Salisbury
	A-549	FMA IA58 Pucara (ZD487)	Imperial War Museum, Duxford
	AE-409	Bell UH-1H Iroquois [656]	Museum of Army Flying, Middle Wallop
	AE-422	Bell UH-1H Iroquois	FAA Museum, RNAS Yeovilton
AUSTRALIA			
	A2-4	Supermarine Seagull V (VH-ALB)	RAF Museum, Hendon
	A16-199	Lockheed Hudson IIIA (G-BEOX) [SF-R]	RAF Museum, Hendon
	A17-48	DH82A Tiger Moth (G-BPHR)	Privately owned, Swindon
	A19-144	Bristol 156 Beaufighter XIc (JM135/A8-324)	The Fighter Collection, Duxford
	A92-480	GAF Jindivik 4A	DERA Llanbedr, on display
	A92-664	GAF Jindivik 4A	Maes Artro Craft Village, Llanbedr
	A92-708	GAF Jindivik 4A	Bristol Aero Collection, stored Kemble
	WH588	Hawker Sea Fury FB11 (N558/ G-EEMV) [114/NW]	Privately owned, Sywell
BELGIUM			
	FT-36	Lockheed T-33A	Dumfries & Galloway Avn Mus, Dumfries
	H-50	Noorduyn AT-16 Harvard IIB (OO-DAF)	Privately owned, Brasschaat, Belgium
	HD-75	Hanriot HD1 (G-AFDX)	RAF Museum, Hendon
	IF-68	Hawker Hunter F6 <ff>	Privately owned, Welshpool
	K-16	Douglas C-53D Skytrooper (OT-CWG/N49G)	Air Dakota, Brussels, Belgium
	L-44	Piper L-18C Super Cub (OO-SPQ)	Privately owned, Belgium
	SG-3	VS379 Spitfire FR XIV (RN201/ SG-31/G-BSKP)	Privately owned, Catfield
	V-18	Stampe SV-4B (OO-GWD)	Antwerp Stampe Centre, Antwerp-Deurne, Belgium
	V-29	Stampe SV-4B (OO-GWB)	Antwerp Stampe Centre, Antwerp-Deurne, Belgium
BOTSWANA			
	OJ1	BAC Strikemaster 83 (ZG805/ G-BXFU)	Global Aviation, Binbrook
	OJ4	BAC Strikemaster 87 (G-AYHR/ G-UNNY)	McCarthy Aviation, North Weald
	OJ7	BAC Strikemaster 83 (ZG809/ G-BXFV)	Global Aviation, Binbrook
	OJ8	BAC Strikemaster 83 (ZG811/ G-BXFX)	Global Aviation, Binbrook
	OJ9	BAC Strikemaster 87 (G-BXFR)	McCarthy Aviation, North Weald
	OJ10	BAC Strikemaster 87 (G-BXFS)	Privately owned
Brazil			
	1317	Embraer T-27 Tucano	Shorts, Belfast (engine test bed)
CANADA			
	622	Piasecki HUP-3 Retriever (51-16622/N6699D)	The Helicopter Museum, Weston-super-Mare
	920	VS Stranraer (CF-BXO) [Q-N]	RAF Museum, Hendon
	2442	Westland Lysander IIIA (OO-SOT)	SABENA Old Timers, Brussels, Belgium
	3349	NA64 Yale (N55904)	ducAir, Lelystad, The Netherlands
	5450	Hawker Hurricane XII (G-TDTW)	Hawker Restorations Ltd, Milden

Serial	Type (other identity)	Owner/operator, location	Notes
9059	Bristol 149 Bolingbroke IVT	Privately owned, Portsmouth	
9893	Bristol 149 Bolingbroke IVT	Imperial War Museum store, Duxford	
9940	Bristol 149 Bolingbroke IVT	Royal Scottish Mus'm of Flight, E Fortune	
15195	Fairchild PT-19A Cornell	RAF Museum, stored Cardington	
16693	Auster J/1N Alpha (G-BLPG) [693]	Privately owned, Headcorn	
18013	DHC1 Chipmunk 22 (G-TRIC) [013]	Privately owned, North Weald	
18393	Avro Canada CF-100 Canuck IVB (G-BCYK)	Imperial War Museum, Duxford	
18671	DHC1 Chipmunk 22 (WP905/ 7438M/G-BNZC) [671]	Privately owned, Wombleton	
20310	CCF T-6J Harvard IV (G-BSBG)	Privately owned, Liverpool	
21417	Canadair CT-133 Silver Star	Yorkshire Air Museum, Elvington	
23140	Canadair CL-13 Sabre [AX] (fuselage)	Midland Air Museum, Coventry	
23380	Canadair CL-13 Sabre <rf>	RAF Millom Museum, Haverigg	
FJ777	Boeing-Stearman PT-13D Kaydet (42-17786/G-BRTK)	Privately owned, Swanton Morley	

CHINA

828	Lavochkin La-9 (G-BWUD)	The Old Flying Machine Company, Duxford	
1532008	Nanchang CJ-6A Chujiao (G-BVFX) [08]	Privately owned, Slinfold	
2232028	Nanchang CJ-6A Chujiao (G-BVVF) [69]	Privately owned, Bishop Auckland	
2632016	Nanchang CJ-6A Chujiao (G-BXZB)	Privately owned, Slinfold	

CZECH REPUBLIC

3677	Letov S-102 (MiG-15) (613677)	Royal Scottish Museum of Flight, E Fortune	
3794	Letov S-102 (MiG-15) (623794)	Imperial War Museum, stored Duxford	
9147	Mil Mi-4	The Helicopter Museum, Weston-super-Mare	

DENMARK

A-011	SAAB A-35XD Draken	NATO Aircraft Museum, New Waltham, Humberside	
AR-107	SAAB S-35XD Draken	Newark Air Museum, Winthorpe	
E-402	Hawker Hunter F51	Privately owned, Kemble	
E-409	Hawker Hunter F51 (*XF383*)	City of Norwich Aviation Museum	
E-419	Hawker Hunter F51	North-East Aircraft Museum, Usworth	
E-420	Hawker Hunter F51 (G-9-442)	Privately owned, Walton-on-Thames	
E-421	Hawker Hunter F51	Brooklands Museum, Weybridge	
E-423	Hawker Hunter F51 (G-9-444)	SWWAPS, Lasham	
E-424	Hawker Hunter F51 (G-9-445)	South Yorkshire Avn Museum, Firbeck	
E-425	Hawker Hunter F51	Midland Air Museum, Coventry	
E-430	Hawker Hunter F51	Vallance By-Ways, Charlwood, Surrey	
ET-272	Hawker Hunter T7 <rf>	McCarthy Aviation, North Weald	
ET-273	Hawker Hunter T7 <rf>	South Yorkshire Avn Museum, Firbeck	
K-682	Douglas C-47A Skytrain (OY-BPB)	Foreningen For Flyvende Mus, Vaerløse, Denmark	
L-866	Consolidated PBY-6A Catalina (8466M)	RAF Cosford Aerospace Museum	
R-756	Lockheed F-104G Starfighter	Midland Air Museum, Coventry	
S-881	Sikorsky S-55C	The Helicopter Museum, Weston-super-Mare	
S-882	Sikorsky S-55C	The Helicopter Museum, Weston-super-Mare	
S-886	Sikorsky S-55C	The Helicopter Museum, Weston-super-Mare	
S-887	Sikorsky S-55C	The Helicopter Museum, Weston-super-Mare	

EGYPT

0446	Mikoyan MiG-21UM <ff>	Thameside Aviation Museum, Tilbury	
2684	Mikoyan MiG-19 <ff>		
7907	Sukhoi Su-7 <ff>	Robertsbridge Aviation Society, Mayfield	

FRANCE

3	Mudry/CAARP CAP-10B (G-BXRA)	Privately owned, Sedlescombe, Sussex	
06	Dewoitine D27 (290/F-AZJD)	The Old Flying Machine Company, Duxford	
20	MH1521C1 Broussard (G-BWGG) [315-SQ]	Privately owned, Rednal	
37	Nord 3400 (G-ZARA) [MAB]	Privately owned, Boston	
57	Dassault Mystère IVA [8-MT]	Imperial War Museum, Duxford	
68	Nord 3400 [MHA]	Privately owned, Coventry	

Historic Aircraft

Notes	Serial	Type (other identity)	Owner/operator, location
	70	Dassault Mystère IVA	Midland Air Museum, Coventry
	78	Nord 3202 (G-BIZK)	Privately owned, Swanton Morley
	79	Dassault Mystère IVA [8-NB]	Norfolk & Suffolk Avn Museum, Flixton
	83	Dassault Mystère IVA [8-MS]	Newark Air Museum, Winthorpe
	84	Dassault Mystère IVA [8-NF]	Lashenden Air Warfare Museum, Headcorn
	85	Dassault Mystère IVA [8-MV]	British Aviation Heritage, Bruntingthorpe
	100	Mudry/CAARP CAP-10B (G-BXRB)	Privately owned, Sedlescombe, Sussex
	101	Dassault Mystère IVA [8-MN]	Bomber County Aviation Museum, Hemswell
	105	Nord N2501F Noratlas (F-AZVM) [62-SI]	Le Noratlas de Provence, Aix-les-Milles, France
	FR108	SO1221 Djinn [CDL]	The Helicopter Museum, Weston-super-Mare
	120	SNCAN Stampe SV4C (G-AZGC)	Privately owned, Reading
	121	Dassault Mystère IVA	City of Norwich Aviation Museum
	134	Mudry/CAARP CAP-10B (G-BXRC)	Privately owned, Sedlescombe, Sussex
	135	Mudry/CAARP CAP-10B (G-BXFE)	Privately owned, Sedlescombe, Sussex
	143	Morane-Saulnier MS733 Alcyon (G-MSAL)	The Squadron, North Weald
	FR145	SO1221 Djinn [CDL]	Privately owned, Luton
	146	Dassault Mystère IVA [8-MC]	North-East Aircraft Museum, Usworth
	185	MH1521M Broussard (G-BWLR)	Privately owned, Longhope
	282	Dassault MD311 Flamant (F-AZFX) [316-KY]	Memorial Flt Association, la Ferté-Alais, France
	316	MH1521M Broussard (G-GGKR) [315-SN]	The Old Flying Machine Company, Duxford
	318	Dassault Mystère IVA [8-NY]	Dumfries & Galloway Avn Mus, Dumfries
	319	Dassault Mystère IVA [8-ND]	Rebel Air Museum, Andrewsfield
	348	SO4050 Vautour IIN (F-AZHP)	Privately owned, Bretigny, France
	396	Stampe SV4A (G-BWRE)	Front Line Aviation Museum, Sandown
	538	Dassault Mirage IIIE	Yorkshire Air Museum, Elvington
	1197	Bleriot XI <R> (G-BPVE)	Bianchi Avn Film Services, Booker
	42157	NA F-100D Super Sabre [11-ML]	North-East Aviation Museum, Usworth
	42204	NA F-100D Super Sabre [11-MQ]	
	63938	NA F-100F Super Sabre [11-MU]	Lashenden Air Warfare Museum, Headcorn
	125716	Douglas AD-4N Skyraider (F-AZFN) [22-DG]	Privately owned, Etampes, France
	517545	NA T-28A Fennec (N14113)	The Aircraft Restoration Company, Duxford
	517692	NA T-28A Fennec (F-AZFV)	The Old Flying Machine Company, Duxford
	18-1528	PA-18 Cub 95 (F-MBCH)	Privately owned, stored Southampton
	56-5395	Piper L-18C Super Cub (52-2436/ G-CUBJ) [CDG]	Privately owned, Oaksey Park
	MS824	Morane-Saulnier Type N <R> (G-AWBU)	Privately owned, Booker

GERMANY

Notes	Serial	Type (other identity)	Owner/operator, location
		Fieseler Fi103R-IV (BAPC91)	Lashenden Air Warfare Mus, Headcorn
	-	Focke-Achgelis Fa330A-1 (8469M)	RAF Cosford Aerospace Museum
	2	Messerschmitt Bf109G-10 (151591/D-HDME)	Privately owned, Mannheim, Germany
	3	Hispano HA1.112M1L Buchon (166238/G-BOML)	The Old Flying Machine Company, Duxford
	3	SNCAN 1101 Noralpha (G-BAYV)	Barton Aviation Heritage Society, Barton
	4	Focke Wulf Fw190 <R> (G-BSLX)	Privately owned, Carlisle
	6	Messerschmitt Bf109G-2/Trop (10639/8478M/G-USTV)	RAF/Imperial War Museum, Duxford
	7	Klemm Kl35D (G-BWRD)	Front Line Aviation Museum, Sandown
	8	Focke Wulf Fw190 <R> (G-WULF)	The Real Aeroplane Company, Breighton
	14	Fiat G46-3B (G-BBII)	Privately owned, stored Staverton
	14	Messerschmitt Bf109 <R> (BAPC 67)	Kent Battle of Britain Museum, Hawkinge
	14	Pilatus P-2 (G-BJAX)	Privately owned, stored Duxford
	102/17	Fokker Dr1 Dreidekker <R> (BAPC 88)	FAA Museum, RNAS Yeovilton
	114	SNCAN 1101 Noralpha (G-BSMD)	Privately owned, North Weald
	152/17	Fokker Dr1 Dreidekker <R> (G-ATJM)	Privately owned, North Weald
	210/16	Fokker EIII (BAPC 56)	Science Museum, South Kensington
	422/15	Fokker EIII <R> (G-AVJO)	Privately owned, Booker
	425/17	Fokker Dr1 Dreidekker <R> (BAPC 133)	Kent Battle of Britain Museum, Hawkinge
	425/17	Fokker Dr1 Dreidekker <R> (G-BWRJ)	Front Line Aviation Museum, Sandown

Serial	Type (other identity)	Owner/operator, location	Notes
450/17	Fokker Dr1 Dreidekker <R> (G-BVGZ)	Museum of Army Flying, Middle Wallop	
626/8	Fokker DVII <R> (N6268)	Blue Max Movie Aircraft Museum, Booker	
959	Mikoyan MiG-21SPS	The Old Flying Machine Company, Duxford	
1190	Messerschmitt Bf109E-3 [4]	Imperial War Museum, Duxford	
1227	Focke-Wulf Fw190A-5 (G-FOKW) [OG+HO]	Flying A Services,	
1342	Messerschmitt Bf109E-3 (G-BYDS)	Hawker Restorations Ltd, Milden	
1480	Messerschmitt Bf109 <R> (BAPC 66) [6]	Kent Battle of Britain Museum, Hawkinge	
2100	Focke-Wulf Fw189A-1 [V7+1H]	Privately owned, Sandtoft	
4101	Messerschmitt Bf109E-3 (DG200/8477M) [12]	RAF Museum, Hendon	
6357	Messerschmitt Bf109 <R> (BAPC 74) [6]	Kent Battle of Britain Museum, Hawkinge	
7198/18	LVG CVI (G-AANJ)	The Shuttleworth Collection, Old Warden	
8147	Messerschmitt Bf109F-4	Charleston Aviation Services, Colchester	
8417/18	Fokker DVII (9207M)	RAF Museum, Hendon	
10132	Messerschmitt Bf109F-4	Privately owned, Milden	
12802	Antonov An-2T (D-FOFM)	Privately owned, Lahr, Germany	
100143	Focke-Achgelis Fa330A-1	Imperial War Museum, Duxford	
100502	Focke-Achgelis Fa330A-1	The Real Aeroplane Company, Breighton	
100509	Focke-Achgelis Fa330A-1	Science Museum, stored Wroughton	
100545	Focke-Achgelis Fa330A-1	Fleet Air Arm Museum stored, Wroughton	
100549	Focke-Achgelis Fa330A-1	Lashenden Air Warfare Museum, Headcorn	
112372	Messerschmitt Me262A-2a (AM.51/VK893/8482M) [9K+XK]	RAF Cosford Aerospace Museum	
120227	Heinkel He162A-2 Salamander (VH513/8472M) [2]	RAF Museum, Hendon	
120235	Heinkel He162A-1 Salamander (AM.68)	Imperial War Museum, Lambeth	
191316	Messerschmitt Me163B Komet	Science Museum, South Kensington	
191614	Messerschmitt Me163B Komet (8481M)	RAF Cosford Aerospace Museum	
191659	Messerschmitt Me163B Komet (8480M) [15]	Royal Scottish Mus'm of Flight, E Fortune	
191660	Messerschmitt Me163B Komet (AM.214) [3]	Imperial War Museum, Duxford	
280020	Flettner Fl282/B-V20 Kolibri (frame only)	Midland Air Museum, Coventry	
360043	Junkers Ju88R-1 (PJ876/8475M) [D5+EV]	RAF Museum, Hendon	
420430	Messerschmitt Me410A-1/U2 (AM.72/8483M) [3U+CC]	RAF Cosford Aerospace Museum	
475081	Fieseler Fi156C-7 Storch (VP546/AM.101/7362M)[GM+AK]	RAF Cosford Aerospace Museum	
494083	Junkers Ju87D-3 (8474M) [RI+JK]	RAF Museum, Hendon	
584219	Focke Wulf Fw190F-8/U1 (AM.29/8470M) [38]	RAF Museum, Hendon	
701152	Heinkel He111H-23 (8471M) [NT+SL]	RAF Museum, Hendon	
730301	Messerschmitt Bf110G-4 (AM.34/8479M) [D5+RL]	RAF Museum, Hendon	
733682	Focke Wulf Fw190A-8/R7 (AM.75/9211M)	Imperial War Museum, Lambeth	
1Z-NK	Amiot AAC1/Ju52 (Port.AF 6316)	Imperial War Museum, Duxford	
2+1	Focke Wulf Fw190 <R> (G-SYFW) [7334]	Privately owned, Guernsey, CI	
6J+PR	CASA 2.111D (G-AWHB)	Privately owned, North Weald	
20+48	Mikoyan MiG-23BN [702]	DERA, Farnborough	
22+35	Lockheed F-104G Starfighter	SWWAPS, Lasham	
22+57	Lockheed F-104G Starfighter	NATO Aircraft Museum, New Waltham, Humberside	
28+02	Aero L-39ZO Albatros (G-OTAF)	The Old Flying Machine Company, Duxford	
96+21	Mil Mi-24D (406)	Imperial War Museum, Duxford	
96+26	Mil Mi-24D (429)	The Helicopter Museum, Weston-super-Mare	
97+04	Putzer Elster B (G-APVF)	Privately owned, Tadlow	
98+14	Sukhoi Su-22M-4	Privately owned, Scampton	
99+24	NA OV-10B Bronco (F-AZKM)	Privately owned, Montelimar, France	
AM+YA	Zlin Z381 Bestmann (G-AMYA)	Privately owned, Wombleton, N Yorks	
BU+CC	CASA 1.131E Jungmann (G-BUCC)	Privately owned, Goodwood	
BU+CK	CASA 1.131E Jungmann (G-BUCK)	Privately owned, White Waltham	
C850	Albatros DV <R>	Macclesfield Hist Avn Society	

Historic Aircraft

Notes	Serial	Type (other identity)	Owner/operator, location
	CC+43	Pilatus P-2 (G-CJCI)	Privately owned, Norwich
	CF+HF	Morane-Saulnier MS502 (EI-AUY)	Imperial War Museum, Duxford
	D5397/17	Albatros DVA <R> (G-BFXL)	FAA Museum, RNAS Yeovilton
	FI+S	Morane-Saulnier MS505 (G-BIRW)	Royal Scottish Mus'm of Flight, E Fortune
	FM+BB	Messerschmitt Bf109G-6 (D-FMBB)	Daimler-Benz Aerospace, Manching, Germany
	JA+120	Canadair CL-13 Sabre 4 (MM19607)	Privately owned
	LG+01	Bücker Bü133C Jungmeister (G-AYSJ)	The Fighter Collection, Duxford
	LG+03	Bücker Bü133C Jungmeister (G-AEZX)	Privately owned, Milden
	NJ+C11	Nord 1002 (G-ATBG)	Privately owned, Sutton Bridge
	S4+A07	CASA 1.131E Jungmann (G-BWHP)	Privately owned, Yarcombe
	S5+B06	CASA 1.131E Jungmann 2000 (G-BSFB)	Privately owned, Stretton
	TA+RC	Morane-Saulnier MS505 (G-BPHZ)	The Aircraft Restoration Co, Duxford
	TQ+BJ	Focke-Wulf Fw44 Stieglitz (LV-ZAU)	Privately owned, Booker

GHANA

Notes	Serial	Type (other identity)	Owner/operator, location
	G-102	SA122 Bulldog	Privately owned, Henstridge
	G-103	SA122 Bulldog (G-BWIB)	Privately owned, Henstridge
	G-105	SA122 Bulldog (G-BXGU)	Privately owned, Old Sarum
	G-107	SA122 Bulldog (G-BCUO)	Privately owned, Henstridge
	G-108	SA122 Bulldog (G-BCUP)	Privately owned, Bourne Park, Hants
	G-357	PBN 2 Islander	Privately owned, Cumbernauld

GREECE

Notes	Serial	Type (other identity)	Owner/operator, location
	51-6171	NA F-86D Sabre	North-East Aircraft Museum, Usworth
	52-6541	Republic F-84F Thunderflash [541]	North-East Aircraft Museum, Usworth

HONG KONG

Notes	Serial	Type (other identity)	Owner/operator, location
	HKG-5	SA128 Bulldog (G-BULL)	Privately owned, Slinfold

HUNGARY

Notes	Serial	Type (other identity)	Owner/operator, location
	501	Mikoyan MiG-21PF	Imperial War Museum, Duxford

INDIA

Notes	Serial	Type (other identity)	Owner/operator, location
	Q497	EE Canberra T4 (fuselage)	BAe Warton Fire Service

IRAQ

Notes	Serial	Type (other identity)	Owner/operator, location
	243	Hawker Fury FB10 (G-BTTA)	The Old Flying Machine Company, Duxford
	333	DH115 Vampire T55 <ff>	Military Aircraft Pres'n Grp, Barton

ISRAEL

Notes	Serial	Type (other identity)	Owner/operator, location
	41	NA P-51D Mustang (G-LYNE)	Privately owned, Tees-side

ITALY

Notes	Serial	Type (other identity)	Owner/operator, location
	MM5701	Fiat CR42 (BT474/8468M) [13-95]	RAF Museum, Hendon
	MM53211	Fiat G46-4 (BAPC 79) [ZI-4]	The Aircraft Restoration Co, stored Duxford
	MM53432	NA T-6D Texan [RM-11]	Privately owned, South Wales
	MM53692	CCF T-6G Texan	RAeS Medway Branch, Rochester
	MM53774	Fiat G59-4B (I-MRSV) [181]	Privately owned, Parma, Italy
	MM54099	NA T-6G Texan (G-BRBC) [RR-56]	Privately owned, Chigwell
	MM54-2372	Piper L-21B Super Cub	Privately owned, Kesgrave, Suffolk
	W7	Avia FL3 (G-AGFT)	Privately owned, Leicester

JAPAN

Notes	Serial	Type (other identity)	Owner/operator, location
	-	Yokosuka MXY 7 Ohka II (BAPC 159)	Defence School, Chattenden
	24	Kawasaki Ki100-1B (8476M/ BAPC 83)	RAF Cosford Aerospace Museum
	5439	Mitsubishi Ki46-III (8484M/ BAPC 84)	RAF Cosford Aerospace Museum
	15-1585	Yokosuka MXY 7 Ohka II (BAPC 58)	Science Museum, at FAA Museum, RNAS Yeovilton
	997	Yokosuka MXY 7 Ohka II (8485M/ BAPC 98)	Gr Manchester Mus of Science & Industry
	I-13	Yokosuka MXY 7 Ohka II (8486M/ BAPC 99)	RAF Cosford Aerospace Museum

Serial	Type (other identity)	Owner/operator, location	Notes

JORDAN

712	Hawker Hunter F58 (J-4025/ G-BWKC) [E]	RJAF Historic Flight, Bournemouth	

NETHERLANDS

204	Lockheed SP-2H Neptune [V]	RAF Cosford Aerospace Museum	
361	Hawker Fury FB10 (N36SF)	Privately owned, Kemble	
39-139	Beech YC-43 Traveler (N295BS)	Dukes of Brabant AF, Eindhoven, The Netherlands	
A-12	DH82A Tiger Moth (PH-TYG)	Privately owned, Gilze-Rijen, The Netherlands	
B-64	Noorduyn AT-16 Harvard IIB (PH-LSK)	Privately owned, Gilze-Rijen, The Netherlands	
B-71	Noorduyn AT-16 Harvard IIB (PH-MLM)	Privately owned, Gilze-Rijen, The Netherlands	
B-118	Noorduyn AT-16 Harvard IIB (PH-IIB)	Privately owned, Gilze-Rijen, The Netherlands	
E-14	Fokker S-11 Instructor (PH-AFS)	Privately owned, Lelystad, The Netherlands	
E-15	Fokker S-11 Instructor (G-BIYU)	Privately owned, White Waltham	
E-18	Fokker S-11 Instructor (PH-HTC)	Dukes of Brabant AF, Eindhoven, The Netherlands	
E-20	Fokker S-11 Instructor (PH-GRB)	Privately owned, Gilze-Rijen, The Netherlands	
E-27	Fokker S-11 Instructor (PH-HOL)	Privately owned, Lelystad, The Netherlands	
E-31	Fokker S-11 Instructor (G-BEPV)	Privately owned, Elstree	
E-32	Fokker S-11 Instructor (PH-HOI)	Privately owned, Gilze-Rijen, The Netherlands	
E-36	Fokker S-11 Instructor (PH-ACG)	Privately owned, Lelystad, The Netherlands	
E-39	Fokker S-11 Instructor (PH-HOG)	Privately owned, Lelystad, The Netherlands	
G-29	Beech D18S (N5369X)	Dutch Dakota Assn, Schiphol, The Netherlands	
N-202	Hawker Hunter F6 [10] <ff>	Privately owned, Eaglescott	
N-250	Hawker Hunter F6 (G-9-185) <ff>	Imperial War Museum, Duxford	
N-268	Hawker Hunter FGA78 (Qatar QA-10)	Yorkshire Air Museum, Elvington	
N-315	Hawker Hunter T7	Jet Avn Preservation Grp, Long Marston	
R-109	Piper L-21B Super Cub (54-2337/ PH-GAZ)	Privately owned, Gilze-Rijen, The Netherlands	
R-122	Piper L-21B Super Cub (54-2412/ PH-PPW)	Privately owned, Gilze-Rijen, The Netherlands	
R-151	Piper L-21B Super Cub (54-2441/ G-BIYR)	Privately owned, Dunkeswell	
R-163	Piper L-21B Super Cub (54-2453/ G-BIRH)	Privately owned, Lee-on-Solent	
R-167	Piper L-21B Super Cub (54-2457/ G-LION)	Privately owned, Turweston, Bucks	
R-177	Piper L-21B Super Cub (54-2467/ PH-KNR)	Privately owned, Gilze-Rijen, The Netherlands	
R-181	Piper L-21B Super Cub (54-2471/ PH-GAU)	Privately owned, Gilze-Rijen, The Netherlands	
R-345	Piper J-3C Cub (PH-UCS)	Privately owned, The Netherlands	
S-9	DHC2 L-20A Beaver (G-BUVF)	Privately owned, Lelystad, The Netherlands	
Y-74	Consolidated PBY-5A Catalina (PH-PBY/C-FHHR)	Cat Air, Lelystad, The Netherlands	

NEW ZEALAND

NZ3902	WS Wasp HAS1 (G-BYCX)	Privately owned, Thruxton	
NZ3909	WS Wasp HAS1	Kennet Aviation, Cranfield	
NZ5648	Goodyear FG-1D Corsair (NX55JP/G-BXUL) [648]	The Old Flying Machine Company, Duxford	
NZ6361	BAC Strikemaster 87 (OJ5/G-BXFP)	McCarthy Aviation, North Weald	

NORTH KOREA

1211	WSK Lim-5 (MiG-17F) (G-BWUF)	The Old Flying Machine Company, Duxford	

NORWAY

423/427	Gloster Gladiator I (L8032/ G-AMRK/*N2308*)	The Shuttleworth Collection, Old Warden	

Historic Aircraft

Notes	Serial	Type (other identity)	Owner/operator, location
	28693	DH100 Vampire FB6 (J-1184/ SE-DXY) [9-G]	Scandinavian Historic Flight, Oslo, Norway
	34668	Hawker Hunter F58 (J-4089/ SE-DXA) [9-G]	Scandinavian Historic Flight, Oslo, Norway
	56321	SAAB S91B Safir (G-BKPY) [U-AB]	Newark Air Museum, Winthorpe

POLAND

	05	WSK SM-2 (Mi-2) (1005)	The Helicopter Museum, Weston-super-Mare
	07	WSK SM-1 (Mi-1) (2007)	The Helicopter Museum, Weston-super-Mare
	309	WSK SBLim-2A (MiG-15UTI) <ff>	Royal Scottish Museum of Flight, E Fortune
	1018	WSK-PZL Mielec TS-11 Iskra (1H-1018)	British Aviation Heritage, Bruntingthorpe
	1120	WSK Lim-2 (MiG-15bis)	RAF Museum, Hendon
	1211	WSK Lim-5 (MiG-17) (G-BWUF)	The Old Flying Machine Company, Duxford
	1408	WSK-PZL Mielec TS-11 Iskra (3H-1408)	The Old Flying Machine Company, Duxford
	09008	WSK SBLim-2A (MiG-15UTI)	Privately owned, Sproughton

PORTUGAL

	1360	OGMA/DHC1 Chipmunk T20 (CS-DAP)	Privately owned, stored Beds
	1366	OGMA/DHC1 Chipmunk T20 (CS-DAO)	Privately owned, stored Beds
	1367	OGMA/DHC1 Chipmunk T20	Privately owned, stored Beds
	1377	DHC1 Chipmunk 22 (G-BARS)	Privately owned, Rugby
	1741	CCF Harvard IV (G-HRVD)	Air Atlantique Historic Flight, Coventry
	1747	CCF T-6J Harvard IV (20385/G-BGPB)	The Aircraft Restoration Co, Duxford

QATAR

	QA12	Hawker Hunter FGA78 <ff>	The Planets Leisure Centre, Woking
	QP30	WS Lynx Mk 28 (G-BFDV/TD 013)	Army SEAE, Arborfield
	QP31	WS Lynx Mk 28	NARO Fleetlands Apprentice School
	QP32	WS Lynx Mk 28 (TAD 016)	AAC Stockwell Hall, Middle Wallop

RUSSIA (& FORMER SOVIET UNION)

	2	Yakovlev Yak-52 (9311708/ G-YAKS)	Privately owned, North Weald
	03	Mil Mi-24D (3532461715415)	Privately owned, Hawarden
	04	Mikoyan MiG-23ML (024003607)	Privately owned, Hawarden
	04	Yakovlev Yak-52 (9211612/ RA-22521)	Privately owned, Wellesbourne Mountford
	05	Yakovlev Yak-50 (832507/YL-CBH)	Privately owned, Strathallan
	06	Mil Mi-24D (3532464505029)	Privately owned, Hawarden
	07	Yakovlev Yak-18M (G-BMJY)	Privately owned, North Weald
	09	Yakovlev Yak-52 (9411809/ G-BVMU)	Privately owned, Sandy, Beds
	12	Let L-29 Delfin (194555/ES-YLM/ G-DELF)	Privately owned, Manston
	15	Yakovlev Yak-52 (844605/ G-BVVW)	Privately owned, Sudbury, Suffolk
	15	Yakovlev Yak-52 (LY-ABQ/866915)	Privately owned, Leicester
	18	Let L-29S Delfin (591771/YL-PAF)	Privately owned, Hawarden
	19	Yakovlev Yak-52 (811202/YL-CBI)	Privately owned, Cumbernauld
	20	Lavochkin La-11	The Fighter Collection, Duxford
	20	Yakovlev Yak-52 (790404/YL-CBJ)	Privately owned, Strathallan
	23	Mikoyan MiG-27D (83712515040)	Privately owned, Hawarden
	26	Yakovlev Yak-52 (9111306/ G-BVXK)	Privately owned, White Waltham
	27	SPP Yak C-11 (G-OYAK)	Privately owned, North Weald
	27	Yakovlev Yak-52 (9111307/ G-YAKX)	Privately owned, Old Sarum
	31	Yakovlev Yak-52 (9111311/ RA-2209)	Privately owned, Rendcomb
	35	Sukhoi Su-17M-3 (25102)	Privately owned, Hawarden
	36	SPP Yak C-11 (G-IYAK)	Privately owned, Earls Colne
	40	Yakovlev Yak-55M (920506/ RA-01333/G-YAKM)	Privately owned,
	42	Yakovlev Yak-52 (833901/LY-AMU)	Privately owned, North Weald
	46	Yakovlev Yak-52 (9111413/ RA-44413)	Privately owned, White Waltham

Serial	Type (other identity)	Owner/operator, location	Notes
49	Yakovlev Yak-55M (880606/RA-44526)	Privately owned, White Waltham	
50	Mikoyan MiG-23MF (023003508)	Privately owned, Hawarden	
50	Yakovlev Yak-50 (812003/G-BWJT)	Privately owned, Breighton	
51	Curtiss P-40E Kittyhawk (41-13570)	Front Line Aviation Museum, Sandown	
51	Let L-29S Delfin (491273/YL-PAG)	Privately owned, Hawarden	
51	Yakovlev Yak-50 (812004/G-BWYK)	Privately owned, Little Gransden	
52	Yakovlev Yak-52 (877610/G-BVVA)	Privately owned, Redhill	
52	Yakovlev Yak-52 (878202/G-BWVR)	Privately owned, Sowerby Bridge, W Yorks	
52	Yakovlev Yak-52 (888802/G-BXID)	Privately owned, Wellesbourne Mountford	
52	Yakovlev Yak-50 (800708/LY-AMP)	Privately owned, Breighton	
53	Curtiss P-40C Warhawk (41-13390/G-TOMA)	The Fighter Collection, Duxford	
54	Sukhoi Su-17M (69004)	Privately owned, Hawarden	
55	Yakovlev Yak-52 (9111505/G-BVOK)	Intrepid Aviation, North Weald	
56	Yakovlev Yak-52 (811504/LY-AKW)	Privately owned, Swanton Morley	
56	Yakovlev Yak-52 (9111506/RA-44516)	Privately owned, White Waltham	
64	Let L-29 Delfin (394912/ES-YLO/G-MAYA)	Privately owned, Lydd	
69	Hawker Hunter FGA9 (8839M/XG194)	RAF North Luffenham Training Area	
69	Yakovlev Yak-50 (G-BTZB)	Privately owned, Audley End	
69	Yakovlev Yak-52 (855509/LY-ALS)	Privately owned, North Weald	
71	Mikoyan MiG-27K (61912507006)	Privately owned, Hawarden	
72	Yakovlev Yak-52 (9111608/G-BXAV)	Privately owned, North Weald	
74	Yakovlev Yak-52 (877404/LY-AOK)	Privately owned, Tollerton	
96	Yakovlev Yak-55 (901103/RA-44525)	Privately owned, White Waltham	
100	Yakovlev Yak-52 (866904/G-YAKI)	Privately owned, Popham	
112	Yakovlev Yak-52 (822610/LY-AFB)	Privately owned, Little Gransden	
503	Mikoyan MiG-21SMT (G-BRAM)	Jet Heritage Museum, Bournemouth	
1342	Yakovlev Yak-1 (G-BTZD)	Privately owned, Milden	
6247	WSK SBLim-2A (MiG-15UTI) (622047/G-OMIG)	The Old Flying Machine Company, Duxford	
866807	Yakovlev Yak-52 (G-BWSW)	Privately owned, Newton, Suffolk	
899404	Yakovlev Yak-52 (G-CCCP)	Privately owned, Little Gransden	
1-12	Yakovlev Yak-52 (9011013/RA-02293)	Privately owned, Halfpenny Green	
BH328	Hawker Hurricane IIB	Privately owned, Isle of Wight	
PT879	VS361 Spitfire LF IX (G-BYDE)	Privately owned, Isle of Wight	
(RK858)	VS361 Spitfire LF IX	The Fighter Collection, Duxford	
(SM639)	VS361 Spitfire LF IX	Privately owned, Catfield	

SAUDI ARABIA

405	Agusta-Bell AB.212	Privately owned, Margate	
420	Agusta-Bell AB.212	Privately owned, Margate	

SINGAPORE

311	BAC Strikemaster 84 (N2146S/G-SARK)	Classic Jets Flying Museum, Biggin Hill	

SLOVAKIA

7708	Mikoyan MiG-21MF	RAF Benevolent Fund, DERA Boscombe Down	

SOUTH AFRICA

6130	Lockheed Ventura II (AJ469)	RAF Cosford Aerospace Museum, stored	

SPAIN

B.2I-27	CASA 2.111B (He111H-16) (B.2I-103)	The Old Flying Machine Company, Duxford	
C.4E-88	Messerschmitt Bf109E	Privately owned, Hungerford	
C.4K-102	Hispano HA 1.112M1L Buchon (G-BWUE)	The Real Aeroplane Company, Breighton	
E.1-9	CASA 1.133L Jungmeister (G-BVXJ)	The Real Aeroplane Company, Breighton	
E.3B-150	CASA 1.131E Jungmann (G-BHPL)	Privately owned, North Weald	
E.3B-153	CASA 1.131E Jungmann (G-BPTS) [781-75]	The Old Flying Machine Company, Duxford	
(E.3B-369)	CASA 1.131E Jungmann (G-BPDM) [781-32]	Privately owned, Chilbolton	

Historic Aircraft

Notes	Serial	Type (other identity)	Owner/operator, location
	E.3B-521	CASA 1.131E Jungmann [781-3]	RAF Museum, Hendon
	E.3B-530	CASA 1.131E Jungmann [05-97]	Privately owned, Kemble
	(E.3B-540)	CASA 1.131E Jungmann (G-BRSH) [781-25]	The Real Aeroplane Company, Breighton
	ES.1-16	CASA 1.133L Jungmeister	Privately owned, Stretton, Cheshire

SWEDEN

Notes	Serial	Type (other identity)	Owner/operator, location
	081	CFM 01 Tummelisa <R> (SE-XIL)	Privately owned, Karlstad, Sweden
	05108	DH60 Moth	Privately owned, Langham
	17239	SAAB B-17A (SE-BYH) [7-J]	Flygvapenmuseum, Linköping, Sweden
	29640	SAAB J-29F [20-08]	Midland Air Museum, Coventry
	29670	SAAB J-29F (SE-DXB) [10-R]	Flygvapenmuseum/F10 Wing, Angelholm, Sweden
	32028	SAAB 32A Lansen (G-BMSG)	Privately owned, Cranfield
	35075	SAAB J-35J Draken [40]	Imperial War Museum, Duxford
	A14	Thulin A/Bleriot XI (SE-XMC)	Privately owned, Karlstad, Sweden
	N3-615	NA P-51D Mustang (26158/SE-BKG)	Privately owned, Hässlo, Sweden

SWITZERLAND

Notes	Serial	Type (other identity)	Owner/operator, location
	A-10	CASA 1.131E Jungmann (G-BECW)	Privately owned, Headcorn
	A-57	CASA 1.131E Jungmann (G-BECT)	Privately owned, Shoreham
	A-701	Junkers Ju52/3m (HB-HOS)	Ju-Air, Dubendorf, Switzerland
	A-702	Junkers Ju52/3m (HB-HOT)	Ju-Air, Dubendorf, Switzerland
	A-703	Junkers Ju52/3m (HB-HOP)	Ju-Air, Dubendorf, Switzerland
	A-806	Pilatus P3-03 (G-BTLL)	Privately owned, stored Headcorn
	C-552	EKW C-3605 (HB-RBJ/G-DORN)	Privately owned, North Weald
	C-558	EKW C-3605	Aerobuild Ltd, stored Gransden
	J-1008	DH100 Vampire FB6	Mosquito Aircraft Museum, London Colney
	J-1149	DH100 Vampire FB6 (G-SWIS)	Jet Heritage, Bournemouth
	J-1172	DH100 Vampire FB6 (8487M)	RAF Museum Restoration Centre, Cardington
	J-1573	DH112 Venom FB50 (G-VICI)	Source Classic Jet Flight, Bournemouth
	J-1605	DH112 Venom FB50 (G-BLID)	Vallance By-Ways, Charlwood, Surrey
	J-1614	DH112 Venom FB50 (G-BLIE)	Privately owned, E Dereham, Norfolk
	J-1626	DH112 Venom FB50	Source Classic Jet Flight, Bournemouth
	J-1632	DH112 Venom FB50 (G-VNOM)	De Havilland Aviation, Swansea
	J-1704	DH112 Venom FB54	RAF Cosford Aerospace Museum
	J-1712	DH112 Venom FB54	Botany Bay Village, Chorley, Lancs)
	J-1758	DH112 Venom FB54 (N203DM)	Privately owned, North Weald
	J-4021	Hawker Hunter F58 (G-BWIU)	Historic Flying Ltd/OFMC, Scampton
	J-4031	Hawker Hunter F58 (G-BWFR)	The Old Flying Machine Company, Scampton
	J-4058	Hawker Hunter F58 (G-BWFS)	The Old Flying Machine Company, Scampton
	J-4066	Hawker Hunter F58 (G-BXNZ)	The Old Flying Machine Company, Kemble
	J-4072	Hawker Hunter F58	Privately owned, Scampton
	J-4081	Hawker Hunter F58 (G-BWKB)	The Old Flying Machine Company, Duxford
	J-4083	Hawker Hunter F58 (G-EGHH)	Jet Heritage, Bournemouth
	J-4090	Hawker Hunter F58 (G-SIAL)	The Old Flying Machine Company, stored Scampton
	J-4091	Hawker Hunter F58	British Aviation Heritage, Bruntingthorpe
	U-80	Bücker Bü133D Jungmeister (G-BUKK)	Privately owned, White Waltham
	U-95	Bücker Bü133C Jungmeister (G-BVGP)	Privately owned, Rednal, Shropshire
	U-110	Pilatus P-2 (G-PTWO)	Privately owned, Earls Colne
	U-142	Pilatus P-2 (G-BONE)	Privately owned, Cheltenhamt
	U-1234	DH115 Vampire T55 (G-DHAV)	De Havilland Aviation, Swansea
	V-54	SE3130 Alouette II (G-BVSD)	Privately owned, Staverton

USA

Notes	Serial	Type (other identity)	Owner/operator, location
	-	Bell UH-1H Iroquois (Arg. AE-406)	Privately owned, Greenford, W London
	-	Noorduyn AT-16 Harvard IIB (KLu B-168)	American Air Museum, Duxford
	1	Spad XIII <R> (G-BFYO/*S3398*)	American Air Museum, Duxford
	2	Boeing-Stearman N2S-5 Kaydet (G-AZLE)	Privately owned, Denham
	5	Boeing P-26A Peashooter <R> (G-BEEW)	Privately owned, Barton
	23	Fairchild PT-23 (N49272)	Privately owned, Halfpenny Green
	26	Boeing-Stearman A75N-1 Kaydet (G-BAVO)	Privately owned, Swanton Morley
	27	NA SNJ-7 Texan (90678/G-BRVG)	Intrepid Aviation Co, North Weald

Serial	Type (other identity)	Owner/operator, location	Notes
43	Noorduyn AT-16 Harvard IIB (43-13064/G-AZSC) [SC]	Privately owned, Duxford	
44	PA-18 Super Cub 95 (51-15541/G-BJLH) [33-K]	Privately owned, Felthorpe	
44	Piper L-21B Super Cub (54-2405/G-BWHH)	Privately owned, Popham	
49	Curtiss P-40M Kittyhawk (43-5802/G-KITT/P8196)	The Fighter Collection, Duxford	
57	WS55 Whirlwind HAS7 (XG592)	Task Force Adventure Park, Cowbridge, S Glam	
85	WAR P-47 Thunderbolt <R> (G-BTBI)	Privately owned, Carlisle	
112	Boeing-Stearman PT-13D Kaydet (42-17397/G-BSWC)	Privately owned, Old Sarum	
118	Boeing-Stearman PT-13A Kaydet (38-470/G-BSDS)	Privately owned, Swanton Morley	
208	Boeing-Stearman N2S-5 Kaydet (42-17223/N75664)	Privately owned, Spanhoe Lodge, Northants	
243	Boeing-Stearman A75N-1 Kaydet (41-25243/G-BUKE)	Privately owned, Goodwood	
295	Ryan PT-22 Recruit (41-20806/N56028)	Privately owned, Oaksey Park, Wilts	
379	Boeing-Stearman PT-13D Kaydet (42-14865/G-ILLE)	Privately owned, Compton Abbas	
441	Boeing-Stearman N2S-4 Kaydet (30010/G-BTFG)	Privately owned, Bryngwyn Bach, Clwyd	
540	Piper L-4H Grasshopper (43-29877/G-BCNX)	Privately owned, Monewden	
628	Beech D17S (44-67761/N18V)	Privately owned, stored North Weald	
796	Boeing-Stearman PT-13D Kaydet (N43SV)	Privately owned, Rendcomb	
854	Ryan PT-22 Recruit (42-17378/G-BTBH)	Privately owned, Wellesbourne Mountford	
855	Ryan PT-22 Recruit (41-15510/N56421)	Privately owned, Halfpenny Green	
897	Aeronca 11AC Chief (G-BJEV) [E]	Privately owned, English Bicknor, Glos	
1164	Beech D18S (G-BKGL)	The Aircraft Restoration Co, Duxford	
1180	Boeing-Stearman N2S-3 Kaydet (3403/G-BRSK)	Privately owned, Tibenham	
2525	Curtiss JN-4D Jenny (N2525)	Aerosuperbatics, Rendcomb	
2807	NA T-6G Texan (49-3072/G-BHTH) [V-103]	Northbrook College, Shoreham	
5547	Lockheed T-33A (51-9036)	Newark Air Museum, Winthorpe	
6771	Republic F-84F Thunderstreak (BAF FU-6)	RAF Cosford Aerospace Museum, stored	
7797	Aeronca L-16A (47-0797/G-BFAF)	Privately owned, Finmere	
8178	NA F-86A Sabre (48-0178/G-SABR) [FU-178]	Golden Apple Operations/OFMC, Duxford	
8242	NA F-86A Sabre (48-0242) [FU-242]	American Air Museum, Duxford	
01532	Northrop F-5E Tiger II <R>	RAF Alconbury on display	
14286	Lockheed T-33A (51-4286)	American Air Museum, Duxford	
O-14419	Lockheed T-33A (51-4419)	Midland Air Museum, Coventry	
14863	NA AT-6D Harvard III (41-33908/G-BGOR)	Privately owned, Goudhurst, Kent	
15154	Bell OH-58A Kiowa (70-15154)	R. Military College of Science, Shrivenham	
16136	Boeing-Stearman A75N-1 Kaydet (42-16136/G-BRUJ) [205]	Privately owned, Liverpool	
16445	Bell AH-1F Hueycobra (69-16445)	R. Military College of Science, Shrivenham	
16579	Bell UH-1H Iroquois (66-16579)	The Helicopter Museum, Weston-super-Mare	
16718	Lockheed T-33A (51-6718)	City of Norwich Aviation Museum	
17473	Lockheed T-33A (51-17473)	Midland Air Museum, Coventry	
18263	Boeing-Stearman PT-17 Kaydet (41-8263/N38940) [822]	Privately owned, Tibenham	
19252	Lockheed T-33A (51-9252)	Tangmere Military Aviation Museum	
20249	Noorduyn AT-16 Harvard IIB (PH-KLU) [XS-249]	Privately owned, Lelystad, The Netherlands	
21605	Bell UH-1H Iroquois (72-21605)	American Air Museum, Duxford	
21714	Grumman F8F-2P Bearcat (121714/G-RUMM) [201-B]	The Fighter Collection, Duxford	
24518	Kaman HH-43F Huskie (62-4535)	Midland Air Museum, Coventry	
28521	CCF Harvard IV (G-TVIJ) [TA-521]	Privately owned, Shoreham	
30861	NA TB-25J Mitchell (44-30861/N9089Z)	Privately owned, North Weald	

Historic Aircraft

Notes	Serial	Type (other identity)	Owner/operator, location
	31145	Piper L-4B Grasshopper (43-1145/ G-BBLH) [26-G]	Privately owned, Biggin Hill
	31171	NA B-25J Mitchell (44-31171/ N7614C)	American Air Museum, Duxford
	31952	Aeronca O-58B Defender (G-BRPR)	Privately owned, Earls Colne
	34037	NA TB-25N Mitchell (44-29366/ N9115Z/8838M)	RAF Museum, Hendon
	37414	McD F-4C Phantom (63-7414)	Midland Air Museum, Coventry
	37699	McD F-4C Phantom (63-7699)	Midland Air Museum, Coventry
	38674	Thomas-Morse S4 Scout <R> (G-MTKM)	Privately owned, Rugby
	39624	Wag Aero Sport Trainer (G-BVMH) [39-D]	Privately owned, Lincoln
	40467	Grumman F6F-5K Hellcat (80141/ G-BTCC) [19]	The Fighter Collection, Duxford
	41386	Thomas-Morse S4 Scout <R> (G-MJTD)	Privately owned, Hitchin
	42163	NA F-100D Super Sabre (54-2163) [HE]	Dumfries & Galloway Avn Mus, Dumfries
	42165	NA F-100D Super Sabre (54-2165) [VM]	American Air Museum, Duxford
	42174	NA F-100D Super Sabre (54-2174) [UH]	Midland Air Museum, Coventry
	42196	NA F-100D Super Sabre (54-2196) [LT]	Norfolk & Suffolk Avn Museum, Flixton
	44846	Boeing B-17E Fortress (44-8846/F-AZDX) [DS-M]	Assoc Fortresse Toujours Volant, Orly, France
	46214	Grumman TBM-3E Avenger (69327/CF-KCG) [X-3]	American Air Museum, Duxford
	46867	Grumman FM-2 Wildcat (N909WJ)	Flying A Services, North Weald
	53319	Grumman TBM-3R Avenger (G-BTDP) [319-RB]	Privately owned, North Weald
	54137	CCF Harvard IV (MM54137/ G-CTKL) [69]	Privately owned, North Weald
	54433	Lockheed T-33A (55-4433)	Norfolk & Suffolk Avn Museum, Flixton
	54439	Lockheed T-33A (55-4439)	North-East Aircraft Museum, Usworth
	58811	NA B-25J Mitchell (45-8811/ F-AZID) [HD]	Privately owned, Athens, Greece
	60312	McD F-101F Voodoo (56-0312) [AR]	Midland Air Museum, Coventry
	60689	Boeing B-52D Stratofortress (56-0689)	American Air Museum, Duxford
	63000	NA F-100D Super Sabre (54-2212) [FW-000]	USAF Croughton, Oxon, at gate
	63319	NA F-100D Super Sabre (54-2269) [FW-319]	RAF Lakenheath, on display
	63428	Republic F-105G Thunderchief (62-4428)	USAF Croughton, Oxon, at gate
	66692	Lockheed U-2CT (56-6692)	American Air Museum, Duxford
	70270	McD F-101B Voodoo (57-270) (fuselage)	Midland Air Museum, Coventry
	79863	Grumman F6F-5K Hellcat (N79863)	Flying A Services, North Weald
	80425	Grumman F7F-3P Tigercat (N7235C/G-RUMT) [WT-14]	The Fighter Collection, Duxford
	82062	DHC U-6A Beaver (58-2062)	Midland Air Museum, Coventry
	85869	Grumman TBM-3E Avenger (F-AZJA) [401-AK]	Privately owned, Etampes, France
	91007	Lockheed T-33A (51-8566/ G-NASA) [TR-007]	De Havilland Aviation, Swansea
	93542	CCF Harvard IV (G-BRLV) [LTA-542]	Privately owned, North Weald
	96995	CV F4U-4 Corsair (OE-EAS) [BR-37]	Tyrolean Jet Services, Innsbruck, Austria
	97264	CV F4U-4 Corsair (F-AZVJ) [403]	Flying Legend, Dijon, France
	111836	NA AT-6C Harvard IIA (41-33262/ G-TSIX) [JZ-6]	The Real Aeroplane Company, Breighton
	111989	Cessna L-19A Bird Dog (51-11989/ N33600)	Museum of Army Flying, Middle Wallop
	115042	NA T-6G Texan (51-15042/ G-BGHU) [TA-042]	Privately owned, Headcorn
	115302	Piper L-18C Super Cub (51-15302/ G-BJTP) [TP]	Privately owned, Bidford
	115684	Piper L-21A Super Cub (51-15684/ G-BKVM) [DC]	Privately owned, Woodhall Spa

Serial	Type (other identity)	Owner/operator, location	Notes
122179	CV F4U-5NL Corsair (N179PT) [NP-9]	Flying A Services, North Weald	
122351	Beech C-45G (51-11665/G-BKRG)	Privately owned, Bruntingthorpe	
124143	Douglas AD-4NA Skyraider (F-AZDP) [205-RM]	Amicale J-B Salis, la Ferté-Alais, France	
124485	Boeing B-17G Fortress (44-85784/ G-BEDF) [DF-A]	B-17 Preservation Ltd, Duxford	
126922	Douglas AD-4NA Skyraider (G-RAID) [402-AK]	The Fighter Collection, Duxford	
126956	Douglas AD-4NA Skyraider (F-AZDQ) [3-RM]	Aéro Retro, St Rambert d'Albon, France	
127002	Douglas AD-4NA Skyraider (F-AZHK) [618-G]	Amicale J-B Salis, la Ferté-Alais, France	
138179	NA T-28A Trojan (OE-ESA) [BA]	Tyrolean Jet Services, Innsbruck, Austria	
140547	NA T-28C Trojan (N2800Q)	Privately owned	
146289	NA T-28C Trojan (N99153) [2W]	Norfolk & Suffolk Aviation Museum, Flixton	
150225	WS58 Wessex 60 (G-AWOX) [123]	The Helicopter Museum, Lu;lsgate	
151632	NA TB-25N Mitchell (44-30925/ G-BWGR)	Privately owned, North Coates	
153008	McD F-4N Phantom	RAF Alconbury, BDRT	
155529	McD F-4S Phantom (ZE359) [AJ-114]	American Air Museum, Duxford	
155848	McD F-4S Phantom [WT-11]	FAA Museum stored, RNAS Yeovilton	
159233	HS AV-8A Harrier [CG-33]	FAA Museum, RNAS Yeovilton	
160810	Bell AH-1T Sea Cobra <ff>	GEC, Rochester	
162068	McD AV-8B Harrier II (9250M) (fuselage)	RAF Wittering, BDRT	
162071	McD AV-8B Harrier II (fuselage)	Rolls-Royce, Filton	
211072	Boeing-Stearman PT-17 Kaydet (N50755)	Privately owned, Swanton Morley	
217786	Boeing-Stearman PT-17 Kaydet (41-8169/CF-EQS) [25]	American Air Museum, Duxford	
219993	Bell P-39Q Airacobra (42-19993/ N319DP)	The Fighter Collection	
226473	Republic P-47D Thunderbolt (45-49192/N47DD) [ZU-N]	American Air Museum, Duxford	
226671	Republic P-47M Thunderbolt (NX47DD/G-THUN)[MX-X]	The Fighter Collection, Duxford	
231983	Boeing B-17G Fortress (44-83735/F-BDRS) [IY-G]	American Air Museum, Duxford	
234539	Fairchild PT-19B Cornell (42-34539/N50429) [63]	Privately owned, Dunkeswell	
236800	Piper L-4A Grasshopper (42-38410/G-BHPK) [44-A]	Privately owned, Tibenham	
237123	Waco CG-4A Hadrian (BAPC 157) (fuselage)	Yorkshire Air Museum, Elvington	
243809	Waco CG-4A Hadrian (BAPC 185)	Museum of Army Flying, Middle Wallop	
252983	Schweizer TG-3A (42-52983/ N66630)	American Air Museum, Duxford	
269097	Bell P-63A Kingcobra (42-69097/ G-BTWR)	The Fighter Collection, Duxford	
290321	Douglas C-53C Skytrooper (43-2022/N32MS)	Bevrijdende Vleugels, Eindhoven, The Netherlands	
314887	Fairchild Argus III (43-14887/ G-AJPI)	Privately owned, Swanton Morley	
315509	Douglas C-47A (43-15509/ G-BHUB) [W7-S]	American Air Museum, Duxford	
329405	Piper L-4H Grasshopper (43-29405/G-BCOB) [23-A]	Privately owned, South Walsham	
329417	Piper L-4A Grasshopper (42-38400/G-BDHK)	Privately owned, Coleford	
329471	Piper L-4H Grasshopper (43-29471/G-BGXA) [44-F]	Privately owned, Martley, Worcs	
329601	Piper L-4H Grasshopper (43-29601/G-AXHR) [44-D]	Privately owned, Nayland	
329854	Piper L-4H Grasshopper (43-29854/G-BMKC) [44-R]	Privately owned, St Just	
329934	Piper L-4H Grasshopper (43-29934/G-BCPH) [72-B]	Privately owned, White Waltham	
330238	Piper L-4H Grasshopper (43-30238/G-LIVH) [24-A]	Privately owned, Barton	
330485	Piper L-4H Grasshopper (43-30485/G-AJES) [44-C]	Privately owned, Saltash	
343251	Boeing-Stearman N2S-5 Kaydet (43517/G-NZSS) [27]	Privately owned, Swanton Morley	

Historic Aircraft

Notes	Serial	Type (other identity)	Owner/operator, location
	413573	NA P-51D Mustang (44-73415/ 9133M/N6526D) [B6-V]	RAF Museum, Hendon
	414151	NA P-51D Mustang (44-73140/ NL314BG) [HO-M]	Flying A Services, North Weald
	434602	Douglas A-26B Invader (44-34602/N167B) [S]	Scandinavian Historic Flight, Oslo, Norway
	435710	Douglas A-26C Invader (44-35710/N7705C)	Historic Invader Avn, Schiphol, The Netherlands
	436021	Piper J-3C Cub 65 (G-BWEZ)	Privately owned, Cumbernauld
	442268	Noorduyn AT-16 Harvard IIB (KF568/LN-TEX) [TA-268]	Scandinavian Historic Flight, Oslo, Norway
	454467	Piper L-4J Grasshopper (45-4467/G-BILI) [44-J]	Privately owned, White Waltham
	454537	Piper L-4J Grasshopper (45-4537/G-BFDL) [04-J]	Privately owned, Pontefract
	461748	Boeing B-29A Superfortress (44-61748/G-BHDK) [Y]	American Air Museum, Duxford
	463209	NA P-51D Mustang <R> (BAPC 255) [WZ-S]	American Air Museum, Duxford
	463221	NA P-51D Mustang (44-73149/ G-BTCD) [G4-S]	The Fighter Collection, Duxford
	463684	NA P-51D Mustang (NL51EA) [SX-B]	Privately owned, Altenrhein, Switzerland
	472035	NA P-51D Mustang (44-72035/ F-AZMU)	Aéro Retro, St Rambert d'Albon, France
	472216	NA P-51D Mustang (44-72216/ G-BIXL) [AJ-L]	Privately owned, North Weald
	472218	CAC-18 Mustang 22 (A68-192/ G-HAEC) [WZ-I]	Privately owned/OFMC, Duxford
	472258	NA P-51D Mustang (44-73979) [WZ-I]	Imperial War Museum, Lambeth
	472773	NA P-51D Mustang (44-72773/ G-SUSY) [AJ-C]	Privately owned, Sywell
	473877	NA P-51D Mustang (44-73877/ N167F) [B6-S]	Scandinavian Historic Flight, Oslo, Norway
	474008	NA P-51D Mustang (44-73339/ G-SIRR) [VF-R]	Intrepid Aviation Co, North Weald
	474832	NA P-51D Mustang (44-74506/ F-AZJJ) [GA-N]	Air B Aviation, Marmaz, France
	474923	NA P-51D Mustang (44-74923/ N6395)	Privately owned, Lelystad, The Netherlands
	479744	Piper L-4H Grasshopper (44-79744/G-BGPD) [49-M]	Privately owned, Marsh, Bucks
	479766	Piper L-4H Grasshopper (44-79766/G-BKHG) [63-D]	Privately owned, Goldcliff, Gwent
	480015	Piper L-4H Grasshopper (44-80015/G-AKIB)	Privately owned, Bodmin
	480133	Piper L-4J Grasshopper (44-80133/G-BDCD) [44-B]	Privately owned, Slinfold
	480321	Piper L-4J Grasshopper (44-80321/G-FRAN) [44-H]	Privately owned, Rayne, Essex
	480480	Piper L-4J Grasshopper (44-80480/G-BECN) [44-E]	Privately owned, Kersey, Suffolk
	480551	Piper L-4J Grasshopper (44-80551/LN-KLT) [43-S]	Scandinavian Historic Flight, Oslo, Norway
	480636	Piper L-4J Grasshopper (44-80636/G-AXHP) [58-A]	Privately owned, Southend
	480752	Piper L-4J Grasshopper (44-80752/G-BCXJ) [39-E]	Privately owned, Old Sarum
	483868	Boeing B-17G Fortress (44-83868/N5237V) [A-N]	RAF Museum, Hendon
	486893	NA B-25J Mitchell (N6123C)	Tyrolean Jet Services, Innsbruck, Austria
	493209	NA T-6G Texan (49-3209/ G-DDMV/41)	Privately owned, Sywell
	511701A	Beech C-45H (51-11701/G-BSZC) [AF258]	Privately owned, Bryngwyn Bach
	607327	PA-18 Super Cub 95 (G-ARAO) [09-L]	Privately owned, Lambley
	2106449	NA P-51C Mustang (43-25147/ N51PR/G-PSIC) [HO-W]	The Fighter Collection, Duxford
	2-134	NA T-6G Texan (114700)	Privately owned, North Weald
	3-1923	Aeronca O-58B Defender (43-1923/G-BRHP)	Privately owned, Chiseldon
	18-2001	Piper L-18C Super Cub (52-2401/ G-BIZV)	Privately owned, Oxenhope

Serial	Type (other identity)	Owner/operator, location	Notes
40-1766	Boeing-Stearman PT-17 Kaydet	Privately owned, Swanton Morley	
41-33275	NA AT-6C Texan (G-BICE) [CE]	Privately owned, Ipswich	
42-12417	NA AT-16 Harvard IIB	Thameside Aviation Museum, East Tilbury	
42-40557	Consolidated B-24D Liberator <ff>	American Air Museum, Duxford	
42-58678	Taylorcraft DF-65 (G-BRIY) [IY]	Privately owned, North Weald	
42-78044	Aeronca 11AC Chief (G-BRXL)	Privately owned, High Cross, Herts	
42-84555	NA AT-6D Harvard III (FAP.1662/ G-ELMH) [EP-H]	Privately owned, Crowfield	
42-93510	Douglas C-47A Skytrain [CM] <ff>	Privately owned, Kew	
42-100611	Douglas C-47A Skytrain (6W-SAF) [4U] <ff>	Museum of Berkshire Aviation, Woodley	
43-9628	Douglas A-20G Havoc <ff>	Privately owned, Hinckley, Leics	
44-14291	NA P-51D Mustang	Classic Warbirds, Norwich	
44-14574	NA P-51D Mustang (fuselage)	East Essex Aviation Museum, Clacton	
44-79609	Piper L-4H Grasshopper (G-BHXY) [PR]	Privately owned, Bodmin	
44-80594	Piper L-4J Grasshopper (G-BEDJ)	Privately owned, White Waltham	
51-14526	NA T-6G Texan (G-BRWB)	Monafield Ltd, Audley End	
51-15227	NA T-6G Texan (G-BKRA) [10]	Privately owned, Shoreham	
51-15673	Piper L-18C Super Cub (53-4781/ G-CUBI)	Privately owned, Felixkirk	
52-8543	CCF T-6J Harvard IV (G-BUKY) [66]	Privately owned, Breighton	
54-2223	NA F-100D Super Sabre (54-2223)	Newark Air Museum, Winthorpe	
54-2447	Piper L-21B Super Cub (G-SCUB)	Privately owned, Anwick	
54-2474	Piper L-21B Super Cub (G-PCUB)	Privately owned, Headcorn	
54-21261	Lockheed T-33A-N Silver Star (N33VC/G-TBRD)	Golden Apple Operations/OFMC, Duxford	
64-17657	Douglas A-26A Invader (N99218) <ff>	Tower Museum, Ludham, Norfolk	
65-777	McD F-4C Phantom (63-7419) [LN]	RAF Lakenheath, on display	
67-120	GD F-111E Aardvark [UH]	American Air Museum, Duxford	
68-0060	GD F-111E Aardvark <ff>	Dumfries & Galloway Avn Mus, Dumfries	
72-1447	GD F-111F Aardvark <ff>	American Air Museum, Duxford	
72-448	GD F-111E Aardvark (68-0011) [LN]	RAF Lakenheath, on display	
77-259	Fairchild A-10A Thunderbolt [AR]	American Air Museum, Duxford	
80-219	Fairchild GA-10A Thunderbolt [AR]	RAF Alconbury, on display	
92-048	McD F-15A Eagle (74-0131) [LN]	RAF Lakenheath, on display	
146-11042	Wolf WII <R> (G-BMZX) [7]	Privately owned, Haverfordwest	
146-11083	Wolf WII <R> (G-BNAI) [5]	Privately owned, Haverfordwest	
I-492	Ryan PT-22 Recruit (41-15236/ G-BPUD)	Privately owned, Swanton Morley	

YUGOSLAVIA

30140	Soko P-2 Kraguj (G-RADA) [140]	Privately owned, Fairoaks	
30146	Soko P-2 Kraguj (G-BSXD) [146]	Privately owned, Elstree	
30149	Soko P-2 Kraguj (G-SOKO) [149]	Privately owned, Liverpool	
51182	UTVA-66 (YU-DMN)	Privately owned, Fairoaks	

This Chipmunk (G-BARS) is painted in Portuguese Air Force colours as 1377. *PRM*

113

Irish Military Aircraft Markings

Notes	Serial	Type (other identity)	Owner/operator, location
	34	Miles M14A Magister (N5392)	IAC Engineering Wing stored, Baldonnel
	141	Avro 652A Anson C19	IAC Engineering Wing stored, Baldonnel
	164	DHC1 Chipmunk T20	IAC Engineering Wing stored, Baldonnel
	168	DHC1 Chipmunk T20	IAC No 2 Support Wing, Gormanston
	172	DHC1 Chipmunk T20	IAC Training Wing stored, Gormanston
	176	DH104 Dove 4 (VP-YKF)	Privately owned,
	177	Percival P56 Provost T51 (G-BLIW)	Privately owned, Shoreham
	183	Percival P56 Provost T51	IAC Engineering Wing stored, Baldonnel
	184	Percival P56 Provost T51	South East Aviation Enthusiasts, Waterford
	187	DH115 Vampire T55	Av'n Society of Ireland, stored, Waterford
	189	Percival P56 Provost T51 (comp XF846)	IAC Baldonnel Fire Section
	191	DH115 Vampire T55	IAC Museum, Baldonnel
	192	DH115 Vampire T55	South East Aviation Enthusiasts, Waterford
	193	DH115 Vampire T55 <ff>	IAC Baldonnel Fire Section
	195	Sud SA316 Alouette III	IAC No 3 Support Wing, Baldonnel
	196	Sud SA316 Alouette III	IAC No 3 Support Wing, Bàldonnel
	197	Sud SA316 Alouette III	IAC No 3 Support Wing, Baldonnel
	198	DH115 Vampire T11 (XE977)	IAC Engineering Wing stored, Baldonnel
	199	DHC1 Chipmunk T22	IAC Training Wing store, Gormanston (spares)
	202	Sud SA316 Alouette III	IAC No 3 Support Wing, Baldonnel (under repair)
	203	Reims-Cessna FR172H	IAC No 2 Support Wing, Gormanston
	205	Reims-Cessna FR172H	IAC No 2 Support Wing, Gormanston
	206	Reims-Cessna FR172H	IAC No 2 Support Wing, Gormanston
	207	Reims-Cessna FR172H	IAC Engineering Wing, Baldonnel, instructional use
	208	Reims-Cessna FR172H	IAC No 2 Support Wing, Gormanston
	209	Reims-Cessna FR172H	IAC No 2 Support Wing, Gormanston, wfu
	210	Reims-Cessna FR172H	IAC No 2 Support Wing, Gormanston
	211	Sud SA316 Alouette III	IAC No 3 Support Wing, Baldonnel
	212	Sud SA316 Alouette III	IAC No 3 Support Wing, Baldonnel
	213	Sud SA316 Alouette III	IAC No 3 Support Wing, Baldonnel
	214	Sud SA316 Alouette III	IAC No 3 Support Wing, Baldonnel
	215	Fouga CM170 Super Magister	IAC, stored Baldonnel
	216	Fouga CM170 Super Magister	IAC Engineering Wing, Baldonnel
	217	Fouga CM170 Super Magister	IAC, stored Baldonnel
	218	Fouga CM170 Super Magister	IAC, stored Baldonnel
	219	Fouga CM170 Super Magister	IAC, stored Baldonnel
	220	Fouga CM170 Super Magister	IAC Training Wing, Baldonnel
	222	SIAI SF-260WE Warrior	IAC Training Wing, Baldonnel
	225	SIAI SF-260WE Warrior	IAC Training Wing, Baldonnel
	226	SIAI SF-260WE Warrior	IAC Training Wing, Baldonnel
	227	SIAI SF-260WE Warrior	IAC Training Wing, Baldonnel
	229	SIAI SF-260WE Warrior	IAC Training Wing, Baldonnel
	230	SIAI SF-260WE Warrior	IAC Training Wing, Baldonnel
	231	SIAI SF-260WE Warrior	IAC Training Wing, Baldonnel
	237	Aérospatiale SA342L Gazelle	IAC No 3 Support Wing, Baldonnel
	240	Beech Super King Air 200MR	IAC No 1 Support Wing, Baldonnel
	241	Aérospatiale SA342L Gazelle	IAC No 3 Support Wing, Baldonnel
	243	Reims-Cessna FR172K	IAC No 2 Support Wing, Gormanston
	244	Aérospatiale SA365F Dauphin II	IAC No 3 Support Wing, Baldonnel
	245	Aérospatiale SA365F Dauphin II	IAC No 3 Support Wing, Baldonnel
	246	Aérospatiale SA365F Dauphin II	IAC No 3 Support Wing, Baldonnel
	247	Aérospatiale SA365F Dauphin II	IAC No 3 Support Wing, Baldonnel
	248	Aérospatiale SA365F Dauphin II	IAC No 3 Support Wing, Baldonnel
	251	Grumman G1159C Gulfstream IV	IAC No 1 Support Wing, Baldonnel
	252	Airtech CN.235 MPA Persuader	IAC No 1 Support Wing, Baldonnel
	253	Airtech CN.235 MPA Persuader	IAC No 1 Support Wing, Baldonnel
	254	PBN-2T Defender 4000 (G-BWPN)	Garda Air Support Unit, Baldonnel
	255	AS355N Twin Squirrel (G-BXEV)	Garda Air Support Unit, Baldonnel

Aircraft included in this section are a selection of those likely to be seen visiting UK civil and military airfields on transport flights, exchange visits, exercises and for air shows. It is not a comprehensive list of *all* aircraft operated by the air arms concerned.

ALGERIA
Force Aérienne Algérienne/
Al Quwwat al Jawwiya al
Jaza'eriya
Lockheed C-130H
Hercules

4911	(7T-WHT)
4912	(7T-WHS)
4913	(7T-WHY)
4914	(7T-WHZ)
4924	(7T-WHR)
4926	(7T-WHQ)
4928	(7T-WHJ)
4930	(7T-WHI)
4934	(7T-WHF)
4935	(7T-WHE)

Lockheed C-130H-30
Hercules

4919	(7T-WHM)
4921	(7T-WHP)
4984	(7T-WHN)
4987	(7T-WHD)
4989	(7T-WHL)
4997	(7T-WHA)
5224	(7T-WHB)

AUSTRALIA
Royal Australian Air Force
Boeing 707-338C/368C*
33 Sqn, Amberley
A20-261*
A20-623
A20-624
A20-627
A20-629

Lockheed C-130H Hercules
36 Sqn, Richmond, NSW
A97-001
A97-002
A97-003
A97-004
A97-005
A97-006
A97-007
A97-008
A97-009
A97-010
A97-011
A97-012

Lockheed C-130E Hercules
37 Sqn, Richmond, NSW
A97-159
A97-160
A97-167
A97-168
A97-171
A97-172
A97-177
A97-178
A97-180

A97-181
A97-189
A97-190

Lockheed C-130J-30
Hercules
36 Sqn, Richmond, NSW
(on order)
A97-440
A97-441
A97-442
A97-447
A97-448
A97-449
A97-450
A97-464
A97-465
A97-466
A97-467
A97-468

Lockheed P-3C Orion
10/11 Sqns, Edinburgh,
NSW

A9-656	11 Sqn
A9-657	11 Sqn
A9-658	11 Sqn
A9-659	11 Sqn
A9-660	11 Sqn
A9-661	11 Sqn
A9-662	11 Sqn
A9-663	11 Sqn
A9-664	11 Sqn
A9-665	11 Sqn
A9-751	10 Sqn
A9-752	10 Sqn
A9-753	10 Sqn
A9-755	10 Sqn
A9-756	10 Sqn
A9-757	10 Sqn
A9-758	10 Sqn
A9-759	10 Sqn
A9-760	10 Sqn

AUSTRIA
Öesterreichische
Luftstreitkräfte
SAAB 35ÖE Draken
Fliegerregiment II
    1 Staffel/Überwg, Zeltweg;
    2 Staffel/Überwg, Graz

01	(351401)	1 Staffel
02	(351402)	1 Staffel
03	(351403)	1 Staffel
04	(351404)	1 Staffel
05	(351405)	1 Staffel
06	(351406)	1 Staffel
07	(351407)	1 Staffel
08	(351408)	1 Staffel
09	(351409)	1 Staffel
10	(351410)	1 Staffel
11	(351411)	1 Staffel
12	(351412)	1 Staffel

13	(351413)	2 Staffel
14	(351414)	2 Staffel
15	(351415)	2 Staffel
16	(351416)	2 Staffel
17	(351417)	2 Staffel
18	(351418)	2 Staffel
19	(351419)	2 Staffel
20	(351420)	2 Staffel
21	(351421)	2 Staffel
22	(351422)	2 Staffel
23	(351423)	2 Staffel
24	(351424)	2 Staffel

SAAB 105ÖE
Fliegerregiment III
    1 Staffel/JbG, Linz
(yellow)

B	(105402)
D	(105404)
E	(105405)
F	(105406)
G	(105407)
I	(105409)
J	(105410)

(green)

A	(105411)
B	(105412)
D	(105414)
GF-16	(105416)
G	(105417)

(red)

B	(105422)
C	(105423)
D	(105424)
E	(105425)
F	(105426)
G	(105427)
H	(105428)
I	(105429)
J	(105430)

(blue)

A	(105431)
B	(105432)
C	(105433)
D	(105434)
E	(105435)
F	(105436)
G	(105437)
I	(105439)
J	(105440)

Short SC7 Skyvan 3M
Fliegerregiment I
    Flachenstaffel, Tulln
5S-TA
5S-TB

BELGIUM
Force Aérienne Belge/
Belgische Luchtmacht
D-BD Alpha Jet E
7/11 Smaldeel (1 Wg),
    Bevekom

Belgium

AT-01
AT-02
AT-03
AT-05
AT-06
AT-08
AT-09
AT-10
AT-11
AT-12
AT-13
AT-14
AT-15
AT-16
AT-17
AT-18
AT-19
AT-20
AT-21
AT-22
AT-23
AT-24
AT-25
AT-26
AT-27
AT-28
AT-29
AT-30
AT-31
AT-32
AT-33

Airbus A.310-322
21 Smaldeel (15 Wg),
  Melsbroek
CA-01
CA-02

Dassault Falcon 900B
21 Smaldeel (15 Wg),
  Melsbroek
CD-01

Swearingen Merlin IIIA
21 Smaldeel (15 Wg),
  Melsbroek
CF-01
CF-02
CF-04
CF-05
CF-06

Lockheed C-130H Hercules
20 Smaldeel (15 Wg),
  Melsbroek
CH-01
CH-02
CH-03
CH-04
CH-05
CH-07
CH-08
CH-09
CH-10
CH-11
CH-12

Dassault Falcon 20E
21 Smaldeel (15 Wg),
  Melsbroek
CM-01
CM-02

**Hawker-Siddeley
HS748 Srs 2A**
21 Smaldeel (15 Wg),
  Melsbroek
CS-01
CS-02
CS-03

**General Dynamics
F-16A/F-16B***
1,2,350 Smaldeel (2 Wg),
  Florennes [FS];
23,31,349 Smaldeel, OCU
  (10 Wg), Kleine-Brogel
  [BL];
SABCA, Gosselies

Reg	Unit
FA-27	2 Wg
FA-39	10 Wg
FA-47	2 Wg
FA-48	2 Wg
FA-49	2 Wg
FA-50	350 Sm
FA-53	2 Wg
FA-55	10 Wg
FA-56	10 Wg
FA-57	10 Wg
FA-58	10 Wg
FA-60	10 Wg
FA-61	2 Wg
FA-65	23 Sm
FA-66	10 Wg
FA-67	31 Sm
FA-68	2 Sm
FA-69	31 Sm
FA-70	10 Wg
FA-71	31 Sm
FA-72	2 Wg
FA-73	10 Wg
FA-74	31 Sm
FA-75	10 Wg
FA-76	10 Wg
FA-77	2 Wg
FA-78	31 Sm
FA-81	2 Wg
FA-82	2 Wg
FA-83	2 Wg
FA-84	10 Wg
FA-86	31 Sm
FA-87	2 Wg
FA-88	349 Sm
FA-89	2 Wg
FA-90	31 Sm
FA-91	10 Wg
FA-92	10 Wg
FA-93	10 Wg
FA-94	2 Wg
FA-95	10 Wg
FA-96	10 Wg
FA-97	10 Wg
FA-98	2 Sm
FA-99	31 Sm
FA-100	349 Sm
FA-101	10 Wg
FA-102	23 Sm
FA-103	349 Sm
FA-104	2 Sm
FA-106	2 Wg
FA-107	2 Wg
FA-108	2 Wg
FA-109	2 Wg
FA-110	2 Wg
FA-111	10 Wg
FA-112	10 Wg
FA-114	10 Wg
FA-115	350 Sm
FA-116	10 Wg
FA-117	2 Wg
FA-118	2 Sm
FA-119	2 Wg
FA-120	31 Sm
FA-121	1 Sm
FA-122	2 Sm
FA-123	2 Wg
FA-124	10 Wg
FA-125	1 Sm
FA-126	10 Wg
FA-127	2 Wg
FA-128	10 Wg
FA-129	2 Wg
FA-130	2 Wg
FA-131	2 Wg
FA-132	2 Wg
FA-133	10 Wg
FA-134	10 Wg
FA-135	10 Wg
FA-136	10 Wg
FB-01*	OCU
FB-02*	OCU
FB-04*	OCU
FB-05*	OCU
FB-07*	OCU
FB-08*	OCU
FB-09*	2 Wg
FB-10*	10 Wg
FB-12*	OCU
FB-14*	1 Sm
FB-15*	10 Wg
FB-17*	OCU
FB-18*	OCU
FB-19*	10 Wg
FB-20*	2 Wg
FB-21*	10 Wg
FB-22*	OCU
FB-23*	10 Wg
FB-24*	OCU

Fouga CM170 Magister
33 Smaldeel (1 Wg),
  Bevekom
MT-04
MT-13
MT-14
MT-26
MT-34
MT-35
MT-36
MT-40
MT-44
MT-48

**Westland Sea King
Mk48/48A***
40 Smaldeel, Koksijde
RS-01
RS-02
RS-03*
RS-04
RS-05

**SIAI Marchetti
SF260MB/SF260D***
Ecole de Pilotage
  Elementaire (5 Sm/1 Wg),
  Bevekom
ST-02
ST-03
ST-04
ST-06

ST-12
ST-15
ST-16
ST-17
ST-18
ST-19
ST-20
ST-21
ST-22
ST-23
ST-24
ST-25
ST-26
ST-27
ST-31
ST-32
ST-35
ST-36
ST-40*
ST-41*
ST-42*
ST-43*
ST-44*
ST-45*
ST-46*
ST-47*
ST-48*

**Aviation Légère de la
Force Terrestre/
Belgische Landmacht**
**Sud SA318C/SE3130*
Alouette II**
16 BnHLn, Bierset;
SLV, Brasschaat

A-22*	16 BnHLn
A-37*	16 BnHLn
A-40	SLV
A-41	SLV
A-42	16 BnHLn
A-43	16 BnHLn
A-44	16 BnHLn
A-46	16 BnHLn
A-47	16 BnHLn
A-49	16 BnHLn
A-50	16 BnHLn
A-53	16 BnHLn
A-54	SLV
A-57	SLV
A-59	16 BnHLn
A-61	SLV
A-62	16 BnHLn
A-64	SLV
A-65	SLV
A-66	SLV
A-68	16 BnHLn
A-69	16 BnHLn
A-70	16 BnHLn
A-72	SLV
A-73	16 BnHLn
A-74	SLV
A-75	16 BnHLn
A-77	16 BnHLn
A-78	16 BnHLn
A-79	SLV
A-80	16 BnHLn
A-81	16 BnHLn

**Britten-Norman BN-2A/
BN-2B-21* Islander**
16 BnHLn, Bierset;
SLV, Brasschaat

B-01	LA	SLV
B-02*	LB	SLV

B-03*	LC	16 BnHLn
B-04*	LD	SLV
B-07*	LG	16 BnHLn
B-08*	LH	16 BnHLn
B-09*	LI	16 BnHLn
B-10*	LJ	16 BnHLn
B-11*	LK	16 BnHLn
B-12	LL	SLV

Agusta A109HA/HO*
17 BnHATk, Bierset;
18 BnHATk, Bierset;
SLV, Brasschaat

H-01*	SLV
H-02*	SLV
H-03*	SLV
H-04*	17 BnHATk
H-05*	17 BnHATk
H-06*	17 BnHATk
H-07*	17 BnHATk
H-08*	18 BnHATk
H-09*	18 BnHATk
H-10*	18 BnHATk
H-11*	SLV
H-12*	SLV
H-13*	SLV
H-14*	SLV
H-15*	SLV
H-16*	18 BnHATk
H-17*	17 BnHATk
H-18*	18 BnHATk
H-19	17 BnHATk
H-20	18 BnHATk
H-21	18 BnHATk
H-22	17 BnHATk
H-23	18 BnHATk
H-24	17 BnHATk
H-25	18 BnHATk
H-26	18 BnHATk
H-27	18 BnHATk
H-28	18 BnHATk
H-29	18 BnHATk
H-30	18 BnHATk
H-31	18 BnHATk
H-32	18 BnHATk
H-33	18 BnHATk
H-34	17 BnHATk
H-35	18 BnHATk
H-36	17 BnHATk
H-37	17 BnHATk
H-38	17 BnHATk
H-39	18 BnHATk
H-40	18 BnHATk
H-41	17 BnHATk
H-42	17 BnHATk
H-43	17 BnHATk
H-44	17 BnHATk
H-45	17 BnHATk
H-46	17 BnHATk

**Force Navale Belge/Belgische
Zeemacht**
Sud SA316B Alouette III
Koksijde Heli Flight

M-1	(OT-ZPA)
M-2	(OT-ZPB)
M-3	(OT-ZPC)

**Gendarmerie/Rijkswacht
Britten-Norman PBN-2T
Islander**
Luchsteundetachment,
Melsbroek

G-05	(OT-GLA)

Cessna 182 Skylane
Luchsteundetachment,
Melsbroek

G-01	C.182Q
G-03	C.182R
G-04	C.182R

MDH MD.900 Explorer
Luchsteundetachment,
Melsbroek
G-10
G-11

Sud Alouette II
Luchsteundetachment,
Melsbroek
G-90
G-93
G-94

BOTSWANA
Botswana Defence Force
**Grumman G.1159C
Gulfstream IV**
OK-1

Lockheed C-130B Hercules
OM-1
OM-2

BRAZIL
Força Aérea Brasileira
Boeing KC-137
2° GT 2° Esq, Galeão
2401
2402
2403
2404

Lockheed C-130E Hercules
1° GT, 1° Esq, Galeão;
1° GTT, 1° Esq, Afonsos

2451	C-130E	1° GTT
2453	C-130E	1° GTT
2454	C-130E	1° GTT
2455	C-130E	1° GTT
2456	C-130E	1° GTT
2458	SC-130E	1° GT
2459	SC-130E	1° GT
2461	KC-130H	1° GT
2462	KC-130H	1° GT
2463	C-130H	1° GT
2464	C-130H	1° GT
2465	C-130H	1° GT
2467	C-130H	1° GT

BULGARIA
**Bulgarsky Voenno-
Vazdushni Sily**
Antonov An-30
16 TAP, Sofia/Dobroslavtzi
055

CANADA
Canadian Forces
**Lockheed CC-130E/
CC-130E(SAR)* Hercules**
402 Sqn, Winnipeg
(17 Wing);
413 Sqn, Greenwood (SAR)
(14 Wing);
424 Sqn, Trenton (SAR)
(8 Wing);
426 Sqn, Trenton (8 Wing);

Canada – Czech Republic

429 Sqn, Trenton (8 Wing);
435 Sqn, Winnipeg
  (17 Wing);
436 Sqn, Trenton (8 Wing);
AETE, Cold Lake

130305*	8 Wing
130306*	8 Wing
130307	8 Wing
130308*	8 Wing
130310*	14 Wing
130311*	14 Wing
130313	8 Wing
130314*	14 Wing
130315*	14 Wing
130316	8 Wing
130317	8 Wing
130319	8 Wing
130320	8 Wing
130323	8 Wing
130324*	8 Wing
130325	8 Wing
130326	8 Wing
130327	8 Wing
130328	8 Wing

**Lockheed CC-130H/
CC-130H(T)* Hercules**

130332	17 Wing
130333	17 Wing
130334	8 Wing
130335	8 Wing
130336	8 Wing
130337	8 Wing
130338*	17 Wing
130339*	AETE
130340*	17 Wing
130341*	17 Wing
130342*	17 Wing

**Lockheed CC-130H-30
Hercules**

130343	8 Wing
130344	17 Wing

Lockheed CP-140 Aurora
404/405/415 Sqns,
  Greenwood (14 Wing);
407 Sqn, Comox (19 Wing)

140101	14 Wing
140102	14 Wing
140103	407 Sqn
140104	407 Sqn
140105	14 Wing
140106	14 Wing
140107	14 Wing
140108	407 Sqn
140109	14 Wing
140110	14 Wing
140111	14 Wing
140112	14 Wing
140113	14 Wing
140114	14 Wing
140115	14 Wing
140116	14 Wing
140117	407 Sqn
140118	14 Wing

**Lockheed
CP-140A Arcturus**

140119	14 Wing
140120	14 Wing
140121	14 Wing

**Canadair CC-144/CE-144
Challenger**
412 Sqn, Trenton (8 Wing);
434 Sqn, Greenwood
  (14 Wing)

144601	CC-144A	434 Sqn
144602	CC-144A	434 Sqn
144603	CE-144A	434 Sqn
144604	CC-144A	434 Sqn
144605	CC-144A	434 Sqn
144606	CE-144A	434 Sqn
144607	CE-144A	434 Sqn
144608	CE-144A	434 Sqn
144609	CE-144A	434 Sqn
144610	CC-144A	434 Sqn
144611	CE-144A	434 Sqn
144614	CC-144B	412 Sqn
144615	CC-144B	412 Sqn
144616	CC-144B	412 Sqn

**Airbus CC-150 Polaris
(A310-304)**
437 Sqn, Trenton (8 Wing)

15001	216
15002	212
15003	202
15004	205
15005	201

CHILE
Fuerza Aérea de Chile
  Boeing 707
  Grupo 10, Santiago

901	707-321B
902	707-351C
903	707-330B
904	707-358C

  Extra EA-300
  Los Halcones

021	[6]
022	[7]
024	[2]
025	[3]
027	[4]
028	[5]
029	[1]

  **Grumman G.1159A
  Gulfstream III**

911	

  **Lockheed C-130B/H
  Hercules**
  Grupo 10, Santiago

993	C-130B
994	C-130H
995	C-130H
996	C-130H
998	C-130B

CZECH REPUBLIC
Ceske Vojenske Letectvo
  Aero L-39/L-59 Albatros
  42 slt/4 zTL, Cáslav;
  321 tpzlt & 322 tlt/32 zTL,
  Náměšt;
  341 vlt/34 zSL, Pardubice;
  LZú, Praha/Kbely

0001	L-39MS	LZO
0004	L-39MS	LZO
0005	L-39MS	LZO
0006	L-39MS	LZO
0103	L-39C	341 vlt/34 zSL

0105	L-39C	341 vlt/34 zSL
0106	L-39C	341 vlt/34 zSL
0107	L-39C	341 vlt/34 zSL
0108	L-39C	341 vlt/34 zSL
0113	L-39C	341 vlt/34 zSL
0115	L-39C	341 vlt/34 zSL
0440	L-39C	341 vlt/34 zSL
0441	L-39C	341 vlt/34 zSL
0444	L-39C	341 vlt/34 zSL
0445	L-39C	341 vlt/34 zSL
0448	L-39C	341 vlt/34 zSL
2341	L-39ZA	42 slt/4 zTL
2344	L-39ZA	42 slt/4 zTL
2347	L-39ZA	42 slt/4 zTL
2350	L-39ZA	42 slt/4 zTL
2415	L-39ZA	42 slt/4 zTL
2418	L-39ZA	42 slt/4 zTL
2421	L-39ZA	42 slt/4 zTL
2424	L-39ZA	32 zTL
2427	L-39ZA	42 slt/4 zTL
2430	L-39ZA	42 slt/4 zTL
2433	L-39ZA	42 slt/4 zTL
2436	L-39ZA	42 slt/4 zTL
3903	L-39ZA	32 zTL
4605	L-39C	341 vlt/34 zSL
4606	L-39C	341 vlt/34 zSL
5013	L-39ZA	32 zTL
5015	L-39ZA	32 zTL
5017	L-39ZA	32 zTL
5019	L-39ZA	32 zTL

Aero L-159 ALCA/L-159T*
LZO, Praha/Kbely

5831*	
5832	

Antonov An-24B*/An-24V
1 dlt/6 zDL, Praha/Kbely

2904*	
5803	
7109	
7110	

**Antonov An-26/
An-26Z-1M***
1 dlt/6 zDL, Praha/Kbely

2408	
2409	
2507	
3209*	
4201	

Antonov An-30FG
344 pzdlt/34 zSL, Pardubice

1107	

Let 410 Turbolet
1 dlt/6 zDL, Praha/Kbely;
344 pzdlt/34 zSL, Pardubice

0402	L-410MA	
		344 pzdlt/34 zSL
0403	L-410MA	
		344 pzdlt/34 zSL
0501	L-410MA	
		344 pzdlt/34 zSL
0503	L-410MA	
		344 pzdlt/34 zSL
0712	L-410UVP-S	
		344 pzdlt/34 zSL
0731	L-410UVP	
		1 dlt/6 zDL
0926	L-410UVP-T	
		1 dlt/6 zDL [4]

Reg	Type / Unit
0928	L-410UVP-T
	1 dlt/6 zDL
0929	L-410UVP-T
	1 dlt/6 zDL [2]
1132	L-410UVP-T
	1 dlt/6 zDL [3]
1134	L-410UVP
	1 dlt/6 zDL
1504	L-410UVP
	1 dlt/6 zDL
1523	L-410FG
	344 pzdlt/34 zSL
1525	L-410FG
	344 pzdlt/34 zSL
1526	L-410FG
	344 pzdlt/34 zSL
2312	L-410UVP-E
	1 dlt/6 zDL
2601	L-410UVP-E
	1 dlt/6 zDL
2602	L-410UVP-E
	1 dlt/6 zDL

Let 610M
1 dlt/6 zDL, Praha/Kbely;
LZú, Praha/Kbely

Reg	Unit
0003	1 dlt/6 zDL
0005	LZO

**Mikoyan MiG-21MF/
MiG-21UM***
42 slt/4 zTL, Cáslav;
LZO, Ceske Budejovice

Reg	Unit
2205	42 slt/4 zTL
2500	42 slt/4 zTL
2614	42 slt/4 zTL
3186*	42 slt/4 zTL
3746*	42 slt/4 zTL
4017	42 slt/4 zTL
4127	42 slt/4 zTL
4175	42 slt/4 zTL
4307	LZO
5031*	42 slt/4 zTL
5201	42 slt/4 zTL
5203	LZO
5209	42 slt/4 zTL
5210	42 slt/4 zTL
5212	42 slt/4 zTL
5213	42 slt/4 zTL
5214	42 slt/4 zTL
5301	42 slt/4 zTL
5302	42 slt/4 zTL
5303	42 slt/4 zTL
5304	42 slt/4 zTL
5305	42 slt/4 zTL
5508	42 slt/4 zTL
5512	42 slt/4 zTL
5581	42 slt/4 zTL
5603	42 slt/4 zTL
7701	42 slt/4 zTL
7802	42 slt/4 zTL
9011*	42 slt/4 zTL
9332*	42 slt/4 zTL
9333*	42 slt/4 zTL
9341*	42 slt/4 zTL
9342*	42 slt/4 zTL
9399*	42 slt/4 zTL
9410	42 slt/4 zTL
9414	42 slt/4 zTL
9707	42 slt/4 zTL
9711	42 slt/4 zTL
9801	42 slt/4 zTL
9802	LZO
9804	42 slt/4 zTL

Reg	Unit
9805	42 slt/4 zTL

**Mikoyan MiG-23ML/
MiG-23UB***
41 slt/4 zTL, Cáslav

2402
2406
2409
2410
2422
2423
2425
3303
3304
3307
4641
4644
4645
4850
4855
4860
8107*
8109*
8327*

Mil Mi-24
331 ltBVr/33 zVrL, Přerov

Reg	Type
0103	Mi-24D
0140	Mi-24D
0142	Mi-24D
0146	Mi-24D
0151	Mi-24D
0214	Mi-24D
0216	Mi-24D
0217	Mi-24D
0218	Mi-24D
0219	Mi-24D
0220	Mi-24D
0701	Mi-24V1
0702	Mi-24V1
0703	Mi-24V1
0705	Mi-24V1
0709	Mi-24V1
0710	Mi-24V1
0788	Mi-24V1
0789	Mi-24V1
0790	Mi-24V1
0812	Mi-24V1
0815	Mi-24V1
0816	Mi-24V1
0834	Mi-24V2
0835	Mi-24V2
0836	Mi-24V2
0837	Mi-24V2
0838	Mi-24V2
0839	Mi-24V2
4010	Mi-24D
4011	Mi-24D
6050	Mi-24DU

**Sukhoi Su-22M-4K/
Su-22UM-3K***
321 tpzlt/32 zTL, Náměšt

Reg	Code	Scheme
2217		
2218		
2619	34	NA-2D
2620	35	NA-2D
2701	36	
3313	24	NA-2A
3314	23	
3315	39	NA-2B
3402	05	
3403	08	NA-1B
3404	09	

Reg	Code	Scheme
3405		
3406		
3407	10	
3701	0	NA-1A
3703	43	NA-1D
3704	44	NA-1D
3705	51	
3706	52	NA-1E
3802	26	NA-2B
3803	27	NA-2B
4005	30	NA-2C
4006	31	NA-2C
4007	32	NA-2C
4008	29	NA-2B
4010	28	NA-2B
4011	22	NA-2A
4208	53	NA-1E
4209	54	NA-1E
6602	55	*
7103	03	NA-1A*
7104	40	NA-2C*
7309	41	NA-2D*
7310	25	NA-2A*

Sukhoi Su-25K/Su-25UBK*
322 tlt/32 zTL, Náměšt

1002
1004
1005
3348*
5003
5006
5007
5008
5039
5040
6019
6020
8076
8077
8078
8079
8080
8081
9013
9014
9093
9094
9098
9099

Tupolev Tu-154B-2
1 dlt/6 zDL, Praha/Kbely
0601

DENMARK
Flyvevåbnet

Lockheed C-130H Hercules
Eskadrille 721, Vaerløse
B-678
B-679
B-680

Canadair CL.604 Challenger
Eskadrille 721, Vaerløse
C-066
C-080

General Dynamics F-16A/F-16B*
Eskadrille 723, Aalborg;
Eskadrille 726, Aalborg;
Eskadrille 727, Skrydstrup;

Denmark – France

Eskadrille 730, Skrydstrup		Eskadrille 721, Vaerløse	H-244
E-004	Esk 726	F-249	H-245
E-005	Esk 726	F-313	H-246
E-006	Esk 726		
E-007	Esk 726	**SAAB T-17 Supporter**	**Aérospatiale AS.550C-2**
E-008	Esk 726	Flyveskolen, Karup (FLSK)	**Fennec**
E-011		T-401	PVH Kmp, Vandel
E-016	Esk 726	T-402	P-090
E-017	Esk 726	T-403	P-234
E-018	Esk 726	T-404	P-254
E-024	Esk 723	T-405	P-275
E-069		T-407	P-276
E-070		T-408	P-287
E-074	Esk 730	T-409	P-288
E-075	Esk 723	T-410	P-319
E-107	Esk 723	T-411	P-320
E-174	Esk 727	T-412	P-339
E-176	Esk 726	T-413	P-352
E-177	Esk 723	T-414	P-369
E-178	Esk 723	T-415	
E-180	Esk 723	T-417	**ECUADOR**
E-181	Esk 723	T-418	**Fuerza Aérea Ecuatoriana**
E-182	Esk 730	T-419	**Lockheed C-130H/L.100-30***
E-183	Esk 730	T-420	**Hercules**
E-184	Esk 727	T-421	Ala de Transporte 11, Quito
E-187	Esk 727	T-423	FAE-812
E-188	Esk 723	T-425	FAE-893*
E-189	Esk 723	T-426	
E-190	Esk 723	T-427	**EGYPT**
E-191	Esk 730	T-428	**Al Quwwat al-Jawwiya ilMisriya**
E-192	Esk 730	T-429	**Lockheed C-130H/**
E-193	Esk 726	T-430	**C-130H-30*Hercules**
E-194	Esk 730	T-431	16 Sqn, Cairo West
E-195	Esk 723	T-432	1271/SU-BAB
E-196	Esk 723		1272/SU-BAC
E-197	Esk 727	**Sikorsky S-61A Sea King**	1273/SU-BAD
E-198	Esk 730	Eskadrille 722, Vaerløse	1274/SU-BAE
E-199	Esk 727	Detachments at:	1275/SU-BAF
E-200	Esk 723	Aalborg, Ronne, Skrydstrup	1277/SU-BAI
E-202	Esk 730	U-240	1278/SU-BAJ
E-203	Esk 723	U-275	1279/SU-BAK
E-596	Esk 723	U-276	1280/SU-BAL
E-597	Esk 730	U-277	1281/SU-BAM
E-598	Esk 730	U-278	1282/SU-BAN
E-599	Esk 730	U-279	1283/SU-BAP
E-600	Esk 727	U-280	1284/SU-BAQ
E-601	Esk 727	U-481	1285/SU-BAR
E-602	Esk 730		1286/SU-BAS
E-603	Esk 723	**SøvaernetsFlyvetjaeneste**	1287/SU-BAT
E-604	Esk 726	**(Navy)**	1288/SU-BAU
E-605	Esk 727	**Westland Lynx Mk 80/90***	1289/SU-BAV
E-606	Esk 727	Eskadrille 722, Vaerløse	1290/SU-BAW
E-607	Esk 723	S-134	1291/SU-BAX
E-608	Esk 723	S-142	1292/SU-BAY
E-609	Esk 727	S-175	1293/SU-BKS*
E-610	Esk 727	S-181	1294/SU-BKT*
E-611	Esk 727	S-191	1295/SU-BKU*
ET-022*	Esk 727	S-249*	
ET-197*	Esk 726	S-256*	**FINLAND**
ET-198*	Esk 726		**Suomen Ilmavoimat**
ET-199*	Esk 726	**Haerens Flyvetjaeneste**	**Fokker F.27 Friendship**
ET-204*	Esk 727	**(Army)**	Tukilentolaivue,
ET-206*	Esk 730	**Hughes 500M**	Jyväskylä/Tikkakoski
ET-207*	Esk 727	OVH Kmp, Vandel;	FF-1 F.27-100
ET-208*	Esk 730	PVH Kmp, Vandel	FF-2 F.27-100
ET-210*	Esk 727	H-201	FF-3 F.27-400M
ET-612*	Esk 727	H-202	
ET-613*	Esk 727	H-203	**FRANCE**
ET-614*	Esk 723	H-205	**Armée de l'Air**
ET-615*	Esk 727	H-206	**Aérospatiale SN601**
ET-626*	Esk 727	H-207	**Corvette**
		H-209	CEV, Bretigny
Grumman G.1159A		H-211	1 MV
Gulfstream III		H-213	2 MW

10	MX

Aérospatiale TB-30 Epsilon
Cartouche Dorée,
(EPAA 00.315) Cognac;
EPAA 00.315, Cognac

1	315-UA
2	315-UB
3	FZ
4	315-UC
5	315-UD
6	315-UE
7	315-UF
8	315-UG
9	315-UH
10	315-UI
12	315-UK
13	315-UL
14	315-UM
15	315-UN
16	315-UO
17	315-UP
18	315-UQ
19	315-UR
20	315-US
21	315-UT
23	315-UV
24	315-UW
25	315-UX
26	315-UY
27	315-UZ
28	315-VA
29	315-VB
30	315-VC
31	315-VD
32	315-VE
33	315-VF
34	315-VG
35	315-VH
36	315-VI
37	315-VJ
38	315-VK
39	315-VL
40	315-VM
41	315-VN
42	315-VO
43	315-VP
44	315-VQ
45	315-VR
46	315-VS
47	315-VT
48	315-VU
49	315-VV
50	315-VW
52	315-VX
53	315-VY
54	315-VZ
56	315-WA
57	F-ZVLB
60	315-WC
61	315-WD
62	315-WE
63	315-WF
64	315-WG
65	315-WH
66	315-WI
67	315-WJ
68	315-WK
69	315-WL
70	315-WM
71	315-WN
72	315-WO
73	315-WP
74	315-WQ
75	315-WR
76	315-WS
77	315-WT
78	315-WU
79	315-WV
80	315-WW
81	315-WX
82	315-WY
83	315-WZ
84	315-XA
85	315-XB
86	315-XC
87	315-XD
88	315-XE
89	315-XF
90	315-XG
91	315-XH
92	F-SEXI [1]*
93	315-XJ
94	315-XK
95	315-XL
96	315-XM
97	315-XN
98	315-XO
99	315-XP
100	F-SEXQ [2]*
101	315-XR
102	315-XS
103	315-XT
104	315-XU
105	F-SEXV [4]*
106	315-XW
107	315-XX
108	315-XY
109	315-XZ
110	315-YA
111	315-YB
112	315-YC
113	315-YD
114	315-YE
115	315-YF
116	315-YG
117	F-SEYH [3]*
118	315-YI
119	315-YJ
120	315-YK
121	315-YL
122	315-YM
123	315-YN
124	315-YO
125	315-YP
126	315-YQ
127	315-YR
128	315-YS
129	315-YT
130	315-YU
131	315-YV
132	315-YW
133	315-YX
134	315-YY
135	315-YZ
136	315-ZA
137	315-ZB
138	315-ZC
139	315-ZD
140	315-ZE
141	315-ZF
142	315-ZG
143	315-ZH
144	315-ZI
145	315-ZJ
146	315-ZK
148	315-ZL
149	315-ZM
150	315-ZN
152	315-ZO
153	315-ZP
154	315-ZQ
155	315-ZR
158	315-ZS
159	315-ZT

Airbus A.300B2-103
CEV, Bretigny

03	(F-BUAD)

Airbus A.310-304
ET 03.060 'Esterel',
Paris/Charles de Gaulle

421	F-RADA
422	F-RADB

Airtech CN-235M-100
ETL 01.062 'Vercours', Creil;
ETOM 00.052 'La Tontouta',
Noumea;
ETOM 00.082 'Maine', Faaa-
Tahiti

043	62-IA	01.062
045	62-IB	01.062
065	82-IC	00.082
066	52-ID	00.052
071	62-IE	01.062
072	82-IF	00.082
105	52-IG	00.052
107	52-IH	00.052
111	62-II	01.062
114	62-IJ	01.062
128	62-IK	01.062

Boeing C-135 Stratotanker
ERV 00.093 'Bretagne',
Istres

470	C-135FR	93-CA
471	C-135FR	93-CB
472	C-135FR	93-CC
474	C-135FR	93-CE
475	C-135FR	93-CF
497	KC-135R	93-CM
525	KC-135R	93-CN
574	KC-135R	93-CP
735	C-135FR	93-CG
736	C-135FR	93-CH
737	C-135FR	93-CI
738	C-135FR	93-CJ
739	C-135FR	93-CK
740	C-135FR	93-CL

Boeing E-3F Sentry
EDCA 00.036, Avord

201	36-CA
202	36-CB
203	36-CC
204	36-CD

CASA 212-300 Aviocar
CEV, Bretigny

377	MO
378	MP
386	MQ
387	MR
388	MS

Cessna 310
CEV, Bretigny, Cazaux,
Istres & Melun

046	310L	AV

185	310N	AU
187	310N	BJ
188	310N	BK
190	310N	BL
192	310N	BM
193	310N	BG
194	310N	BH
242	310K	AW
244	310K	AX
513	310N	BE
693	310N	BI
820	310Q	CL
981	310Q	BF

D-BD Alpha Jet
AMD-BA, Istres;
CEV, Bretigny;
EAC 00.314, Tours;
EC 01.002 'Cicogne', Dijon;
EC 02.007 'Argonne',
  St Dizier;
ERS 01.091 'Gascogne',
  Mont-de-Marsan;
ETO 01.008 'Saintonge'&
ETO 02.008 'Nice' Cazaux;
CEAM (EC 05.330),
  Mont-de-Marsan;
EPNER, Istres;
Patrouille de France (PDF)
  (EPAA 20.300),
  Salon de Provence

01	F-ZJTS	CEV
E1		CEV
E3		
E4		CEV
E5	7-PE	02.007
E7		
E8		CEV
E9	8-MJ	01.008
E10	8-NM	02.008
E11	8-MW	01.008
E12		CEV
E13	314-TK	00.314
E14		
E15	314-TT	00.314
E17	8-NK	02.008
E18	8-MD	01.008
E19	314-TS	00.314
E20	2-EF	01.002
E21	314-UO	00.314
E22	314-TG	00.314
E23	8-MQ	01.008
E24	314-TW	00.314
E25	314-LL	00.314
E26		
E28	8-MI	01.008
E29	314-TM	00.314
E30	8-NR	02.008
E31	314-TY	00.314
E32	8-NQ	02.008
E33	8-NN	02.008
E34	314-TC	00.314
E35	314-UF	00.314
E36	314-LT	00.314
E37	8-NI	02.008
E38	8-NJ	02.008
E41	314-TR	00.314
E42	7-PX	02.007
E43	2-EI	01.002
E44		CEV
E45	330-AK	CEAM
E46		CEV
E47	314-LO	00.314
E48	8-MH	01.008
E49	8-NO	02.008
E51	314-UB	00.314
E52		
E53	314-LV	00.314
E55	314-UC	00.314
E58	314-TH	00.314
E59	314-LY	00.314
E60		EPNER
E61		
E63	314-TA	00.314
E64	314-TL	00.314
E65	8-MU	01.008
E66	8-ME	01.008
E67	314-TB	00.314
E68	2-EL	01.002
E69	8-NX	02.008
E70		
E72	314-LA	00.314
E73	314-TV	00.314
E74	8-MS	01.008
E75	2-EM	01.002
E76	7-PW	02.007
E79	314-LN	00.314
E80		CEV
E81	F-TERI	PDF [3]
E82	8-NB	02.008
E83	8-NG	02.008
E84	8-MH	01.008
E85	330-AL	CEAM
E86		
E87	314-LU	00.314
E88	314-TF	00.314
E89	314-TQ	00.314
E90	314-LF	00.314
E91	8-NL	02.008
E92	314-UE	00.314
E93	314-LD	00.314
E94	314-TE	00.314
E95		
E96	314-UA	00.314
E97	314-UN	00.314
E98		
E99	314-LW	00.314
E100		EPNER
E101	314-LX	00.314
E102		
E103	314-LM	00.314
E104	F-TERB	PDF [4]
E105		
E106	314-UL	00.314
E107	314-LS	00.314
E108	8-NF	02.008
E109		
E110		
E112	DA	01.091
E113	314-LK	00.314
E114	314-TU	00.314
E115	8-NW	02.008
E116	8-MG	01.008
E117		
E118		
E119	7-PZ	02.007
E120	F-TERG	PDF [5]
E121		
E122	F-TERD	PDF [1]
E123	8-ML	01.008
E124		
E125	314-LP	00.314
E126	314-LI	00.314
E127		
E128	F-TERN	PDF [2]
E129	314-TO	00.314
E130	314-LG	00.314
E131	314-UD	00.314
E132	314-UJ	00.314
E133	8-NE	02.008
E134	8-MA	01.008
E135		
E136	314-TN	00.314
E137	314-LB	00.314
E138	F-TERM	PDF [0]
E139	330-AH	CEAM
E140	314-UH	00.314
E141		
E142	8-NV	02.008
E143	8-MM	01.008
E144	8-NA	02.008
E145	314-LZ	00.314
E146	8-MC	01.008
E147	8-NH	02.008
E148	314-TD	00.314
E149	8-MO	01.008
E150	8-NC	02.008
E151	F-TERJ	PDF
E152	8-MP	01.008
E153	F-TERH	PDF [7]
E154	8-NT	02.008
E155	314-TP	00.314
E156	314-TI	00.314
E157	314-LG	00.314
E158	F-TERG	PDF [6]
E159	7-PP	02.007
E160	F-TERC	PDF [8]
E161		
E162	314-TZ	00.314
E163	314-UM	00.314
E164	8-MB	01.008
E165	F-TERE	PDF [9]
E166	314-TX	00.314
E167	8-MN	01.008
E168	8-MK	01.008
E169	8-NU	02.008
E170	2-EO	01.002
E171	314-LR	00.314
E173	314-LH	00.314
E175	F-TER.	PDF
E176	8-MA	01.008

Dassault Falcon 20
CEV, Bretigny[1], Cazaux[2],
  Istres[3] & Melun[4];
CITac 00.339
  'Aquitaine', Luxeuil;
ETEC 00.065, Villacoublay;
SIET 98.120, Cazaux

22	CS	CEV[3]
49	120-FA	98.120
79	CT	CEV[1]
86	CG	CEV[2]
93	F-RAED	00.065
96	CB	CEV[1]
104	CW	CEV[1]
115	339-JG	00.339
124	CC	CEV[1]
131	CD	CEV[1]
138	CR	CEV[2]
145	CU	CEV[1]
182	339-JA	00.339
188	CX	CEV[4]
238	F-RAEE	00.065
252	CA	CEV[1]
260	F-RAEA	00.065
263	CY	CEV[1]
268	F-RAEF	00.065
288	CV	CEV[1]
291	(F-RAEG)	00.065
342	F-RAEC	00.065
375	CZ	CEV[1]

422	65-EH	00.065
451	339-JC	00.339
483	339-JI	00.339

Dassault Falcon 50
ETEC 00.065, Villacoublay

5	F-RAFI
27	(F-RAFK)
34	(F-RAFL)
78	F-RAFJ

Dassault Falcon 900
ETEC 00.065, Villacoublay

2	(F-RAFP)
4	(F-RAFQ)

Dassault Mirage IVP
ERS 01.091 'Gascogne', Mont-de-Marsan

11	AJ
23	AV
31	BD
36	BI
52	BY
53	BZ
59	CF
62	CI

Dassault Mirage F.1B
CEAM (EC 05.330) Mont-de-Marsan;
EC 03.033 'Lorraine', Reims

501		
502	330-AD	CEAM
503	33-FG	03.033
504	33-FB	03.033
505		
507	33-FA	03.033
509		
510	33-FV	03.033
511	33-FF	03.033
512		
513	33-FY	03.033
514	33-FZ	03.033
516	33-FP	03.033
517	33-FH	03.033
518	33-FI	03.033
519	33-FM	03.033
520	33-FL	03.033

Dassault Mirage F.1C/F.1CT*
CEAM (EC 05.330), Mont-de-Marsan;
CEV, Bretigny & Istres;
GC 01.030 'Alsace' & GC 02.030 'Normandie Niemen', Colmar;
EC 03.033 'Lorraine', Reims;
EC 04.033 'Vexin', Djibouti

5	33-FV	03.033
15		
24		
31	330-AC	CEAM
32	33-FJ	03.033
33	33-FN	03.033
52	33-FK	03.033
62	33-FD	03.033
64		
72		
74		
76		
80	33-FQ	03.033
81		

82	33-FO	03.033
83	33-LI	04.033
84	33-LC	04.033
85	33-FR	03.033
87	33-L	04.033
90	33-FC	03.033
100		
103	33-FU	03.033
201	33-FW	03.033
202	33-LG	04.033
203	33-FX	03.033
205	33-FS	03.033
206	33-LA	04.033
207*	330-AO	CEAM
210	33-L	04.033
211	33-L	04.033
213	33-LF	04.033
214		
218	33-FE	03.033
219*	30-SF	01.030
220*	30-QM	02.030
221*	30-SY	01.030
223*	30-QT	02.030
224	33-FT	03.033
225*	30-QC	02.030
226*	30-QO	02.030
227*	330-AP	CEAM
228*	30-SN	01.030
229*		
230*	30-SP	01.030
231*		
232*	30-QW	02.030
233*	30-QG	02.030
234*	30-QL	02.030
235*	30-QS	02.030
236*	30-SB	01.030
237*		
238*	30-QN	02.030
239*	30-QT	02.030
241*	30-SI	01.030
242*	30-SG	01.030
243*		
244*	30-QH	02.030
245*	30-SA	01.030
246*	30-QJ	02.030
247*	30-QP	02.030
248*	30-QQ	02.030
251*	330-AI	CEAM
252*	30-SK	01.030
253*		
254*	30-QV	02.030
255*	30-QI	02.030
256*	30-QK	02.030
257*	30-SD	01.030
258*	30-SZ	01.030
259*	30-QU	02.030
260*	30-SO	01.030
261*	30-SL	01.030
262*	30-SE	01.030
264*	30-SW	01.030
265*	30-SH	01.030
267*	30-QB	02.030
268*	30-SR	01.030
271*	30-SM	01.030
272*	30-SQ	01.030
273*	30-QL	02.030
274*	330-AJ	CEAM
275*	30-SX	01.030
278*	30-QA	02.030
279*	30-SC	01.030
280*	30-QE	02.030
281*	30-QF	02.030
283*	30-SV	01.030

Dassault Mirage F.1CR
CEAM (EC 05.330),
Mont-de-Marsan;
CEV, Istres;
ER 01.033 'Belfort' &
ER 02.033 'Savoie', Reims

602		CEV
603	33-CB	01.033
604	33-CF	01.033
605	330-AF	CEAM
606	33-NP	02.033
607	33-CE	01.033
608	33-NG	02.033
610	33-NQ	02.033
611	33-CO	01.033
612	33-NJ	02.033
613	33-NK	02.033
614	33-NF	02.033
615	33-CU	01.033
616	33-NM	02.033
617	33-N0	02.033
620	33-CT	01.033
622	33-CR	01.033
623	33-CM	01.033
624		
627	33-NI	02.033
628	33-NN	02.033
629	33-CG	01.033
630	33-NL	02.033
631	330-AB	CEAM
632	33-NE	02.033
634	33-CK	01.033
635	33-NS	02.033
636	33-NZ	02.033
637	33-CP	01.033
638	33-CI	01.033
640	33-CH	01.033
641	33-CD	01.033
642	33-NC	02.033
643	33-NR	02.033
645	33-CC	01.033
646	33-NW	02.033
647	33-NX	02.033
648	33-NT	02.033
649	33-CZ	01.033
650	33-CJ	01.033
651	33-NB	02.033
653	33-NV	02.033
654	33-CL	01.033
655	330-AT	CEAM
656	33-CS	01.033
657	33-CV	01.033
658	33-CW	01.033
659	33-CA	01.033
660	33-ND	02.033
661	33-CX	01.033
662	33-NA	02.033

Dassault Mirage 2000B/2000-5*
AMD-BA, Istres;
CEV, Bretigny;
EC 02.002 'Côte d'Or', Dijon;
EC 01.005 'Vendée' &
EC 02.005 'Ile de France', Orange;
EC 01.012 'Cambrésis' &
EC 02.012 'Picardie', Cambrai

501*	(BX1)	CEV
502	5-OH	02.005
504*	BOB	CEV
505		
506	5-OY	02.005

507	2-FD	02.002
508	5-OT	02.005
509	5-OP	02.005
510	5-OQ	02.005
511	5-OR	02.005
512	5-OU	02.005
513	5-OI	02.005
514	5-OE	02.005
515	5-OG	02.005
516	5-OL	02.005
518	5-OM	02.005
519	5-OW	02.005
520	2-FW	02.002
521	2-FX	02.002
522	5-OV	02.005
523	2-FT	02.002
524	330-AZ	CEAM
525	2-FV	02.002
526	12-KM	02.012
527	12-KJ	02.012
528	330-AN	CEAM
529	2-FS	02.002
530	12-YA	01.012

Dassault Mirage 2000C/2000-5*
CEAM (EC 05.330),
  Mont-de-Marsan;
CEV, Istres;
EC 01.002 'Cicogne' &
EC 02.002 'Côte d'Or', Dijon;
EC 01.005 'Vendée' &
EC 02.005 'Ile de France',
  Orange;
EC 01.012 'Cambrésis' &
EC 02.012 'Picardie',
  Cambrai

1	2-EP	CEV
2		CEV
3	5-OO	02.005
4	5-OD	02.005
5	5-OS	02.005
8	2-ER	01.002
9	5-NQ	01.005
11	2-ET	01.002
12	5-NN	01.005
13	2-ES	01.002
14	5-OB	02.005
15	2-EK	01.002
16	5-NE	01.005
17	5-NR	01.005
18	5-OF	02.005
19	2-EA	01.002
20	2-EQ	01.002
21	2-EG	01.002
22	5-ND	01.005
25	2-EJ	01.002
27	5-NT	01.005
28	5-OK	02.005
29	2-ED	01.002
30	2-EC	01.002
32	2-EP	01.002
34		
35	5-NL	01.005
36	5-OC	02.005
37	5-OJ	02.005
38*	2-EU	CEAM
39*	2-EE	CEAM
40	5-NI	01.005
41*		
42	5-NJ	01.005
43	5-NK	01.005
44	5-ON	02.005
45		

46		
47		
48		
49		
51*	330-AS	CEAM
52		
53		
54		
55		
56	5-OA	02.005
57		
58		
59		
61	5-NP	01.005
62	5-NW	01.005
63	5-NF	01.005
64	330-AQ	CEAM
65		
66		
67		
68	5-NU	01.005
69		
70	5-NV	01.005
71*	2-EH	CEAM
72	5-NG	01.005
73*	2-EA	CEAM
74	5-NB	01.005
76		
77*	330-AX	CEAM
78*	2-EA	CEAM
79	2-FN	02.002
80	12-YJ	01.012
81	12-YI	01.012
82	12-YH	01.012
83	12-YC	01.012
84	12-KT	02.012
85	12-YE	01.012
86	12-KH	02.012
87	12-YQ	01.012
88	12-YG	01.012
89	2-FL	02.002
90	12-KO	02.012
91	12-YO	01.012
92	330-AW	CEAM
93	330-AR	CEAM
94	12-KA	02.012
95	12-YF	01.012
96	12-KK	02.012
97	12-KP	02.012
98	12-YB	01.012
99	2-FM	02.002
100	2-FZ	02.002
101	2-FB	02.002
102	2-FE	02.002
103	12-YN	01.012
104	12-YK	01.012
105	12-YL	01.012
106	2-FP	02.002
107	12-YR	01.012
108	12-KE	02.012
109		
111	12-KI	02.012
112	2-FR	02.002
113	12-KN	02.012
114	12-KS	02.012
115	12-KC	02.012
116	12-KG	02.012
117	12-YD	01.012
118	2-FJ	02.002
119	12-KD	02.012
120	12-YM	01.012
121	2-FG	02.002
122		
123	12-KR	02.012

124	12-KB	02.012

Dassault Mirage 2000D
AMD-BA, Istres;
CEAM (EC 05.330),
  Mont-de-Marsan;
EC 01.003 'Navarre',
EC 02.003 'Champagne' &
EC 03.003 'Ardennes',
  Nancy

601	3-IA	01.003
602	3-XG	03.003
603	3-IC	01.003
604	3-XK	03.003
605	3-IE	01.003
606	3-XL	03.003
607		CEV
609	3-XD	03.003
610	3-II	01.003
611	3-XS	03.003
612	3-IL	01.003
613	3-IF	01.003
614	3-IJ	01.003
615	330-AM	CEAM
616	330-AA	CEAM
617	3-XA	03.003
618	3-IG	01.003
619	3-JE	02.003
620	3-IM	01.003
621	3-XC	03.003
622	3-JF	02.003
623	3-IB	01.003
624	3-XF	03.003
625	3-IK	01.003
626	3-XH	03.003
627	3-JG	02.003
628	3-XI	03.003
629	3-XJ	03.003
630	3-JI	02.003
631	330-AE	CEAM
632	3-XM	03.003
633	3-JT	02.003
634	3-ID	01.003
635	3-XP	03.003
636	3-JJ	02.003
637	3-JH	02.003
638	3-IQ	01.003
639	3-XQ	03.003
640	3-IR	01.003
641	3-JA	02.003
642	3-JB	02.003
643	3-JC	02.003
644	3-JD	02.003
645	3-JO	02.003
646	3-JP	02.003
647	3-JQ	02.003
648	3-XT	03.003
649	3-IS	01.003
650	3-IN	01.003
651	3-IH	01.003
652	3-XN	03.003
653	3-JK	02.003
654	3-IT	01.003
655	3-XE	03.003
656	3-JL	02.003
657		
658		
659		
660		

Dassault Mirage 2000N
CEAM (EC 05.330),
  Mont-de-Marsan;
EC 01.004 'Dauphiné' &

EC 02.004 'Lafayette', Luxeuil;
EC 03.004 'Limousin', Istres

301		CEV
303		CEV
304	4-CB	03.004
305	4-CS	03.004
306	4-CQ	03.004
307	4-CC	03.004
309	4-CT	03.004
310	4-CE	03.004
311	4-CA	03.004
312	4-CF	03.004
313	4-CU	03.004
314	4-CG	03.004
315	4-CD	03.004
316	4-CH	03.004
317		
318	4-CI	03.004
319	4-BI	02.004
320	4-CK	03.004
322	4-CL	03.004
323	4-CJ	03.004
325	4-BT	02.004
326	4-CM	03.004
327		
329	4-CN	03.004
330	4-CO	03.004
331	4-CP	03.004
332	4-BN	02.004
333	4-AB	01.004
334	330-AV	CEAM
335	4-BJ	02.004
336	4-BP	02.004
337	4-BU	02.004
338	4-AC	01.004
339	4-AD	01.004
340		
341	4-AF	01.004
342	4-AG	01.004
343	4-AH	01.004
344	4-AJ	01.004
345	4-AA	01.004
348	4-AL	01.004
349	4-BA	02.004
350	4-AO	01.004
351	4-AQ	01.004
353	4-BL	02.004
354	4-BF	02.004
355	4-AE	01.004
356	4-AI	01.004
357	4-BD	02.004
358	4-AL	01.004
359	4-BG	02.004
360	4-AI	01.004
361		
362	4-BM	02.004
363	4-BK	02.004
364	4-BB	02.004
365	4-BE	02.004
366	4-BO	02.004
367	4-AS	01.004
368	4-AR	01.004
369	4-BQ	02.004
370	4-AT	01.004
371	4-AV	02.004
372	4-BR	02.004
373	4-BH	02.004
374	4-BS	02.004
375	4-BC	02.004

Dassault Rafale-B
AMD-BA, Istres
B01   AMD-BA

Dassault Rafale-C

B1	AMD-BA
301	CEV

AMD-BA, Istres
C01   AMD-BA

DHC-6 Twin Otter 200/300*
CEAM (EET 06.330), Mont-de-Marsan;
EdC 00.070, Chateaudun;
ETL 01.062 'Vercours', Creil;
GAM 00.056 'Vaucluse', Evreux

292	CC	00.056
298	CD	00.056
300	CE	00.056
603*	70-MB	00.070
730*	CA	01.062
742*	IA	CEAM
743*	70-MA	00.070
745*	IB	CEAM
786*	CT	01.062
790*	CW	01.062

Douglas DC-8-53[1]/55F[2]/72CF[3]
EE 00.051 'Aubrac', Evreux;
ET 03.060 'Esterel', Paris/Charles de Gaulle

45570[1]	FE	00.051
46013[3]	F-RAFG	03.060
46043[3]	FD	00.051
46130[3]	F-RAFF	03.060

Embraer EMB.121AA/AN* Xingu
EAT 00.319, Avord

054	YX
055*	
064	YY
066*	
069*	
070*	
072	YA
073	YB
075	YC
076	YD
077*	
078	YE
080	YF
082	YG
083*	ZE
084	YH
086	YI
089	YJ
090*	
091	YK
092	YL
095	YM
096	YN
098	YO
099	YP
101	YR
102	YS
103	YT
105	YU
107	YV
108	YW
111	YQ

Embraer EMB.312F Tucano
GI 00.312, Salon de Provence

438	312-UW
439	312-UX
456	312-JA
457	312-JB
458	312-JC
459	312-JD
460	312-JE
461	312-JF
462	312-JG
463	312-JH
464	312-JI
466	312-JK
467	312-JL
468	312-JM
469	312-JN
470	312-JO
471	312-JP
472	312-JQ
473	312-JR
474	312-JS
475	312-JT
477	312-JU
478	312-JV
479	312-JX
480	312-JY
481	312-JZ
483	312-UB
484	312-UC
485	312-UD
486	312-UE
487	312-UF
488	312-UG
489	312-UH
490	312-UI
491	312-UJ
492	312-UK
493	312-UL
494	312-UM
495	312-UN
496	312-UO
497	312-UP
498	312-UQ
499	312-UR
500	312-US
501	312-UT
502	312-UU
503	312-UV
504	312-UX

Eurocopter AS.332 Super Puma/AS.532 Cougar
EH 03.067 'Parisis', Villacoublay;
ETOM 00.082 'Maine', Faaa-Tahiti;
GAM 00.056 'Vaucluse', Evreux

2014	AS.332C		
2057	AS.332C	82-PO	00.082
2093	AS.332C	82-PP	00.082
2233	AS.332M	67-FY	03.067
2235	AS.332M	67-FZ	03.067
2244	AS.332C	82-PM	00.082
2337	AS.532UL		03.067
2342	AS.532M1	FX	00.056
2369	AS.532M1	FW	00.056
2375	AS.532M1	FV	00.056
2377	AS.532M	67-FU	03.067

France

Lockheed C-130H/C-130H-30* Hercules

ET 02.061 'Franche-Comté', Orléans

4588	61-PM	
4589	61-PN	
5114	61-PA	
5116	61-PB	
5119	61-PC	
5140	61-PD	
5142*	61-PE	
5144*	61-PF	
5150*	61-PG	
5151*	61-PH	
5152*	61-PI	
5153*	61-PJ	
5226*	61-PK	
5227*	61-PL	

Morane Saulnier MS.760 Paris

CEV, Bretigny & Istres;
EAC 00.314, Tours;
EAM 09.112, Reims;
EAM 09.115, Orange;
EAM 09.116, Luxeuil;
EAM 09.128, Metz;
EAM 09.132, Colmar;
EAM 09.133, Nancy;
ENOSA 00.316, Toulouse;
GI00.312, Salon de Provence

25	314-DC	00.314
26	112-CP	09.112
27	132-CC	09.132
30	4-WA	09.116
34	133-CG	09.133
36	316-DH	00.316
38	115-MF	09.115
45		
54		
56		
57	316-DJ	00.316
58	312-DG	00.312
59	133-CF	09.133
61	316-DI	00.316
65	316-DD	00.316
68	NB	CEV
71	316-DO	00.316
75	116-CB	09.116
83	NC	CEV
91	316-DM	00.316
92	316-DL	00.316
93	132-CN	09.132
94	115-MF	09.115
115	OV	CEV
116	ON	CEV
118	NQ	CEV
119	NL	CEV

Nord 262A[A]/262D[D]/262D-AEN[N] Frégate

CEV, Istres;
ENOSA 00.316, Toulouse;
EPNER, Istres;
ETE 00.041 'Verdun', Metz;
ETE 00.043 'Médoc', Bordeaux;
ETE 00.044 'Mistral', Aix-en-Provence;
ETEC 00.065, Villacoublay

58[A]	MJ	EPNER
64[D]	AA	00.065
66[D]	AB	00.065
67[A]	MI	CEV
68[D]	AC	00.065
76[N]	316-DA	00.316
77[D]	AK	00.044
78[D]	AF	00.065
80[D]	AW	00.041
81[D]	AH	00.065
83[N]	316-DB	00.316
86[N]	316-DD	00.316
87[N]	316-DC	00.316
88[D]	AL	00.044
89[D]	AZ	00.041
91[D]	AT	00.043
92[N]	316-DE	00.316
93[D]	AP	00.065
94[D]	AU	00.044
95[D]	AR	00.065
105[D]	AE	00.065
106[D]	AY	00.041
107[D]	AX	00.065
108[D]	AG	00.041
109[D]	AM	00.043
110[D]	AS	00.041

SEPECAT Jaguar A

CEV, Bretigny & Istres;
CEAM (EC 05.330), Mont-de-Marsan;
CITac 00.339 'Aquitaine', Luxeuil;
EC 01.007 'Provence',
EC 02.007 'Argonne' &
EC 03.007 'Languedoc', St Dizier

A1		
A15		
A17		
A25	7-PU	02.007
A28		
A29		
A34		
A35	7-IH	02.007
A43	7-HF	01.007
A47	7-PJ	02.007
A50		
A53	7-P	02.007
A55	7-PA	02.007
A58	7-HE	01.007
A61		
A64	7-IS	03.007
A66	7-IB	03.007
A75	7-IJ	03.007
A82	7-HM	01.007
A84	7-PY	02.007
A87	7-PF	02.007
A88	7-PC	02.007
A90		
A92	7-HC	01.007
A93	7-IO	03.007
A94	7-IG	03.007
A96	7-HD	01.007
A97	7-IQ	03.007
A98		
A99		
A100		
A101	7-HB	01.007
A103	7-IE	03.007
A104	7-IT	03.007
A107	7-IR	03.007
A108	7-HQ	01.007
A112	7-HS	01.007
A113	7-II	03.007
A115	7-HT	01.007
A117	7-HA	01.007
A120	7-IN	03.007
A122	7-IM	03.007
A123		
A124		
A126	7-HJ	01.007
A127	7-IP	03.007
A128	7-HV	01.007
A129	7-IC	03.007
A130	7-HU	01.007
A133	7-IK	03.007
A135	7-HL	01.007
A137	7-HG	01.007
A138		
A139		
A140	7-HI	01.007
A141	7-HW	01.007
A144	7-IF	03.007
A145		
A148	7-IK	03.007
A149	7-HP	01.007
A150		
A151	7-HH	01.007
A153	7-ID	03.007
A154		
A157	7-HK	01.007
A158	7-IA	03.007
A159	7-HO	01.007
A160	7-IV	03.007

SEPECAT Jaguar E

E2	339-WM	00.339
E3	339-WF	00.339
E4	7-PG	02.007
E5	339-WH	00.339
E6	339-WG	00.339
E7	7-PL	02.007
E8		
E9	7-PE	02.007
E10		
E12	339-WI	00.339
E15		
E18	339-WL	00.339
E19	7-PN	02.007
E20	339-WN	00.339
E21	7-PM	02.007
E22	339-WK	00.339
E23	7-PB	02.007
E24	7-PH	02.007
E25		
E27		
E28	7-PS	02.007
E29	339-WJ	00.339
E30	7-PK	02.007
E32		
E35		
E36		
E37	7-PQ	02.007
E39		
E40	7-PI	02.007

SOCATA TBM 700

CEAM (EET 06.330), Mont-de-Marsan;
CEV, Bordeaux;
ETE 00.041 'Verdun', Metz;
ETE 00.043 'Médoc', Bordeaux;
ETE 00.044 'Mistral', Aix-en-Provence;
ETEC 00.065, Villacoublay;
EdC 00.070, Chateaudun

33	330-ID	CEAM
35	43-XB	00.043

70	43-XC	00.043
77	65-XD	00.065
78	65-XE	00.044
80	41-XF	00.041
93	330-IC	CEAM
94	65-XG	00.070
95	65-XH	00.065
103	41-XI	00.041
104	65-XJ	00.065
105	65-XK	00.065
106	MN	CEV
110	XP	00.041
111	65-XM	00.065
117	65-XN	00.065
125	XO	00.065
131	XQ	

**Transall C-160A/C-160F/
C-160H/C-160NG/s C-160NG
GABRIEL*/C-160R**
CEAM (EET 06.330),
 Mont-de-Marsan;
CEV, Bretigny;
EA 01.059 'Bigorre', Evreux;
EET 01.054 'Dunkerque',
 Metz;
ET 01.061 'Touraine' &
ET 03.061 'Poitou', Orléans;
ET 01.064 'Bearn' &
ET 02.064 'Anjou', Evreux;
ETOM 00.055 'Ouessant',
 Dakar

RA02	C-160R	61-MI	01.061
RA04	C-160R	61-MS	01.061
RA06	C-160R	61-ZB	03.061
R1	C-160R	61-MA	01.061
R2	C-160R	61-MB	01.061
R3	C-160R	61-MC	01.061
R4	C-160R	61-MD	01.061
R5	C-160R	61-ME	01.061
R11	C-160R	61-MF	01.061
R12	C-160R	61-MG	01.061
R13	C-160R	61-MH	01.061
R15	C-160R	61-MJ	01.061
R16	C-160R	61-MK	01.061
R17	C-160R	61-ML	01.061
R18	C-160R	61-MM	01.061
R42	C-160R	61-MN	01.061
R43	C-160R	61-MO	01.061
R44	C-160R	61-MP	01.061
R45	C-160R	61-MQ	01.061
R46	C-160R	61-MR	01.061
R48	C-160R	61-MT	01.061
R49	C-160R	59-MU	CEV
R51	C-160R	61-MW	01.061
R52	C-160R	61-MX	01.061
R53	C-160R	61-MY	01.061
R54	C-160R	61-MZ	01.061
F55	C-160F	61-ZC	03.061
R86	C-160R	61-ZD	03.061
F87	C-160F	61-ZE	03.061
F88	C-160F	61-ZF	03.061
R89	C-160R	61-ZG	03.061
F90	C-160F	61-ZH	03.061
R91	C-160R	61-ZI	03.061
R92	C-160R	61-ZJ	03.061
R93	C-160R	61-ZK	03.061
R94	C-160R	61-ZL	03.061
R95	C-160R	61-ZM	03.061
R96	C-160R	61-ZN	03.061
R97	C-160R	61-ZO	03.061
R98	C-160R	61-ZP	03.061
R99	C-160R	61-ZQ	03.061
F100	C-160F	61-ZR	03.061
R153	C-160R	61-ZS	03.061
R154	C-160R	61-ZT	03.061
R157	C-160R	61-ZW	03.061
R158	C-160R	61-ZX	03.061
R159	C-160R	61-ZY	03.061
R160	C-160R	61-ZZ	03.061
F201	C-160NG	64-GA	01.064
R202	C-160R	64-GB	02.064
R203	C-160R	64-GC	01.064
R204	C-160R	64-GD	02.064
F205	C-160NG	64-GE	01.064
F206	C-160NG	64-GF	02.064
F207	C-160NG	64-GG	01.064
R208	C-160R	64-GH	02.064
F210	C-160NG	64-GJ	02.064
F211	C-160NG	64-GK	01.064
R212	C-160R	64-GL	02.064
F213	C-160NG	64-GM	01.064
F214	C-160NG	64-GN	02.064
F215	C-160NG	64-GO	01.064
F216	C-160NG*	54-GT	01.054
F217	C-160NG	64-GQ	01.064
F218	C-160NG	64-GR	02.064
F221	C-160NG*	54-GS	01.054
F223	C-160NG	64-GW	01.064
F224	C-160NG	64-GX	02.064
R225	C-160R	64-GY	01.064
R226	C-160R	64-GZ	02.064
H01	C-160H	59-BA	01.059
H02	C-160H	59-BB	01.059
H03	C-160H	59-BC	01.059
H04	C-160H	59-BD	01.059

**Aéronavale/Marine
Aérospatiale SA.321G
Super Frelon**
32 Flotille, Lanvéoc/Poulmic;
33 Flotille, San Mandrier

101	32F
102	32F
106	32F
118	33F
134	32F
137	32F
144	32F
148	33F
160	32F
162	32F
163	33F
164	33F
165	33F

Breguet Br 1050M Alizé
6 Flotille, Nimes/Garons

22
47
49
50
52
53
55
56
59

**Breguet Br 1150
Atlantique 2**
21 Flotille,
 Nimes/Garons;
23 Flotille,
 Lorient/Lann Bihoué

1	21F
2	23F
3	21F
4	21F

France

Dassault (23F/21F series)

5	23F
6	23F
7	21F
8	21F
9	23F
10	23F
11	23F
12	21F
13	21F
14	21F
15	23F
16	21F
17	21F
18	21F
19	23F
20	23F
21	21F
22	23F
23	21F
24	21F
25	21F
26	23F
27	21F
28	
29	
30	

Dassault Etendard IVPM
16 Flotille, Landivisiau

101
107
109
115
118
153
163

Dassault Falcon 10(MER)
ES 57, Landivisiau

32	
101	
129	
133	
143	
185	

Dassault Falcon 20G Guardian
ES 9 Tontouta;
ES 12 Papeete

48	12S
65	9S
72	12S
77	9S
80	

Dassault Falcon 50
24 Flotille, Lorient/Lann Bihoué

30
36

Dassault Rafale-M

M01	AMD-BA
M02	AMD-BA
M1	CEV

Dassault Super Etendard
11 Flotille, Landivisiau;
17 Flotille, Landivisiau;
CEV, Bretigny & Istres

1	17F
2	11F
3	17F
4	11F
6	
8	11F
10	11F
11	17F
12	17F
13	11F
14	11F
15	
16	17F
17	11F
18	
19	11F
23	11F
24	11F
25	17F
26	11F
28	17F
30	11F
31	11F
32	17F
33	17F
35	CEV
37	11F
38	11F
39	17F
41	11F
43	11F
44	17F
45	11F
46	11F
47	17F
48	11F
49	11F
50	17F
51	11F
52	17F
55	17F
57	17F
59	17F
60	11F
61	17F
62	11F
64	11F
65	11F
66	11F
68	CEV
69	17F
71	11F

Embraer EMB.121AN Xingu
ES 2, Lorient/Lann Bihoué

30
47
65
67
68
71
74
79
81
85
87

Eurocopter SA.365/AS.565 Panther
ES 23, St Mandrier;
32 Flotille, Lanvéoc/Poulmic (with detachments at Cherbourg, Hyères, La Rochelle & Le Touquet)
36 Flotille, St Mandrier

17	SA.365N	32F
19	SA.365N	32F
24	SA.365N	32F
81	SA.365N	32F
91	SA.365N	32F
313	SA.365F1	23S
316	AS.565MA	23S
318	SA.365F1	23S
319	AS.565MA	32F
322	SA.365F1	23S
355	AS.565MA	36F
362	AS.565MA	32F
436	AS.565MA	36F
452	AS.565MA	36F
453	AS.565MA	32F
466	AS.565MA	36F
482	AS.565MA	32F
486	AS.565SA	36F
503	AS.565MA	36F
505	AS.565MA	23S
506	AS.565MA	36F
511	AS.565SA	
522	AS.565SA	36F

LTV F-8P Crusader
12 Flotille, Landivisiau

3
4
7
8
10
11
19
23
29
32
34
35
39

Nord 262 Frégate
28 Flotille, Hyères;
ES 55, Aspretto;
ES 56, Nimes/Garons

45	262E	56S
46	262E	56S
51	262E	56S
52	262E	56S
53	262E	56S
60	262E	
63	262E	56S
69	262E	56S
70	262E	
71	262E	56S
72	262E	56S
73	262E	56S
75	262E	56S
79	262E	
100	262E	56S

Northrop Grumman E-2C Hawkeye
4 Flotille, Lorient/Lann Bihoué

1	(165455)
2	(165456)

Westland Lynx HAS2(FN)/HAS4(FN)*
31 Flotille, St Mandrier;
34 Flotille, Lanvéoc/Poulmic

260	
262	34F
263	31F
264	31F
265	34F
266	31F

267	31F
268	
269	31F
270	31F
271	34F
272	31F
274	34F
275	31F
276	34F
620	34F
621	34F
622	34F
623	34F
624	31F
625	34F
627	34F
801*	31F
802*	31F
803*	31F
804*	31F
806*	34F
807*	34F
808*	34F
810*	34F
811*	34F
812*	31F
813*	34F
814*	31F

Aviation Legére de l'Arme de Terre (ALAT)
Cessna F.406 Caravan II

0008	ABM
0010	ABN

SOCATA TBM 700

99	ABO
100	ABP
115	ABQ

GERMANY
Luftwaffe, Marineflieger
Boeing 707-307C
1/FBS, Köln-Bonn
10+02

Airbus A.310-304
1/FBS, Köln-Bonn

10+21
10+22
10+23
10+24
10+25
10+26
10+27

Tupolev Tu-154M
1/FBS, Köln-Bonn
11+01

Canadair CL601-1A Challenger
1/FBS, Köln-Bonn

12+01
12+02
12+03
12+04
12+05
12+06
12+07

Mikoyan MiG-29G/ MiG-29GT*
JG-73 'Steinhoff', Laage

29+01	
29+02	
29+03	
29+04	
29+05	
29+06	
29+07	
29+08	
29+10	
29+11	
29+12	
29+14	
29+15	
29+16	
29+17	
29+18	
29+19	
29+20	
29+21	
29+22*	
29+23*	
29+24*	
29+25*	

McD F-4F Phantom
JG-71 'Richthoven', Wittmundhaven;
JG-72 'Westfalen', Hopsten;
JG-73 'Steinhoff', Laage;
JG-74 'Molders', Neuburg/ Donau;
TsLw-1, Kaufbeuren;
WTD-61, Ingolstadt

37+01	JG-72
37+03	JG-71
37+04	TsLw-1
37+06	JG-72
37+07	JG-72
37+08	JG-74
37+09	JG-72
37+10	JG-72
37+11	JG-73
37+12	JG-72
37+13	JG-74
37+14	TsLw-1
37+15	WTD-61
37+16	WTD-61
37+17	JG-74
37+22	JG-71
37+26	JG-73
37+28	JG-71
37+29	JG-72
37+31	JG-72
37+32	JG-71
37+33	JG-72
37+34	JG-72
37+35	JG-72
37+36	JG-72
37+37	JG-72
37+38	JG-72
37+39	JG-71
37+42	JG-72
37+43	JG-72
37+44	JG-72
37+45	JG-72
37+47	JG-72
37+48	JG-74
37+49	JG-71
37+50	JG-72
37+52	JG-72
37+54	JG-74
37+55	JG-71
37+58	JG-72
37+61	JG-74

37+63	JG-71
37+64	JG-74
37+65	JG-71
37+66	JG-74
37+67	JG-74
37+71	JG-74
37+73	JG-71
37+75	JG-72
37+76	JG-71
37+77	JG-74
37+79	JG-74
37+81	JG-71
37+82	JG-71
37+83	JG-71
37+84	JG-74
37+85	JG-71
37+86	JG-71
37+88	JG-73
37+89	JG-73
37+92	JG-74
37+93	JG-72
37+94	JG-74
37+96	JG-72
37+97	JG-74
37+98	JG-74
38+00	JG-74
38+01	JG-73
38+02	JG-71
38+03	JG-72
38+04	JG-72
38+05	JG-73
38+06	JG-74
38+07	JG-71
38+09	JG-74
38+10	JG-74
38+12	JG-71
38+13	WTD-61
38+14	JG-71
38+16	JG-74
38+17	JG-74
38+18	JG-74
38+20	JG-72
38+24	JG-74
38+25	JG-74
38+26	JG-74
38+27	JG-71
38+28	JG-74
38+29	JG-71
38+30	JG-73
38+31	JG-72
38+32	JG-71
38+33	JG-73
38+34	JG-72
38+36	JG-71
38+37	JG-72
38+40	JG-71
38+42	JG-72
38+43	JG-72
38+44	JG-72
38+45	JG-72
38+46	JG-72
38+48	JG-74
38+49	JG-71
38+50	JG-72
38+53	JG-74
38+54	JG-73
38+55	JG-72
38+56	JG-73
38+57	JG-74
38+58	JG-73
38+60	JG-74
38+61	JG-72
38+62	JG-72
38+64	JG-72

Germany

38+66	JG-73		43+65	JbG-38		44+57	JbG-31	
38+67	JG-73		43+67	JbG-34		44+58	JbG-31	
38+68	JG-72		43+68	JbG-34		44+60	JbG-31	
38+69	JG-74		43+69	JbG-38		44+61	AkG-51	
38+70	JG-74		43+70	JbG-38		44+62	JbG-33	
38+73	JG-72		43+71	JbG-38		44+63	JbG-33	
38+74	JG-74		43+72	JbG-38		44+64	AkG-51	
38+75	JG-71		43+73	AkG-51		44+65	AkG-51	
99+91	WTD-61		43+75	[G-77]	TTTE	44+66	JbG-31	
			43+76	JbG-38		44+68	AkG-51	

**Panavia Tornado
Strike/Trainer[1]/ECR[2]**
AkG-51 'Immelmann',
   Schleswig/Jagel;
JbG-31 'Boelcke', Nörvenich;
JbG-32, Lechfeld;
JbG-33, Büchel;
JbG-34 'Algäu', Memmingen;
JbG-38 'Ostfriesland', Jever;
MFG-2, Eggebek;
TsLw-1, Kaufbeuren;
TTTE, RAF Cottesmore;
WTD-61, Ingolstadt

43+01[1]	[G-20]	TTTE	43+77	JbG-34		44+69	AkG-51	
43+02[1]	[G-21]	TTTE	43+78	JbG-38		44+70	JbG-31	
43+03[1]	[G-22]	TTTE	43+79	AkG-51		44+71	JbG-31	
43+04[1]	JbG-33		43+80	AkG-51		44+72[1]	JbG-33	
43+05[1]	[G-24]	TTTE	43+81	AkG-51		44+73[1]	JbG-32	
43+06[1]	[G-25]	TTTE	43+82	AkG-51		44+75[1]	JbG-33	
43+07[1]	[G-26]	TTTE	43+85	JbG-38		44+76	JbG-34	
43+08[1]	JbG-32		43+86	JbG-38		44+77	JbG-31	
43+09[1]	[G-28]	TTTE	43+87	MFG-2		44+78	JbG-31	
43+10[1]			43+90[1]	JbG-38		44+79	JbG-33	
43+11[1]	[G-30]	TTTE	43+92[1]	JbG-31		44+80	JbG-33	
43+13	[G-71]	TTTE	43+94[1]	JbG-38		44+81	JbG-34	
43+14	[G-72]	TTTE	43+96	AkG-51		44+83	JbG-33	
43+15[1]	[G-31]	TTTE	43+97[1]	JbG-32		44+84	JbG-34	
43+16[1]	[G-32]	TTTE	43+98	AkG-51		44+85	JbG-33	
43+17[1]	[G-33]	TTTE	43+99	JbG-34		44+86	AkG-51	
43+18	JbG-31		44+00	JbG-31		44+87	AkG-51	
43+20	AkG-51		44+02	JbG-31		44+88	AkG-51	
43+22[1]	JbG-38		44+03	JbG-31		44+89	JbG-33	
43+23[1]	JbG-38		44+04	AkG-51		44+90	JbG-33	
43+25	[G-75]	TTTE	44+05[1]	AkG-51		44+91	JbG-33	
43+27	JbG-34		44+06	JbG-34		44+92	JbG-38	
43+29	JbG-31		44+07	JbG-31		44+93	JbG-33	
43+30	JbG-31		44+08	JbG-38		44+94	JbG-33	
43+31[1]	JbG-31		44+09	JbG-33		44+95	JbG-38	
43+32	[G-73]	TTTE	44+10[1]	JbG-38		44+96	JbG-31	
43+33[1]	JbG-38		44+11	JbG-34		44+97	JbG-38	
43+34	TsLw-1		44+13	JbG-31		44+98	JbG-34	
43+35[1]	JbG-38		44+14	JbG-31		45+00	JbG-33	
43+37[1]	JbG-38		44+15	JbG-38		45+01	JbG-38	
43+38	JbG-53		44+16[1]	JbG-31		45+02	JbG-34	
43+40	JbG-38		44+17	AkG-51		45+03	JbG-34	
43+41	JbG-31		44+19	JbG-31		45+04	JbG-33	
43+42[1]	[G-39]	TTTE	44+21	JbG-31		45+05	JbG-33	
43+43[1]	JbG-38		44+22	JbG-31		45+06	AkG-51	
43+44[1]	AkG-51		44+23	JbG-33		45+07	JbG-33	
43+45[1]	AkG-51		44+24	AkG-51		45+08	JbG-33	
43+46	AkG-51		44+25[1]	JbG-38		45+09	JbG-31	
43+47	AkG-51		44+26	JbG-31		45+10	JbG-31	
43+48	AkG-51		44+27	JbG-33		45+11	JbG-31	
43+50	AkG-51		44+29	JbG-31		45+12[1]	MFG-2	
43+52	JbG-38		44+30	JbG-31		45+13[1]	MFG-2	
43+53	JbG-38		44+31	JbG-31		45+14[1]	JbG-38	
43+54	JbG-34		44+32	JbG-38		45+15[1]	MFG-2	
43+55	MFG-2		44+33	JbG-33		45+16[1]	MFG-2	
43+59	JbG-38		44+34	AkG-51		45+17	JbG-33	
43+60	JbG-34		44+35	JbG-31		45+18	JbG-33	
43+61	TsLw-1		44+37[1]	JbG-38		45+19	JbG-33	
43+62	JbG-34		44+38[1]	JbG-33		45+20	AkG-51	
43+63	JbG-34		44+40	JbG-33		45+21	JbG-33	
43+64	JbG-38		44+41	JbG-31		45+22	JbG-33	
			44+42	AkG-51		45+23	JbG-31	
			44+43	JbG-34		45+24	JbG-33	
			44+44	JbG-31		45+25	AkG-51	
			44+46	JbG-34		45+27	MFG-2	
			44+48	JbG-33		45+28	MFG-2	
			44+49	JbG-31		45+29	WTD-61	
			44+50	AkG-51		45+30	MFG-2	
			44+51	JbG-38		45+31	MFG-2	
			44+52	JbG-31		45+33	MFG-2	
			44+53	AkG-51		45+34	MFG-2	
			44+54	JbG-33		45+35	MFG-2	
			44+55	JbG-38		45+36	MFG-2	
			44+56	JbG-34		45+37	MFG-2	
						45+38	MFG-2	

45+39	MFG-2
45+40	MFG-2
45+41	MFG-2
45+42	MFG-2
45+43	MFG-2
45+44	MFG-2
45+45	MFG-2
45+46	MFG-2
45+47	MFG-2
45+49	MFG-2
45+50	MFG-2
45+51	AkG-51
45+52	MFG-2
45+53	MFG-2
45+54	MFG-2
45+55	MFG-2
45+56	MFG-2
45+57	JbG-34
45+59	MFG-2
45+60[1]	JbG-38
45+61[1]	JbG-34
45+62[1]	JbG-38
45+64	TsLw-1
45+66	MFG-2
45+67	AkG-51
45+68	MFG-2
45+69	MFG-2
45+70[1]	JbG-33
45+71	MFG-2
45+72	MFG-2
45+73[1]	JbG-31
45+74	MFG-2
45+76	JbG-38
45+77[1]	JbG-33
45+78	JbG-33
45+79	JbG-31
45+81	JbG-34
45+82	JbG-31
45+84	AkG-51
45+85	AkG-51
45+86	JbG-33
45+87	JbG-34
45+88	JbG-33
45+89	JbG-34
45+90	JbG-31
45+91	AkG-51
45+93	AkG-51
45+94	JbG-33
45+95	JbG-34
45+98	AkG-51
45+99[1]	AkG-51
46+00	JbG-34
46+01	JbG-34
46+02	JbG-33
46+03[1]	JbG-34
46+04[1]	JbG-38
46+05[1]	MFG-2
46+07[1]	JbG-34
46+08[1]	JbG-38
46+09[1]	JbG-34
46+10	WTD-61
46+11	MFG-2
46+12	MFG-2
46+13	JbG-34
46+14	JbG-34
46+15	MFG-2
46+18	MFG-2
46+19	MFG-2
46+20	MFG-2
46+21	MFG-2
46+22	MFG-2
46+23[2]	JbG-32
46+24[2]	JbG-32
46+25[2]	JbG-32

46+26[2]	JbG-32
46+27[2]	JbG-32
46+28[2]	JbG-32
46+29[2]	JbG-32
46+30[2]	JbG-32
46+31[2]	JbG-32
46+32[2]	JbG-32
46+33[2]	JbG-32
46+34[2]	JbG-32
46+35[2]	JbG-32
46+36[2]	JbG-32
46+37[2]	JbG-32
46+38[2]	JbG-32
46+39[2]	JbG-32
46+40[2]	JbG-32
46+41[2]	JbG-32
46+42[2]	JbG-32
46+43[2]	JbG-32
46+44[2]	JbG-32
46+45[2]	JbG-32
46+46[2]	JbG-32
46+47[2]	JbG-32
46+48[2]	JbG-32
46+49[2]	JbG-32
46+50[2]	JbG-32
46+51[2]	JbG-32
46+52[2]	JbG-32
46+53[2]	JbG-32
46+54[2]	JbG-32
46+55[2]	JbG-32
46+56[2]	JbG-32
46+57[2]	JbG-32
98+03[2]	WTD-61
98+59	WTD-61
98+60	WTD-61
98+79[2]	WTD-61

Transall C-160D
LTG-61, Landsberg;
LTG-62, Wunstorf;
LTG-63, Hohn;
WTD-61, Ingolstadt

50+06	LTG-63
50+07	LTG-61
50+08	LTG-61
50+09	LTG-62
50+10	LTG-62
50+17	LTG-62
50+29	LTG-62
50+33	LTG-62
50+34	LTG-61
50+35	LTG-62
50+36	LTG-63
50+37	LTG-62
50+38	LTG-62
50+40	LTG-61
50+41	LTG-62
50+42	LTG-63
50+44	LTG-61
50+45	LTG-61
50+46	LTG-62
50+47	LTG-62
50+48	LTG-61
50+49	LTG-61
50+50	LTG-62
50+51	LTG-61
50+52	LTG-62
50+53	LTG-62
50+54	LTG-63
50+55	LTG-62
50+56	LTG-63
50+57	LTG-63
50+58	LTG-62

50+59	LTG-63
50+60	LTG-62
50+61	LTG-63
50+62	LTG-62
50+64	LTG-61
50+65	LTG-63
50+66	LTG-63
50+67	LTG-61
50+68	LTG-62
50+69	LTG-61
50+70	LTG-62
50+71	LTG-61
50+72	LTG-63
50+73	LTG-63
50+74	LTG-61
50+75	WTD-61
50+76	LTG-63
50+77	LTG-62
50+78	LTG-62
50+79	LTG-63
50+81	LTG-62
50+82	LTG-62
50+83	LTG-62
50+84	LTG-61
50+85	LTG-63
50+86	LTG-61
50+87	LTG-63
50+88	LTG-61
50+89	LTG-62
50+90	WTD-61
50+91	LTG-62
50+92	LTG-61
50+93	LTG-63
50+94	LTG-63
50+95	LTG-61
50+96	LTG-61
50+97	LTG-62
50+98	LTG-63
50+99	LTG-61
51+00	LTG-62
51+01	LTG-62
51+02	LTG-63
51+03	LTG-62
51+04	LTG-61
51+05	LTG-62
51+06	LTG-61
51+07	LTG-62
51+08	LTG-63
51+09	LTG-63
51+10	LTG-61
51+11	LTG-62
51+12	LTG-62
51+13	LTG-63
51+14	LTG-63
51+15	LTG-61

LET L-410UVP-S
3/FBS, Berlin-Tegel

53+09
53+10
53+11
53+12

Dornier Do.228/Do.228LM*
MFG-3, Nordholz;
WTD-61, Ingolstadt

57+01	MFG-3
57+02	MFG-3
57+03	MFG-3
57+04*	MFG-3
98+78	WTD-61

Breguet Br.1151 Atlantic
*Elint

Germany

MFG-3, Nordholz
61+03*
61+04
61+05
61+06*
61+08
61+09
61+10
61+11
61+12
61+13
61+14
61+15
61+16
61+17
61+18*
61+19*
61+20

Eurocopter AS.532U2 Cougar
3/FBS, Berlin/Tegel
82+01
82+02
82+03

Westland Lynx Mk88
MFG-3, Nordholz
83+02
83+03
83+04
83+05
83+06
83+07
83+08
83+09
83+10
83+11
83+12
83+13
83+14
83+15
83+17
83+18
83+19

Westland Sea King HAS41
MFG-5, Kiel-Holtenau
89+50
89+51
89+52
89+53
89+54
89+55
89+56
89+57
89+58
89+59
89+60
89+61
89+62
89+63
89+64
89+65
89+66
89+67
89+68
89+69
89+70
89+71

Eurofighter EF2000 Typhoon
WTD-61, Ingolstadt

98+29	WTD-61
98+30	WTD-61

Heeresfliegertruppe
MBB Bo.105
HFlgRgt-15, Rheine-Bentlage;
HFlgRgt-16, Celle;
HFlgRgt-25, Laupheim;
HFlgRgt-26, Roth;
HFlgRgt-35, Mendig;
HFlgRgt-36, Fritzlar;
HFS-400, Cottbus;
HFVS-910, Bückeburg;
HFWS, Bückeburg;
TsLw-3, Fassberg;
WTD-61, Ingolstadt

80+01	Bo.105M HFR-35
80+02	Bo.105M TsLw-3
80+03	Bo.105M HFWS
80+04	Bo.105M HFWS
80+05	Bo.105M HFR-35
80+06	Bo.105M HFWS
80+07	Bo.105M HFR-35
80+08	Bo.105M HFR-25
80+09	Bo.105M HFR-35
80+10	Bo.105M HFR-25
80+11	Bo.105M HFWS
80+12	Bo.105M HFWS
80+13	Bo.105M HFR-15
80+14	Bo.105M HFWS
80+15	Bo.105M HFR-15
80+16	Bo.105M HFR-15
80+17	Bo.105M HFS-400
80+18	Bo.105M HFR-15
80+19	Bo.105M HFR-15
80+20	Bo.105M HFS-400
80+21	Bo.105M HFR-15
80+22	Bo.105M HFS-400
80+23	Bo.105M HFR-15
80+24	Bo.105M HFR-15
80+25	Bo.105M HFR-15
80+26	Bo.105M HFR-35
80+27	Bo.105M HFR-35
80+28	Bo.105M HFWS
80+29	Bo.105M HFR-35
80+30	Bo.105M HFR-35
80+31	Bo.105M HFR-35
80+32	Bo.105M HFR-35
80+33	Bo.105M HFR-35
80+34	Bo.105M HFR-25
80+35	Bo.105M HFS-400
80+36	Bo.105M HFR-25
80+37	Bo.105M HFS-400
80+38	Bo.105M HFR-25
80+39	Bo.105M HFR-25
80+40	Bo.105M HFR-26
80+41	Bo.105M HFR-25
80+42	Bo.105M HFR-25
80+43	Bo.105M HFR-25
80+44	Bo.105M HFR-25
80+46	Bo.105M TsLw-3
80+47	Bo.105M HFR-25
80+48	Bo.105M HFR-25
80+49	Bo.105M HFS-400
80+50	Bo.105M HFS-400
80+51	Bo.105M HFR-15
80+52	Bo.105M HFR-15
80+53	Bo.105M HFS-400
80+54	Bo.105M HFR-15
80+55	Bo.105M HFS-400
80+56	Bo.105M HFS-400
80+57	Bo.105M HFR-35
80+58	Bo.105M HFR-35
80+59	Bo.105M HFR-35
80+60	Bo.105M HFR-35
80+61	Bo.105M HFS-400
80+62	Bo.105M HFR-35
80+64	Bo.105M HFR-35
80+65	Bo.105M HFR-15
80+66	Bo.105M HFR-15
80+67	Bo.105M HFR-15
80+68	Bo.105M HFR-15
80+69	Bo.105M HFR-15
80+70	Bo.105M HFR-15
80+71	Bo.105M HFR-15
80+72	Bo.105M HFR-15
80+73	Bo.105M HFR-15
80+74	Bo.105M HFR-15
80+76	Bo.105M HFR-35
80+77	Bo.105M HFR-35
80+78	Bo.105M HFR-35
80+79	Bo.105M HFR-35
80+80	Bo.105M HFR-35
80+81	Bo.105M HFR-25
80+82	Bo.105M HFR-25
80+83	Bo.105M HFR-25
80+84	Bo.105M HFR-25
80+85	Bo.105M HFR-25
80+86	Bo.105M HFS-400
80+87	Bo.105M HFR-25
80+88	Bo.105M HFS-400
80+89	Bo.105M HFS-400
80+90	Bo.105M HFS-400
80+91	Bo.105M HFR-35
80+92	Bo.105M HFR-35
80+93	Bo.105M HFS-400
80+94	Bo.105M HFR-25
80+95	Bo.105M HFS-400
80+96	Bo.105M HFR-25
80+97	Bo.105M HFR-35
80+98	Bo.105M HFR-25
80+99	Bo.105M HFR-26
81+00	Bo.105M HFR-25
86+01	Bo.105P HFR-16
86+02	Bo.105P HFWS
86+03	Bo.105P HFWS
86+04	Bo.105P HFR-36
86+05	Bo.105P HFWS
86+06	Bo.105P HFWS
86+07	Bo.105P HFWS
86+08	Bo.105P HFWS
86+09	Bo.105P HFWS
86+10	Bo.105P HFR-16
86+11	Bo.105P HFWS
86+12	Bo.105P HFWS
86+13	Bo.105P HFWS
86+14	Bo.105P HFR-16
86+15	Bo.105P HFR-16
86+16	Bo.105P HFWS
86+17	Bo.105P HFVS-910
86+18	Bo.105P HFR-26
86+19	Bo.105P HFR-26
86+20	Bo.105P HFWS
86+21	Bo.105P HFR-36
86+22	Bo.105P HFWS
86+23	Bo.105P HFWS
86+24	Bo.105P HFVS-910
86+25	Bo.105P HFR-16
86+26	Bo.105P HFR-36
86+27	Bo.105P HFR-26
86+28	Bo.105P HFR-16
86+29	Bo.105P HFR-16
86+30	Bo.105P HFR-26
86+31	Bo.105P HFR-16
86+32	Bo.105P HFR-26
86+33	Bo.105P HFR-26
86+34	Bo.105P HFR-26
86+35	Bo.105P HFR-26

Reg	Type	Unit	Reg	Type	Unit	Reg	Type	Unit
86+36	Bo.105P	HFR-36	87+13	Bo.105P	HFR-36	87+89	Bo.105P	HFR-26
86+37	Bo.105P	HFR-16	87+14	Bo.105P	HFR-36	87+90	Bo.105P	HFWS
86+38	Bo.105P	HFR-36	87+15	Bo.105P	HFR-36	87+91	Bo.105P	HFR-26
86+39	Bo.105P	HFR-16	87+16	Bo.105P	HFR-36	87+92	Bo.105P	HFR-26
86+41	Bo.105P	HFR-26	87+17	Bo.105P	HFR-26	87+93	Bo.105P	HFR-26
86+42	Bo.105P	HFR-26	87+18	Bo.105P	HFR-36	87+94	Bo.105P	HFR-26
86+43	Bo.105P	HFR-16	87+19	Bo.105P	HFR-36	87+95	Bo.105P	HFR-26
86+44	Bo.105P	HFR-26	87+20	Bo.105P	HFR-26	87+96	Bo.105P	HFR-26
86+45	Bo.105P	HFR-26	87+21	Bo.105P	TsLw-3	87+97	Bo.105P	HFR-26
86+46	Bo.105P	HFR-26	87+22	Bo.105P	HFR-16	87+98	Bo.105P	HFR-26
86+47	Bo.105P	HFR-16	87+23	Bo.105P	HFWS	87+99	Bo.105P	HFR-36
86+48	Bo.105P	HFR-16	87+24	Bo.105P	HFR-16	88+01	Bo.105P	HFR-26
86+49	Bo.105P	HFR-26	87+25	Bo.105P	HFR-26	88+02	Bo.105P	HFR-36
86+50	Bo.105P	HFR-16	87+26	Bo.105P	HFR-35	88+03	Bo.105P	HFR-36
86+51	Bo.105P	HFR-36	87+27	Bo.105P	HFR-16	88+04	Bo.105P	HFR-16
86+52	Bo.105P	HFR-16	87+28	Bo.105P	HFR-16	88+05	Bo.105P	HFVS-910
86+53	Bo.105P	HFR-36	87+29	Bo.105P	HFR-26	88+06	Bo.105P	HFR-36
86+54	Bo.105P	TsLw-3	87+30	Bo.105P	HFR-16	88+07	Bo.105P	HFR-36
86+55	Bo.105P	TsLw-3	87+31	Bo.105P	HFR-16	88+08	Bo.105P	HFR-36
86+56	Bo.105P	HFR-36	87+32	Bo.105P	HFR-16	88+09	Bo.105P	HFR-36
86+57	Bo.105P	HFR-16	87+33	Bo.105P	HFWS	88+10	Bo.105P	HFVS-910
86+58	Bo.105P	HFR-36	87+34	Bo.105P	HFR-26	88+11	Bo.105P	HFR-36
86+59	Bo.105P	HFWS	87+35	Bo.105P	HFR-26	88+12	Bo.105P	HFR-36
86+60	Bo.105P	HFR-16	87+36	Bo.105P	HFR-26	98+21	Bo.105C	WTD-61
86+61	Bo.105P	HFR-26	87+37	Bo.105P	HFR-26	98+28	Bo.105C	WTD-61
86+62	Bo.105P	HFVS-910	87+38	Bo.105P	HFR-36			
86+63	Bo.105P	HFR-26	87+39	Bo.105P	HFR-36			
86+64	Bo.105P	HFR-26	87+41	Bo.105P	HFR-16			
86+65	Bo.105P	HFR-26	87+42	Bo.105P	HFR-36			
86+66	Bo.105P	HFVS-910	87+43	Bo.105P	HFR-36			
86+67	Bo.105P	HFR-26	87+44	Bo.105P	HFR-36			
86+68	Bo.105P	HFR-36	87+45	Bo.105P	HFR-16			
86+69	Bo.105P	HFR-26	87+46	Bo.105P	HFR-16			
86+70	Bo.105P	HFR-16	87+47	Bo.105P	HFR-16			
86+71	Bo.105P	HFR-36	87+48	Bo.105P	HFR-16			
86+72	Bo.105P	HFR-36	87+49	Bo.105P	HFR-16			
86+73	Bo.105P	HFWS	87+50	Bo.105P	HFWS			
86+74	Bo.105P	HFR-16	87+51	Bo.105P	HFR-16			
86+75	Bo.105P	HFR-36	87+52	Bo.105P	HFR-16			
86+76	Bo.105P	HFR-26	87+53	Bo.105P	HFWS			
86+77	Bo.105P	HFR-16	87+55	Bo.105P	HFVS-910			
86+78	Bo.105P	HFR-26	87+56	Bo.105P	HFR-26			
86+80	Bo.105P	HFR-16	87+57	Bo.105P	HFR-26			
86+81	Bo.105P	HFR-16	87+58	Bo.105P	HFR-26			
86+83	Bo.105P	HFR-16	87+59	Bo.105P	HFR-36			
86+84	Bo.105P	HFR-16	87+60	Bo.105P	HFR-36			
86+85	Bo.105P	HFR-16	87+61	Bo.105P	HFR-35			
86+86	Bo.105P	HFR-16	87+62	Bo.105P	HFR-36			
86+87	Bo.105P	HFR-16	87+63	Bo.105P	HFWS			
86+88	Bo.105P	HFR-16	87+64	Bo.105P	HFR-36			
86+89	Bo.105P	HFR-16	87+65	Bo.105P	HFR-36			
86+90	Bo.105P	HFR-26	87+66	Bo.105P	HFR-36			
86+91	Bo.105P	HFR-26	87+67	Bo.105P	HFWS			
86+92	Bo.105P	HFR-36	87+68	Bo.105P	HFR-16			
86+93	Bo.105P	HFVS-910	87+69	Bo.105P	HFR-26			
86+94	Bo.105P	HFWS	87+70	Bo.105P	HFR-16			
86+95	Bo.105P	HFR-16	87+71	Bo.105P	HFR-26			
86+96	Bo.105P	HFR-16	87+72	Bo.105P	HFR-16			
86+97	Bo.105P	HFR-36	87+73	Bo.105P	HFR-16			
86+98	Bo.105P	HFR-16	87+74	Bo.105P	HFVS-910			
86+99	Bo.105P	HFR-26	87+75	Bo.105P	HFR-16			
87+00	Bo.105P	HFR-26	87+76	Bo.105P	HFR-16			
87+01	Bo.105P	HFR-26	87+77	Bo.105P	HFR-16			
87+02	Bo.105P	HFR-26	87+78	Bo.105P	HFR-16			
87+03	Bo.105P	HFR-26	87+79	Bo.105P	HFR-16			
87+04	Bo.105P	HFR-26	87+80	Bo.105P	HFR-16			
87+05	Bo.105P	HFR-26	87+81	Bo.105P	HFR-16			
87+06	Bo.105P	HFR-36	87+82	Bo.105P	HFR-16			
87+07	Bo.105P	HFR-26	87+83	Bo.105P	HFR-16			
87+08	Bo.105P	HFR-16	87+84	Bo.105P	HFVS-910			
87+09	Bo.105P	HFR-36	87+85	Bo.105P	HFR-26			
87+10	Bo.105P	HFR-26	87+86	Bo.105P	HFR-26			
87+11	Bo.105P	HFR-36	87+87	Bo.105P	HFR-16			
87+12	Bo.105P	HFR-36	87+88	Bo.105P	HFR-26			

Sikorsky/VFW CH-53G
HFlgRgt-15, Rheine-Bentlage;
HFlgRgt-25, Laupheim;
HFlgRgt-35, Mendig;
HFWS, Bückeburg;
TsLw-3, Fassberg;
WTD-61, Ingolstadt

Reg	Unit
84+01	WTD-61
84+02	WTD-61
84+03	HFR-15
84+04	HFWS
84+05	HFR-35
84+06	HFR-15
84+07	HFWS
84+08	HFR-35
84+09	HFR-25
84+10	HFWS
84+11	HFWS
84+12	HFR-15
84+13	TsLw-3
84+14	HFWS
84+15	HFR-25
84+16	HFWS
84+17	HFR-25
84+18	HFWS
84+19	HFWS
84+20	HFR-35
84+21	HFWS
84+22	HFR-15
84+23	HFR-35
84+24	HFR-35
84+25	HFR-35
84+26	HFR-35
84+27	HFR-35
84+28	HFR-25
84+29	HFR-35
84+30	HFR-35
84+31	HFR-35
84+32	HFR-35
84+33	HFR-35
84+34	HFR-35
84+35	HFR-35
84+36	HFR-35
84+37	HFR-35
84+38	HFR-35
84+39	HFR-35
84+40	HFR-25
84+41	HFWS

84+42	HFR-25
84+43	HFR-25
84+44	HFR-25
84+45	HFR-25
84+46	HFR-35
84+47	HFR-25
84+48	HFR-25
84+49	HFWS
84+50	HFR-25
84+51	HFR-25
84+52	HFR-25
84+53	HFR-25
84+54	HFR-25
84+55	HFR-25
84+56	HFR-35
84+57	HFR-25
84+58	HFR-25
84+59	HFR-25
84+60	HFR-25
84+62	HFR-25
84+63	HFR-25
84+64	HFR-35
84+65	HFR-35
84+66	HFR-35
84+67	HFR-35
84+68	HFR-15
84+69	HFR-15
84+70	HFR-15
84+71	HFR-15
84+72	HFR-15
84+73	HFR-15
84+74	HFR-15
84+75	HFR-15
84+76	HFR-15
84+77	HFR-15
84+78	HFR-15
84+79	HFR-15
84+80	HFR-15
84+82	HFR-35
84+83	HFR-15
84+84	HFR-15
84+85	HFR-15
84+86	HFR-15
84+87	HFR-15
84+88	HFR-15
84+89	HFR-15
84+90	HFR-15
84+91	HFR-15
84+92	HFR-35
84+93	HFR-35
84+94	HFR-35
84+95	HFR-25
84+96	HFR-25
84+97	HFR-25
84+98	HFR-15
84+99	HFR-15
85+00	WTD-61
85+01	HFR-35
85+02	HFR-35
85+03	HFR-35
85+04	HFR-25
85+05	HFR-25
85+06	HFR-25
85+07	HFR-15
85+08	HFR-15
85+09	HFR-15
85+10	HFR-35
85+11	HFR-25
85+12	HFR-15

Eurocopter AS.665 Tiger
WTD-61, Ingolstadt

98+23	
98+25	

GHANA
Ghana Air Force
  Fokker F-28
  Fellowship 3000
  VIP Flight, Accra
  G-530

GREECE
Ellinikí Polemikí Aeroporía
  Lockheed C-130H Hercules
  356 MTM/112 PM, Elefsís

*ECM	
741*	
742	
743	
744	
745	
746	
747	
749	
751	
752	

  Lockheed F-16C/F-16D*
  Fighting Falcon
  330 Mira/111 PM,
    Nea Ankhialos;
  341 Mira/111 PM,
    Nea Ankhialos;
  346 MAPK/110 PM, Larissa;
  347 Mira/111 PM,
    Nea Ankhialos

045	
046	
047	341 Mira
048	341 Mira
049	
050	
051	
052	
053	
054	
055	
056	
057	
058	
059	347 Mira
060	
061	
062	
063	
064	
065	
066	
077*	
078*	341 Mira
079*	341 Mira
080*	
081*	347 Mira
082*	
083*	347 Mira
084*	
110	346 MAPK
111	
112	346 MAPK
113	330 Mira
114	346 MAPK
115	330 Mira
116	346 MAPK
117	330 Mira
118	346 MAPK
119	330 Mira
120	346 MAPK
121	330 Mira
122	346 MAPK
123	330 Mira
124	346 MAPK
125	330 Mira
126	346 MAPK
127	330 Mira
128	346 MAPK
129	330 Mira
130	346 MAPK
131	330 Mira
132	346 MAPK
133	330 Mira
134	346 MAPK
136	346 MAPK
138	346 MAPK
139	330 Mira
140	346 MAPK
141	330 Mira
143	330 Mira
144*	330 Mira
145*	330 Mira
146*	346 MAPK
147*	330 Mira
148*	346 MAPK
149*	330 Mira

HUNGARY
Magyar Honvédség Repülö
Csapatai
  Antonov An-26
  89 VSD, Szolnok

203	(02203)
204	(02204)
208	(02208)
209	(02209)
405	(03405)
406	(03406)
407	(03407)
603	(03603)

ISRAEL
Heyl ha'Avir
  Boeing 707
  122 Sqn, 134 Sqn, Tel Aviv

120/4X-JYP	RC-707
128/4X-JYL	RC-707
137/4X-JYM	RC-707
140/4X-JYT	KC-707
242/4X-JYQ	VC-707
246/4X-JYS	EC-707
248/4X-JYU	KC-707
250/4X-JYY	KC-707
258/4X-JYC	EC-707
260/4X-JYN	KC-707
264/4X-JYH	VC-707

  Lockheed C-130 Hercules
  103 Sqn, 131 Sqn, Tel Aviv

102	C-130H
106	C-130H
208/4X-FBP	C-130E
301	C-130E
304	C-130E
305	C-130E
307	C-130E
309	C-130H
310/4X-FBG	C-130E
311/4X-FBD	C-130E
312	C-130E
313	C-130E
314	C-130E
316	C-130E
318	C-130E
420	C-130H

Reg	Code	Unit
423	C-130H	
427	C-130H	
428	C-130H	
435	C-130H	
436	C-130H	
448	C-130H	
522	KC-130H	
545	KC-130H	

ITALY
Aeronautica Militare Italiana
Aeritalia G222
9ª Brigata Aerea, Pratica di Mare:
8° Gruppo & 71° Gruppo;
46ª Brigata Aerea, Pisa:
2° Gruppo & 98° Gruppo;
RSV, Pratica di Mare

G222TCM

Reg	Code	Unit
MM62101	RS-45	RSV
MM62102	46-20	2
MM62104	46-91	98
MM62105	46-82	98
MM62109	46-96	98
MM62111	46-83	98
MM62114	46-80	98
MM62115	46-22	2
MM62117	46-25	2
MM62119	46-21	2
MM62120	46-90	98
MM62121	RS-46	RSV
MM62122	46-23	2
MM62123	46-28	2
MM62124	46-88	98
MM62125	46-87	98
MM62126	46-26	2
MM62127	46-27	2
MM62130	46-31	2
MM62133	46-93	98
MM62134	46-33	2
MM62135	46-94	98
MM62136	46-97	98
MM62137	46-95	98
MM62143	46-36	2
MM62144	46-98	98
MM62152	46-38	2
MM62153	46-99	98

G222VS

Reg	Code	Unit
MM62107		71
MM62138		71

G222RM

Reg	Code	Unit
MM62139	14-20	8
MM62140	14-21	8
MM62141	14-22	8
MM62142		8

G222PROCIV

Reg	Code	Unit
MM62145	46-50	2
MM62146	46-51	2
MM62147	46-52	2
MM62154	46-54	2
MM62153	46-53	2

Aeritalia-EMB AMX/AMX-T*
2° Stormo, Rivolto:
14° Gruppo;
32° Stormo, Amendola:
13° Gruppo & 101° Gruppo;
51° Stormo, Istrana:
103° Gruppo;
RSV, Pratica di Mare

Reg	Code	Unit
MMX595	Alenia	
MMX596	Alenia	
MMX597	Alenia	
MMX599	Alenia	
MM7089		
MM7090	2-14	14
MM7091	32-64	101
MM7092	RS-14	RSV
MM7093		
MM7094		
MM7095		
MM7096	32-03	13
MM7097		
MM7098		
MM7099		
MM7100	32-66	101
MM7101		
MM7102	2-03	14
MM7103		
MM7104	51-32	103
MM7105	32-20	13
MM7106	51-36	103
MM7107		
MM7110		
MM7111		
MM7112		
MM7114	32-15	13
MM7115	2-12	14
MM7116	32-11	13
MM7117		
MM7118	2-11	14
MM7119		
MM7120		
MM7122		
MM7123		
MM7124		
MM7125	RS-11	RSV
MM7126	32-12	13
MM7127		
MM7128		
MM7129	0	
MM7130	32-02	13
MM7131	51-52	103
MM7132	51-35	103
MM7133		
MM7134	51-30	103
MM7135		
MM7138	51-31	103
MM7139	51-33	103
MM7140	51-43	103
MM7141	51-55	103
MM7142		
MM7143	51-41	103
MM7144		
MM7145		
MM7146		
MM7147	32-04	13
MM7148	51-51	103
MM7149		
MM7150	32-65	101
MM7151	51-52	103
MM7152	51-53	103
MM7153	32-60	101
MM7154	51-54	103
MM7155	32-05	13
MM7156	32-10	13
MM7157	32-06	13
CMX7158	RS-12	RSV
MM7159		
MM7160	32-14	13
MM7161	2-21	14
MM7162	51-45	103
MM7163	51-63	103
MM7164		
MM7165		
MM7166		
MM7167	2-01	14
MM7168	2-04	14
MM7169		
MM7170	2-23	14
MM7171	2-15	14
MM7172	2-07	14
MM7173	2-16	14
MM7174		
MM7175		
MM7176	2-20	14
MM7177	2-22	14
MM7178	2-24	14
MM7179	2-02	14
MM7180		
MM7181		
MM7182		132
MM7183		
MM7184		
MM7185		
MM7186	51-56	103
MM7187	32-16	13
MM7188		
MM7189	51-62	103
MM7190	32-17	13
MM7191	32-01	13
MM7192	51-50	103
MM7193	51-60	103
MM7194	32-07	13
MM7195		
MM7196	32-13	13
MM7197	32-21	13
MM7198		
MM55024*	15	RSV
MM55025*	RS-16	RSV
MM55026*	32-43	101
MM55027*	32-42	101
MM55028*		
MM55029*		
MM55030*	32-41	101
MM55031*	32-40	101
MM55034*	18	RSV
MM55035*	32-50	101
MM55036*	32-51	101
MM55037*		
MM55038*	32-53	101
MM55039*	32-54	101
MM55040*	32-52	101
MM55041*	32-55	101
MM55042*	32-56	101
MM55043*	51-61	103
MM55044*	32-57	101
MM55045*	2-10	14
MM55046*	32-47	101
MM55047*	32-45	101
MM55048*	32-44	101
MM55049*	32-46	101
MM55050*		
MM55051*		

Aermacchi MB339A/MB339CD*
61° Stormo, Lecce:
212° Gruppo & 213° Gruppo Aermacchi, Venegono;
Frecce Tricolori [FT] (MB339PAN)
(313 Gruppo), Rivolto;
RSV, Pratica di Mare

Reg	Code	Unit
MM54438	61-93	
MM54439		[FT]
MM54440	61-00	
MM54441	RS-28	RSV

Italy

<table>
<tr><td>MM54442</td><td>61-95</td><td></td></tr>
<tr><td>MM54443</td><td>61-50</td><td></td></tr>
<tr><td>MM54445</td><td></td><td>[FT]</td></tr>
<tr><td>MM54446</td><td>61-01</td><td></td></tr>
<tr><td>MM54447</td><td>61-02</td><td></td></tr>
<tr><td>MM54448</td><td>61-03</td><td></td></tr>
<tr><td>MM54449</td><td>61-04</td><td></td></tr>
<tr><td>MM54450</td><td>61-94</td><td></td></tr>
<tr><td>MM54451</td><td>61-86</td><td></td></tr>
<tr><td>MM54452</td><td></td><td></td></tr>
<tr><td>MM54453</td><td>61-05</td><td></td></tr>
<tr><td>MM54454</td><td></td><td></td></tr>
<tr><td>MM54455</td><td>61-07</td><td></td></tr>
<tr><td>MM54456</td><td>61-10</td><td></td></tr>
<tr><td>MM54457</td><td>61-11</td><td></td></tr>
<tr><td>MM54458</td><td>61-12</td><td></td></tr>
<tr><td>MM54459</td><td>61-13</td><td></td></tr>
<tr><td>MM54460</td><td>61-14</td><td></td></tr>
<tr><td>MM54461</td><td>61-15</td><td></td></tr>
<tr><td>MM54462</td><td>61-16</td><td></td></tr>
<tr><td>MM54463</td><td>61-17</td><td></td></tr>
<tr><td>MM54467</td><td>61-23</td><td></td></tr>
<tr><td>MM54468</td><td>61-24</td><td></td></tr>
<tr><td>MM54471</td><td>61-27</td><td></td></tr>
<tr><td>MM54472</td><td>61-30</td><td></td></tr>
<tr><td>MM54474</td><td></td><td>[FT]</td></tr>
<tr><td>MM54475</td><td>1</td><td>[FT]</td></tr>
<tr><td>MM54477</td><td>11</td><td>[FT]</td></tr>
<tr><td>MM54478</td><td>0</td><td>[FT]</td></tr>
<tr><td>MM54479</td><td>12</td><td>[FT]</td></tr>
<tr><td>MM54480</td><td>8</td><td>[FT]</td></tr>
<tr><td>MM54482</td><td>10</td><td>[FT]</td></tr>
<tr><td>MM54483</td><td>7</td><td>[FT]</td></tr>
<tr><td>MM54484</td><td></td><td>[FT]</td></tr>
<tr><td>MM54485</td><td>9</td><td>[FT]</td></tr>
<tr><td>MM54486</td><td>6</td><td>[FT]</td></tr>
<tr><td>MM54487</td><td>61-31</td><td></td></tr>
<tr><td>MM54488</td><td>61-32</td><td></td></tr>
<tr><td>MM54489</td><td>61-33</td><td></td></tr>
<tr><td>MM54490</td><td>61-34</td><td></td></tr>
<tr><td>MM54491</td><td>61-35</td><td></td></tr>
<tr><td>MM54492</td><td>61-36</td><td></td></tr>
<tr><td>MM54493</td><td>61-37</td><td></td></tr>
<tr><td>MM54494</td><td>61-40</td><td></td></tr>
<tr><td>MM54496</td><td>61-42</td><td></td></tr>
<tr><td>MM54497</td><td>61-43</td><td></td></tr>
<tr><td>MM54498</td><td>61-44</td><td></td></tr>
<tr><td>MM54499</td><td>61-45</td><td></td></tr>
<tr><td>MM54500</td><td>4</td><td>[FT]</td></tr>
<tr><td>MM54503</td><td>61-51</td><td></td></tr>
<tr><td>MM54504</td><td>61-52</td><td></td></tr>
<tr><td>MM54505</td><td>61-53</td><td></td></tr>
<tr><td>MM54506</td><td>61-54</td><td></td></tr>
<tr><td>MM54507</td><td>61-55</td><td></td></tr>
<tr><td>MM54508</td><td>61-56</td><td></td></tr>
<tr><td>MM54509</td><td>61-57</td><td></td></tr>
<tr><td>MM54510</td><td>61-60</td><td></td></tr>
<tr><td>MM54511</td><td>61-61</td><td></td></tr>
<tr><td>MM54512</td><td>61-62</td><td></td></tr>
<tr><td>MM54513</td><td>61-63</td><td></td></tr>
<tr><td>MM54514</td><td>61-64</td><td></td></tr>
<tr><td>MM54515</td><td>61-65</td><td></td></tr>
<tr><td>MM54516</td><td>61-66</td><td></td></tr>
<tr><td>MM54517</td><td>3</td><td>[FT]</td></tr>
<tr><td>MM54518</td><td>61-70</td><td></td></tr>
<tr><td>MM54532</td><td>61-71</td><td></td></tr>
<tr><td>MM54533</td><td>61-72</td><td></td></tr>
<tr><td>MM54534</td><td>61-73</td><td></td></tr>
<tr><td>MM54535</td><td>61-74</td><td></td></tr>
<tr><td>MM54536</td><td></td><td></td></tr>
<tr><td>MM54537</td><td></td><td></td></tr>
<tr><td>MM54538</td><td>61-75</td><td></td></tr>
<tr><td>MM54539</td><td>61-76</td><td></td></tr>
<tr><td>MM54541</td><td>61-80</td><td></td></tr>
</table>

<table>
<tr><td>MM54542</td><td>61-81</td><td></td></tr>
<tr><td>MM54543</td><td>61-82</td><td></td></tr>
<tr><td>MM54544*</td><td>(Aermacchi)</td><td></td></tr>
<tr><td>MM54545</td><td>61-84</td><td></td></tr>
<tr><td>MM54546</td><td>61-85</td><td></td></tr>
<tr><td>MM54547</td><td>61-87</td><td></td></tr>
<tr><td>MM54548</td><td>61-90</td><td></td></tr>
<tr><td>MM54549</td><td>61-107</td><td></td></tr>
<tr><td>MM54550</td><td>61-92</td><td></td></tr>
<tr><td>MM54551</td><td>2</td><td>[FT]</td></tr>
<tr><td>MM55052</td><td>61-96</td><td></td></tr>
<tr><td>MM55053</td><td>61-97</td><td></td></tr>
<tr><td>MM55054</td><td>61-15</td><td></td></tr>
<tr><td>MM55055</td><td>61-20</td><td></td></tr>
<tr><td>MM55058</td><td>61-41</td><td></td></tr>
<tr><td>MM55059</td><td>61-26</td><td></td></tr>
<tr><td>MM55062*</td><td>RS-26</td><td>RSV</td></tr>
<tr><td>MM55063*</td><td>RS-27</td><td>RSV</td></tr>
<tr><td>MM55064*</td><td>61-130</td><td></td></tr>
<tr><td>MM55065*</td><td>61-131</td><td></td></tr>
<tr><td>MM55066*</td><td>61-132</td><td></td></tr>
<tr><td>MM55067*</td><td>61-133</td><td></td></tr>
<tr><td>MM55068*</td><td>61-134</td><td></td></tr>
<tr><td>MM55069*</td><td>61-135</td><td></td></tr>
<tr><td>MM55070*</td><td>61-136</td><td></td></tr>
<tr><td>MM55072*</td><td>61-140</td><td></td></tr>
<tr><td>MM55073*</td><td>61-141</td><td></td></tr>
<tr><td>MM55074*</td><td>61-142</td><td></td></tr>
<tr><td>MM55075*</td><td>61-143</td><td></td></tr>
</table>

Boeing 707-328B/-3F5C*
9ª Brigata Aerea, Pratica di Mare:
  8º Gruppo;

<table>
<tr><td>MM62148</td><td>14-01</td></tr>
<tr><td>MM62149</td><td>14-02</td></tr>
<tr><td>MM62150*</td><td>14-03</td></tr>
<tr><td>MM62151*</td><td>14-04</td></tr>
</table>

Breguet Br.1150 Atlantic
30º Stormo, Cagliari:
  86º Gruppo;
41º Stormo, Catania:
  88º Gruppo

<table>
<tr><td>MM40108</td><td>41-70</td></tr>
<tr><td>MM40109</td><td>30-71</td></tr>
<tr><td>MM40110</td><td>41-72</td></tr>
<tr><td>MM40111</td><td>41-73</td></tr>
<tr><td>MM40112</td><td>30-74</td></tr>
<tr><td>MM40113</td><td>30-75</td></tr>
<tr><td>MM40114</td><td>41-76</td></tr>
<tr><td>MM40115</td><td>41-77</td></tr>
<tr><td>MM40116</td><td>30-01</td></tr>
<tr><td>MM40117</td><td>41-02</td></tr>
<tr><td>MM40118</td><td>30-03</td></tr>
<tr><td>MM40119</td><td>30-04</td></tr>
<tr><td>MM40120</td><td>41-05</td></tr>
<tr><td>MM40121</td><td>41-06</td></tr>
<tr><td>MM40122</td><td>30-07</td></tr>
<tr><td>MM40123</td><td>30-10</td></tr>
<tr><td>MM40124</td><td>41-11</td></tr>
<tr><td>MM40125</td><td>30-12</td></tr>
</table>

Dassault Falcon 50
31º Stormo, Roma-Ciampino:
  93º Gruppo

MM62020
MM62021
MM62026
MM62029

Eurofighter
EF2000 Typhoon
Aeritalia, Torino/Caselle

MMX602
MMX603

Grumman G.1159A
Gulfstream III
31º Stormo, Roma-Ciampino:
  306º Gruppo

MM62022
MM62025

Lockheed F-104 Starfighter
4º Stormo, Grosseto:
  9º Gruppo & 20º Gruppo;
5º Stormo, Cervia:
  23º Gruppo;
9º Stormo, Grazzanise:
  10º Gruppo;
37º Stormo, Trapani:
  18º Gruppo;
RSV, Pratica di Mare
F-104S-ASA/F104ASA-M*

<table>
<tr><td>CMX611*</td><td>RS-06</td><td>RSV</td></tr>
<tr><td>MM6701</td><td>9-35</td><td>10</td></tr>
<tr><td>MM6703</td><td></td><td></td></tr>
<tr><td>MM6704</td><td>4-7</td><td>9</td></tr>
<tr><td>MM6705</td><td>4-5</td><td>9</td></tr>
<tr><td>MM6710</td><td></td><td></td></tr>
<tr><td>MM6713</td><td>37-01</td><td>18</td></tr>
<tr><td>MM6714</td><td></td><td></td></tr>
<tr><td>MM6717*</td><td>5-41</td><td>23</td></tr>
<tr><td>MM6719*</td><td>5-40</td><td>23</td></tr>
<tr><td>MM6720</td><td></td><td></td></tr>
<tr><td>MM6721</td><td></td><td></td></tr>
<tr><td>MM6726</td><td>4-6</td><td>9</td></tr>
<tr><td>MM6727</td><td>9-45</td><td>10</td></tr>
<tr><td>MM6731</td><td></td><td></td></tr>
<tr><td>MM6733</td><td></td><td></td></tr>
<tr><td>MM6734*</td><td>5-37</td><td>23</td></tr>
<tr><td>MM6735*</td><td>5-35</td><td>23</td></tr>
<tr><td>MM6736</td><td></td><td></td></tr>
<tr><td>MM6737</td><td></td><td></td></tr>
<tr><td>MM6739</td><td></td><td></td></tr>
<tr><td>MM6744</td><td>5-07</td><td></td></tr>
<tr><td>MM6748</td><td></td><td></td></tr>
<tr><td>MM6756*</td><td>5-42</td><td>23</td></tr>
<tr><td>MM6759*</td><td>5-45</td><td>23</td></tr>
<tr><td>MM6760</td><td>4-50</td><td>20</td></tr>
<tr><td>MM6761</td><td>4-3</td><td>9</td></tr>
<tr><td>MM6762</td><td></td><td></td></tr>
<tr><td>MM6763</td><td>37-02</td><td>18</td></tr>
<tr><td>MM6768</td><td></td><td></td></tr>
<tr><td>MM6769</td><td>4-53</td><td>20</td></tr>
<tr><td>MM6770</td><td></td><td></td></tr>
<tr><td>MM6771</td><td></td><td>22</td></tr>
<tr><td>MM6773</td><td></td><td></td></tr>
<tr><td>MM6774</td><td>4-1</td><td>9</td></tr>
<tr><td>MM6775</td><td></td><td></td></tr>
<tr><td>MM6776</td><td></td><td></td></tr>
<tr><td>MM6781</td><td></td><td></td></tr>
<tr><td>MM6785</td><td>5-25</td><td></td></tr>
<tr><td>MM6786</td><td>4-21</td><td>9</td></tr>
<tr><td>MM6788</td><td>5-01</td><td></td></tr>
<tr><td>MM6789</td><td></td><td></td></tr>
<tr><td>MM6795</td><td></td><td></td></tr>
<tr><td>MM6796</td><td>5-37</td><td>23</td></tr>
<tr><td>MM6797</td><td></td><td></td></tr>
<tr><td>MM6800</td><td>37-25</td><td>18</td></tr>
<tr><td>MM6805</td><td>4-10</td><td>9</td></tr>
<tr><td>MM6807</td><td></td><td></td></tr>
<tr><td>MM6809</td><td></td><td></td></tr>
<tr><td>MM6810</td><td></td><td></td></tr>
<tr><td>MM6812</td><td>9-41</td><td>10</td></tr>
<tr><td>MM6816</td><td>9-40</td><td>10</td></tr>
<tr><td>MM6817</td><td></td><td></td></tr>
</table>

MM6818		
MM6821	5-16	
MM6822	9-30	10
MM6823		
MM6824	9-43	10
MM6825	37-10	18
MM6826	4-51	20
MM6830	4-42	20
MM6833	5-22	
MM6836	5-10	
MM6838		
MM6839		
MM6840	4-2	9
MM6841		
MM6842	4-54	20
MM6844	37-23	18
MM6845	5-11	
MM6847	37-11	18
MM6848*	5-46	23
MM6849*		
MM6850	9-50	10
MM6870		
MM6873	9-31	10
MM6875	9-33	10
MM6876*	5-47	23
MM6879	9-53	10
MM6880*		
MM6881		
MM6886	5-02	
MM6887*	5-47	23
MM6909		
MM6912	4-20	9
MM6913	37-04	18
MM6915	5-15	
MM6918	RS-06	RSV
MM6920		
MM6921		
MM6922	9-35	10
MM6923		
MM6924		
MM6925	37-05	18
MM6926	4-56	20
MM6929		
MM6932		
MM6934	9-51	10
MM6935*	5-30	23
MM6936	5-36	23
MM6937	9-42	10
MM6938*	5-43	23
MM6939*	5-31	23
MM6940		
MM6941	4-4	9
MM6942	4-16	9
MM6943	37-15	18
MM6944		
MM6946	37-06	18

TF-104G

MM54226	4-23	20
MM54228	4-26	20
MM54232	4-29	20
MM54237	4-32	20
MM54250	4-33	20
MM54253	4-35	20
MM54254	4-36	20
MM54255	4-37	20
MM54256	4-38	20
MM54258	4-40	20
MM54260	4-41	20
MM54553	4-44	20
MM54554	4-48	20
MM54555	4-45	20
MM54556	4-47	20
MM54558	4-46	20

Lockheed
C-130H Hercules
46ª Brigata Aerea, Pisa:
50º Gruppo

MM61988	46-02
MM61989	46-03
MM61990	46-04
MM61991	46-05
MM61992	46-06
MM61993	46-07
MM61994	46-08
MM61995	46-09
MM61997	46-11
MM61998	46-12
MM61999	46-13
MM62001	46-15

McDonnell Douglas
DC-9-32
31º Stormo, Roma-Ciampino:
306º Gruppo

MM62012
MM62013

Panavia Tornado
ADV/Trainer[1]
36º Stormo, Gioia del Colle:
12º Gruppo;
53º Stormo, Cameri:
21º Gruppo

MM7202	36-12	(ZE832)
MM7203	36-02	(ZE761)
MM7204	36-05	(ZE730)
MM7205	36-06	(ZE787)
MM7206	36-07	(ZE760)
MM7207	53-10	(ZE762)
MM7208		(ZE811)
MM7209	53-07	(ZE835)
MM7210	36-14	(ZE836)
MM7211	36-16	(ZE792)
MM7225	36-04	(ZE252)
MM7226	36-12	(ZE911)
MM7227	36-22	(ZG732)
MM7228	53-03	(ZG733)
MM7229	53-06	(ZG728)
MM7230	36-11	(ZG730)
MM7231	53-11	(ZG734)
MM7232	36-10	(ZG735)
MM7233	53-04	(ZG768)
MM7234	53-14	(ZE167)
MM55056[1]	36-01	(ZE202)
MM55057[1]	36-03	(ZE837)
MM55060[1]	53-01	(ZE208)
MM55061[1]	53-12	(ZE205)

Panavia Tornado Strike/
Trainer[1]/ECR[2]
TTTE, RAF Cottesmore;
6º Stormo, Ghedi:
102º Gruppo &
154º Gruppo;
36º Stormo, Gioia del Colle:
156º Gruppo;
50º Stormo, Piacenza:
155º Gruppo;
RSV, Pratica di Mare

MM586		
MM7002	6-10	154
MM7003	I-93	TTTE
MM7004	36-46	156
MM7005	6-05	154
MM7006	6-16	154
MM7007	36-37	156
MM7008		
MM7009	50-45	155
MM7010	6-33	102
MM7011	36-32	156
MM7013	36-40	156
MM7014	50-43	155
MM7015	6-25	154
MM7016	RS-01	RSV
MM7018	6-18	154
MM7019[2]	50-05	155
MM7020[2]	50-41	155
MM7021	6-21	154
MM7022	6-22	154
MM7023	36-31	156
MM7025	6-43	102
MM7026		
MM7027	6-47	102
MM7028	6-18	154
MM7029	6-19	154
MM7030	6-35	102
MM7031	50-01	155
MM7033	6-11	154
MM7034	6-30	154
MM7035	36-47	156
MM7036	6-36	102
MM7037	6-07	154
MM7038	36-41	156
MM7039	50-03	155
CMX7040	36-35	156
MM7041	6-21	154
MM7042	6-31	102
MM7043	6-13	154
MM7044	6-20	154
MM7046	6-06	154
MM7047	36-36	156
MM7048	36-54	Alenia
MM7049	6-34	102
MM7050	36-44	156
MM7051	6-01	154
MM7052	6-32	102
MM7053[2]	50-07	155
MM7054[2]		Alenia
MM7055	36-33	156
MM7056		
MM7057	6-47	102
MM7058		
MM7059		
MM7060	50-06	155
MM7061	36-41	156
MM7062[2]	50-44	155
MM7063	36-42	156
MM7064		
MM7065	6-14	154
MM7066	6-44	102
MM7067	67	156
MM7068[2]		Alenia
MM7070	6-01	154
MM7071	6-42	102
MM7072	6-36	102
MM7073	36-43	156
MM7075	50-04	155
MM7078	50-02	155
CMX7079[2]		Alenia
MM7080	6-41	102
MM7081	6-02	154
MM7082[2]	50-40	155
MM7083	6-37	102
MM7084		
CMX7085	36-50	Alenia
MM7086	6-04	154
MM7087	36-35	156
MM7088		
MM55000[1]	I-42	TTTE
MM55001[1]	I-40	TTTE
MM55002[1]	I-41	TTTE

MM55003[1]	I-43	TTTE
MM55004[1]	6-15	154
MM55005[1]	6-40	102
MM55006[1]	6-03	154
MM55007[1]	50-51	155
MM55008[1]	6-45	102
MM55009[1]	36-56	156
MM55010[1]	50-50	155
MM55011[1]	36-55	156

Piaggio P-180AM Avanti
53° Stormo, Cameri:
   653ª SC;
303° Gruppo, Guidonia;
RSV, Pratica di Mare

MM62159		RSV
MM62160	54	RSV
MM62161		653
MM62162		303
MM62163		303
MM62164		RSV

Piaggio-Douglas PD-808-GE/ PD-808-RM/PD-808-TA
9ª Brigata Aerea, Pratica di Mare:
   8° Gruppo & 71° Gruppo;
RSV, Pratica di Mare

MM61952	TA	71
MM61952	GE	71
MM61954	TA	71
MM61955	GE	71
MM61960	GE	71
MM61961	GE	71
MM61962	GE	71
MM62014	RM	8

Guardia di Finanza Aérospatiale
   ATR.42-400MP
   2° Gruppo EM, Pratica di Mare

MM62165	GF-13
MM62166	GF-14

Marina Militare Italiana
   McDonnell Douglas AV-8B/TAV-8B Harrier II+
   Gruppo Aerei Imbarcarti, Taranto/Grottaglie
   AV-8B

MM7199	1-03
MM7200	1-04
MM7201	1-05
MM7212	1-06
MM7213	1-07
MM7214	1-08
MM7215	1-09
MM7216	1-10
MM7217	1-11
MM7218	1-12
MM7219	1-13
MM7220	1-14
MM7221	1-15
MM7222	1-16
MM7223	1-17
MM7224	1-18

   TAV-8B

MM55032	1-01
MM55033	1-02

JAPAN
Japan Air Self Defence Force
   Boeing 747-47C
   701st Flight Sqn, Chitose
   20-1101
   20-1102

JORDAN
Al Quwwat al Jawwiya al Malakiya al Urduniya
   Lockheed C-130H Hercules
   3 Sqn, Al Matar AB/Amman
   344
   345
   346
   347
   348

KENYA
Kenya Air Force
   Fokker 70ER
   KAF 308

KUWAIT
Al Quwwat al Jawwiya al Kuwaitiya
   Lockheed L100-30 Hercules
   41 Sqn, Kuwait International
   KAF 323
   KAF 324
   KAF 325

LITHUANIA
Karines Oro Pajegos
   Let 410 Turbolet
   I Transporto Eskadrile, Zokniai
   01
   02

LUXEMBOURG NATO
   Boeing E-3A
   NAEWF, Geilenkirchen
   LX-N90442
   LX-N90443
   LX-N90444
   LX-N90445
   LX-N90446
   LX-N90447
   LX-N90448
   LX-N90449
   LX-N90450
   LX-N90451
   LX-N90452
   LX-N90453
   LX-N90454
   LX-N90455
   LX-N90456
   LX-N90458
   LX-N90459

   Boeing 707-307C/329C*
   NAEWF, Geilenkirchen
   LX-N19996*
   LX-N19997
   LX-N19999
   LX-N20000
   LX-N20198*
   LX-N20199*

MALAYSIA
Royal Malaysian Air Force/ Tentera Udara Diraja Malaysia

   Lockheed C-130 Hercules
   14 Sqn, Labuan;
   20 Sqn, Subang

M30-01	C-130H	14 Sqn
M30-02	C-130H	14 Sqn
M30-03	C-130H	14 Sqn
M30-04	C-130H	14 Sqn
M30-05	C-130H	14 Sqn
M30-06	C-130H	14 Sqn
M30-07	C-130T	20 Sqn
M30-08	C-130H(MP)	20 Sqn
M30-09	C-130H(MP)	20 Sqn
M30-10	C-130H-30	20 Sqn
M30-11	C-130H-30	20 Sqn
M30-12	C-130H-30	20 Sqn
M30-13	C-130H-30	20 Sqn
M30-14	C-130H-30	20 Sqn
M30-15	C-130H-30	20 Sqn
M30-16	C-130H-30	20 Sqn

MEXICO
Fuerza Aérea Mexicana
   Boeing 757-225
   8° Grupo Aéreo, Mexico City
   TP-01   (XC-UJM)

MOROCCO
Force Aérienne Royaume Marocaine/ Al Quwwat al Jawwiya al Malakiya Marakishiya
   Airtech CN.235M-100
   Escadrille de Transport, Rabat

023	CNA-MA
024	CNA-MB
025	CNA-MC
026	CNA-MD
027	CNA-ME
028	CNA-MF
031	CNA-MG

   CAP-230
   Marche Verte

04	CN-ABD
05	CN-ABF
06	CN-ABI
07	CN-ABJ
08	CN-ABK
09	CN-ABL
22	CN-ABM
23	CN-ABN
24	CN-ABO

   Lockheed C-130H Hercules
   Escadrille de Transport, Rabat

4535	CN-AOA
4551	CN-AOC
4575	CN-AOD
4581	CN-AOE
4583	CN-AOF
4713	CN-AOG
4717	CN-AOH
4733	CN-AOI
4738	CN-AOJ
4739	CN-AOK
4742	CN-AOL
4875	CN-AOM
4876	CN-AON
4877	CN-AOO
4888	CN-AOP
4892	CN-AOQ
4907	CN-AOR

4909	CN-AOS	J-003	322 Sqn	J-254	312 Sqn
4940	CN-AOT	J-004	322 Sqn	J-255	311 Sqn
		J-005	322 Sqn	J-256	311 Sqn
NETHERLANDS		J-006	322 Sqn	J-257	313 Sqn
Koninklijke Luchtmacht		J-008	322 Sqn	J-259*	311 Sqn
Agusta-Bell AB.412SP		J-009	322 Sqn	J-261*	313 Sqn
303 Sqn, Leeuwarden		J-010	312 Sqn	J-264*	313 Sqn
R-01		J-011	322 Sqn	J-265*	313 Sqn
R-02		J-013	322 Sqn	J-266*	313 Sqn
R-03		J-014	322 Sqn	J-267*	311 Sqn
		J-015	312 Sqn	J-268*	313 Sqn
Boeing-Vertol		J-016	311 Sqn	J-269*	313 Sqn
CH-47D Chinook		J-017	312 Sqn	J-270*	313 Sqn
298 Sqn, Soesterberg		J-018	322 Sqn	J-360	313 Sqn
D-101		J-019	311 Sqn	J-361	312 Sqn
D-102		J-020	315 Sqn	J-362	315 Sqn
D-103		J-021	312 Sqn	J-363	323 Sqn
D-104		J-055	322 Sqn	J-364	323 Sqn
D-105		J-057	322 Sqn	J-365	315 Sqn
D-106		J-058	315 Sqn	J-366	322 Sqn
D-661		J-059	315 Sqn	J-367	323 Sqn
D-662		J-060	311 Sqn	J-368*	312 Sqn
D-663		J-061	322 Sqn	J-369*	315 Sqn
D-664		J-062	322 Sqn	J-508	315 Sqn
D-665		J-063	322 Sqn	J-509	322 Sqn
D-666		J-064*	322 Sqn	J-510	313 Sqn
D-667		J-065*	315 Sqn	J-511	311 Sqn
		J-066*	315 Sqn	J-512	311 Sqn
Eurocopter AS.532U2		J-067*	315 Sqn	J-513	312 Sqn
Cougar		J-068*	322 Sqn	J-514	315 Sqn
300 Sqn, Gilze-Rijen		J-135	315 Sqn	J-515	312 Sqn
S-400		J-136	322 Sqn	J-516	312 Sqn
S-419		J-137	322 Sqn	J-616	313 Sqn
S-433		J-138	315 Sqn	J-617	322 Sqn
S-438		J-139	323 Sqn	J-619	312 Sqn
S-440		J-141	315 Sqn	J-620	323 Sqn
S-441		J-142	312 Sqn	J-622	311 Sqn
S-442		J-143	315 Sqn	J-623	323 Sqn
S-444		J-144	323 Sqn	J-624	313 Sqn
S-445		J-145	315 Sqn	J-627	306 Sqn
S-447		J-146	315 Sqn	J-628	306 Sqn
S-450		J-192	312 Sqn	J-630	306 Sqn
S-453		J-193	312 Sqn	J-631	306 Sqn
S-454		J-194	311 Sqn	J-632	306 Sqn
S-456		J-196	313 Sqn	J-633	306 Sqn
S-457		J-197	323 Sqn	J-635	306 Sqn
S-458		J-198	311 Sqn	J-636	306 Sqn
S-459		J-199	306 Sqn	J-637	306 Sqn
		J-201	312 Sqn	J-638	306 Sqn
Fokker F-27-200MPA		J-202	311 Sqn	J-640	306 Sqn
336 Sqn, Hato, Antilles		J-203	311 Sqn	J-641	306 Sqn
M-1		J-204	323 Sqn	J-642	306 Sqn
M-2		J-205	323 Sqn	J-643	306 Sqn
		J-206	312 Sqn	J-644	306 Sqn
Fokker 50		J-207	323 Sqn	J-646	306 Sqn
334 Sqn, Eindhoven		J-208*	323 Sqn	J-647	306 Sqn
U-05		J-209*	315 Sqn	J-648	306 Sqn
U-06		J-210*	312 Sqn	J-649*	311 Sqn
		J-211*	313 Sqn	J-650*	315 Sqn
Fokker 60UTA-N		J-215	312 Sqn	J-651*	306 Sqn
334 Sqn, Eindhoven		J-220	311 Sqn	J-652*	306 Sqn
U-01		J-226	312 Sqn	J-653*	TGp
U-02		J-231	312 Sqn	J-654*	313 Sqn
U-03		J-232	313 Sqn	J-655*	306 Sqn
U-04		J-235	311 Sqn	J-656*	323 Sqn
		J-236	323 Sqn	J-657*	323 Sqn
General Dynamics		J-239	312 Sqn	J-864	306 Sqn
F-16A/F-16B*		J-243	311 Sqn	J-866	306 Sqn
TGp/306/311/312 Sqns,		J-246	313 Sqn	J-867	306 Sqn
Volkel;		J-248	323 Sqn	J-868	323 Sqn
313/315 Sqns, Twenthe;		J-249	311 Sqn	J-869	323 Sqn
322/323 Sqns, Leeuwarden		J-250	311 Sqn	J-870	323 Sqn
J-001	322 Sqn	J-251	322 Sqn	J-871	323 Sqn
J-002	311 Sqn	J-253	312 Sqn	J-872	323 Sqn

J-873	323 Sqn
J-874	311 Sqn
J-875	323 Sqn
J-876	313 Sqn
J-877	323 Sqn
J-878	312 Sqn
J-879	312 Sqn
J-881	323 Sqn
J-882*	323 Sqn
J-884*	313 Sqn
J-885*	311 Sqn

Grumman G-1159C Gulfstream IV
334 Sqn, Eindhoven
V-11

Lockheed C-130H-30 Hercules
334 Sqn, Eindhoven
G-273
G-275

MBB Bo.105CB/Bo.105CB-4*
299 Sqn, Gilze-Rijen
B-37*
B-38
B-39*
B-40*
B-41*
B-42
B-43
B-44
B-47
B-48
B-63
B-64
B-66
B-67
B-68
B-69
B-70
B-71
B-72
B-74
B-75
B-76
B-77
B-78*
B-79
B-80
B-83

MDH AH-64A Apache/ NAH-64D Longbow Apache
AH-64A
301 Sqn, Gilze-Rijen;
302 Sqn, Gilze-Rijen

25430	301 Sqn
25465	301 Sqn
2547	301 Sqn
25472	301 Sqn
25474	301 Sqn
25480	301 Sqn
25482	301 Sqn
25485	301 Sqn
68970	301 Sqn
68983	301 Sqn
69029	301 Sqn
69033	301 Sqn

NAH-64D

Q-01	302 Sqn
Q-02	302 Sqn
Q-03	302 Sqn
Q-04	302 Sqn
Q-05	302 Sqn
Q-06	302 Sqn
Q-07	302 Sqn
Q-08	302 Sqn
Q-09	302 Sqn
Q-10	302 Sqn

McDonnell Douglas KDC-10
334 Sqn, Eindhoven
T-235
T-264

Pilatus PC-7
131 EMV Sqn, Woensdrecht
L-01
L-02
L-03
L-04
L-05
L-06
L-07
L-08
L-09
L-10
L-11
L-12
L-13

Sud Alouette III
300 Sqn, Soesterberg
A-247
A-253
A-275
A-292
A-301

Marine Luchtvaart Dienst
Lockheed P-3C Orion
MARPAT (320 Sqn & 321 Sqn), Valkenburg and Keflavik
300
301
302
303
304
305
306
307
308
309
310
311
312

Westland SH-14D Lynx
HELIGRP (7 Sqn & 860 Sqn), De Kooij
(7 Sqn operates 860 Sqn aircraft on loan)
260
261
262
264
265
266
267
268
269
270
271
272

273
274
276
277
278
279
280
281
283

NEW ZEALAND
Royal New Zealand Air Force
Boeing 727-22C
40 Sqn, Whenuapai
NZ7271
NZ7272

Lockheed C-130H Hercules
40 Sqn, Whenuapai
NZ7001
NZ7002
NZ7003
NZ7004
NZ7005

Lockheed P-3K Orion
5 Sqn, Whenuapai
NZ4201
NZ4202
NZ4203
NZ4204
NZ4205
NZ4206

NIGERIA
Federal Nigerian Air Force
Lockheed C-130H Hercules
Lagos
NAF-910
NAF-912
NAF-913
NAF-914
NAF-915
NAF-916
NAF-917
NAF-918

NORWAY
Kongelige Norske Luftforsvaret
Bell 412SP
339 Skv, Bardufoss;
720 Skv, Rygge

139	339 Skv
140	720 Skv
141	720 Skv
142	339 Skv
143	339 Skv
144	339 Skv
145	339 Skv
146	339 Skv
147	720 Skv
148	339 Skv
149	339 Skv
161	339 Skv
162	339 Skv
163	720 Skv
164	720 Skv
165	720 Skv
166	720 Skv
167	720 Skv
194	720 Skv

Dassault Falcon 20 ECM
717 Skv, Rygge
041
053
0125

DHC-6 Twin Otter
719 Skv, Bodø
057
184
7062

**General Dynamics
F-16A/F-16B***
331 Skv, Bodø (r/w/bl);
332 Skv, Rygge (y/bk);
334 Skv, Bodø (r/w);
338 Skv, Ørland

272	332 Skv
273	332 Skv
275	332 Skv
276	338 Skv
277	332 Skv
279	332 Skv
281	332 Skv
282	332 Skv
284	332 Skv
285	338 Skv
288	338 Skv
289	338 Skv
291	338 Skv
292	338 Skv
293	338 Skv
295	338 Skv
297	338 Skv
298	338 Skv
299	338 Skv
302*	338 Skv
304*	334 Skv
305*	332 Skv
306*	332 Skv
658	334 Skv
659	334 Skv
660	334 Skv
661	334 Skv
662	334 Skv
663	334 Skv
664	331 Skv
665	334 Skv
666	334 Skv
667	334 Skv
668	334 Skv
669	334 Skv
670	338 Skv
671	334 Skv
672	331 Skv
673	331 Skv
674	331 Skv
675	331 Skv
677	331 Skv
678	334 Skv
680	338 Skv
681	331 Skv
682	331 Skv
683	331 Skv
686	331 Skv
687	338 Skv
688	331 Skv
689*	338 Skv
690*	338 Skv
691*	338 Skv
692*	334 Skv
693*	338 Skv

711*	331 Skv
712*	331 Skv

Lockheed C-130H Hercules
335 Skv, Gardermoen
952
953
954
955
956
957

Lockheed P-3C Orion
333 Skv, Andøya
3296
3297
3298
3299

Lockheed P-3N Orion
333 Skv, Andøya
4576
6603

Northrop F-5A
336 Skv, Rygge
128
130
131
133
134
896
902

Northrop F-5B
336 Skv, Rygge
136
243
244
387
906
907
908
909

Westland Sea King
330 Skv:
A Flt, Bodø; B Flt, Banek;
C Flt, Ørland; D Flt, Sola
060 Mk 43
062 Mk 43
066 Mk 43
069 Mk 43
070 Mk 43
071 Mk 43B
072 Mk 43A
073 Mk 43
074 Mk 43
189 Mk 43A
322 Mk 43B
329 Mk 43B
330 Mk 43B

**Kystvakt (Coast Guard)
Westland Lynx Mk86**
337 Skv, Bardufoss
207
216
228
232
237
350

**OMAN
Royal Air Force of Oman
BAC 1-11/485GD**
4 Sqn, Seeb
551
552
553

Lockheed C-130H Hercules
4 Sqn, Seeb
501
502
503

**Short Skyvan 3M/
Seavan 3M***
2 Sqn, Seeb
901
902
903
904
905
906
907
908
910*
911
912
913
914
915*
916*

**PAKISTAN
Pakistan Fiza'ya
Boeing 707-340C**
68-19866   12 Sqn
69-19635   12 Sqn

**PERU
Fuerza Aérea Peruana**
Douglas DC-8-62AF
370 (OB-1372)
371 (OB-1373)

**POLAND
Polskie Wojska Lotnicze
Antonov An-26**
13 PLT, Belice
1307
1310
1402
1403
1406
1407
1508
1509
1602
1603
1604

Mikoyan MiG-29A/UB*
1 PLM, Minsk/Mazowiecki
15*
28*
29
38
40
42*
54
56
59
64*
65

Poland – Romania

66
67
70
77
83
89
92
105
108
111
114
115

Tupolev Tu-134A
36 SPLT, Warszawa
102

Tupolev Tu-154M
36 SPLT, Warszawa
101

Yakovlev Yak-40
36 SPLT, Warszawa
032
034
036
037
038
039
040
041
042
043
044
045
047
048

PORTUGAL
Força Aérea Portuguesa
  Aérospatiale SA.330C Puma
  Esq 751, Montijo;
  Esq 752, Lajes

19502	Esq 751
19503	Esq 751
19504	Esq 751
19505	Esq 751
19506	Esq 752
19508	Esq 752
19509	Esq 751
19511	Esq 752
19512	Esq 751
19513	Esq 752

CASA 212A/212ECM*
Aviocar
Esq 401, Sintra;
Esq 502, Sintra;
Esq 503, Lajes

16501*	Esq 401
16502*	Esq 502
16503	Esq 502
16504	Esq 502
16505	Esq 502
16506	Esq 502
16507	Esq 502
16508	Esq 502
16509	Esq 502
16510	Esq 401
16511	Esq 502
16512	Esq 401
16513	Esq 503
16514	Esq 503
16515	Esq 503

16517	Esq 503
16519	Esq 502
16520	Esq 503
16521*	Esq 401
16522*	Esq 401
16523*	Esq 401
16524*	Esq 401

CASA 212-300 Aviocar
Esq 401, Sintra
17201
17202

D-BD Alpha Jet
Esq 103, Beja;
Esq 301, Beja
15201
15202
15204
15205
15206
15208
15209
15210
15211
15213
15214
15215
15216
15217
15218
15219
15220
15221
15222
15223
15224
15225
15226
15227
15228
15229
15230
15231
15232
15233
15234
15235
15236
15237
15238
15239
15240
15241
15242
15243
15244
15246
15247
15248
15249
15250

Dassault Falcon 20DC
Esq 504, Lisbon/Montijo
17103

Dassault Falcon 50
Esq 504, Lisbon/Montijo
17401
17402
17403

Lockheed C-130H/
C-130H-30* Hercules
Esq 501, Lisbon/Montijo
16801*
16802*
16803
16804
16805
16806*

Lockheed (GD)
F-16A/F-16B*
Esq 201, Monte Real
15101
15102
15103
15104
15105
15106
15107
15108
15109
15110
15111
15112
15113
15114
15115
15116
15117
15118*
15119*
15120*

Lockheed P-3P Orion
Esq 601, Lisbon/Montijo
14801
14802
14803
14804
14805
14806

LTV A-7P/TA-7P* Corsair II
Esq 304, Monte Real
15509
15511
15512
15514
15515
15519
15521
15524
15531
15545*
15546*
15549*
15550*

Marinha Westland Super
Lynx Mk 95
Esq de Helicopteros,
Lisbon/Montijo
19201
19202
19203
19204
19205

ROMANIA
Fortele Aeriene Romania
  Lockheed C-130B Hercules
  19 FMT, Bucharest/Otapeni
  5927

5930
6150
6166

RUSSIA
Voenno-Vozdushniye Sily
 Rossioki Federatsii (Russian Air Force)
 Sukhoi Su-27
 TsAGI, Gromov Flight Institute Zhukhovsky

595	(27595)	Su-27P
597	(27597)	Su-30
598	(27598)	Su-27P

SAUDI ARABIA
Al Quwwat al Jawwiya as Sa'udiya
 Boeing E-3A/KE-3A* Sentry
 18 Sqn, Riyadh

1801
1802
1803
1804
1805
1811*
1812*
1813*
1814*
1815*
1816*
1817*
1818*

Lockheed C-130 Hercules
1 Sqn, Riyadh;
4 Sqn, Jeddah;
16 Sqn, Jeddah;
32 Sqn, Jeddah

111	VC-130H	1 Sqn
112	VC-130H	1 Sqn
451	C-130E	4 Sqn
452	C-130H	4 Sqn
455	C-130E	4 Sqn
461	C-130H	4 Sqn
462	C-130H	4 Sqn
463	C-130H	4 Sqn
464	C-130H	4 Sqn
465	C-130H	4 Sqn
466	C-130H	4 Sqn
467	C-130H	4 Sqn
468	C-130H	4 Sqn
471	C-130H-30	4 Sqn
472	C-130H	4 Sqn
473	C-130H	4 Sqn
474	C-130H	4 Sqn
475	C-130H	4 Sqn
476	C-130H	4 Sqn
477	C-130H	4 Sqn
478	C-130H	4 Sqn
479	C-130H	4 Sqn
1601	C-130H	16 Sqn
1602	C-130H	16 Sqn
1603	C-130H	16 Sqn
1604	C-130H	16 Sqn
1605	C-130H	16 Sqn
1606	C-130E	16 Sqn
1607	C-130E	16 Sqn
1608	C-130E	16 Sqn
1609	C-130E	16 Sqn
1610	C-130E	16 Sqn
1611	C-130E	16 Sqn
1612	C-130H	16 Sqn
1613	C-130H	16 Sqn

1614	C-130H	16 Sqn
1615	C-130H	16 Sqn
1618	C-130H	16 Sqn
1619	C-130H	16 Sqn
1622	C-130H-30	16 Sqn
1623	C-130H-30	16 Sqn
1624	C-130H	16 Sqn
1625	C-130H	16 Sqn
1626	C-130H	16 Sqn
1627	C-130H	16 Sqn
1628	C-130H	16 Sqn
3201	KC-130H	32 Sqn
3202	KC-130H	32 Sqn
3203	KC-130H	32 Sqn
3204	KC-130H	32 Sqn
3205	KC-130H	32 Sqn
3206	KC-130H	32 Sqn
3207	KC-130H	32 Sqn
3208	KC-130H	32 Sqn

SINGAPORE
Republic of Singapore Air Force
 Lockheed C-130 Hercules
 122 Sqn, Paya Labar

720	KC-130B
721	KC-130B
724	KC-130B
725	KC-130B
730	C-130H
731	C-130H
732	C-130H
733	C-130H
734	KC-130H
735	C-130H

SLOVAKIA
Slovenské Vojenske Letectvo
 Aero L-39/L-59 (L-39MS) Albatros
 31 SLK/3 Letka, Sliač [SL];
 VSL, Košice;
 White Albatroses, Košice (WA)

0002	L-39MS	VSL
0003	L-39MS	VSL
0101	L-39C	WA [4]
0102	L-39C	WA [6]
0103	L-39C	VSL
0111	L-39C	WA [5]
0112	L-39C	WA [1]
0442	L-39C	WA [2]
0443	L-39C	WA [7]
0730	L-39V	VSL
0745	L-39V	VSL
1701	L-39ZA	31 SLK
1725	L-39ZA	31 SLK
1730	L-39ZA	31 SLK
3905	L-39ZA	31 SLK
4355	L-39C	WA [3]
4701	L-39ZA	31 SLK
4703	L-39ZA	31 SLK
4705	L-39ZA	31 SLK
4707	L-39ZA	WA
4711	L-39ZA	31 SLK

Antonov An-24V
32 ZmDK/1 Letka, Piešťany
2903
5605

Antonov An-26
32 ZmDK/1 Letka, Piešťany
2506
3208

Let 410 Turbolet
31 SLK/4 Letka, Sliač [SL];
32 ZmDK/1 Letka, Piešťany;
VSL, Košice

0404	L-410MA	32 ZmDK
0405	L-410MA	32 ZmDK
0730	L-410UVP	32 ZmDK
0927	L-410T	31 SLK
0930	L-410T	32 ZmDK
1133	L-410T	VSL
1203	L-410FG	32 ZmDK
1521	L-410FG	32 ZmDK
2311	L-410UVP	32 ZmDK

Mikoyan MiG-29A/UB*
31 SLK/1 & 2 Letka, Sliač [SL]
0619
0820
0921
1303*
2022
2123
3709
3911
4401*
5113
5304*
5515
5817
6124
6425
6526
6627
6728
6829
6930
7501
8003
8605
9308

Sukhoi Su-25K/UBK*
33 SBoLK/2 Letka, Malacky
1006
1007
1008
1027
3237*
5033
5036
6017
6018
8072
8073
8074
8075

SLOVENIA
Slovene Army
 Let 410UVP-E
 15 Brigada, Ljubljana
 L4-01

Pilatus PC-9
15 Brigada, Ljubljana
L9-51
L9-52
L9-53
L9-61
L9-62
L9-63
L9-64
L9-65
L9-66

Slovenia – Spain

L9-67	
L9-68	

SOUTH AFRICA
South African Air Force/
Suid Afrikaanse Lugmag
Boeing 707
60 Sqn, Waterkloof

AF-615(1415)	328C
AF-617(1417)	328C
AF-619(1419)	328C
AF-621(1421)	344C
AF-623(1423)	344C

Lockheed C-130B/C-130F*
Hercules
28 Sqn, Waterkloof

401
402
403
404
405
406
407
408*
409*
410*
411*
412*

SPAIN
Ejército del Aire
Airtech CN.235M-10 (T.19A)/
CN.235M-100 (T.19B)
Ala 35, Getafe

T.19A-01	35-60
T.19A-02	35-61
T.19B-03	35-21
T.19B-04	35-22
T.19B-05	35-23
T.19B-06	35-24
T.19B-07	35-25
T.19B-08	35-26
T.19B-09	35-27
T.19B-10	35-28
T.19B-11	35-29
T.19B-12	35-30
T.19B-13	35-31
T.19B-14	35-32
T.19B-15	35-33
T.19B-16	35-34
T.19B-17	35-35
T.19B-18	35-36
T.19B-19	35-37
T.19B-20	35-38

Boeing 707
408 Esc, Torrejón;
Grupo 45, Torrejón

T.17-1	331B	45-10
T.17-2	331B	45-11
T.17-3	368C	45-12
TM.17-4	351C	408-21

CASA 101 Aviojet
Grupo 54, Torrejón
Grupo de Escuelas de
Matacán (74);
AGA, San Javier (79);
*Patrulla Aguila, San Javier**

E.25-01	79-01	
E.25-05	79-05	
E.25-06	79-06	
E.25-07	79-07	[1]*
E.25-08	79-08	[5]*
E.25-09	79-09	
E.25-10	79-10	
E.25-11	79-11	
E.25-12	79-12	
E.25-13	79-13	[3]*
E.25-14	79-14	
E.25-15	79-15	
E.25-16	79-16	
E.25-17	74-40	
E.25-18	74-42	
E.25-19	79-19	
E.25-20	79-20	
E.25-21	79-21	
E.25-22	79-22	
E.25-23	74-02	[6]*
E.25-24	79-24	
E.25-25	79-25	
E.25-26	79-26	
E.25-27	79-27	
E.25-28	79-28	[8]*
E.25-29	79-29	
E.25-31	79-31	
E.25-33	74-02	
E.25-34	79-34	
E.25-35	79-35	
E.25-36	79-36	
E.25-37	74-04	
E.25-38	79-38	
E.25-40	79-40	[2]*
E.25-41	74-41	
E.25-43		
E.25-44	79-44	
E.25-45	79-45	
E.25-46	79-46	
E.25-47	79-47	
E.25-48	79-48	
E.25-49	79-49	
E.25-50	79-33	
E.25-51	74-07	
E.25-52	79-34	[4]*
E.25-53	411-07	
E.25-54	79-35	
E.25-55	44-05	
E.25-56	74-11	
E.25-57	74-12	
E.25-59	74-13	
E.25-61		
E.25-62	74-16	
E.25-63	74-17	
E.25-64	74-18	
E.25-65	79-95	
E.25-66	74-20	
E.25-67	74-21	
E.25-68	74-22	
E.25-69	79-97	
E.25-71	74-25	
E.25-72	74-26	
E.25-73	79-98	
E.25-74	74-28	
E.25-75	74-29	
E.25-76	74-30	
E.25-78	79-02	
E.25-79	74-32	
E.25-80	74-33	
E.25-81	74-34	
E.25-83	74-35	
E.25-84	79-04	
E.25-86	79-32	[7]*
E.25-87	74-38	
E.25-88	74-39	

CASA 212 Aviocar
212 (XT.12)/212A (T.12B)/
212B (TR.12A)/
212D (TE.12B)/
212DE (TM.12D)/
212E (T.12C)/
212S (D.3A)/212S1 (D.3B)/
212-200 (T.12D)/
212-200 (TR.12D)
Ala 22, Morón; Ala 37;
Villanubla;
Ala 46, Gando, Las Palmas;
CLAEX, Torrejón (54);
Grupo 72, Alcantarilla;
Grupo Esc, Matacán (74);
AGA (Ala 79), San Javier;
403 Esc, Getafe;
408 Esc, Torrejón;
il721 Esc, Alcantarilla;
801 Esc, Palma/Son San
Juan;
803 Esc, Cuatro Vientos;
INTA, Torrejón

D.3A-1	(801 Esc)
D.3A-2	803-11
D.3B-3	(803 Esc)
D.3B-4	(801 Esc)
D.3B-5	(801 Esc)
D.3B-6	803-12
D.3B-7	(803 Esc)
D.3B-8	22-92
XT.12A-1	54-10
TR.12A-3	403-01
TR.12A-4	403-02
TR.12A-5	403-03
TR.12A-6	403-04
TR.12A-8	403-06
T.12B-9	74-83
TE.12B-10	79-92
T.12B-12	74-82
T.12B-13	74-70
T.12B-14	37-01
T.12B-15	37-02
T.12B-16	74-71
T.12B-17	37-03
T.12B-18	46-31
T.12B-19	46-32
T.12B-20	37-04
T.12B-21	37-05
T.12B-22	37-06
T.12B-23	72-01
T.12B-24	37-07
T.12B-25	74-72
T.12B-26	72-02
T.12B-27	46-33
T.12B-28	72-03
T.12B-29	37-08
T.12B-30	74-73
T.12B-31	46-34
T.12B-33	72-04
T.12B-34	74-74
T.12B-35	37-09
T.12B-36	37-10
T.12B-37	72-05
T.12B-39	74-75
TE.12B-40	79-93
TE.12B-41	79-94
T.12C-43	46-50
T.12C-44	37-50
T.12B-46	74-76
T.12B-47	72-06
T.12B-48	37-11
T.12B-49	72-07
T.12B-50	74-77
T.12B-51	74-78
T.12B-52	46-35

T.12B-53	46-36
T.12B-54	46-37
T.12B-55	46-38
T.12B-56	74-79
T.12B-57	72-08
T.12B-58	46-39
T.12C-59	37-51
T.12C-60	37-52
T.12C-61	37-53
T.12B-63	37-14
T.12B-64	46-40
T.12B-65	74-80
T.12B-66	72-09
T.12B-67	74-81
T.12B-68	37-15
T.12B-69	37-16
T.12B-70	37-17
T.12B-71	37-18
TM.12D-72	408-01
TM.12D-73	408-02
TM.12D-74	54-11
T.12D-75	(403 Esc)
TR.12D-76	37-60
TR.12D-77	37-61
TR.12D-78	37-62
TR.12D-79	37-63
TR.12D-80	37-64
TR.12D-81	37-65

Cessna 560 Citation VI
403 Esc, Getafe

TR.20-01	403-11
TR.20-02	403-12
TR.20-03	403-13

Dassault Falcon 20D/E/F
Grupo 45, Torrejón;
408 Esc, Torrejón

T.11-1	20E	45-02
TM.11-2	20D	45-03
TM.11-3	20D	408-11
TM.11-4	20E	45-01
T.11-5	20F	45-05

Dassault Falcon 50
Grupo 45, Torrejón;

T.16-1	45-20

Dassault Falcon 900
Grupo 45, Torrejón

T.18-1	45-40
T.18-2	45-41

Eurofighter EF2000 Typhoon
CASA, Getafe
XCE.16-01

Fokker F.27M Friendship 400MPA
802 Esc, Gando, Las Palmas

D.2-01	802-10
D.2-02	802-11
D.2-03	802-12

Lockheed Hercules C-130H/ C-130H-30/KC-130H
311 Esc/312 Esc (Ala 31), Zaragoza

TL.10-01	C-130H-30	31-01
T.10-02	C-130H	31-02
T.10-03	C-130H	31-03
T.10-04	C-130H	31-04
TK.10-5	KC-130H	31-50
TK.10-06	KC-130H	31-51
TK.10-7	KC-130H	31-52
T.10-8	C-130H	31-05
T.10-9	C-130H	31-06
T.10-10	C-130H	31-07
TK.10-11	KC-130H	31-53
TK.10-12	KC-130H	31-54

Lockheed P-3A/P-3B* Orion
Grupo 22, Morón

P.3-01	22-21
P.3-03	22-22
P.3-08	22-31*
P.3-09	22-32*
P.3-10	22-33*
P.3-11	22-34*
P.3-12	22-35*

McDonnell Douglas EF-18A/EF-18B* Hornet
Ala 12, Torrejón;
Grupo 15, Zaragoza;
Grupo 21, Morpón

CE.15-1	15-70*
CE.15-2	15-71*
CE.15-3	15-72*
CE.15-4	15-73*
CE.15-5	15-74*
CE.15-6	15-75*
CE.15-7	15-76*
CE.15-8	12-71*
CE.15-9	15-77*
CE.15-10	12-73*
CE.15-11	12-74*
CE.15-12	12-75*
C.15-13	12-01
C.15-14	15-01
C.15-15	15-02
C.15-16	15-03
C.15-18	15-05
C.15-20	15-07
C.15-21	15-08
C.15-22	15-09
C.15-23	15-10
C.15-24	15-11
C.15-25	15-12
C.15-26	15-13
C.15-27	15-14
C.15-28	15-15
C.15-29	15-16
C.15-30	15-17
C.15-31	15-18
C.15-32	15-19
C.15-33	15-20
C.15-34	15-21
C.15-35	15-22
C.15-36	15-23
C.15-37	15-24
C.15-38	15-25
C.15-39	15-26
C.15-40	15-27
C.15-41	15-28
C.15-42	15-29
C.15-43	15-30
C.15-44	12-02
C.15-45	12-03
C.15-46	12-04
C.15-47	15-31
C.15-48	12-06
C.15-49	12-07
C.15-50	12-08
C.15-51	12-09
C.15-52	12-10
C.15-53	12-11
C.15-54	12-12
C.15-55	12-13
C.15-56	12-14
C.15-57	12-15
C.15-58	12-16
C.15-59	12-17
C.15-60	12-18
C.15-61	12-19
C.15-62	12-20
C.15-63	15-32
C.15-64	12-22
C.15-65	12-23
C.15-66	12-24
C.15-67	15-33
C.15-68	12-26
C.15-69	12-27
C.15-70	12-28
C.15-72	12-30
C.15-73	21-01
C.15-74	21-02
C.15-75	21-03
C.15-76	21-04
C.15-77	21-05
C.15-78	21-06
C.15-79	21-07
C.15-80	21-08
C.15-81	21-09
C.15-82	21-10
C.15-83	21-11
C.15-84	21-12
C.15-85	21-13
C.15-86	
C.15-87	
C.15-88	
C.15-89	
C.15-90	
C.15-91	
C.15-92	
C.15-93	
C.15-94	
C.15-95	
C.15-96	

Arma Aérea del'Armada Española
BAe/McDonnell Douglas EAV-8B/EAV-8B+/TAV-8B+ Harrier II
EAV-8B
Esc 009, Rota

VA.2-3	01-903
VA.2-4	01-904
VA.2-5	01-905
VA.2-6	01-906
VA.2-7	01-907
VA.2-9	01-909
VA.2-10	01-910
VA.2-11	01-911
VA.2-12	01-912

EAV-8B+

VA.2-14	01-914
VA.2-15	01-915
VA.2-16	01-916
VA.2-17	01-917
VA.2-18	01-918
VA.2-19	01-919
VA.2-20	01-920
VA.2-21	01-922
VA.2-22	01-922

TAV-8B+

VA.2-23	01-923

Cessna 550 Citation 2
Esc 004, Rota

U.20-1	01-405
U.20-2	01-406
U.20-3	01-407

SUDAN

Silakh al Jawwiya as'Sudaniya
Lockheed C-130H Hercules

1100
1101
1102
1103
1104
1105

SWEDEN

Svenska Flygvapnet
Aerospatiale AS.332M-1 Super Puma (Hkp.10)
Flottiljer 7, Såtenäs;
Flottiljer 15, Söderhamn;
Flottiljer 17,
Ronneby/Kallinge;
Flottiljer 21, Luleå/Kallax

10401	91	F7
10402	92	F7
10403	93	F21
10404	94	F21
10405	95	F15
10406	96	F15
10407	97	F17
10408	98	F15
10409	99	F17
10410	90	F17
10411	88	F21
10412	89	F15

Beechcraft Super King Air (Tp.101)
Flottiljer 7, Såtenäs;
Flottiljer 17, Ronneby/
  Kallinge;
Flottiljer 21, Lulea/Kallax

101002	012	F21
101003	013	F17
101004	014	F7

Cessna 550 Citation 2 (Tp.103)
Flottiljer 17,
Ronneby/Kallinge

103001	

Grumman G.1159C Gulfstream 4 (Tp.102A/S.102B Korpen*)
Flottiljer 16, Uppsala;
Flottiljer 16M, Malmslätt

102001	021	F16
102002*	022	F16M
102003*	023	F16M

Lockheed C-130 Hercules (Tp.84)
Flottiljer 7, Såtenäs

84001	841	C-130E
84002	842	C-130E
84003	843	C-130H
84004	844	C-130H
84005	845	C-130H
84006	846	C-130H
84007	847	C-130H
84008	848	C-130H

Rockwell Sabreliner-40 (Tp.86)
FMV, Malmslätt

86001	861
86002	862

SAAB JAS 39 Gripen
Flottiljer 7, Såtenäs [G];
FMV, Malmslätt

39-2	JAS 39	[52]	FMV
39-3	JAS 39	[53]	FMV
39-4	JAS 39	[54]	SAAB
39-5	JAS 39	[55]	SAAB
39101	JAS 39	[51]	FMV
39103	JAS 39	[03]	F7
39104	JAS 39	[04]	F7
39105	JAS 39	[05]	F7
39106	JAS 39	[06]	F7
39107	JAS 39	[07]	F7
39108	JAS 39	[08]	F7
39109	JAS 39	[09]	F7
39110	JAS 39	[10]	F7
39111	JAS 39	[11]	F7
39112	JAS 39	[12]	F7
39113	JAS 39	[13]	F7
39114	JAS 39	[14]	F7
39115	JAS 39	[15]	F7
39116	JAS 39	[16]	F7
39117	JAS 39	[17]	F7
39118	JAS 39	[18]	SAAB
39119	JAS 39	[19]	F7
39120	JAS 39	[20]	F7
39121	JAS 39	[21]	F7
39122	JAS 39	[22]	F7
39123	JAS 39	[23]	F7
39124	JAS 39	[24]	F7
39125	JAS 39	[25]	F7
39126	JAS 39	[26]	F7
39127	JAS 39	[27]	F7
39128	JAS 39	[28]	F7
39129	JAS 39	[29]	F7
39130	JAS 39	[30]	F7
39131	JAS 39	[31]	F7
39132	JAS 39	[32]	F7
39133	JAS 39	[33]	F7
39134	JAS 39	[34]	F7
39135	JAS 39	[35]	F7
39136	JAS 39	[36]	F7
39137	JAS 39	[37]	F7
39138	JAS 39	[38]	F7
39139	JAS 39	[39]	F7
39140	JAS 39	[40]	F7
39141	JAS 39	[41]	F7
39142	JAS 39	[42]	F7
39143	JAS 39	[43]	F7
39144	JAS 39	[44]	F7
39145	JAS 39	[45]	F7
39146	JAS 39	[46]	F7
39147	JAS 39	[47]	F7
39148	JAS 39	[48]	F7
39149	JAS 39	[49]	F7
39150	JAS 39	[50]	F7
39151	JAS 39	[51]	F7
39152	JAS 39	[52]	F7
39153	JAS 39	[53]	F7
39154	JAS 39	[54]	F7
39155	JAS 39	[55]	F7
39156	JAS 39	[56]	F7
39157	JAS 39	[57]	F7
39158	JAS 39		
39159	JAS 39		
39160	JAS 39		
39161	JAS 39		
39162	JAS 39		
39163	JAS 39		
39164	JAS 39		
39165	JAS 39		
39166	JAS 39		
39167	JAS 39		
39168	JAS 39		
39169	JAS 39		
39170	JAS 39		
39800	JAS 39B	[58]	FMV
39801	JAS 39B	[70]	F7
39802	JAS 39B	[71]	F7
39803	JAS 39B	[72]	F7
39804	JAS 39B	[73]	F7
39805	JAS 39B	[74]	F7

SAAB SF.340B (Tp.100A)/ SF.340AEW&C (S.100B) Argus*
Flottiljer 16, Uppsala;
Flottiljer 16M, Malmslätt

100001	001	F16
100002	002	F16M
100003*	003	F16
100004*	004	F16M
100005*	005	F16M
100006*	006	F16
100007*	007	F16M

Marine Flygtjänst
Vertol 107-II-15 (Hkp.4B)
11 Hkp Div, Berga

04061	61
04063	63
04064	64

Kawasaki-Vertol KV.107-II-16 (Hkp.4C)
11 Hkp Div, Berga;
12 Hkp Div, Säve;
13 Hkp Div, Ronneby/
  Kallinge;
FC, Malmslätt (Air Force)

04065	65	12 Hkp Div
04067	67	12 Hkp Div
04068	68	12 Hkp Div
04069	69	11 Hkp Div
04070	70	11 Hkp Div
04071	71	12 Hkp Div
04072	72	FC

Vertol 107-II-15 (Hkp.4A)
11 Hkp Div, Berga;
12 Hkp Div, Säve;
13 Hkp Div, Ronneby/
  Kallinge;

04073	73	11 Hkp Div
04074	74	13 Hkp Div
04075	75	13 Hkp Div
04076	76	13 Hkp Div

Armen
Agusta-Bell AB.412 (Hkp.11)
Armeflyget 1 (AF1), Boden

11331	31
11332	32
11333	33
11334	34
11335	35
11336	36
11337	37
11338	38
11339	39
11340	40

11341	41	
11342	42	

MBB Bo.105CB (Hkp.9B)
Armeflyget 1 (AF1), Boden;
Armeflyget 2 (AF2),
 Malmslätt;
FC, Malmslätt (Air Force)

09201	01	AF2
09202	02	AF1
09203	03	AF1
09204	04	AF2
09205	05	AF1
09206	06	AF1
09207	07	AF1
09208	08	AF1
09209	09	AF2
09210	10	AF1
09211	11	AF1
09212	12	AF1
09213	13	AF2
09214	14	AF2
09215	15	AF2
09216	16	AF1
09217	17	AF2
09218	18	AF1
09219	19	AF1
09220	20	AF2
09221	90	FC

SWITZERLAND
Schweizerische Flugwaffe
(Most aircraft are pooled
centrally. Some carry unit
badges but these rarely
indicate actual operators.)

**Aérospatiale AS.532
Super Puma**
Leichte Flieger Staffel 5
 (LtSt 5), Interlaken;
Leichte Flieger Staffel 6
 (LtSt 6), Alpnach;
Leichte Flieger Staffel 8
 (LtSt 8), Ulrichen
Detachments at Alpnach,
 Emmen, Meiringen,
 Payerne & Sion

T-311
T-312
T-313
T-314
T-315
T-316
T-317
T-318
T-319
T-320
T-321
T-322
T-323
T-324
T-325

Dassault Falcon 50
VIP Flight, Dübendorf
T-783

Dassault Mirage III
Flieger Staffel 3 (FlSt 3),
 Sion;
Flieger Staffel 4 (FlSt 4),
 Payerne;
Flieger Staffel 10 (FlSt 10),
 Buochs;

Flieger Staffel 16 (FlSt 16),
 Buochs;
Gruppe fur Rustungdienste
 (GRD), Emmen;
Instrumentation Flieger
 Staffel 14 (InstruFlSt 14),
 Payerne

Mirage IIIBS
J-2001   InstruFlSt 14
Mirage IIIUDS
J-2011   InstruFlSt 14
J-2012   InstruFlSt 14
Mirage IIIS
J-2301
J-2302   GRD
J-2303   GRD
J-2304
J-2305
J-2306
J-2308
J-2309
J-2311
J-2312
J-2313
J-2314
J-2315
J-2317
J-2318
J-2319
J-2321
J-2322
J-2324
J-2325
J-2327
J-2330
J-2331
J-2332
J-2334
J-2335
Mirage IIIRS
R-2102
R-2103
R-2104
R-2105
R-2106
R-2107
R-2108
R-2109
R-2110
R-2111
R-2112
R-2113
R-2114
R-2115
R-2116
R-2117
R-2118
Mirage IIIBS
U-2004   InstruFlSt 14

Gates Learjet 35A
VIP Flight, Dübendorf
T-781

**McDonnell Douglas
F/A-18 Hornet**
Flieger Staffel 11 (FlSt 11),
 Meiringen;
Flieger Staffel 17 (FlSt 17),
 Payerne;
Flieger Staffel 18 (FlSt 18),
 Payerne
F/A-18C
J-5001

J-5002
J-5003
J-5004
J-5005
J-5006
J-5007
J-5008
J-5009
J-5010
J-5011
J-5012
J-5013
J-5014
J-5015
J-5016
J-5017
J-5018
J-5019
J-5020
J-5021
J-5022
J-5023
J-5024
J-5025
J-5026
F/A-18D
J-5232
J-5233
J-5234
J-5235
J-5236
J-5237
J-5238

Northrop F-5 Tiger II
Flieger Staffel 1 (FlSt 1),
 Turtman;
Flieger Staffel 6 (FlSt 6),
 Sion;
Flieger Staffel 8 (FlSt 8),
 Meiringen;
Flieger Staffel 11 (FlSt 11),
 Meiringen;
Flieger Staffel 13 (FlSt 13),
 Meiringen;
Flieger Staffel 18 (FlSt 18),
 Payerne;
Flieger Staffel 19 (FlSt 19),
 Mollis;
Gruppe fur Rustunggdienste
 (GRD), Emmen;
Instrumentation Flieger
 Staffel 14 (InstruFlSt 14),
 Dübendorf;
Patrouille Suisse, Emmen
 (P. Suisse)
F-5E
J-3001
J-3002
J-3003
J-3004
J-3005
J-3006
J-3007
J-3008   InstruFlSt 14
J-3009
J-3010
J-3011
J-3012
J-3014
J-3015
J-3016
J-3019
J-3020

J-3021		J-3202		039
J-3022		J-3203		040	12-040
J-3023		J-3204	GRD	
J-3024		J-3205		**TUSAS-GD F-16C/F-16D***
J-3025		J-3206		**Fighting Falcon**
J-3026		J-3207		4 AJÜ, Mürted:
J-3027		J-3208		141 Filo, 142 Filo
J-3029		J-3209		& Öncel Filo;
J-3030		J-3210		5 AJÜ, Merzifon:
J-3031		J-3211		151 Filo & 152 Filo;
J-3032		J-3212		6 AJÜ, Bandirma:
J-3033				161 Filo & 162 Filo;
J-3034		**TURKEY**		8 AJÜ, Diyarbakir:
J-3035		**Türk Hava Kuvvetleri**		181 Filo & 182 Filo;
J-3036		**Boeing KC-135R**		9 AJÜ, Balikesir:
J-3037		**Stratotanker**		191 Filo & 192 Filo
J-3038		Tanker Filo, Incirlik		86-0066	Öncel Filo
J-3039		00325		86-0068	Öncel Filo
J-3040		23539		86-0069	Öncel Filo
J-3041		23563		86-0070	Öncel Filo
J-3043		23567		86-0071	Öncel Filo
J-3044		72609		86-0072	Öncel Filo
J-3045		80110		86-0191*	Öncel Filo
J-3046				86-0192*	191 Filo
J-3047		**Cessna 650 Citation VII**		86-0193*	Öncel Filo
J-3049		224 Filo, Ankara/Etimesğut		86-0194*	Öncel Filo
J-3050		93-7024 ETI-024		86-0195*	Öncel Filo
J-3051		93-7026 ETI-026		86-0196*	Öncel Filo
J-3052				87-0002*	142 Filo
J-3053		**Grumman G.1159C**		87-0003*	Öncel Filo
J-3054		**Gulfstream 4**		87-0009	Öncel Filo
J-3055		224 Filo, Ankara/Etimesğut		87-0010	Öncel Filo
J-3056		003		87-0011	Öncel Filo
J-3057				87-0013	Öncel Filo
J-3058		**Lockheed C-130B Hercules**		87-0014	Öncel Filo
J-3060		222 Filo, Erkilet		87-0015	Öncel Filo
J-3061		3496 (23496)		87-0016	Öncel Filo
J-3062		10960		87-0017	141 Filo
J-3063		10963		87-0018	142 Filo
J-3064		70527		87-0019	Öncel Filo
J-3065		80736		87-0020	Öncel Filo
J-3066		91527		87-0021	191 Filo
J-3067				88-0013*	Öncel Filo
J-3068		**Lockheed C-130E Hercules**		88-0014*	141 Filo
J-3069		222 Filo, Erkilet		88-0015*	141 Filo
J-3070		00991		88-0019	Öncel Filo
J-3072		01468 12-468		88-0020	Öncel Filo
J-3073		01947		88-0021	Öncel Filo
J-3074		13186 12-186		88-0024	Öncel Filo
J-3075		13187 12-187		88-0025	Öncel Filo
J-3076		13188		88-0026	Öncel Filo
J-3077		13189		88-0027	Öncel Filo
J-3079				88-0028	191 Filo
J-3080	P. Suisse	**Transall C-160D**		88-0029	Öncel Filo
J-3081	P. Suisse	221 Filo, Erkilet		88-0030	191 Filo
J-3082	P. Suisse	019		88-0031	Öncel Filo
J-3083	P. Suisse	020		88-0032	Öncel Filo
J-3084	P. Suisse [4]	021		88-0033	141 Filo
J-3085	P. Suisse [3]	022		88-0034	141 Filo
J-3086	P. Suisse [6]	023		88-0035	141 Filo
J-3087	P. Suisse	024		88-0036	141 Filo
J-3088	P. Suisse [5]	025 12-025		88-0037	141 Filo
J-3089	P. Suisse	026		89-0022	141 Filo
J-3090	P. Suisse [2]	027		89-0023	141 Filo
J-3091	P. Suisse [1]	028 12-028		89-0024	141 Filo
J-3092		029		89-0025	141 Filo
J-3093		031		89-0026	141 Filo
J-3094		032		89-0027	141 Filo
J-3095		033		89-0028	141 Filo
J-3096		034		89-0030	142 Filo
J-3097	GRD	035		89-0031	142 Filo
J-3098		036		89-0032	161 Filo
F-5F		037 12-037		89-0034	162 Filo
J-3201		038		89-0035	162 Filo

89-0036	161 Filo	92-0021	181 Filo	94-0087	
89-0037	162 Filo	92-0022*	181 Filo	94-0088	
89-0038	162 Filo	92-0023*	191 Filo	94-0089	
89-0039	162 Filo	92-0024*	161 Filo	94-0090	
89-0040	162 Filo	93-0001	181 Filo	94-0091	
89-0041	162 Filo	93-0002	181 Filo	94-0092	
89-0042*	141 Filo	93-0003	181 Filo	94-0093	
89-0043*	162 Filo	93-0004	181 Filo	94-0094	
89-0044*	162 Filo	93-0005	181 Filo	94-0095	
89-0045*	162 Filo	93-0006	181 Filo	94-0096	
90-0001	162 Filo	93-0007	142 Filo	94-0097	
90-0003	162 Filo	93-0008	181 Filo	94-0098	
90-0004	162 Filo	93-0009	182 Filo	94-0099	
90-0005	161 Filo	93-0010	181 Filo	94-0100	
90-0006	162 Filo	93-0011	182 Filo	94-0101	
90-0007	162 Filo	93-0012	181 Filo	94-0102	
90-0008	162 Filo	93-0013	182 Filo	94-0103	
90-0009	162 Filo	93-0014	181 Filo	94-0104	
90-0010	192 Filo	93-0657	141 Filo	94-0105*	191 Filo
90-0011	162 Filo	93-0658		94-0106*	191 Filo
90-0012	6 AJÜ	93-0659		94-0107*	
90-0013	161 Filo	93-0660	152 Filo	94-0108*	
90-0014	192 Filo	93-0661		94-0109*	
90-0015	162 Filo	93-0662		94-0110*	
90-0016	162 Filo	93-0663			
90-0017	162 Filo	93-0664		**UNITED ARAB EMIRATES**	
90-0018	162 Filo	93-0665		**United Arab Emirates Air Force**	
90-0019	6 AJÜ	93-0666		*Abu Dhabi*	
90-0020	162 Filo	93-0667		**Lockheed C-130H Hercules**	
90-0021	162 Filo	93-0668		1211	
90-0022*	182 Filo	93-0669	152 Filo	1212	
90-0023*	191 Filo	93-0670		1213	
90-0024*	161 Filo	93-0671		1214	
91-0001	161 Filo	93-0672	152 Filo		
91-0002	162 Filo	93-0673	Öncel Filo	*Dubai*	
91-0003	162 Filo	93-0674	192 Filo	**Lockheed L.100-30**	
91-0004	162 Filo	93-0675	192 Filo	**Hercules**	
91-0005	162 Filo	93-0676	192 Filo	311	
91-0006	192 Filo	93-0677	192 Filo	312	
91-0007	192 Filo	93-0678	192 Filo		
91-0008	141 Filo	93-0679	192 Filo		
91-0010	192 Filo	93-0680	192 Filo		
91-0011	141 Filo	93-0681			
91-0012	191 Filo	93-0682			
91-0013	192 Filo	93-0683	192 Filo		
91-0014	191 Filo	93-0684	192 Filo		
91-0015	192 Filo	93-0685			
91-0016	192 Filo	93-0686	192 Filo		
91-0017	192 Filo	93-0687	Öncel Filo		
91-0018	192 Filo	93-0688	192 Filo		
91-0019	192 Filo	93-0689	192 Filo		
91-0020	182 Filo	93-0690	192 Filo		
91-0022*	141 Filo	93-0691*			
91-0024*	141 Filo	93-0692*	152 Filo		
92-0001	191 Filo	93-0693*	Öncel Filo		
92-0002	192 Filo	93-0694*			
92-0003	191 Filo	93-0695*	192 Filo		
92-0004	191 Filo	93-0696*	192 Filo		
92-0005	192 Filo	94-0071	192 Filo		
92-0006	182 Filo	94-0072	192 Filo		
92-0007	182 Filo	94-0073			
92-0008	182 Filo	94-0074			
92-0009	191 Filo	94-0075			
92-0010	142 Filo	94-0076			
92-0011	182 Filo	94-0077			
92-0012	192 Filo	94-0078			
92-0013	191 Filo	94-0079			
92-0014	191 Filo	94-0080			
92-0015	182 Filo	94-0081			
92-0016	191 Filo	94-0082			
92-0017	191 Filo	94-0083			
92-0018	191 Filo	94-0084			
92-0019	142 Filo	94-0085			
92-0020	142 Filo	94-0086			

US Military Aircraft Markings

All USAF aircraft have been allocated a fiscal year (FY) number since 1921. Individual aircraft are given a serial according to the fiscal year in which they are ordered. The numbers commence at 0001 and are prefixed with the year of allocation. For example F-15C Eagle 84-001 (84-0001) was the first aircraft ordered in 1984. The fiscal year (FY) serial is carried on the technical data block which is usually stencilled on the left-hand side of the aircraft just below the cockpit. The number displayed on the fin is a corruption of the FY serial. Most tactical aircraft carry the fiscal year in small figures followed by the last three or four digits of the serial in large figures. For example Aviano-based F-16C Fighting Falcon 89-2009 carries 89-009/AV on its tail. Large transport and tanker aircraft such as C-130s and KC-135s sometimes display a five-figure number commencing with the last digit of the appropriate fiscal year and four figures of the production number. An example of this is KC-135R 58-0128 which displays 80128 on its fin.

USN serials follow a straightforward numerical sequence which commenced, for the present series, with the allocation of 00001 to an SB2C Helldiver by the Bureau of Aeronautics in 1940. Numbers in the 165000 series are presently being issued. They are usually carried in full on the rear fuselage of the aircraft.

UK based USAF Aircraft

The following aircraft are normally based in the UK. They are listed in numerical order of type with individual aircraft in serial number order, as depicted on the aircraft. The number in brackets is either the alternative presentation of the five-figure number commencing with the last digit of the fiscal year, or the fiscal year where a five-figure serial is presented on the aircraft. Where it is possible to identify the allocation of aircraft to individual squadrons by means of colours carried on fin or cockpit edge, this is also provided.

Notes	Type				Notes	Type			
	McDonnell Douglas F-15C Eagle/					86-0173	(86-0173)	F-15C	y
	F-15D Eagle/F-15E Strike Eagle					86-0174	(86-0174)	F-15C	y
	LN: 48th FW, RAF Lakenheath:					86-0175	(86-0175)	F-15C	y
	492nd FS blue/white					86-0176	(86-0176)	F-15C	y
	493rd FS black/yellow					86-0178	(86-0178)	F-15C	y
	494th FS red/white					86-0180	(86-0180)	F-15C	y
	84-0001	(84-0001)	F-15C	y				[48th OG]	
	84-0009	(84-0009)	F-15C	y		86-0182	(86-0182)	F-15D	y
	84-0010	(84-0010)	F-15C	y		90-0248	(90-0248)	F-15E	m
	84-0014	(84-0014)	F-15C	y				[48th FW]	
	84-0015	(84-0015)	F-15C	y		90-0251	(90-0251)	F-15E	bl
	84-0019	(84-0019)	F-15C	y				[492nd FS]	
	84-0044	(84-0044)	F-15D	y		90-0255	(90-0255)	F-15E	bl
	86-0147	(86-0147)	F-15C	y		90-0256	(90-0256)	F-15E	bl
	86-0154	(86-0154)	F-15C	y		90-0257	(90-0257)	F-15E	bl
	86-0156	(86-0156)	F-15C	y		90-0258	(90-0258)	F-15E	bl
	86-0159	(86-0159)	F-15C	y		90-0259	(90-0259)	F-15E	bl
	86-0160	(86-0160)	F-15C	y		90-0260	(90-0260)	F-15E	bl
	86-0163	(86-0163)	F-15C	y		90-0261	(90-0261)	F-15E	bl
	86-0164	(86-0164)	F-15C	y		90-0262	(90-0262)	F-15E	bl
			[493rd FS]					[48th OG]	
	86-0165	(86-0165)	F-15C	y		91-0300	(91-0300)	F-15E	bl
	86-0166	(86-0166)	F-15C	y		91-0301	(91-0301)	F-15E	bl
	86-0167	(86-0167)	F-15C	y		91-0302	(91-0302)	F-15E	bl
	86-0169	(86-0169)	F-15C	y		91-0303	(91-0303)	F-15E	bl
	86-0171	(86-0171)	F-15C	y		91-0304	(91-0304)	F-15E	bl
	86-0172	(86-0172)	F-15C	y		91-0305	(91-0305)	F-15E	bl

Type			Notes	Type		Notes
91-0306	(91-0306)	F-15E		01630	(FY70)	
91-0307	(91-0307)	F-15E *bl*		10924	(FY68)	
91-0308	(91-0308)	F-15E *bl*		14993	(FY67)	
91-0309	(91-0309)	F-15E *bl*		31648	(FY73)	
91-0310	(91-0310)	F-15E *bl*		95784	(FY69)	
91-0311	(91-0311)	F-15E *bl*		95790	(FY69)	
91-0312	(91-0312)	F-15E *bl*				
91-0313	(91-0313)	F-15E *m*		**Lockheed C-130 Hercules**		
		[3rd AF]		352nd SOG, RAF Mildenhall:		
91-0314	(91-0314)	F-15E *r*		7th SOS* & 67th SOS,		
		[494th FS]		37814	(FY63) C-130E	
91-0315	(91-0315)	F-15E *r*		40476	(FY84) MC-130H*	
91-0316	(91-0316)	F-15E *r*		60223	(FY66) MC-130P	
91-0317	(91-0317)	F-15E		61699	(FY86) MC-130H*	
91-0318	(91-0318)	F-15E *r*		70023	(FY87) MC-130H*	
91-0319	(91-0319)	F-15E		80193	(FY88) MC-130H*	
91-0320	(91-0320)	F-15E *r*		80194	(FY88) MC-130H*	
91-0321	(91-0321)	F-15E *r*		95820	(FY69) MC-130P	
91-0322	(91-0322)	F-15E *r*		95823	(FY69) MC-130P	
91-0323	(91-0323)	F-15E *r*		95826	(FY69) MC-130P	
91-0324	(91-0324)	F-15E *r*		95828	(FY69) MC-130P	
91-0325	(91-0325)	F-15E *bl*		95831	(FY69) MC-130P	
91-0326	(91-0326)	F-15E *bl*				
91-0328	(91-0328)	F-15E *r*		**Boeing KC-135R**		
91-0329	(91-0329)	F-15E *bl*		**Stratotanker**		
91-0330	(91-0330)	F-15E *r*		351st ARS/100th ARW,		
91-0331	(91-0331)	F-15E *r*		RAF Mildenhall [D] (*r/w/bl*)		
91-0332	(91-0332)	F-15E *bl*		10267	(FY61)	
91-0333	(91-0333)	F-15E *r*		10284	(FY61)	
91-0334	(91-0334)	F-15E *r*		10288	(FY61)	
91-0335	(91-0335)	F-15E *r*		10312	(FY61)	
91-0601	(91-0601)	F-15E *r*		23498	(FY62)	
91-0602	(91-0602)	F-15E *r*		23517	(FY62)	
91-0603	(91-0603)	F-15E *r*		23528	(FY62)	
91-0604	(91-0604)	F-15E *r*		23533	(FY62)	
91-0605	(91-0605)	F-15E *r*		23538	(FY62)	
92-0364	(92-0364)	F-15E *r*		23561	(FY62)	
				23564	(FY62)	
Sikorsky MH-53J				23578	(FY62)	
21st SOS/352nd SOG,				37979	(FY63)	
RAF Mildenhall				38017	(FY63)	
01625	(FY70)			71474	(FY57)	
01626	(FY70)					

UK based US Navy Aircraft

Beech UC 12M
Super King Air
Naval Air Facility, Mildenhall
3840 (163840)
3843 (163843)

European based USAF Aircraft

These aircraft are normally based in Western Europe with the USAFE. They are shown in numerical order of type designation, with individual aircraft in serial number order as carried on the aircraft. An alternative five-figure presentation of the serial is shown in brackets where appropriate. Fiscal year (FY) details are also provided if necessary. The unit allocation and operating bases are given for most aircraft.

Notes	Type				Notes	Type			
	Lockheed U-2S					40180	C-12F[3]		
	OL-FR/9th RW, Istres, France [BB]					*FY76*			
	01082 (FY80)					60171	C-12C[1]		
	01083 (FY80)					60173	C-12C[1]		
	McDonnell Douglas					**Lockheed (GD) F-16C/F-16D***			
	C-9A Nightingale					**AV:** 31st FW, Aviano, Italy:			
	86th AW, Ramstein, Germany:					510th FS *purple/white*			
	75th AAS & 76th AS[1];					555th FS *green/yellow*			
	Det 1, 86th OG/SHAPE, Chievres,					**SP:** 52nd FW, Spangdahlem, Germany:			
	Belgium[2]					22nd FS *red/white*			
	FY71					23rd FS *blue/white*			
	10876[2] (VIP)					87-350 (87-0350)	AV *gn*		
	10879					87-351 (87-0351)	AV *gn*		
	10880[1] (VIP)					87-355 (87-0355)	AV *pr*		
	10881					87-359 (87-0359)	AV *pr*		
	10882					88-413 (88-0413)	AV *pr*	[510th FS]
	FY67					88-425 (88-0425)	AV *gn*		
	22585					88-435 (88-0435)	AV *gn*		
	FY68					88-443 (88-0443)	AV *pr*		
	88934					88-444 (88-0444)	AV *pr*		
						88-446 (88-0446)	AV *pr*		
	Fairchild A-10A/OA-10A*					88-491 (88-0491)	AV *pr*		
	Thunderbolt II					88-525 (88-0525)	AV *pr*		
	SP: 52nd FW, Spangdahlem, Germany:					88-526 (88-0526)	AV *pr*		
	81st FS *black*					88-529 (88-0529)	AV *pr*		
	81-951 (81-0951)	*bk*				88-532 (88-0532)	AV *gn*	[31st OG]
	81-952 (81-0952)*	*m*	[52nd FW]			88-535 (88-0535)	AV *gn*		
	81-954 (81-0954)*	*bk*				88-541 (88-0541)	AV *pr*		
	81-956 (81-0956)*	*bk*				88-550 (88-0550)	AV *gn*	[555th FS]
	81-962 (81-0962)	*bk*				89-001 (89-2001)	AV *m*	[31st FW]
	81-963 (81-0963)	*bk*				89-009 (89-2009)	AV *pr*		
	81-966 (81-0966)	*bk*				89-011 (89-2011)	AV *pr*		
	81-976 (81-0976)	*bk*				89-016 (89-2016)	AV *gn*	[16th AF]
	81-978 (81-0978)*	*bk*				89-018 (89-2018)	AV *gn*		
	81-980 (81-0980)	*bk*	81st FS]			89-023 (89-2023)	AV *gn*		
	81-983 (81-0983)	*bk*				89-024 (89-2024)	AV *gn*		
	81-984 (81-0984)	*bk*				89-026 (89-2026)	AV *pr*		
	81-985 (81-0985)*	*bk*				89-029 (89-2029)	AV *pr*		
	81-988 (81-0988)	*bk*				89-030 (89-2030)	AV *pr*		
	81-991 (81-0991)*	*bk*				89-035 (89-2035)	AV *gn*		
	81-992 (81-0992)	*bk*				89-038 (89-2038)	AV *gn*		
	82-649 (82-0649)*	*bk*				89-039 (89-2039)	AV *gn*		
	82-650 (82-0650)	*bk*				89-044 (89-2044)	AV *gn*		
	82-654 (82-0654)	*bk*				89-046 (89-2046)	AV *pr*		
	82-655 (82-0655)	*bk*				89-047 (89-2047)	AV *pr*		
	82-656 (82-0656)	*bk*				89-049 (89-2049)	AV *pr*		
						89-050 (89-2050)	AV *pr*		
	Beech C-12C/C-12D/C-12F					89-057 (89-2057)	AV *gn*		
	[1]JUSMG, Ankara, Turkey					89-137 (89-2137)	AV *pr*		
	[2]US Embassy Flight, Athens					89-178 (89-2178)*	AV *pr*		
	[3]US Embassy Flight, Budapest					90-709 (90-0709)	AV *pr*		
	FY83					90-795 (90-0795)*	AV *gn*		
	30495 C-12D[3]					90-796 (90-0796)*	AV *gn*		
	FY73					90-800 (90-0800)*	AV *gn*		
	31206 C-12C[1]					90-813 (90-0813)	SP *r*		
	31216 C-12C[1]					90-818 (90-0818)	SP *r*		
	31218 C-12C[2]					90-827 (90-0827)	SP *r*		
	FY84					90-828 (90-0828)	SP *r*		

Type			Notes	Type	Notes
90-829	(90-0829)	SP r	[22nd FS]	*7005th ABS/HQ USEUCOM,	
90-831	(90-0831)	SP r		Stuttgart, Germany	
90-833	(90-0833)	SP r		*FY84*	
90-843	(90-0843)*	SP r		40068*	
90-846	(90-0846)*	SP r		40081*	
91-336	(91-0336)	SP r		40082*	
91-337	(91-0337)	SP r		40083*	
91-338	(91-0338)	SP r		40084	
91-339	(91-0339)	SP r	[22nd FS]	40085	
91-340	(91-0340)	SP r		40086	
91-341	(91-0341)	SP r		40087	
91-342	(91-0342)	SP r		40108	
91-343	(91-0343)	SP r		40109	
91-344	(91-0344)	SP r		40110	
91-351	(91-0351)	SP r		40111	
91-352	(91-0352)	SP m	[52nd FW]	40112	
91-402	(91-0402)	SP bl			
91-403	(91-0403)	SP bl	[23rd FS]	**Sikorsky HH-60G Blackhawk**	
91-405	(91-0405)	SP bl		56th RQS/85th Group, Keflavik,	
91-406	(91-0406)	SP bl	[23rd FS]	Iceland [IS]	
91-407	(91-0407)	SP bl		26117	(FY88)
91-408	(91-0408)	SP bl		26205	(FY89)
91-409	(91-0409)	SP bl		26206	(FY89)
91-410	(91-0410)	SP bl		26208	(FY89)
91-412	(91-0412)	SP m	[52nd FW]	26212	(FY89)
91-414	(91-0414)	SP bl			
91-415	(91-0415)	SP bl		**Lockheed C-130E Hercules**	
91-416	(91-0416)	SP bl		37th AS/86th AW, Ramstein,	
91-417	(91-0417)	SP bl		Germany [RS] (*bl/w*)	
91-418	(91-0418)	SP bl		01260	(FY70)
91-419	(91-0419)	SP bl		01264	(FY70)
91-420	(91-0420)	SP bl		01271	(FY70)
91-421	(91-0421)	SP bl		01274	(FY70)
91-464	(91-0464)*	SP r		10935	(FY68)
91-472	(91-0472)*	SP bl		10938	(FY68)
91-474	(91-0474)*	SP bl		10943	(FY68)
92-915	(92-3915)	SP bl		10947	(FY68)
92-918	(92-3918)	SP bl		17681	(FY64)
				18240	(FY64)

Grumman C-20A Gulfstream III
76th AS/86th AW, Ramstein,
Germany
FY83
30500
30501
30502

37885	(FY63)
37887	(FY63)
40502	(FY64)
40527	(FY64)
40533	(FY64)
40550	(FY64)
96566	(FY69)
96582	(FY69)
96583	(FY69)

Gates C-21A Learjet
76th AS/86th AW, Ramstein,
Germany

European based US Navy Aircraft

Type			Notes	Type			Notes
Lockheed P-3 Orion				3837	(163837)	Sigonella	
CinCAFSE, NAF Sigonella, Italy;				3838	(163838)	Sigonella	
NAF Keflavik, Iceland;				3839	(163839)	Rota	
VQ-2, NAF Rota, Spain				3841	(163841)	Sigonella	
150495		UP-3A	NAF Keflavik	3842	(163842)	Rota	
150511		VP-3A	CinCAFSE	3844	(163844)	Sigonella	
156520	[10]	P-3C	VQ-2	**Sikorsky MH-53E**			
156525	[11]	P-3C	VQ-2	**Sea Stallion**			
156529	[24]	EP-3E	VQ-2	HC-4, NAF Sigonella, Italy			
157316	[23]	EP-3E	VQ-2	162505	HC-47		
157320	[21]	EP-3E	VQ-2	162506	HC-48		
157325	[25]	EP-3E	VQ-2	162509	HC-49		
157326	[22]	EP-3E	VQ-2	162516	HC-46		
				163053	HC-44		
Beech UC-12M Super King Air				163055	HC-45		
NAF Rota, Spain;				163057	HC-41		
NAF Sigonella, Italy				163065	HC-43		
				163068	HC-42		

Type		Notes	Type			Notes
Bell UH-1H Iroquois			40161	C-12F	6th Avn Co	
LANDSOUTHEAST, Cigli, Turkey;			40162	C-12F	6th Avn Co	
'B Co, 2nd Btn, 502nd Avn Reg't,			40164	C-12F	LANDSOUTHEAST	
Coleman Barracks;			40165	C-12F	LANDSOUTHEAST	
7th Army Training Center,			*FY94*			
Grafenwöhr;			40315	C-12R	A/2-228th Avn	
Combat Manoeuvre Training Centre,			40317	C-12R	A/2-228th Avn	
Hohenfels;			40318	C-12R	A/2-228th Avn	
HQ/USEUCOM, Stuttgart;			40319	C-12R	A/2-228th Avn	
6th Avn Co, Vicenza, Italy			*FY95*			
FY69			50088	C-12R	A/2-228th Avn	
15605	HQ/USEUCOM		*FY85*			
15606	HQ/USEUCOM		50147	RC-12K	1st MIB	
FY68			50148	RC-12K	1st MIB	
16341	LANDSOUTHEAST		50150	RC-12K	1st MIB	
16662	LANDSOUTHEAST		50151	RC-12K	1st MIB	
FY72			50152	RC-12K	1st MIB	
21569	CMTC		50153	RC-12K	1st MIB	
21632	CMTC		50154	RC-12K	1st MIB	
21636	CMTC		50155	RC-12K	1st MIB	
FY73						
21668	CMTC		**Beech C-12J**			
21700	6th Avn Co		HQ/USEUCOM, Stuttgart			
21714	6th Avn Co		*FY86*			
21786	CMTC		60079			
21806	LANDSOUTHEAST					
21824	7th ATC		**Cessna UC-35A Citation V**			
22123	B/2-502nd Avn		207th Avn Co, Heidelberg			
22127	B/2-502nd Avn		*FY95*			
FY74			50123			
22303	CMTC		50124			
22318	6th Avn Co		*FY97*			
22330	CMTC		70101			
22337	6th Avn Co		70102			
22347	CMTC					
22355	CMTC		**Boeing-Vertol CH-47D Chinook**			
22368	HQ/USEUCOM		'F' Co, 159th Avn Reg't Giebelstadt			
22370	CMTC		*FY87*			
22410	CMTC		70072			
22411	6th Avn Co		70073			
22444	6th Avn Co		*FY88*			
22448	CMTC		80098			
22465	CMTC		80099			
22483	6th Avn Co		80100			
22496	6th Avn Co		80101			
22504	7th ATC		80102			
22513	HQ/USEUCOM		80103			
22514	HQ/USEUCOM		80104			
			80106			
Beech C-12 Super King Air			*FY89*			
7th Army Training Center,			90138			
Grafenwöhr;			90139			
207th Avn Co, Heidelberg;			90140			
'LANDSOUTHEAST, Izmir, Turkey;			90141			
HQ/USEUCOM, Stuttgart;			90142			
6th Avn Co, Vicenza, Italy;			90143			
'A' Co, 5th Btn, 158th Avn Reg't,			90144			
Wiesbaden;			90145			
1st Military Intelligence Btn,						
Wiesbaden			**Bell OH-58D(I) Kiowa Warrior**			
FY84			1st Btn, 1st Cavalry Reg't, Budingen;			
40144	C-12F	7th ATC	1st Btn, 4th Cavalry Reg't, Schweinfurt			
40152	C-12F	207th Avn Co	*FY90*			
40153	C-12F	1st MIB	00348	1-1st Cav		
40155	C-12F	207th Avn Co	00371	1-1st Cav		
40156	C-12F	207th Avn Co	00373	1-4th Cav		
40157	C-12F	207th Avn Co	*FY91*			
40158	C-12F	HQ/USEUCOM	10540	1-1st Cav		
40160	C-12F	HQ/USEUCOM	10544	1-1st Cav		

Type			Notes	Type			Notes
10564	1-1st Cav			23755	UH-60A	45th Med Co	
FY92				23756	UH-60A	236th Med Co	
20520	1-1st Cav			23757	UH-60A	207th Avn Co	
20529	1-1st Cav			23761	UH-60A	2-501st Avn	
20545	1-1st Cav			FY83			
FY93				23854	UH-60A	A/5-158th Avn	
30971	1-4th Cav			23855	UH-60A	207th Avn Co	
30996	1-4th Cav			23868	UH-60A	207th Avn Co	
30998	1-4th Cav			23869	UH-60A	207th Avn Co	
31002	1-4th Cav			FY84			
31005	1-4th Cav			23951	UH-60A	45th Med Co	
31006	1-4th Cav			24019	EH-60A		
31007	1-4th Cav			FY85			
31008	1-4th Cav			24391	UH-60A	45th Med Co	
FY94				24467	EH-60A	2-1st Avn	
40149	1-4th Cav			24475	EH-60A	2-1st Avn	
40150	1-4th Cav			24478	EH-60A	2-1st Avn	
40151	1-4th Cav			FY86			
40152	1-1st Cav			24498	UH-60A	2-501st Avn	
40153	1-4th Cav			24530	UH-60A	2-501st Avn	
40154	1-4th Cav			24531	UH-60A	45th Med Co	
40174	1-4th Cav			24532	UH-60A	45th Med Co	
40175	1-1st Cav			24538	UH-60A	207th Avn Co	
40176	1-4th Cav			24550	UH-60A	236th Med Co	
40178	1-1st Cav			24551	UH-60A	236th Med Co	
40179	1-1st Cav			24552	UH-60A	159th Med Co	
40180	1-1st Cav			24554	UH-60A	2-501st Avn	
FY89				24555	UH-60A	159th Med Co	
90114	1-1st Cav			24566	EH-60C	2-501st Avn	
90116	1-1st Cav			FY87			
90117	1-1st Cav			24579	UH-60A	A/5-158th Avn	
				24581	UH-60A	159th Med Co	
				24583	UH-60A	357th Avn Det	
				24584	UH-60A	357th Avn Det	
				24589	UH-60A	207th Avn Co	
				24621	UH-60A	207th Avn Co	
				24628	UH-60A	C/158th Avn	
				24634	UH-60A	159th Med Co	
				24642	UH-60A	207th Avn Co	
				24643	UH-60A	3-3rd Avn	
				24644	UH-60A	45th Med Co	
				24645	UH-60A	236th Med Co	
				24646	UH-60A	2-1st Avn	
				24647	UH-60A	2-501st Avn	
				24650	UH-60A	159th Med Co	
				24656	UH-60A	159th Med Co	
				24660	EH-60C	2-501st Avn	
				24664	EH-60A	2-501st Avn	
				24667	EH-60A	2-501st Avn	
				26001	UH-60A	45th Med Co	
				26002	UH-60A	159th Med Co	
				26003	UH-60A	B/5-158th Avn	
				26004	UH-60A	3-3rd Avn	

Sikorsky H-60 Black Hawk

2nd Btn, 1st Avn Reg't, Ansbach;
3rd Btn, 3rd Avn Reg't, Ansbach;
45th Medical Co, Ansbach;
'B' Co, 5th Btn, 158th Avn Regt,
   Aviano
'A' Co, 127th Divisional Avn Support
   Btn Bad Kreuznach;
357th Avn Det/SHAPE, Chievres;
'B' Co, 70th Transportation Reg't,
   Coleman Barracks;
'C' Co, 158th Avn Reg't, Giebelstadt;
'D' Co, 159th Avn Reg't, Giebelstadt;
2nd Btn, 501st Avn Reg't, Hanau;
207th Avn Co, Heidelberg;
236th Medical Co (HA), Landstuhl;
6th Avn Co, Vicenza, Italy;
'A' Co, 5th Btn, 158th Avn Reg't,
   Wiesbaden;
159th Medical Co, Wiesbaden

FY82			
23660	UH-60A	C/158th Avn	
23672	UH-60A	207th Avn Co	
23675	UH-60A	45th Med Co	
23685	UH-60A	236th Med Co	
23692	UH-60A	C/158th Avn	
23693	UH-60A	45th Med Co	
23727	UH-60A	236th Med Co	
23729	UH-60A	45th Med Co	
23735	UH-60A	236th Med Co	
23736	UH-60A	236th Med Co	
23737	UH-60A	236th Med Co	
23738	UH-60A	159th Med Co	
23744	UH-60A		
23745	UH-60A	236th Med Co	
23749	UH-60A	236th Med Co	
23750	UH-60A	159th Med Co	
23751	UH-60A		
23752	UH-60A	236th Med Co	
23753	UH-60A	159th Med Co	
23754	UH-60A	45th Med Co	

FY88			
26019	UH-60A	2-501st Avn	
26020	UH-60A	B/7-159th Avn	
26021	UH-60A	A/5-158th Avn	
26023	UH-60A	236th Med Co	
26025	UH-60A	207th Avn Co	
26026	UH-60A	6th Avn Co	
26027	UH-60A	207th Avn Co	
26028	UH-60A	2-501st Avn	
26031	UH-60A	2-501st Avn	
26034	UH-60A	2-501st Avn	
26037	UH-60A	2-501st Avn	
26038	UH-60A	A/5-158th Avn	
26039	UH-60A	45th Med Co	
26040	UH-60A	45th Med Co	
26041	UH-60A	A/5-158th Avn	
26042	UH-60A	A/5-158th Avn	
26045	UH-60A	45th Med Co	
26050	UH-60A	2-501st Avn	
26051	UH-60A	A/5-158th Avn	

Notes	Type			Notes	Type		
	26052	UH-60A	B/5-158th Avn		26691	UH-60L	C/158th Avn
	26053	UH-60A	2-501st Avn		26692	UH-60L	C/158th Avn
	26054	UH-60A	236th Med Co		*FY97*		
	26055	UH-60A	2-501st Avn		26762	UH-60L	2-501st Avn
	26056	UH-60A	A/5-158th Avn		26763	UH-60L	2-501st Avn
	26058	UH-60A	159th Med Co		26764	UH-60L	2-501st Avn
	26063	UH-60A	A/5-158th Avn		26767	UH-60L	2-501st Avn
	26067	UH-60A	2-501st Avn		26787	UH-60L	2-501st Avn
	26068	UH-60A	2-501st Avn		26795	UH-60L	
	26070	UH-60A			26796	UH-60L	2-501st Avn
	26071	UH-60A	2-501st Avn		26802	UH-60L	2-501st Avn
	26072	UH-60A	45th Med Co		27623	UH-60L	2-501st Avn
	26075	UH-60A	2-501st Avn				
	26077	UH-60A	2-501st Avn		**MDH AH-64A Apache**		
	26080	UH-60A	159th Med Co		1st Btn, 1st Avn Reg't, Ansbach;		
	26083	UH-60A	2-501st Avn		1st Btn, 501st Avn Reg't, Hanau;		
	26085	UH-60A	2-501st Avn		2nd Btn, 6th Cavalry Reg't, Illesheim;		
	26086	UH-60A	2-501st Avn		6th Btn, 6th Cavalry Reg't, Illesheim;		
	FY89				'A' Co, 7th Btn, 159th Avn Reg't,		
	26138	UH-60A	45th Med Co		Illesheim		
	26142	UH-60A	2-501st Avn		*FY85*		
	26145	UH-60A	6th Avn Co		25357		1-501st Avn
	26146	UH-60A	159th Med Co		25460		A/7-159th Avn
	26151	UH-60A	159th Med Co		25473		1-501st Avn
	26153	UH-60A	2-501st Avn		*FY86*		
	26164	UH-60A	2-501st Avn		68940		2-6th Cav
	26165	UH-60A	207th Avn Co		68941		6-6th Cav
	FY95				68942		2-6th Cav
	26621	UH-60L	2-1st Avn		68943		2-6th Cav
	26628	UH-60L	2-1st Avn		68946		6-6th Cav
	26629	UH-60L	2-1st Avn		68947		6-6th Cav
	26630	UH-60L	2-1st Avn		68948		2-6th Cav
	26631	UH-60L	2-1st Avn		68949		6-6th Cav
	26632	UH-60L	2-1st Avn		68950		6-6th Cav
	26633	UH-60L	2-1st Avn		68951		2-6th Cav
	26635	UH-60L	2-1st Avn		68952		2-6th Cav
	26636	UH-60L	2-1st Avn		68955		2-6th Cav
	26637	UH-60L	2-1st Avn		68956		2-6th Cav
	26638	UH-60L	2-1st Avn		68957		2-6th Cav
	26639	UH-60L	2-1st Avn		68959		2-6th Cav
	26640	UH-60L	2-1st Avn		68960		2-6th Cav
	26641	UH-60L	D/159th Avn		68961		2-6th Cav
	26642	UH-60L	D/159th Avn		68981		2-6th Cav
	26643	UH-60L	D/159th Avn		69010		2-6th Cav
	26644	UH-60L	2-1st Avn		69011		2-6th Cav
	26646	UH-60L	2-1st Avn		69019		2-6th Cav
	26647	UH-60L	2-1st Avn		69026		2-6th Cav
	26648	UH-60L	2-1st Avn		69030		2-6th Cav
	26649	UH-60L	D/159th Avn		69032		2-6th Cav
	26650	UH-60L	D/159th Avn		69037		2-6th Cav
	26651	UH-60L	C/158th Avn		69039		2-6th Cav
	26652	UH-60L	C/158th Avn		69041		1-501st Avn
	26653	UH-60L	C/158th Avn		69048		2-6th Cav
	26654	UH-60L	C/158th Avn		*FY87*		
	26655	UH-60L	C/158th Avn		70409		1-1st Avn
	FY96				70410		1-501st Avn
	26674	UH-60L	D/159th Avn		70411		6-6th Cav
	26675	UH-60L	D/159th Avn		70412		1-1st Avn
	26676	UH-60L	D/159th Avn		70413		1-1st Avn
	26677	UH-60L	D/159th Avn		70415		1-501st Avn
	26678	UH-60L	D/159th Avn		70417		1-1st Avn
	26679	UH-60L			70418		1-501st Avn
	26680	UH-60L	D/159th Avn		70420		1-1st Avn
	26681	UH-60L	D/159th Avn		70428		2-6th Cav
	26682	UH-60L	D/159th Avn		70435		1-501st Avn
	26683	UH-60L	C/158th Avn		70436		1-1st Avn
	26684	UH-60L	C/158th Avn		70437		1-1st Avn
	26685	UH-60L	C/158th Avn		70438		1-501st Avn
	26686	UH-60L	A/5-158th Avn		70439		1-1st Avn
	26687	UH-60L	C/158th Avn		70440		1-501st Avn
	26688	UH-60L	C/158th Avn		70441		2-6th Cav
	26689	UH-60L	C/158th Avn		70442		1-1st Avn
	26690	UH-60L	C/158th Avn		70443		2-6th Cav

Type		Notes	Type		Notes
70444	1-501st Avn		*FY88*		
70445	1-501st Avn		80197	1-501st Avn	
70446	1-501st Avn		80198	1-501st Avn	
70447	1-501st Avn		80203	6-6th Cav	
70449	1-501st Avn		80212	6-6th Cav	
70451	1-501st Avn		80213	6-6th Cav	
70455	1-501st Avn		80214	6-6th Cav	
70457	1-1st Avn		80215	6-6th Cav	
70470	1-1st Avn		80216	6-6th Cav	
70471	1-1st Avn		80217	6-6th Cav	
70474	1-1st Avn		80219	6-6th Cav	
70475	1-1st Avn		80222	6-6th Cav	
70476	1-1st Avn		80225	6-6th Cav	
70477	1-1st Avn		80228	6-6th Cav	
70478	1-1st Avn		80229	6-6th Cav	
70481	1-1st Avn		80232	6-6th Cav	
70487	1-501st Avn		80233	6-6th Cav	
70496	1-501st Avn		80234	6-6th Cav	
70503	1-501st Avn		80236	6-6th Cav	
70504	1-501st Avn		80243	6-6th Cav	
70505	1-501st Avn		80246	6-6th Cav	
			80250	6-6th Cav	

Kansas ANG B-1B 60136 making a powerful take-off. *PRM*

The following aircraft are normally based in the USA but are likely to be seen visiting the UK from time to time. The presentation is in numerical order of the type, commencing with the B-**1B** and concluding with the C-**141**. The aircraft are listed in numerical progression by the serial actually carried externally. Fiscal year information is provided, together with details of mark variations and in some cases operating units. Where base-code letter information is carried on the aircrafts' tails, this is detailed with the squadron/base data; for example the 7th Wing's B-1B 30069 carries the letters DY on its tail, thus identifying the Wing's home base as Dyess AFB, Texas.

Rockwell B-1B Lancer
7th BW, Dyess AFB, Texas [DY]:
  9th BS (*bk*) & 28th BS (*bl/w*);
28th BW, Ellsworth AFB,
  South Dakota [EL]:
  13th BS (*bl/br*), 37th BS (*bk/y*)
  & 77th BS (*bl*);
127th BS/184th BW, Kansas ANG,
  McConnell AFB, Kansas (*r/w*);
128th BS/116th BW, Georgia ANG,
  Robins AFB, Georgia [GA];
34th BS/366th Wg, Mountain Home
  AFB, Idaho [MO] (*r/bk*);
419th FLTS/412th TW, Edwards AFB,
  California [ED]

Notes	Type				Notes	Type		
	FY83					50084	28th BW	*bk/y*
	30065	7th BW	*bk*			50085	28th BW	*bk/y*
	30066	7th BW	*bl/w*			50086	28th BW	*bk/y*
	30067	7th BW	*bk*			50087	28th BW	*bl/br*
	30068	7th BW	*bl/w*			50088	127th BS	*/w*
	30069	7th BW	*bl/w*			50089	128th BS	
	30070	7th BW	*bl/w*			50090	28th BW	*bk/y*
	30071	7th BW	*bk*			50091	366th Wg	*/bk*
	FY84					50092	128th BS	
	40049	412th TW				*FY86*		
	40050	7th BW	*bl/w*			60093	28th BW	*bk/y*
	40051	7th BW	*bk*			60094	28th BW	*bk/y*
	40053	7th BW	*bl/w*			60095	127th BS	*r/w*
	40054	7th BW	*bk*			60096	28th BW	*bk/y*
	40055	7th BW	*bl/w*			60097	366th Wg	*r/bk*
	40056	7th BW	*bl/w*			60098	128th BS	
	40058	7th BW	*bk*			60099	28th BW	*bk/y*
	FY85					60100	7th BW	*bl/w*
	50059	128th BS				60101	7th BW	*bl/w*
	50060	127th BS	*r/w*			60102	28th BW	*bk/y*
	50061	128th BS				60103	7th BW	*bk*
	50062	7th BW	*bl/w*			60104	366th Wg	*/bk*
	50064	127th BS	*/w*			60105	7th BW	*bl/w*
	50065	128th BS				60107	128th BS	
	50066	28th BW	*bk/y*			60108	7th BW	*bl/w*
	50067	7th BW	*bl/w*			60109	7th BW	*bl/w*
	50068	412th TW				60110	7th BW	*bl/w*
	50069	127th BS	*r/w*			60111	28th BW	*bk/y*
	50070	127th BS	*r/w*			60112	7th BW	*bk*
	50071	128th BS				60113	28th BW	*bk/y*
	50072	7th BW	*bk*			60114	28th BW	*bk/y*
	50073	7th BW	*bl/w*			60115	127th BS	*r/w*
	50074	7th BW	*bk*			60116	366th Wg	*r/bk*
	50075	28th BW	*bk/y*			60117	7th BW	*bl/w*
	50077	28th BW	*bk/y*			60118	366th Wg	*r/bk*
	50079	28th BW	*bk/y*			60119	7th BW	*bl/w*
	50080	127th BS	*r/w*			60120	7th BW	*bk*
	50081	127th BS	*/w*			60121	366th Wg	*r/bk*
	50082	7th BW	*bl/w*			60122	7th BW	*bl/w*
	50083	128th BS				60123	7th BW	*bk*
						60124	128th BS	
						60125	366th Wg	*r/bk*
						60126	7th BW	*bl/w*
						60127	128th BS	
						60129	127th BS	*r/w*
						60130	7th BW	*bl/w*
						60131	366th Wg	*r/bk*
						60132	7th BW	*bl/w*
						60133	128th BS	
						60134	366th Wg	*r/bk*
						60135	7th BW	*bk*
						60136	127th BS	*/w*
						60137	7th BW	*bl/w*
						60138	366th Wg	*r/bk*
						60139	366th Wg	*r/bk*

Type			Notes
60140	7th BW	*bk*	

Northrop B-2 Spirit
419th FLTS/412th TW, Edwards AFB,
 California [ED];
509th BW, Whiteman AFB,
Missouri [WM]:
 325th BS, 393rd BS & 715th BS
(Names are given where known.
Each begins *Spirit of ...*)
FY90

Type			Notes
00040	509th BW	*Alaska*	
00041	509th BW	*Hawaii*	
FY92			
20700	509th BW	*Florida*	
FY82			
21066	Northrop		
21067	509th BW	*Arizona*	
21068	412th TW	*New York*	
21069	Northrop		
21070	Northrop	*Ohio*	
21071	509th BW	*Mississippi*	
FY93			
31085	Northrop	*Oklahoma*	
31086	509th BW	*Kitty Hawk*	
31087	509th BW	*Pennsylvania*	
31088	509th BW	*Louisiana*	
FY88			
80328	509th BW	*Texas*	
80329	509th BW	*Missouri*	
80330	509th BW	*California*	
80331	509th BW	*South Carolina*	
80332	509th BW	*Washington*	
FY89			
90127	509th BW	*Kansas*	
90128	509th BW	*Nebraska*	
90129	509th BW	*Georgia*	

Boeing E-3 Sentry
552nd ACW, Tinker AFB,
 Oklahoma [OK]:
963rd AACS (*bk*), 964th AACS (*r*)
965th AACS (*y*) & 966th AACTS (*bl*)
961st AACS/18th Wg, Kadena AB,
 Japan [ZZ] (*or*);
962nd AACS/3rd Wg, Elmendorf AFB,
 Alaska [AK] (*gn*);
FY80

Type			Notes
00137	E-3C	*bk*	
00138	E-3C	*y*	
00139	E-3C	*bk*	
FY81			
10004	E-3C	*bk*	
10005	E-3C	*bk*	
FY71			
11407	E-3B	*bl*	
11408	E-3B	*bk*	
FY82			
20006	E-3C	*y*	
20007	E-3C	*m*	
FY83			
30008	E-3C	*r*	
30009	E-3C	*bk*	
FY73			
31674	JE-3C	Boeing	
31675	E-3B	*bl*	
FY75			
50556	E-3B	*r*	
50557	E-3B	*r*	
50558	E-3B	*y*	
50559	E-3B	*m*	
50560	E-3B	*bk*	
FY76			

Type			Notes
61604	E-3B	*gn*	
61605	E-3B	*m*	
61606	E-3B	*r*	
61607	E-3B	*bl*	
FY77			
70351	E-3B	*y*	
70352	E-3B	*r*	
70353	E-3B	*m*	
70355	E-3B	*r*	
70356	E-3B	*y*	
FY78			
80576	E-3B	*bk*	
80577	E-3B	*r*	
80578	E-3B	*y*	
FY79			
90001	E-3B	*y*	
90002	E-3B	*m*	
90003	E-3B	*bl*	

Boeing E-4B
1st ACCS/55th Wg, Offutt AFB,
 Nebraska [OF]

Type			Notes
31676	(FY73)		
31677	(FY73)		
40787	(FY74)		
50125	(FY75)		

Lockheed C-5 Galaxy
60th AMW, Travis AFB, California:
 21st AS & 22nd AS (*bk/bl* & *bk/gd*);
56th AS/97th AMW, Altus AFB,
 Oklahoma (*r/y*);
137th AS/105th AW, Stewart AFB,
 New York (*bl*)
68th AS/433rd AW AFRC, Kelly AFB,
 Texas;
436th AW, Dover AFB, Delaware:
 3rd AS & 9th AS (*y/r* & *y/bl*);
337th AS/439th AW AFRC,
Westover ARB, Massachusetts (*bl/r*)
FY70

Type			Notes
00445	C-5A	433rd AW	
00446	C-5A	433rd AW	
00447	C-5A	436th AW	*y/r*
00448	C-5A	439th AW	*bl/r*
00449	C-5A	97th AMW	*y*
00450	C-5A	97th AMW	*r/y*
00451	C-5A	436th AW	*y/bl*
00452	C-5A	97th AMW	*r/y*
00453	C-5A	97th AMW	*r/y*
00454	C-5A	60th AMW	*bk/bl*
00455	C-5A	436th AW	*y/bl*
00456	C-5A	60th AMW	*bk/gd*
00457	C-5A	60th AMW	*bk/gd*
00458	C-5A	436th AW	*y/r*
00459	C-5A	60th AMW	*bk/gd*
00460	C-5A	105th AW	*bl*
00461	C-5A	433rd AW	
00462	C-5A	97th AMW	*r/y*
00463	C-5A	436th AW	*y/bl*
00464	C-5A	60th AMW	*bk/bl*
00465	C-5A	436th AW	*y/r*
00466	C-5A	433rd AW	
00467	C-5A	97th AMW	*r/y*
FY83			
31285	C-5B	436th AW	*y/r*
FY84			
40059	C-5B	436th AW	*y/r*
40060	C-5B	60th AMW	*bk/bl*
40061	C-5B	436th AW	*y/r*
40062	C-5B	60th AMW	*bk/gd*
FY85			
50001	C-5B	436th AW	*m*

Notes	Type			
	50002	C-5B	60th AMW	bk/bl
	50003	C-5B	436th AW	y/bl
	50004	C-5B	60th AMW	bk/bl
	50005	C-5B	436th AW	y/bl
	50006	C-5B	60th AMW	bk/gd
	50007	C-5B	436th AW	y/bl
	50008	C-5B	60th AMW	bk/gd
	50009	C-5B	436th AW	y/r
	50010	C-5B	60th AMW	bk/gd
FY86				
	60011	C-5B	436th AW	y/bl
	60012	C-5B	60th AMW	bk/bl
	60013	C-5B	436th AW	y/bl
	60014	C-5B	60th AMW	bk/bl
	60015	C-5B	436th AW	y/r
	60016	C-5B	60th AMW	bk/bl
	60017	C-5B	436th AW	y/bl
	60018	C-5B	60th AMW	bk/gd
	60019	C-5B	436th AW	y/r
	60020	C-5B	436th AW	y/bl
	60021	C-5B	60th AMW	bk/gd
	60022	C-5B	60th AMW	bk/bl
	60023	C-5B	436th AW	/bl
	60024	C-5B	60th AMW	bk/bl
	60025	C-5B	436th AW	y/bl
	60026	C-5B	60th AMW	bk/gd
FY66				
	68304	C-5A	439th AW	bl/r
	68305	C-5A	433rd AW	
	68306	C-5A	433rd AW	
	68307	C-5A	433rd AW	
FY87				
	70027	C-5B	436th AW	y/bl
	70028	C-5B	60th AMW	bk/bl
	70029	C-5B	436th AW	/r
	70030	C-5B	60th AMW	bk/bl
	70031	C-5B	436th AW	y/r
	70032	C-5B	60th AMW	bk/bl
	70033	C-5B	436th AW	y/r
	70034	C-5B	60th AMW	bk/gd
	70035	C-5B	436th AW	y/bl
	70036	C-5B	60th AMW	bk/gd
	70037	C-5B	436th AW	y/r
	70038	C-5B	60th AMW	bk/bl
	70039	C-5B	436th AW	y/r
	70040	C-5B	60th AMW	bk/gd
	70041	C-5B	436th AW	y/bl
	70042	C-5B	60th AMW	bk/gd
	70043	C-5B	436th AW	y/bl
	70044	C-5B	60th AMW	bk/gd
	70045	C-5B	436th AW y	/r
FY67				
	70167	C-5A	105th AW	bl
	70168	C-5A	433rd AW	
	70169	C-5A	105th AW	bl
	70170	C-5A	105th AW	bl
	70171	C-5A	433rd AW	
	70173	C-5A	105th AW	bl
	70174	C-5A	105th AW	bl
FY68				
	80211	C-5A	439th AW	bl/r
	80212	C-5A	105th AW	bl
	80213	C-5C	60th AMW	bk/bl
	80214	C-5A	436th AW	y/r
	80215	C-5A	439th AW	bl/r
	80216	C-5C	60th AMW	bk/bl
	80217	C-5A	97th AMW	r/y
	80219	C-5A	439th AW	bl/r
	80220	C-5A	433rd AW	
	80221	C-5A	433rd AW	
	80222	C-5A	439th AW	bl/r
	80223	C-5A	433rd AW	
	80224	C-5A	105th AW	bl

Notes	Type			
	80225	C-5A	439th AW	bl/w
	80226	C-5A	105th AW	bl
FY69				
	90001	C-5A	97th AMW r	/y
	90002	C-5A	433rd AW	
	90003	C-5A	439th AW	bl/r
	90004	C-5A	433rd AW	
	90005	C-5A	439th AW	bl/r
	90006	C-5A	433rd AW	
	90007	C-5A	433rd AW	
	90008	C-5A	105th AW	bl
	90009	C-5A	105th AW	bl
	90010	C-5A	60th AMW	bk/gd
	90011	C-5A	439th AW	bl/r
	90012	C-5A	105th AW	bl
	90013	C-5A	439th AW	bl/r
	90014	C-5A	97th AMW	r/y
	90015	C-5A	105th AW	bl
	90016	C-5A	433rd AW	
	90017	C-5A	439th AW	bl/r
	90018	C-5A	97th AMW	r/y
	90019	C-5A	439th AW	bl/r
	90020	C-5A	439th AW	bl/r
	90021	C-5A	105th AW	bl
	90022	C-5A	439th AW	bl/r
	90023	C-5A	60th AMW	bk/bl
	90024	C-5A	97th AMW	r/y
	90025	C-5A	60th AMW	bk/gd
	90026	C-5A	60th AMW	
	90027	C-5A	436th AW	y/bl

Boeing E-8 J-STARS
Grumman, Melbourne, Florida;
12th ACCS/93rd ACW, Robins AFB,
  Georgia [WR] (*gn*)

Notes	Type		
FY90			
	00175	E-8A	Grumman
FY92			
	23289	E-8C	93rd ACW
	23290	E-8C	93rd ACW
FY93			
	30011	E-8C	93rd ACW
FY66			
	30052	E-8C	93rd ACW
FY93			
	30597	E-8C	93rd ACW
	30598	E-8C	
	31097	E-8C	93rd ACW
FY94			
	40284	E-8C	
	40285	E-8C	
FY95			
	50121	E-8C	
	50122	E-8C	
FY86			
	60416	E-8A	93rd ACW
	60417	E-8A	

McDonnell Douglas C-9 Nightingale
86th AW, Ramstein, Germany:
  75th AAS & 76th AS;
Det 1, 86th OG/SHAPE, Chievres,
  Belgium;
99th AS/89th AW, Andrews AFB,
  Maryland;
30th AS/374th AW, Yokota AB, Japan
11th AS/375th AW, Scott AFB, Illinois

Notes	Type		
FY71			
	10874	C-9A	374th AW
	10875	C-9A	374th AW
	10876	C-9A	86th OG (VIP)
	10877	C-9A	374th AW
	10878	C-9A	375th AW

Type			Notes	Type			Notes
10879	C-9A	75th AAS		60038	60th AMW	bk/r	
10880	C-9A	76th AS (VIP)		FY87			
10881	C-9A	75th AAS		70117	60th AMW	bk/r	
10882	C-9A	75th AAS		70118	60th AMW	bk/bl	
FY68				70119	60th AMW	bk/r	
10958	C-9A	375th AW		70120	305th AMW	bl	
10959	C-9A	375th AW		70121	305th AMW	bl/r	
10960	C-9A	375th AW		70122	305th AMW	bl/r	
10961	C-9A	375th AW		70123	305th AMW	bl	
FY67				70124	305th AMW	bl/r	
22583	C-9A	374th AW		FY79			
22584	C-9A	375th AW		90433	305th AMW	bl	
22585	C-9A	75th AAS		90434	305th AMW	bl/r	
FY73				91710	305th AMW	bl/r	
31681	C-9C	89th AW		91711	305th AMW	bl/r	
31682	C-9C	89th AW		91712	305th AMW	bl/r	
31683	C-9C	89th AW		91713	305th AMW	bl	
FY68				91946	60th AMW	bk/r	
88932	C-9A	375th AW		91947	305th AMW	bl r	
88933	C-9A	375th AW		91948	60th AMW	bk/bl	
88934	C-9A	375th AW		91949	305th AMW	bl/r	
88935	C-9A	375th AW		91950	60th AMW	bk/bl	
				91951	60th AMW	bk/bl	

McDonnell Douglas KC-10A Extender
60th AMW, Travis AFB, California:
  6th ARS (*bk/r*) & 9th ARS (*bk/bl*);
305th AMW, McGuire AFB, New Jersey:
  2nd ARS (*bl/r*) & 32nd ARS (*bl*)

McDonnell Douglas C-17 Globemaster III
58th AS/97th AMW, Altus AFB, Oklahoma (*r/y*);
417th FLTS/412th TW, Edwards AFB, California [ED];
437th AW, Charleston AFB, South Carolina:
  14th AS, 15th AS & 17th AS (*y/bl*)

Type			Notes	Type			Notes
FY82				FY90			
20191	60th AMW	bk/bl		00532	C-17A	437th AW	y/bl
20192	60th AMW	bk/r		00533	C-17A	437th AW	y/bl
20193	60th AMW	bk/bl		00534	C-17A	97th AMW	r/y
FY83				00535	C-17A	97th AMW	r/y
30075	60th AMW			FY92			
30076	60th AMW	bk/bl		23291	C-17A	437th AW	y/bl
30077	60th AMW	bk/r		23292	C-17A	437th AW	y/bl
30078	60th AMW	bk/bl		23293	C-17A	97th AMW	r/y
30079	305th AMW	bl/r		23294	C-17A	437th AW	y/bl
30080	60th AMW	bk/bl		FY93			
30081	305th AMW	bl/bk		30599	C-17A	437th AW	y/bl
30082	305th AMW	bl		30600	C-17A	437th AW	y/bl
FY84				30601	C-17A	437th AW	y/bl
40185	60th AMW	bk/bl		30602	C-17A	437th AW	y/bl
40186	305th AMW	bl/r		30603	C-17A	437th AW	y/bl
40187	60th AMW	bk/bl		30604	C-17A	97th AMW	r/y
40188	305th AMW	bl		FY94			
40189	60th AMW	bk/bl		40065	C-17A	437th AW	y/bl
40190	305th AMW	bl/r		40066	C-17A	437th AW	y/bl
40191	60th AMW	bk/bl		40067	C-17A	437th AW	y/bl
40192	305th AMW	b/r		40068	C-17A	97th AMW	r/y
FY85				40069	C-17A	437th AW	y/bl
50027	305th AMW	bl/r		40070	C-17A	97th AMW	r/y
50028	305th AMW	bl/r		FY95			
50029	60th AMW	bk/r		50102	C-17A	437th AW	y/bl
50030	305th AMW	bl/r		50103	C-17A	437th AW	y/bl
50031	305th AMW	bl/r		50104	C-17A	437th AW	y/bl
50032	305th AMW	bl		50105	C-17A	437th AW	y/bl
50033	305th AMW	bl		50106	C-17A	437th AW	y/bl
50034	305th AMW	bl/r		50107	C-17A	437th AW	y/bl
FY86				FY96			
60027	305th AMW	bl		60001	C-17A	437th AW	y/bl
60028	305th AMW	bl/r		60002	C-17A	437th AW	y/bl
60029	60th AMW	bk/r		60003	C-17A	437th AW	y/bl
60030	305th AMW	bl/r		60004	C-17A	437th AW	y/bl
60031	60th AMW	bk/r		60005	C-17A	437th AW	y/bl
60032	60th AMW	bk/r		60006	C-17A	437th AW	y/bl
60033	60th AMW	bk/r		60007	C-17A	437th AW	y/bl
60034	60th AMW	bk/r		60008	C-17A	437th AW	y/bl
60035	305th AMW	bl/r					
60036	305th AMW	bl/r					
60037	60th AMW	bk/r					

C-17 – B-52H

Notes	Type			
	FY87			
	70025	YC-17A	412th TW	
	FY97			
	70041	C-17A	437th AW	*y/bl*
	70042	C-17A	437th AW	*y/bl*
	70043	C-17A	437th AW	*y/bl*
	70044	C-17A	437th AW	*y/bl*
	70045	C-17A		
	70046	C-17A		
	70047	C-17A		
	70048	C-17A		
	FY98			
	80049	C-17A		
	80050	C-17A		
	80051	C-17A		
	80052	C-17A		
	80053	C-17A		
	80054	C-17A		
	80055	C-17A		
	80056	C-17A		
	80057	C-17A		
	FY88			
	80265	C-17A	97th AMW	*r/y*
	80266	C-17A	437th AW	*y/bl*
	FY89			
	91189	C-17A	437th AW	*y/bl*
	91190	C-17A	437th AW	*y/bl*
	91191	C-17A	437th AW	*y/bl*
	91192	C-17A	437th AW	*y/bl*

Boeing C-18
12th ACCS/93rd ACW, Robins AFB, Georgia [WR] (*gn*);
452nd FLTS/412th TW, Edwards AFB, California [ED];
966th AACTS/552nd ACW, Tinker AFB, Oklahoma [OK] (*bl*)

	FY81		
	10891	EC-18B	412th TW
	10892	EC-18B	412th TW
	10893	EC-18B	93rd ACW
	10894	EC-18B	412th TW
	FY84		
	41398	TC-18E	552nd ACW
	41399	TC-18E	552nd ACW

Grumman C-20 Gulfstream III/IV
99th AS/89th AW, Andrews AFB, Maryland;
OSAC/PAT, US Army, Andrews AFB, Maryland;
Pacific Flight Detachment, Hickam AFB, Hawaii

C-20B Gulfstream III
	FY86	
	60201	89th AW
	60202	89th AW
	60203	89th AW
	60204	89th AW
	60206	89th AW
	60403	89th AW

C-20C Gulfstream III
	FY85	
	50049	89th AW
	50050	89th AW

C-20E Gulfstream III
	FY87	
	70139	Pacific Flt Det
	70140	OSAC/PAT

C-20F Gulfstream IV
	FY91	
	10108	OSAC/PAT

C-20H Gulfstream IV

Notes	Type	
	FY90	
	00300	89th AW
	FY92	
	20375	89th AW

Boeing C-22B/C-22C*
88th ABW, Wright-Patterson AFB, Ohio;
201st AS/113th FW DC ANG, Andrews AFB, Maryland

	FY83	
	34610	201st AS
	34615	201st AS
	34616	201st AS
	34618*	88th ABW

Boeing VC-25A
89th AW, Andrews AFB, Maryland
	FY82
	28000
	FY92
	29000

Boeing C-32A
1st AS/89th AW, Andrews AFB, Maryland
	FY98
	80001
	80002
	FY99
	90003
	90004

Gulfstream Aerospace C-37A Gulfstream V
99th AS/89th AW, Andrews AFB, Maryland
	FY97
	70400
	70401

Boeing CT-43A
562nd FTS/12th FTW, Randolph AFB, Texas [RA] (*bk/y*);
201st AS/113th FW DC ANG, Andrews AFB, Maryland;
CinC CentCom (CinC CC)/6th ARW, MacDill AFB, Florida

	FY71		
	11403	12th FTW	*bk/y*
	11404	12th FTW	*bk/y*
	11405	12th FTW	*bk/y*
	FY72		
	20283	6th ARW	
	20288	201st AS	
	FY73		
	31150	12th FTW	*bk/y*
	31151	12th FTW	*bk/y*
	31152	12th FTW	*bk/y*
	31153	12th FTW	*bk/y*
	31154	201st AS	
	31156	12th FTW	*bk/y*

Boeing B-52H Stratofortress
2nd BW, Barksdale AFB, [LA]: 11th BS (*gd*), 20th BS (*bl*) & 96th BS (*r*);
23rd BS/5th BW, Minot AFB, North Dakota [MT] (*r/y*);
93rd BS/917th Wg AFRC, Barksdale AFB, Louisiana [BD] (*y/bl*);

Type		Notes	Type			Notes
419th FLTS/412th TW Edwards AFB, California [ED]			10014	5th BW	r/y	
FY60			10015	2nd BW	gd	
00001	2nd BW	bl	10016	2nd BW	gd	
00002	2nd BW	gd	10017	93rd BS	y/bl	
00003	93rd BS	y/bl	10018	5th BW	r/y	
00004	5th BW	r/y	10019	2nd BW	r	
00005	5th BW	r/y	10020	2nd BW	r	
00007	5th BW	r/y	10021	93rd BS	y/bl	
00008	2nd BW	r	10022	93rd BS	y/bl	
00009	5th BW	r/y	10023	2nd BW	bl	
00010	2nd BW	r	10024	2nd BW	r	
00011	2nd BW	bl	10025	2nd BW	gd	
00012	5th BW	r/y	10027	5th BW	r/y	
00013	2nd BW	r	10028	2nd BW	r	
00014	2nd BW	bl	10029	93rd BS	y/bl	
00015	5th BW	r/y	10031	2nd BW	gd	
00016	2nd BW	r	10032	93rd BS	y/bl	
00017	2nd BW	gd	10034	5th BW	r/y	
00018	5th BW	r/y	10035	5th BW	r/y	
00019	2nd BW	gd	10036	5th BW	r/y	
00020	2nd BW	bl	10038	2nd BW	gd	
00022	2nd BW	r	10039	2nd BW	gd	
00023	5th BW	r/y	10040	5th BW	r/y	
00024	5th BW	r/y				
00025	2nd BW	bl	**Lockheed F-117A Nighthawk**			
00026	5th BW	r/y	49th FW, Holloman AFB, New Mexico [HO]:			
00028	2nd BW	r	7th FS (*si*), 8th FS (*y*) & 9th FS (*r*)			
00029	5th BW	r/y	53rd Wg, Nellis AFB, Nevada [OT];			
00030	2nd BW	bl	445th FLTS/412th TW, Edwards AFB, California [ED]			
00031	2nd BW	bl	79-783	(79-10783)	ED	
00032	2nd BW	gd	79-784	(79-10784)	ED	
00033	5th BW	r/y	80-786	(80-0786)	HO	
00034	5th BW	r/y	80-787	(80-0787)	HO	si
00035	2nd BW	gd	80-788	(80-0788)	HO	si
00036	5th BW	r/y	80-789	(80-0789)	HO	r
00037	2nd BW	r	80-790	(80-0790)	HO	r
00038	2nd BW	gd	80-791	(80-0791)	HO	
00041	93rd BS	y/bl	81-794	(81-10794)	HO	
00042	5th BW	r/y	81-795	(81-10795)	HO	y
00043	2nd BW	bl	81-796	(81-10796)	HO	si
00044	5th BW	r/y	81-797	(81-10797)	HO	r
00045	93rd BS	y/bl	81-798	(81-10798)	HO	y
00046	2nd BW	gd	82-799	(82-0799)	HO	y
00048	2nd BW	gd	82-800	(82-0800)	HO	y
00049	2nd BW	bl	82-801	(82-0801)	HO	
00050	412th TW		82-802	(82-0802)	HO	y
00051	5th BW	r/y	82-803	(82-0803)	HO	m [49th FW]
00052	2nd BW	r	82-804	(82-0804)	HO	si [7th FS]
00053	2nd BW	r	82-805	(82-0805)	HO	r
00054	2nd BW	r	82-806	(82-0806)	HO	r
00055	5th BW	r/y	83-807	(83-0807)	HO	r
00056	5th BW	r/y	83-808	(83-0808)	HO	si
00057	2nd BW	bl	84-809	(84-0809)	HO	r [9th FS]
00058	2nd BW	gd	84-810	(84-0810)	HO	r
00059	2nd BW	r	84-811	(84-0811)	HO	si
00060	5th BW	r/y	84-812	(84-0812)	HO	r [49th OG]
00061	2nd BW	gd	84-824	(84-0824)	HO	r
00062	2nd BW	bl	84-826	(84-0826)	HO	r
FY61			84-827	(84-0827)	HO	y
10001	5th BW	r/y	84-828	(84-0828)	HO	si
10002	2nd BW	bl	85-813	(85-0813)	HO	
10003	2nd BW	gd	85-814	(85-0814)	HO	y
10004	2nd BW	bl	85-816	(85-0816)	HO	y [49th FW]
10005	5th BW	r/y	85-817	(85-0817)	HO	y
10006	2nd BW	gd	85-818	(85-0818)	HO	r
10007	5th BW	r/y	85-819	(85-0819)	HO	si [49th FW]
10008	93rd BS	y/bl	85-820	(85-0820)	HO	r
10009	2nd BW	r	85-829	(85-0829)	HO	y
10010	2nd BW	bl	85-830	(85-0830)	HO	r
10011	2nd BW	gd	85-831	(85-0831)	ED	
10012	2nd BW	gd	85-832	(85-0832)	HO	si
10013	2nd BW	r				

Notes	Type				Notes	Type

85-833 (85-0833) HO y
85-834 (85-0834) HO y
85-835 (85-0835) HO r
85-836 (85-0836) HO r
86-821 (86-0821) HO r
86-822 (86-0822) HO
86-823 (86-0823) HO r
86-837 (86-0837) OT
86-838 (86-0838) HO y [8th FS]
86-839 (86-0839) HO r
86-840 (86-0840) HO si
88-841 (88-0841) HO
88-842 (88-0842) HO y
88-843 (88-0843) HO y

Lockheed C-130 Hercules
1st SOS/353rd SOG, Kadena AB,
  Japan;
517th AS/3rd Wg, Elmendorf AFB,
  Alaska [AK] (*w*);
4th SOS/16th SOW, Hurlburt Field,
  Florida;
5th SOS/919th SOW AFRC, Duke
  Field, Florida;
7th SOS/352nd SOG,
  RAF Mildenhall, UK;
8th SOS/16th SOW, Hurlburt Field,
  Florida;
9th SOS/16th OG, Eglin AFB, Florida;
15th SOS/16th SOW, Hurlburt Field,
  Florida;
16th SOS/16th SOW, Hurlburt Field,
  Florida;
17th SOS/353rd SOG, Kadena AB,
  Japan;
37th AS/86th AW, Ramstein AB,
  Germany [RS] (*bl/w*);
39th RQS/939th RQW AFRC,
  Patrick AFB, Florida [FL];
41st ECS/355th Wg, Davis-Monthan
  AFB, Arizona [DM] (*bl*);
42nd ACCS/355th Wg,
  Davis-Monthan
  AFB, Arizona [DM] (*w*);
43rd AW, Pope AFB,
  North Carolina [FT]:
  2nd AS (*bl/y*) & 41st AS (*gn/or*);
43rd ECS/355th Wg, Davis-Monthan
  AFB, Arizona [DM] (*r*);
53rd WRS/403rd AW AFRC,
  Keesler AFB, Missouri;
550th SOS/58th SOW, Kirtland AFB,
  New Mexico;
67th SOS/352nd SOG,
  RAF Mildenhall, UK;
71st RQS/347th Wg, Moody AFB,
  Georgia [MY] (*bl*);
95th AS/440th AW AFRC,
  General Mitchell ARS,
  Wisconsin (*y/w*);
96th AS/934th AW AFRC,
  Minneapolis/St Paul,
  Minnesota (*pr*);
102nd RQS/106th RQW, Suffolk
  Field, New York ANG [LI];
105th AS/118th AW, Nashville,
  Tennessee ANG (*or*);
109th AS/133rd AW,
  Minneapolis/St Paul,
  Minnesota ANG [MN] (*gn/bl*);
115th AS/146th AW,
  Channel Island ANGS,
  California ANG [CI] (*gn*);

122nd FS/159th FW,
  NAS New Orleans,
  Louisiana ANG [JZ];
129th RQS/129th RQW, Moffet Field,
  California ANG [CA] (*bl*);
130th AS/130th AW, Yeager Int'l
  Airport, Charleston
  West Virginia ANG [WV] (*bk/w*);
135th AS/135th AW, Martin State
  Airport,
  Maryland ANG [MD] (*bk/y*);
139th AS/109th AW, Schenectady,
  New York ANG [NY];
142nd AS/166th AW, Greater
  Wilmington, Delaware ANG [DE] (*bl*);
143rd AS/143rd AW, Quonset,
  Rhode Island ANG [RI] (*r*);
144th AS/176th CW, Kulis ANGB,
  Alaska ANG (*bk/y*);
154th TS/189th AW, Little Rock,
  Arkansas ANG (*r*);
156th AS/145th AW, Charlotte,
  North Carolina ANG [NC] (*bl*);
157th FS/169th FW, McEntire ANGS,
  South Carolina ANG [SC];
158th AS/165th AW, Savannah,
  Georgia ANG [GA] (*r*);
164th AS/179th AW, Mansfield,
  Ohio ANG [OH] (*bl*);
165th AS/123rd AW, Standiford Field,
  Kentucky ANG [KY];
167th AS/167th AW, Martinsburg,
  West Virginia ANG [WV] (*r*);
169th AS/182nd AW, Peoria,
  Illinois ANG [IL];
171st AS/127th Wg, Selfridge ANGB,
  Michigan ANG (*y/bk*);
180th AS/139th AW, Rosencrans
  Memorial Airport, Missouri ANG
  [XP];
181st AS/136th AW, NAS Dallas,
  Texas ANG [TX];
185th AS/137th AW, Will Rogers
  World Airport, Oklahoma ANG
  [OK] (*bl*);
187th AS/153rd AW, Cheyenne,
  Wyoming ANG [WY];
189th AS/124th Wg, Boise,
  Idaho ANG [ID];
192nd AS/152nd AW, Reno,
  Nevada ANG [NV] (*w*);
193rd SOS/193rd SOW, Harrisburg,
  Pennsylvania ANG [PA];
198th AS/156th AW, Muniz ANGB,
  San Juan, Puerto Rico
204th AS/154th Wg, Hickam AFB,
  Hawaii ANG;
210th RQS/176th CW, Kulis ANGB,
  Alaska ANG [AK];
303rd RQS/939th RQW AFRC,
  Portland, Oregon ((*y*);
314th AW, Little Rock AFB, Arkansas:
  53rd AS (*bk*) & 62nd AS (*bl*);
317th AG, Dyess AFB, Texas:
  39th AS (*r*) & 40th AS (*bl*);
327th AS/913th AW AFRC,
  NAS Willow Grove, Pennsylvania
  (*bk*);
328th AS/914th AW AFRC,
  Niagara Falls, New York (*gn*);
357th AS/908th AW AFRC,
  Maxwell AFB, Alabama (*bl*);
36th AS/374th AW, Yokota AB,

Type			Notes
Japan [YJ] (r);			
418th FLTS/412th TW Edwards AFB, California [ED];			
463rd AG Little Rock AFB, Arkansas [LK]:			
50th AS (r) & 61st AS (gn);			
645th Materiel Sqn, Palmdale, California [D4];			
700th AS/94th AW AFRC, Dobbins ARB, Georgia (bk/w);			
711th SOS/919th SOW AFRC, Duke Field, Florida;			
731st AS/302nd AW AFRC, Peterson AFB, Colorado (gn);			
757th AS/910th AW AFRC, Youngstown ARS, Ohio (bl);			
758th AS/911th AW AFRC, Pittsburgh ARS, Pennsylvania [PI] (bk/y);			
773rd AS/910th AW AFRC, Youngstown ARS, Ohio [YO] (r);			
815th AS/403rd AW AFRC, Keesler AFB, Missouri (r)			
FY90			
00161	MC-130H	15th SOS	
00162	MC-130H	15th SOS	
00163	AC-130U	4th SOS	
00164	AC-130U	4th SOS	
00165	AC-130U	4th SOS	
00166	AC-130U	4th SOS	
00167	AC-130U	4th SOS	
FY80			
00320	C-130H	158th AS	r
00321	C-130H	158th AS	r
00322	C-130H	158th AS	r
00323	C-130H	158th AS	r
00324	C-130H	158th AS	r
00325	C-130H	158th AS	r
00326	C-130H	158th AS	r
00332	C-130H	158th AS	r
FY90			
01057	C-130H	181st AS	
01058	C-130H	130th AS	bk/w
FY70			
01259	C-130E	43rd AW	gn/or
01260	C-130E	37th AS	bl/w
01261	C-130E	43rd AW	bl/y
01262	C-130E	43rd AW	gn/or
01263	C-130E	43rd AW	gn/or
01264	C-130E	37th AS	bl/w
01265	C-130E	43rd AW	bl/y
01266	C-130E	43rd AW	gn/or
01267	C-130E	43rd AW	gn/or
01268	C-130E	43rd AW	bl/y
01270	C-130E	43rd AW	gn/or
01271	C-130E	37th AS	bl/w
01272	C-130E	43rd AW	bl/y
01273	C-130E	43rd AW	gn/or
01274	C-130E	37th AS	bl/w
01275	C-130E	43rd AW	bl/y
01276	C-130E	43rd AW	gn/or
FY90			
01791	C-130H	164th AS	bl
01792	C-130H	164th AS	bl
01793	C-130H	164th AS	bl
01794	C-130H	164th AS	bl
01795	C-130H	164th AS	bl
01796	C-130H	164th AS	bl
01797	C-130H	164th AS	bl
01798	C-130H	164th AS	bl
02103	HC-130N	210th RQS	
09107	C-130H	757th AS	bl
09108	C-130H	757th AS	bl
FY81			
10626	C-130H	700th AS	bk/w
10627	C-130H	700th AS	bk/w
10628	C-130H	700th AS	bk/w
10629	C-130H	700th AS	bk/w
10630	C-130H	700th AS	bk/w
10631	C-130H	700th AS	bk/w
FY68			
10934	C-130E	43rd AW	bl/y
10935	C-130E	37th AS	bl/w
10937	C-130E	43rd AW	gn/or
10938	C-130E	37th AS	bl/w
10939	C-130E	43rd AW	gn/or
10940	C-130E	43rd AW	gn/or
10941	C-130E	43rd AW	bl/y
10942	C-130E	43rd AW	bl/y
10943	C-130E	37th AS	bl/w
10947	C-130E	37th AS	bl/w
10948	C-130E	463rd AG	gn
FY91			
11231	C-130H	165th AS	
11232	C-130H	165th AS	
11233	C-130H	165th AS	
11234	C-130H	165th AS	
11235	C-130H	165th AS	
11236	C-130H	165th AS	
11237	C-130H	165th AS	
11238	C-130H	165th AS	
11239	C-130H	165th AS	
11651	C-130H	165th AS	
11652	C-130H	165th AS	
11653	C-130H	165th AS	
FY61			
12358	C-130E	171st AS	y/bk
12359	C-130E	115th AS	gn
12361	C-130E	192nd AS	w
12367	C-130E	115th AS	gn
12369	C-130E	115th AS	gn
12370	C-130E	171st AS	y/bk
12371	C-130E	171st AS	y/bk
12372	C-130E	115th AS	gn
FY64			
14852	HC-130P	58th SOW	
14853	HC-130P	71st RQS	bl
14854	MC-130P	9th SOS	
14855	HC-130P	303rd RQS	y
14858	MC-130P	58th SOW	
14859	C-130E	711th SOS	
14860	HC-130P	303rd RQS	y
14861	WC-130H	53rd WRS	
14862	EC-130H	645th MS	
14863	HC-130P	71st RQS	bl
14864	HC-130P	39th RQS	
14865	HC-130P	71st RQS	bl
14866	WC-130H	53rd WRS	
17680	C-130E	314th AW	bk
17681	C-130E	37th AS	bl/w
18240	C-130E	37th AS	bl/w
FY91			
19141	C-130H	773rd AS	r
19142	C-130H	773rd AS	r
19143	C-130H	773rd AS	r
19144	C-130H	773rd AS	r
FY82			
20054	C-130H	144th AS	bk/y

Notes	Type				Notes	Type			
	20055	C-130H	144th AS	bk/y		21832	EC-130E	42nd ACCS	w
	20056	C-130H	144th AS	bk/y		21833	C-130E	115th AS	gn
	20057	C-130H	144th AS	bk/y		21834	C-130E	374th AW	r
	20058	C-130H	144th AS	bk/y		21835	C-130E	96th AS	pr
	20059	C-130H	144th AS	bk/y		21836	EC-130E	42nd ACCS	w
	20060	C-130H	144th AS	bk/y		21837	C-130E	189th AS	
	20061	C-130H	144th AS	bk/y		21839	C-130E	96th AS	pr
	FY92					21842	C-130E	171st AS	
	20253	AC-130U	4th SOS						y/bk
	20547	C-130H	463rd AG	r		21843	MC-130E	711th SOS	
	20548	C-130H	463rd AG	r		21844	C-130E	96th AS	pr
	20549	C-130H	463rd AG	r		21846	C-130E	189th AS	
	20550	C-130H	463rd AG	r		21847	C-130E	96th AS	pr
	20551	C-130H	463rd AG	r		21848	C-130E	96th AS	pr
	20552	C-130H	463rd AG	r		21849	C-130E	815th AS	r
	20553	C-130H	463rd AG	r		21850	C-130E	314th AW	bk
	20554	C-130H	463rd AG	r		21851	C-130E	115th AS	gn
	21094	LC-130H	139th AS			21852	C-130E	96th AS	pr
	21095	LC-130H	139th AS			21855	MC-130E	16th SOS	
	FY72					21856	C-130E	143rd AS	r
	21288	C-130E	374th AW	r		21857	EC-130E	42nd ACCS	w
	21289	C-130E	374th AW	r		21858	C-130E	192nd AS	w
	21290	C-130E	374th AW	r		21859	C-130E	192nd AS	w
	21291	C-130E	314th AW	bk		21862	C-130E	115th AS	gn
	21292	C-130E	463rd AG	gn		21863	EC-130E	42nd ACCS	gy
	21293	C-130E	463rd AG	gn		21864	C-130E	189th AS	
	21294	C-130E	463rd AG	gn		21866	C-130E	314th AW	bk
	21295	C-130E	314th AW	bl		*FY92*			
	21296	C-130E	314th AW	bk		22104	HC-130N	210th RQS	
	21298	C-130E	374th AW	r		23021	C-130H	773rd AS	r
	21299	C-130E	374th AW	r		23022	C-130H	773rd AS	r
	FY92					23023	C-130H	773rd AS	r
	21451	C-130H	156th AS	bl		23024	C-130H	773rd AS	r
	21452	C-130H	156th AS	bl		23281	C-130H	328th AS	gn
	21453	C-130H	156th AS	bl		23282	C-130H	328th AS	gn
	21454	C-130H	156th AS	bl		23283	C-130H	328th AS	gn
	21531	C-130H	187th AS			23284	C-130H	328th AS	gn
	21532	C-130H	187th AS			23285	C-130H	328th AS	gn
	21533	C-130H	187th AS			23286	C-130H	328th AS	gn
	21534	C-130H	187th AS			23287	C-130H	328th AS	gn
	21535	C-130H	187th AS			23288	C-130H	328th AS	gn
	21536	C-130H	187th AS			*FY83*			
	21537	C-130H	187th AS			30486	C-130H	139th AS	
	21538	C-130H	187th AS			30487	C-130H	139th AS	
	FY62					30488	C-130H	139th AS	
	21784	C-130E	154th TS	r		30489	C-130H	139th AS	
	21786	C-130E	189th AS			30490	LC-130H	139th AS	
	21787	C-130E	154th TS	r		30491	LC-130H	139th AS	
	21788	C-130E	154th TS	r		30492	LC-130H	139th AS	
	21789	C-130E	314th AW	bk		30493	LC-130H	139th AS	
	21790	C-130E	154th TS	r		*FY93*			
	21791	EC-130E	42nd ACCS	w		31036	C-130H	463rd AG	r
	21792	C-130E	463rd AG	gn		31037	C-130H	463rd AG	r
	21793	C-130E	463rd AG	gn		31038	C-130H	463rd AG	r
	21795	C-130E	154th TS	r		31039	C-130H	463rd AG	r
	21798	C-130E	314th AW	bk		31040	C-130H	463rd AG	r
	21799	C-130E	115th AS	gn		31041	C-130H	463rd AG	r
	21801	C-130E	115th AS	gn		31096	LC-130H	139th AS	
	21804	C-130E	154th TS	r		*FY83*			
	21806	C-130E	96th AS	pr		31212	MC-130H	15th SOS	
	21808	C-130E	314th AW	bk		*FY93*			
	21810	C-130E	314th AW	bl		31455	C-130H	156th AS	bl
	21811	C-130E	115th AS	gn		31456	C-130H	156th AS	bl
	21812	C-130E	192nd AS	w		31457	C-130H	156th AS	bl
	21816	C-130E	314th AW	bl		31458	C-130H	156th AS	bl
	21817	C-130E	189th AS			31459	C-130H	156th AS	bl
	21818	EC-130E	42nd ACCS	w		31561	C-130H	156th AS	bl
	21820	C-130E	171st AS	y/bk		31562	C-130H	156th AS	bl
	21823	C-130E	96th AS	pr		31563	C-130H	156th AS	bl
	21824	C-130E	154th TS	r		*FY73*			
	21825	EC-130E	42nd ACCS	w		31580	EC-130H	43rd ECS	r
	21826	C-130E	115th AS	gn		31581	EC-130H	43rd ECS	r
	21829	C-130E	192nd AS	w		31582	C-130H	317th AG	

Type			Notes	Type			Notes
31583	EC-130H	43rd ECS	r	37838	C-130E	314th AW	bl
31584	EC-130H	43rd ECS	r	37839	C-130E	463rd AG	gn
31585	EC-130H	41st ECS	bl	37840	C-130E	143rd AS	r
31586	EC-130H	41st ECS	bl	37841	C-130E	198th AS	gn
31587	EC-130H	41st ECS	bl	37842	C-130E	1st SOS	
31588	EC-130H	41st ECS	bl	37845	C-130E	463rd AG	
31590	EC-130H	43rd ECS	r	37846	C-130E		
31592	EC-130H	43rd ECS	r	37847	C-130E	154th TS	r
31594	EC-130H	41st ECS	bl	37848	C-130E	327th AS	bk
31595	EC-130H	43rd ECS	r	37849	C-130E	314th AW	bl
31597	C-130H	317th AG	bl	37850	C-130E	374th AW	r
31598	C-130H	3rd Wg	w	37851	C-130E	192nd AS	w
FY93				37852	C-130E	815th AS	r
32041	C-130H	204th AS		37853	C-130E	327th AS	bk
32042	C-130H	204th AS		37854	C-130E	463rd AG	gn
32105	HC-130N	210th RQS		37856	C-130E	815th AS	r
32106	HC-130N	210th RQS		37857	C-130E	463rd AG	gn
37311	C-130H	731st AS	gn	37858	C-130E	169th AS	
37312	C-130H	731st AS	gn	37859	C-130E	143rd AS	r
37313	C-130H	731st AS	gn	37860	C-130E	314th AW	bl
37314	C-130H	731st AS	gn	37861	C-130E	463rd AG	gn
FY63				37864	C-130E	314th AW	bl
37764	C-130E	815th AS	r	37865	C-130E	374th AW	r
37765	C-130E	314th AW	bl	37866	C-130E	314th AW	bk
37767	C-130E	314th AW	bl	37867	C-130E	327th AS	bk
37768	C-130E	314th AW	bl	37868	C-130E	143rd AS	r
37769	C-130E	327th AS	bk	37869	EC-130E	193rd SOS	
37770	C-130E	815th AS	r	37871	C-130E	374th AW	r
37773	EC-130E	193rd SOS		37872	C-130E	169th AS	
37776	C-130E	327th AS	bk	37874	C-130E	314th AW	bk
37777	C-130E	192nd AS	w	37876	C-130E	463rd AG	gn
37778	C-130E	314th AW	bk	37877	C-130E	169th AS	
37781	C-130E	463rd AG	gn	37879	C-130E	374th AW	r
37782	C-130E	143rd AS	r	37880	C-130E	314th AW	bl
37783	EC-130E	193rd SOS		37882	C-130E	314th AW	bk
37784	C-130E	314th AW	bl	37883	C-130E	327th AS	bk
37785	MC-130E	711th SOS		37884	C-130E	463rd AG	gn
37786	C-130E	171st AS	y/bk	37885	C-130E	37th AS	bl/w
37788	C-130E	143rd AS	r	37887	C-130E	37th AS	bl/w
37790	C-130E	374th AW	r	37888	C-130E	463rd AG	gn
37791	C-130E	314th AW	bl	37889	C-130E	143rd AS	r
37792	C-130E	169th AS		37890	C-130E	314th AW	bl
37796	C-130E	314th AW	bk	37892	C-130E	327th AS	bk
37799	C-130E	314th AW	bl	37893	C-130E	314th AW	bk
37800	C-130E	169th AS		37894	C-130E	463rd AG	gn
37804	C-130E	314th AW	bl	37895	C-130E	171st AS	y/bk
37805	C-130E	815th AS	r	37896	C-130E	463rd AG	gn
37808	C-130E	463rd AG	gn	37897	C-130E	169th AS	
37809	C-130E			37898	C-130E	8th SOS	
37811	C-130E	143rd AS	r	37899	C-130E	314th AW	bl
37812	C-130E	169th AS		39810	C-130E	71st RQS	bl
37813	C-130E	314th AW	bl	39812	C-130E	314th AW	bk
37814	C-130E	67th SOS		39813	C-130E	171st AS	y/bk
37815	C-130E	193rd SOS		39814	C-130E	314th AW	bl
37816	C-130E	193rd SOS		39815	C-130E	171st AS	y/bk
37817	C-130E	815th AS	r	39816	EC-130E	193rd SOS	
37818	C-130E	169th AS		39817	EC-130E	193rd SOS	
37819	C-130E	374th AW	r	FY84			
37821	C-130E	374th AW	r	40204	C-130H	700th AS	bk/w
37822	C-130E	815th AS	r	40205	C-130H	700th AS	bk/w
37823	C-130E	327th AS	bk	40206	C-130H	142nd AS	bl
37824	C-130E	143rd AS	r	40207	C-130H	142nd AS	bl
37825	C-130E	135th AS	bk/y	40208	C-130H	142nd AS	bl
37826	C-130E	327th AS	bk	40209	C-130H	142nd AS	bl
37828	EC-130E	193rd SOS		40210	C-130H	142nd AS	bl
37829	C-130E	463rd AG	gn	40211	C-130H	142nd AS	bl
37830	C-130E	314th AW	bk	40212	C-130H	142nd AS	bl
37831	C-130E	135th AS	bk/y	40213	C-130H	142nd AS	bl
37832	C-130E	96th AS	pr	40475	MC-130H	15th SOS	
37833	C-130E	327th AS	bk	40476	MC-130H	7th SOS	
37834	C-130E	327th AS	bk	FY64			
37835	C-130E	314th AW	bk	40495	C-130E	43rd AW	gn/or
37837	C-130E	374th AW	r	40496	C-130E	43rd AW	bl/y

C-130

Notes	Type				Notes	Type			
	40498	C-130E	43rd AW	bl/y		41692	C-130H	3rd Wg	w
	40499	C-130E	43rd AW	bl/y		42061	C-130H	317th AG	r
	40500	NC-130E	645th MS			42062	C-130H	3rd Wg	w
	40502	C-130E	37th AS	bl/w		42063	C-130H	317th AG	bl
	40504	C-130E	43rd AW	bl/y		42065	C-130H	317th AG	bl
	40510	C-130E	135th AS	bk/y		42066	C-130H	3rd Wg	w
	40512	C-130E	154th TS	r		42067	C-130H	317th AG	r
	40514	C-130E	135th AS	bk/y		42069	C-130H	317th AG	r
	40515	C-130E	135th AS	bk/y		42070	C-130H	3rd Wg	w
	40517	C-130E	43rd AW	gn/or		42071	C-130H	3rd Wg	w
	40518	C-130E	463rd AG	gn		42072	C-130H	317th AG	bl
	40519	C-130E	314th AW	bl		42130	C-130H	317th AG	r
	40520	C-130E	135th AS	bk/y		42131	C-130H	3rd Wg	w
	40521	C-130E	135th AS	bk/y		42132	C-130H	317th AG	r
	40523	MC-130E	8th SOS			42133	C-130H	3rd Wg	w
	40525	C-130E	43rd AW	gn/or		42134	C-130H	317th AG	r
	40526	C-130E	135th AS	bk/y		FY94			
	40527	C-130E	37th AS	bl/w		46701	C-130H	167th AS	r
	40529	C-130E	43rd AW	gn/or		46702	C-130H	167th AS	r
	40531	C-130E	43rd AW	bl/y		46703	C-130H	167th AS	r
	40533	C-130E	37th AS	bl/w		46704	C-130H	167th AS	r
	40535	C-130E	314th AW	bl		46705	C-130H	167th AS	r
	40537	C-130E	43rd AW	gn/or		46706	C-130H	167th AS	r
	40538	C-130E	314th AW	bk		46707	C-130H	167th AS	r
	40539	C-130E	43rd AW	gn/or		46708	C-130H	167th AS	r
	40540	C-130E	43rd AW	bl/y		47310	C-130H	731st AS	gn
	40541	C-130E	314th AW	bk		47315	C-130H	731st AS	gn
	40542	C-130E	314th AW	bk		47316	C-130H	731st AS	gn
	40544	C-130E	135th AS	bk/y		47317	C-130H	731st AS	gn
	40550	C-130E	37th AS	bl/w		47318	C-130H	731st AS	gn
	40551	MC-130E	711th SOS			47319	C-130H	731st AS	gn
	40555	MC-130E	8th SOS			47320	C-130H	731st AS	gn
	40557	C-130E	314th AW	bl		47321	C-130H	731st AS	gn
	40559	MC-130E	8th SOS			FY85			
	40561	MC-130E	711th SOS			50011	MC-130H	58th SOW	
	40562	MC-130E	711th SOS			50012	MC-130H	15th SOS	
	40565	MC-130E	711th SOS			50035	C-130H	357th AS	bl
	40566	MC-130E	8th SOS			50036	C-130H	357th AS	bl
	40567	MC-130E	8th SOS			50037	C-130H	357th AS	bl
	40568	MC-130E	8th SOS			50038	C-130H	357th AS	bl
	40569	C-130E	314th AW	bl		50039	C-130H	357th AS	bl
	40570	C-130E	43rd AW	gn/or		50040	C-130H	357th AS	bl
	40571	MC-130E	711th SOS			50041	C-130H	357th AS	bl
	40572	MC-130E	711th SOS			50042	C-130H	357th AS	bl
	FY74					FY65			
	41658	C-130H	3rd Wg	w		50962	EC-130H	42nd ACCS	w
	41659	C-130H	3rd Wg	w		50963	WC-130H	53rd WRS	
	41660	C-130H	3rd Wg	w		50964	C-130E	39th RQS	
	41661	C-130H	3rd Wg	w		50966	WC-130H	53rd WRS	
	41663	C-130H	317th AG	bl		50967	WC-130H	53rd WRS	
	41664	C-130H	3rd Wg	w		50968	WC-130H	53rd WRS	
	41665	C-130H	317th AG	bl		50969	C-130E	711th SOS	
	41666	C-130H	317th AG	bl		50970	HC-130P	303rd RQS	y
	41667	C-130H	317th AG	r		50971	MC-130P	5th SOS	
	41668	C-130H	3rd Wg	w		50973	HC-130P	71st RQS	bl
	41669	C-130H	317th AG	r		50974	HC-130P	102nd RQS	
	41670	C-130H	317th AG	r		50975	MC-130P	58th SOW	
	41671	C-130H	317th AG	bl		50976	HC-130P	303rd RQS	y
	41673	C-130H	317th AG	bl		50977	WC-130H	53rd WRS	
	41674	C-130H	317th AG	r		50978	HC-130P	102nd RQS	
	41675	C-130H	317th AG	r		50979	NC-130H	412th TW	
	41676	C-130H	3rd Wg	m		50980	WC-130H	53rd WRS	
	41677	C-130H	317th AG	bl		50981	HC-130P	129th RQS	bl
	41679	C-130H	317th AG	bl		50982	HC-130P	71st RQS	bl
	41680	C-130H	317th AG	r		50983	HC-130N	129th RQS	bl
	41682	C-130H	3rd Wg	w		50984	WC-130H	53rd WRS	
	41684	C-130H	3rd Wg	w		50985	WC-130H	53rd WRS	
	41685	C-130H	3rd Wg	w		50986	HC-130P	71st RQS	bl
	41687	C-130H	317th AG	r		50987	HC-130P	71st RQS	bl
	41688	C-130H	317th AG	bl		50988	HC-130P	71st RQS	bl
	41689	C-130H	317th AG	bl		50989	EC-130H	41st ECS	bl
	41690	C-130H	3rd Wg	w		50991	MC-130P	9th SOS	
	41691	C-130H	317th AG	r		50992	MC-130P	17th SOS	

Type			Notes
50993	MC-130P	17th SOS	
50994	MC-130P	17th SOS	
FY95			
51001	C-130H	109th AS	gn/bl
51002	C-130H	109th AS	gn/bl
FY85			
51361	C-130H	181st AS	
51362	C-130H	181st AS	
51363	C-130H	181st AS	
51364	C-130H	181st AS	
51365	C-130H	181st AS	
51366	C-130H	181st AS	
51367	C-130H	181st AS	
51368	C-130H	181st AS	
FY95			
56709	C-130H	167th AS	r
56710	C-130H	167th AS	r
56711	C-130H	167th AS	r
56712	C-130H	167th AS	r
FY66			
60212	MC-130P	58th SOW	
60213	MC-130P	9th SOS	
60215	MC-130P	17th SOS	
60216	MC-130P	5th SOS	
60217	MC-130P	9th SOS	
60219	MC-130P	5th SOS	
60220	MC-130P	9th SOS	
60221	HC-130P	129th RQS	bl
60222	HC-130P	102nd RQS	
60223	MC-130P	67th SOS	
60224	HC-130P	129th RQS	bl
60225	MC-130P	9th SOS	
FY86			
60410	C-130H	758th AS	bk/y
60411	C-130H	758th AS	bk/y
60412	C-130H	758th AS	bk/y
60413	C-130H	758th AS	bk/y
60414	C-130H	758th AS	bk/y
60415	C-130H	758th AS	bk/y
60418	C-130H	758th AS	bk/y
60419	C-130H	758th AS	bk/y
FY96			
61003	C-130H	109th AS	gn/bl
61004	C-130H	109th AS	gn/bl
61005	C-130H	109th AS	gn/bl
61006	C-130H	109th AS	gn/bl
61007	C-130H	109th AS	gn/bl
61008	C-130H	109th AS	gn/bl
FY86			
61391	C-130H	180th AS	
61392	C-130H	180th AS	
61393	C-130H	180th AS	
61394	C-130H	180th AS	
61395	C-130H	180th AS	
61396	C-130H	180th AS	
61397	C-130H	180th AS	
61398	C-130H	180th AS	
61699	MC-130H	7th SOS	
FY96			
65300	WC-130J	53rd WRS	
65301	WC-130J	53rd WRS	
65302	WC-130J	53rd WRS	
67322	C-130H	731st AS	gn
67323	C-130H	731st AS	gn
67324	C-130H	731st AS	gn
67325	C-130H	731st AS	gn
68151	C-130J		
68152	C-130J		
68153	C-130J		
68154	C-130J		
FY87			
70023	MC-130H	7th SOS	
70024	MC-130H	15th SOS	

Type			Notes
70125	MC-130H	58th SOW	
70126	MC-130H	58th SOW	
70127	MC-130H	58th SOW	
70128	AC-130U	4th SOS	
70157	NC-130H	412th TW	
FY97			
71351	C-130J	135th AS	bk/y
71352	C-130J	135th AS	bk/y
71353	C-130J	135th AS	bk/y
71354	C-130J	135th AS	bk/y
75303	WC-130J	53rd WRS	
75304	WC-130J	53rd WRS	
75305	WC-130J	53rd WRS	
75306	WC-130J	53rd WRS	
FY87			
79281	C-130H	95th AS	y/w
79282	C-130H	95th AS	y/w
79283	C-130H	95th AS	y/w
79284	C-130H	700th AS	bk
79285	C-130H	95th AS	y/w
79286	C-130H	357th AS	bl
79287	C-130H	95th AS	y/w
79288	C-130H	758th AS	bk/y
FY88			
80191	MC-130H	1st SOS	
80192	MC-130H	1st SOS	
80193	MC-130H	7th SOS	
80194	MC-130H	7th SOS	
80195	MC-130H	1st SOS	
80264	MC-130H	1st SOS	
FY78			
80806	C-130H	185th AS	bl
80807	C-130H	185th AS	bl
80808	C-130H	185th AS	bl
80809	C-130H	185th AS	bl
80810	C-130H	185th AS	bl
80811	C-130H	185th AS	bl
80812	C-130H	185th AS	bl
80813	C-130H	185th AS	bl
FY88			
81301	C-130H	130th AS	bk/w
81302	C-130H	130th AS	bk/w
81303	C-130H	130th AS	bk/w
81304	C-130H	130th AS	bk/w
81305	C-130H	130th AS	bk/w
81306	C-130H	130th AS	bk/w
81307	C-130H	130th AS	bk/w
81308	C-130H	130th AS	bk/w
81803	MC-130H	1st SOS	
82101	HC-130N	102nd RQS	
82102	HC-130N	102nd RQS	
84401	C-130H	95th AS	y/w
84402	C-130H	95th AS	y/w
84403	C-130H	95th AS	y/w
84404	C-130H	95th AS	y/w
84405	C-130H	95th AS	y/w
84406	C-130H	95th AS	y/w
84407	C-130H	95th AS	y/w
FY98			
85308	WC-130J	53rd WRS	
85309	WC-130J	53rd WRS	
FY89			
90280	MC-130H	15th SOS	
90281	MC-130H	15th SOS	
90282	MC-130H	15th SOS	
90283	MC-130H	15th SOS	
FY79			
90473	C-130H	144th AS	bk/y
90474	C-130H	185th AS	bl
90475	C-130H	204th AS	
90476	C-130H	157th FS	
90477	C-130H	158th AS	r

Notes	Type			Notes	Type

	Type	Unit	Notes
	90478	C-130H	204th AS	
	90479	C-130H	204th AS	
	90480	C-130H	122nd FS	
FY89				
	90509	AC-130U	4th SOS	
	90510	AC-130U	4th SOS	
	90511	AC-130U	4th SOS	
	90512	AC-130U	4th SOS	
	90513	AC-130U	4th SOS	
	90514	AC-130U	4th SOS	
	91051	C-130H	105th AS	*or*
	91052	C-130H	105th AS	*or*
	91053	C-130H	105th AS	*or*
	91054	C-130H	105th AS	*or*
	91055	C-130H	142nd AS	*bl*
	91056	C-130H	180th AS	
	91181	C-130H	105th AS	*or*
	91182	C-130H	105th AS	*or*
	91183	C-130H	105th AS	*or*
	91184	C-130H	105th AS	*or*
	91185	C-130H	105th AS	*or*
	91186	C-130H	105th AS	*or*
	91187	C-130H	105th AS	*or*
	91188	C-130H	105th AS	*or*
FY69				
	95819	MC-130P	55th SOS	
	95820	MC-130P	67th SOS	
	95821	MC-130P	58th SOW	
	95822	MC-130P	9th SOS	
	95823	MC-130P	67th SOS	
	95824	HC-130N	39th RQS	
	95825	MC-130P	5th SOS	
	95826	MC-130P	67th SOS	
	95827	MC-130P	5th SOS	
	95828	MC-130P	67th SOS	
	95829	HC-130N	39th RQS	
	95830	HC-130N	39th RQS	
	95831	MC-130P	67th SOS	
	95832	MC-130P	9th SOS	
	95833	HC-130N	39th RQS	
	96566	C-130E	37th AS	*bl/w*
	96568	AC-130H	16th SOS	
	96569	AC-130H	16th SOS	
	96570	AC-130H	16th SOS	
	96572	AC-130H	16th SOS	
	96573	AC-130H	16th SOS	
	96574	AC-130H	16th SOS	
	96575	AC-130H	16th SOS	
	96577	AC-130H	16th SOS	
	96579	C-130E	463rd AG	*gn*
	96580	C-130E	43rd AW	*gn/or*
	96582	C-130E	37th AS	*bl/w*
	96583	C-130E	37th AS	*bl/w*
FY89				
	99101	C-130H	757th AS	*bl*
	99102	C-130H	757th AS	*bl*
	99103	C-130H	757th AS	*bl*
	99104	C-130H	757th AS	*bl*
	99105	C-130H	757th AS	*bl*
	99106	C-130H	757th AS	*bl*

Boeing C-135/C-137

91st ARS/6th ARW, MacDill AFB, Florida (*y/bl*);
65th AS/15th ABW, Hickam AFB, Hawaii;
909th ARS/18th Wg, Kadena AB, Japan [ZZ] (*w*);
99th ARS/19th ARG, Robins AFB, Georgia (*y/bl*);
22nd ARW, McConnell AFB, Kansas:
344th ARS (*y/bk*), 349th ARS (*y/bl*)
350th ARS (*y/r*) & 384th ARS (*y/pr*)

55th Wg, Offutt AFB, Nebraska [OF]:
38th RS (*gn*) & 45th RS (*bk*);
88th ABW, Wright-Patterson AFB, Ohio;
1st AS/89th AW, Andrews AFB, Maryland;
92nd ARW, Fairchild AFB, Washington:
43rd ARS (*bl*), 92nd ARS (*bk*), 96th ARS (*gn*), 97th ARS (*y*) & 98th ARS (*r*);
55th ARS/97th AMW, Altus AFB, Oklahoma (*y/r*);
351st ARS/100th ARW, RAF Mildenhall, UK [D] (*r/w/bl*);
132nd ARS/101st ARW, Bangor, Maine ANG (*w/gn*);
136th ARS/107th ARW, Niagara Falls, New York ANG (*bl*);
108th ARW, McGuire AFB, New Jersey ANG:
141st ARS (*bk/y*) & 150th ARS (*bl*);
106th ARS/117th ARW, Birmingham, Alabama ANG (*w/r*);
121st ARW, Rickenbacker ANGB, Ohio ANG:
145th ARS & 166th ARS (*bl*);
108th ARS/126th ARW, Greater Peoria Airport, Illinois ANG (*w/bl*);
126th ARS/128th ARW, Mitchell Field, Wisconsin ANG (*w/bl*);
151st ARS/134th ARW, Knoxville, Tennessee ANG (*w/or*);
116th ARS/141st ARW, Fairchild AFB, Washington ANG (*gn/w*);
191st ARS/151st ARW, Salt Lake City, Utah ANG (*bl/bk*);
203rd ARS/154th Wg, Hickam AFB, Hawaii ANG (*y/bk*);
173rd ARS/155th ARW, Lincoln, Nebraska ANG (*r/w*);
133rd ARS/157th ARW, Pease ANGB, New Hampshire ANG (*bl*);
197th ARS/161st ARW, Phoenix, Arizona ANG;
196th ARS/163rd ARW, March ARB, California ANG (*bl/w*);
168th ARS/168th ARW, Eielson AFB, Alaska ANG (*bl/y*);
171st ARW, Greater Pittsburgh, Pennsylvania ANG:
146th ARS (*y/bk*) & 147th ARS (*bk/y*);
153rd ARS/186th ARW, Meridian, Mississippi ANG (*bk/gd*);
117th ARS/190th ARW, Forbes Field, Kansas ANG (*bl/y*);
319th ARW, Grand Forks AFB, North Dakota:
905th ARS (*bl*), 906th ARS (*y*), 911th ARS (*r*) & 912th ARS (*w*);
22nd ARS/366th Wg, Mountain Home AFB, Idaho [MO] (*y/gn*);
452nd FLTS/412th TW, Edwards AFB, California [ED] (*bl*);
434th ARW AFRC, Grissom AFB, Indiana:
72nd ARS (*bl*) & 74th ARS (*r/w*);
336th ARS/452nd AMW AFRC,

March ARB, California (*y*);
465th ARS/507th ARW AFRC,
Tinker AFB, Oklahoma (*bl/y*);
645th Materiel Sqn, Greenville,
Texas;
77th ARS/916th ARW AFRC,
Seymour Johnson AFB,
North Carolina (*gn*);
63rd ARS/927th ARW AFRC,
Selfridge ANGB, Michigan (*pr/w*);
314th ARS/940th ARW AFRC,
McClellan AFB, California (*or/bk*);
CinC CentCom (CinC CC)/6th ARW,
MacDill AFB, Florida

FY60

Type			Notes
00313	KC-135R	22nd ARW	
00314	KC-135R	434th ARW	/w
00315	KC-135R	128th ARW	w/bl
00316	KC-135E	141st ARW	
00318	KC-135E	154th Wg	y/bk
00319	KC-135R	319th ARW	
00320	KC-135R	319th ARW	w
00321	KC-135R	97th AMW	y/r
00322	KC-135R	434th ARW	bl
00323	KC-135R	154th Wg	y/bk
00324	KC-135R	319th ARW	bl
00327	KC-135E	151st ARW	bl/bk
00328	KC-135R	92nd ARW	bk
00329	KC-135R	154th Wg	y/bk
00331	KC-135R	97th AMW	y/r
00332	KC-135R	6th ARW	/bl
00333	KC-135R	97th AMW	y/r
00334	KC-135R	168th ARW	bl/y
00335	KC-135T	22nd ARW	y/bk
00336	KC-135T	92nd ARW	gn
00337	KC-135T	92nd ARW	bl
00339	KC-135T	92nd ARW	bk
00341	KC-135R	121st ARW	bl
00342	KC-135T	319th ARW	y
00343	KC-135T	319th ARW	w
00344	KC-135T	22nd ARW	y/bk
00345	KC-135T	92nd ARW	bl
00346	KC-135T	92nd ARW	bk
00347	KC-135R	121st ARW	bl
00348	KC-135R	6th ARW	/bl
00349	KC-135R	916th ARW	gn
00350	KC-135R	22nd ARW	y/bk
00351	KC-135R	22nd ARW	
00353	KC-135R	319th ARW	y
00355	KC-135R	319th ARW	y
00356	KC-135R	22nd ARW	y/bl
00357	KC-135R	22nd ARW	y/bk
00358	KC-135R	107th ARW	bl
00359	KC-135R	434th ARW	r/w
00360	KC-135R	319th ARW	r
00362	KC-135R	22nd ARW	
00363	KC-135R	434th ARW	bl
00364	KC-135R	434th ARW	r/w
00365	KC-135R	366th Wg	y/gn
00366	KC-135R	19th ARG	y/bl
00367	KC-135R	121st ARW	bl
00372	C-135E	412th TW	bl
00374	EC-135E	412th TW	bl
00375	C-135E	412th TW	bl
00376	C-135E	15th ABW	

FY61

Type			Notes
10264	KC-135R	121st ARW	bl
10266	KC-135R	155th ARW	r/w
10267	KC-135R	100th ARW	r/w/bl
10268	KC-135E	940th ARW	or/bk
10270	KC-135E	927th ARW	pr/w
10271	KC-135E	927th ARW	pr/w

Type			Notes
10272	KC-135R	434th ARW	r/w
10275	KC-135R	22nd ARW	y/r
10276	KC-135R	155th ARW	r/w
10277	KC-135R	366th Wg	y/gn
10280	KC-135E	452nd AMW	y
10281	KC-135E	161st ARW	
10284	KC-135R	100th ARW	r/w/bl
10288	KC-135R	100th ARW	r/w/bl
10290	KC-135R	154th Wg	y/bk
10292	KC-135R	22nd ARW	y/pr
10293	KC-135R	22nd ARW	y/r
10294	KC-135R	6th ARW	y/bl
10295	KC-135R	319th ARW	bl
10298	KC-135R	128th ARW	w/bl
10299	KC-135R	92nd ARW	bk
10300	KC-135R	19th ARG	y/bl
10302	KC-135R	319th ARW	w
10303	KC-135E	452nd AMW	y
10304	KC-135R	92nd ARW	y
10305	KC-135R	22nd ARW	y/bk
10306	KC-135R	22nd ARW	
10307	KC-135R	434th ARW	r/w
10308	KC-135R	97th AMW	y/r
10309	KC-135R	128th ARW	w/bl
10310	KC-135R	157th ARW	bl
10311	KC-135R	22nd ARW	y/r
10312	KC-135R	100th ARW	r/w/bl
10313	KC-135R	916th ARW	gn
10314	KC-135R	97th AMW	y/r
10315	KC-135R	22nd ARW	
10317	KC-135R	319th ARW	bl
10318	KC-135R	6th ARW	y/bl
10320	KC-135R	92nd ARW	y
10321	KC-135R	92nd ARW	y
10323	KC-135R	6th ARW	y/bl
10324	KC-135R	452nd AMW	y
10327	EC-135N	CinC CC	
10330	EC-135E	412th TW	bl
12662	RC-135S	55th Wg	bk
12663	RC-135S	55th Wg	bk
12666	WC-135W	645th MS	
12667	WC-135W	55th Wg	bk
12669	C-135C	412th TW	bl
12670	OC-135B	55th Wg	bl
12672	OC-135B	55th Wg	bl

FY64

Type			Notes
14828	KC-135R	22nd ARW	y/pr
14829	KC-135R	319th ARW	r
14830	KC-135R	6th ARW	y/bl
14831	KC-135R	92nd ARW	
14832	KC-135R	154th Wg	y/bk
14833	KC-135R	6th ARW	/bl
14834	KC-135R	434th ARW	r/w
14835	KC-135R	22nd ARW	y/bk
14836	KC-135R	18th Wg	w
14837	KC-135R	18th Wg	w
14838	KC-135R	6th ARW	y/bl
14839	KC-135R	107th ARW	bl
14840	KC-135R	121st ARW	bl
14841	RC-135V	55th Wg	gn
14842	RC-135V	55th Wg	gn
14843	RC-135V	55th Wg	gn
14844	RC-135V	55th Wg	gn
14845	RC-135V	55th Wg	gn
14846	RC-135V	55th Wg	gn
14847	RC-135U	55th Wg	gn
14848	RC-135V	55th Wg	gn
14849	RC-135U	55th Wg	gn

FY67

Type			Notes
19417	EC-137D	6th ARW	

FY62

Type			Notes
23498	KC-135R	100th ARW	r/w/bl
23499	KC-135R	22nd ARW	y/pr

Notes	Type				Notes	Type			
	23500	KC-135R	128th ARW	w/bl		24131	RC-135W	55th Wg	gn
	23502	KC-135R	319th ARW	r		24132	RC-135W	55th Wg	gn
	23503	KC-135R	319th ARW	r		24133	TC-135S	55th Wg	bk
	23504	KC-135R	319th ARW	bl		24134	RC-135W	55th Wg	gn
	23505	KC-135R	6th ARW	y/bl		24135	RC-135W	55th Wg	gn
	23506	KC-135R	157th ARW	bl		24138	RC-135W	55th Wg	gn
	23507	KC-135R	22nd ARW			24139	RC-135W	55th Wg	gn
	23508	KC-135R	19th ARG	y/bl		FY72			
	23509	KC-135R	916th ARW	gn		27000	C-137C	89th AW	
	23510	KC-135R	434th ARW	r/w		FY63			
	23511	KC-135R	121st ARW	bl		37976	KC-135R	319th ARW	bl
	23512	KC-135R	128th ARW	w/bl		37977	KC-135R	319th ARW	bl
	23513	KC-135R	366th Wg	y/gn		37978	KC-135R	97th AMW	y/r
	23514	KC-135R	154th Wg	y/bk		37979	KC-135R	100th ARW	r/w/bl
	23515	KC-135R	157th ARW	bl		37980	KC-135R	22nd ARW	y/bk
	23516	KC-135R				37981	KC-135R	107th ARW	bl
	23517	KC-135R	100th ARW	r/w/bl		37982	KC-135R	18th Wg	w
	23518	KC-135R	434th ARW	bl		37984	KC-135R	117th ARW	w/r
	23519	KC-135R	319th ARW	r		37985	KC-135R	507th ARW	bl/y
	23520	KC-135R	319th ARW	w		37987	KC-135R	319th ARW	
	23521	KC-135R	434th ARW			37988	KC-135R	155th ARW	r/w
	23523	KC-135R	19th ARG	/bl		37991	KC-135R	155th ARW	r/w
	23524	KC-135R	117th ARW	w/r		37992	KC-135R	121st ARW	bl
	23526	KC-135R	155th ARW	r/w		37993	KC-135R	121st ARW	m
	23527	KC-135E	108th ARW	bk/y		37995	KC-135R	507th ARW	bl/y
	23528	KC-135R	100th ARW	r/w/bl		37996	KC-135R	434th ARW	bl
	23529	KC-135R	97th AMW	y/r		37997	KC-135R	19th ARG	y/bl
	23530	KC-135R	434th ARW	bl		37999	KC-135R	18th Wg	w
	23531	KC-135R	121st ARW	bl		38000	KC-135R	19th ARG	y/bl
	23533	KC-135R	100th ARW	r/w/bl		38002	KC-135R	19th ARG	y/bl
	23534	KC-135R	22nd ARW	y/pr		38003	KC-135R	22nd ARW	y/r
	23537	KC-135R	18th Wg	w		38004	KC-135R	366th Wg	y/gn
	23538	KC-135R	100th ARW	r/w/bl		38006	KC-135R	19th ARG	y/bl
	23540	KC-135R	92nd ARW	gn		38007	KC-135R	117th ARW	w/r
	23541	KC-135R	22nd ARW			38008	KC-135R	22nd ARW	y/r
	23542	KC-135R	916th ARW	gn		38011	KC-135R	18th Wg	w
	23543	KC-135R	434th ARW	bl		38012	KC-135R	319th ARW	bl
	23544	KC-135R	19th ARG	y/bl		38013	KC-135R	121st ARW	bl
	23545	KC-135R	319th ARW	bl		38014	KC-135R	92nd ARW	r
	23546	KC-135R	97th AMW	y/r		38015	KC-135R	168th ARW	bl/y
	23547	KC-135R	157th ARW	bl		38017	KC-135R	100th ARW	r/w/bl
	23548	KC-135R	22nd ARW	y/r		38018	KC-135R	155th ARW	r/w
	23549	KC-135R	97th AMW	y/r		38019	KC-135R	22nd ARW	y/pr
	23550	KC-135R	97th AMW	y/r		38020	KC-135R	97th AMW	y/r
	23551	KC-135R	97th AMW	y/r		38021	KC-135R	319th ARW	bl
	23552	KC-135R	319th ARW	w		38022	KC-135R	22nd ARW	m
	23553	KC-135R	19th ARG	y/bl		38023	KC-135R		
	23554	KC-135R	19th ARG	y/bl		38024	KC-135R	507th ARW	bl/y
	23556	KC-135R	916th ARW	gn		38025	KC-135R	319th ARW	bl
	23557	KC-135R	319th ARW	bl		38026	KC-135R	319th ARW	y
	23558	KC-135R	22nd ARW	y/bk		38027	KC-135R	92nd ARW	gn
	23559	KC-135R	22nd ARW	y/pr		38028	KC-135R	168th ARW	bl/y
	23561	KC-135R	100th ARW	/w/bl		38029	KC-135R	128th ARW	w/bl
	23562	KC-135R	319th ARW	w		38030	KC-135R	154th Wg	y/bk
	23564	KC-135R	100th ARW	r/w/bl		38031	KC-135R	19th ARG	
	23565	KC-135R	97th AMW	y/r		38032	KC-135R	434th ARW	bl
	23566	KC-135E	101st ARW	w/gn		38033	KC-135R	92nd ARW	y
	23568	KC-135R	6th ARW	y/bl		38034	KC-135R	319th ARW	y
	23569	KC-135R	19th ARG	y/bl		38035	KC-135R	117th ARW	w/r
	23571	KC-135R	168th ARW	bl/y		38036	KC-135R	107th ARW	bl
	23572	KC-135R	366th Wg	y/gn		38037	KC-135R	97th AMW	y/r
	23573	KC-135R	22nd ARW			38038	KC-135R	157th ARW	bl
	23575	KC-135R	22nd ARW			38039	KC-135R	507th ARW	bl/y
	23576	KC-135R	157th ARW	bl		38040	KC-135R	319th ARW	y
	23577	KC-135R	916th ARW	gn		38041	KC-135R	434th ARW	bl
	23578	KC-135R	100th ARW	r/w/bl		38043	KC-135R	168th ARW	bl/y
	23580	KC-135R	97th AMW	y/r		38044	KC-135R	319th ARW	y
	24125	RC-135W	55th Wg			38045	KC-135R	319th ARW	r
	24126	C-135B	108th ARW	bk/y		38050	NKC-135B	412th TW	bl
	24127	C-135B				38058	KC-135D	190th ARW	bl/y
	24128	RC-135X	55th Wg			38059	KC-135D	190th ARW	bl/y
	24129	TC-135W	55th Wg	gn					
	24130	RC-135W	55th Wg						

Type			Notes	Type			Notes
38060	KC-135D	190th ARW	bl/y	71438	KC-135E	927th ARW	pr/w
38061	KC-135D	190th ARW	bl/y	71439	KC-135R		
38871	KC-135R	319th ARW	r	71440	KC-135R	18th Wg	w
38872	KC-135R	107th ARW	bl	71441	KC-135E	126th ARW	w/bl
38873	KC-135R	66th ARW	y/bl	71443	KC-135R	101st ARW	w/gn
38874	KC-135R	319th ARW	w	71445	KC-135R	108th ARW	bk/y
38875	KC-135R	366th Wg	y/gn	71447	KC-135E	171st ARW	y/bk
38876	KC-135R	18th Wg	w	71448	KC-135R	101st ARW	w/gn
38877	KC-135R	92nd ARW	bl	71450	KC-135R	101st ARW	w/gn
38878	KC-135R	97th AMW	y/r	71451	KC-135E	141st ARW	gn/w
38879	KC-135R	22nd ARW		71452	KC-135R	161st ARW	
38880	KC-135R	507th ARW	bl/y	71453	KC-135R	117th ARW	w/r
38881	KC-135R	97th AMW	y/r	71454	KC-135R	6th ARW	y/bl
38883	KC-135R	319th ARW	w	71455	KC-135R	134th ARW	w/or
38884	KC-135R	22nd ARW	y/r	71456	KC-135R		
38885	KC-135R	18th Wg	w	71458	KC-135E	126th ARW	w/bl
38886	KC-135R	97th AMW	y/r	71459	KC-135R	163rd ARW	bl/w
38887	KC-135R	97th AMW	y/r	71460	KC-135R	190th ARW	bl/y
38888	KC-135R	319th ARW	bl	71461	KC-135R	155th ARW	r/w
39792	RC-135V	55th Wg	gn	71462	KC-135E	121st ARW	bl
FY55				71463	KC-135R	190th ARW	bl/y
53125	EC-135Y	CinC CC		71464	KC-135R	108th ARW	bk/y
53132	NKC-135E	412th TW	bl	71465	KC-135R	134th ARW	w/or
53135	NKC-135E	412th TW	bl	71468	KC-135R	452nd AMW	y
53141	KC-135E	141st ARW	gn/w	71469	KC-135R	121st ARW	bl
53143	KC-135E	161st ARW		71471	KC-135R	101st ARW	w/gn
53145	KC-135E	940th ARW		71472	KC-135R	452nd AMW	y
			or/bk	71473	KC-135R	319th ARW	
53146	KC-135E	108th ARW	bl	71474	KC-135R	100th ARW	r/w/bl
FY85				71475	KC-135R	161st ARW	
56973	C-137C	89th AW		71478	KC-135E	134th ARW	w/or
FY56				71479	KC-135R	452nd AMW	y
63593	KC-135E	108th ARW	bk/y	71480	KC-135E	126th ARW	w/bl
63604	KC-135E	108th ARW	bk/y	71482	KC-135R	190th ARW	bl/y
63606	KC-135E	101st ARW	w/gn	71483	KC-135R	92nd ARW	gn
63607	KC-135E	134th ARW	w/or	71484	KC-135R	161st ARW	
63609	KC-135E	134th ARW	w/or	71485	KC-135R	134th ARW	w/or
63611	KC-135E	171st ARW	y/bk	71486	KC-135R	92nd ARW	r
63612	KC-135E	171st ARW	y/bk	71487	KC-135R	434th ARW	bl
63622	KC-135E	101st ARW	w/gn	71488	KC-135R	97th AMW	y/r
63623	KC-135E	452nd AMW	y	71491	KC-135E	101st ARW	w/gn
63626	KC-135E	171st ARW	y/bk	71492	KC-135R	134th ARW	w/or
63630	KC-135E	171st ARW	y/bk	71493	KC-135R	6th ARW	y/bl
63631	KC-135E	151st ARW	bl/bk	71494	KC-135E	126th ARW	w/bl
63638	KC-135E	161st ARW		71495	KC-135E	161st ARW	
63640	KC-135E	101st ARW	w/gn	71496	KC-135E	161st ARW	
63641	KC-135E	190th ARW	bl/y	71497	KC-135E	151st ARW	bl/bk
63643	KC-135E	134th ARW	w/or	71499	KC-135R		
63645	KC-135E	940th ARW		71501	KC-135E	141st ARW	gn/w
			or/bk	71502	KC-135R	319th ARW	y
63648	KC-135E	171st ARW	y/bk	71503	KC-135E	134th ARW	w/or
63650	KC-135E	141st ARW	gn/w	71504	KC-135E	927th ARW	pr/w
63654	KC-135E	101st ARW	w/gn	71505	KC-135E	101st ARW	w/gn
63658	KC-135E	190th ARW	bl/y	71506	KC-135R	319th ARW	
FY57				71507	KC-135E	108th ARW	bk/y
71418	KC-135R	186th ARW	bk/gd	71508	KC-135R	154th Wg	y/bk
71419	KC-135R	18th Wg	w	71509	KC-135R	171st ARW	bk/y
71421	KC-135E	141st ARW	gn/w	71510	KC-135R	151st ARW	bl/bk
71422	KC-135E	927th ARW	pr/w	71511	KC-135R	940th ARW	or/bk
71423	KC-135E	171st ARW	bk/y	71512	KC-135R	452nd AMW	y
71425	KC-135E	134th ARW	w/or	71514	KC-135R	128th ARW	w/bl
71426	KC-135E	161st ARW		72589	KC-135E	15th ABW	
71427	KC-135R	121st ARW	bl	72593	KC-135R	121st ARW	bl
71428	KC-135R	163rd ARW	bl/w	72594	KC-135E	126th ARW	w/bl
71429	KC-135R	190th ARW	bl/y	72595	KC-135E	171st ARW	bk/y
71430	KC-135R	157th ARW	bl	72597	KC-135R	186th ARW	bk/gd
71431	KC-135R	108th ARW	bk/y	72598	KC-135R	452nd AMW	y
71432	KC-135R	117th ARW	w/r	72599	KC-135R	916th ARW	gn
71433	KC-135E	161st ARW		72600	KC-135E	141st ARW	gn/w
71434	KC-135R	141st ARW	gn/w	72601	KC-135R	134th ARW	w/or
71435	KC-135R	22nd ARW	y/r	72602	KC-135E	108th ARW	bl
71436	KC-135R	163rd ARW	bl/w	72603	KC-135E	927th ARW	pr/w
71437	KC-135R	916th ARW	gn	72604	KC-135E	171st ARW	y/bk

C-135

Notes	Type				Notes	Type			
	72605	KC-135R	6th ARW	y/bl		80083	KC-135R	121st ARW	bl
	72606	KC-135E	108th ARW	bl		80084	KC-135T	92nd ARW	r
	72607	KC-135E	171st ARW	bk/y		80085	KC-135E	452nd AMW	y
	72608	KC-135E	171st ARW	bk/y		80086	KC-135T	92nd ARW	gn
	FY58					80087	KC-135E	108th ARW	bl
	80001	KC-135R	97th AMW	y/r		80088	KC-135R	22nd ARW	y/bk
	80003	KC-135E	126th ARW	w/bl		80089	KC-135T	22nd ARW	y/bk
	80004	KC-135R	186th ARW	bk/gd		80090	KC-135E	940th ARW	o/bk
	80005	KC-135E	190th ARW	bl/y		80092	KC-135R	157th ARW	bl
	80006	KC-135R	151st ARW	bl/bk		80093	KC-135R	319th ARW	r
	80008	KC-135R	157th ARW	bl		80094	KC-135T	92nd ARW	bk
	80009	KC-135R	128th ARW	w/bl		80095	KC-135T	22nd ARW	y/bk
	80010	KC-135R	186th ARW	bk/gd		80096	KC-135E	940th ARW	or/bk
	80011	KC-135R	22nd ARW	y/bl		80098	KC-135R	157th ARW	bl
	80012	KC-135E	151st ARW	bl/bk		80099	KC-135T	92nd ARW	bl
	80013	KC-135E	927th ARW	pr/w		80100	KC-135R	22nd ARW	
	80014	KC-135E	126th ARW	w/bl		80102	KC-135R	434th ARW	r/w
	80015	KC-135R	434th ARW	r/w		80103	KC-135T	92nd ARW	r
	80016	KC-135R	22nd ARW	y/bk		80104	KC-135R	107th ARW	bl
	80017	KC-135E	171st ARW	y/bk		80106	KC-135R	117th ARW	w/r
	80018	KC-135R	22nd ARW	y/pr		80107	KC-135E	151st ARW	bl/bk
	80020	KC-135E	141st ARW	gn/w		80108	KC-135E	940th ARW	or/bk
	80021	KC-135R	128th ARW	w/bl		80109	KC-135R	186th ARW bk/gd	
	80023	KC-135R	107th ARW	bl					
	80024	KC-135E	171st ARW	y/bk		80111	KC-135E	108th ARW	bk/y
	80027	KC-135R	22nd ARW	y/bl		80112	KC-135T	92nd ARW	bl
	80030	KC-135R	117th ARW	w/r		80113	KC-135R	18th Wg	w
	80032	KC-135E	108th ARW	bl		80114	KC-135R	319th ARW	r
	80034	KC-135R	97th AMW	y/r		80115	KC-135E	108th ARW	bl
	80035	KC-135R	22nd ARW	y/bl		80116	KC-135E	161st ARW	
	80036	KC-135R	18th Wg	w		80117	KC-135T	92nd ARW	r
	80037	KC-135E	171st ARW	bk/y		80118	KC-135R	22nd ARW	y/bl
	80038	KC-135R	916th ARW	gn		80119	KC-135R	319th ARW	r
	80040	KC-135E	108th ARW	bl		80120	KC-135R	97th AMW	y/r
	80041	KC-135E	927th ARW	pr/w		80121	KC-135R	507th ARW	bl/y
	80042	KC-135T	319th ARW	y		80122	KC-135R	168th ARW	bl/y
	80043	KC-135E	151st ARW	bl/bk		80123	KC-135R	22nd ARW	
	80044	KC-135E	108th ARW	bk/y		80124	KC-135R	22nd ARW	y/bl
	80045	KC-135T	92nd ARW	bl		80125	KC-135T	92nd ARW	y
	80046	KC-135T	92nd ARW	r		80126	KC-135R	22nd ARW	y/bl
	80047	KC-135T	319th ARW	w		80128	KC-135R	6th ARW	y/bl
	80049	KC-135T	92nd ARW	bl		80129	KC-135T	92nd ARW	y
	80050	KC-135T	92nd ARW	r		80130	KC-135R	128th ARW	w/bl
	80051	KC-135R	507th ARW	bl/y		*FY88*			
	80052	KC-135E	452nd AMW	y		86005	EC-137D	88th ABW	
	80053	KC-135E	940th ARW	r/bk		*FY59*			
	80054	KC-135T	92nd ARW	gn		91444	KC-135R	121st ARW	bl
	80055	KC-135T	92nd ARW	r		91445	KC-135E	141st ARW	gn/w
	80056	KC-135R	186th ARW	o/bl		91446	KC-135R	186th ARW	
	80057	KC-135E	126th ARW	w/bl					bk/gd
	80058	KC-135E	940th ARW	o/bk		91447	KC-135E	927th ARW	pr/w
	80059	KC-135R	186th ARW			91448	KC-135R	163rd ARW	bl/w
	80060	KC-135T	92nd ARW	bl		91450	KC-135R	163rd ARW	bl/w
	80061	KC-135T	319th ARW	r		91451	KC-135R	927th ARW	pr/w
	80062	KC-135T	92nd ARW	gn		91453	KC-135R	121st ARW	bl
	80063	KC-135R	507th ARW	bl/y		91455	KC-135R	186th ARW	
	80064	KC-135E	940th ARW	obk					bk/gd
	80065	KC-135T	319th ARW	bl		91456	KC-135E	108th ARW	bk/y
	80066	KC-135R	507th ARW	bl/y		91457	KC-135E	171st ARW	bk/y
	80067	KC-135E	126th ARW	w/bl		91458	KC-135R	121st ARW	bl
	80068	KC-135E	126th ARW	w/bl		91459	KC-135R	97th AMW	y/r
	80069	KC-135T	92nd ARW	bl		91460	KC-135T	92nd ARW	bk
	80071	KC-135T	22nd ARW	y/bk		91461	KC-135R	168th ARW	bl/y
	80072	KC-135T	92nd ARW	gn		91462	KC-135T	22nd ARW	y/bk
	80073	KC-135R	117th ARW	w/r		91463	KC-135R	155th ARW	r/w
	80074	KC-135T	92nd ARW	r		91464	KC-135T	92nd ARW	bk
	80075	KC-135R	434th ARW	bl		91465	KC-135R	107th ARW	bl
	80076	KC-135R	434th ARW	r/w		91466	KC-135T	92nd ARW	bl
	80077	KC-135T	92nd ARW	bk		91467	KC-135T	92nd ARW	y
	80078	KC-135E	108th ARW	bl		91468	KC-135T	92nd ARW	r
	80079	KC-135R	507th ARW	bl/y		91469	KC-135R	916th ARW	gn
	80080	KC-135E	151st ARW	bl/bk		91470	KC-135T	92nd ARW	bl
	80082	KC-135E	141st ARW	gn/w		91471	KC-135T	92nd ARW	r
						91472	KC-135R	154th Wg	y/bk

Type			Notes	Type			Notes
91473	KC-135E	151st ARW	bl/bk		California:		
91474	KC-135T	92nd ARW	y		729th AS & 730th AS (r/y);		
91475	KC-135R	6th ARW	y/bl		756th AS/459th AW, AFRC,		
91476	KC-135R	97th AMW	y/r		Andrews AFB, Maryland (y/bk)		
91477	KC-135E	927th ARW	pr/w	**C-141B/C-141C***			
91478	KC-135R	186th ARW		FY61			
bk/gd				12778	164th AW	r	
91479	KC-135E	171st ARW	y/bk	FY63			
91480	KC-135T	92nd ARW	y	38076	62nd AW	gn/r	
91482	KC-135R			38080	164th AW	r	
91483	KC-135E	121st ARW	bl	38081	62nd AW	gn/bl	
91484	KC-135E	171st ARW	bk/y	38082	62nd AW	gn/r	
91485	KC-135E	108th ARW	bl	38084	452nd AMW	r/y	
91486	KC-135R	22nd ARW	y	38085	452nd AMW	r/y	
91487	KC-135E	126th ARW	w/bl	38087	97th AMW	r/y	
91488	KC-135R	22nd ARW	y/r	38088	60th AMW	bk/si	
91489	KC-135E	151st ARW	b/l	FY64			
91490	KC-13ST	92nd ARW	bk	40610	437th AW	y/bl	
91492	KC-135R	18th Wg	w	40611	62nd AW	gn/r	
91493	KC-135R	101st ARW	w/gn	40612	305th AMW	bl	
91495	KC-135R	155th ARW	r/w	40614	172nd AW	bl	
91496	KC-135E	171st ARW	y/bk	40615	62nd AW	gn/si	
91497	KC-135E	108th ARW	bl	40616	305th AMW	bl	
91498	KC-135R	366th Wg	y/gn	40618	437th AW	y/bl	
91499	KC-135R	163rd ARW	bl/w	40619	305th AMW	bl	
91500	KC-135R	19th ARG	y/bl	40620	459th AW	y/bk	
91501	KC-135R	22nd ARW	y/r	40621	305th AMW	bl	
91502	KC-135R	22nd ARW	y/pr	40622	172nd AW	bl	
91503	KC-135R	108th ARW	bk/y	40623	305th AMW	bl	
91504	KC-135T	92nd ARW	bl	40627	164th AW	r	
91505	KC-135R	163rd ARW	bl/w	40628	305th AMW	bl	
91506	KC-135E	171st ARW	bk/y	40629	97th AMW	r/y	
91507	KC-135R	22nd ARW	y/bl	40630	437th AW	y/bl	
91508	KC-135R	319th ARW	r	40631	62nd AW	gn/bl	
91509	KC-135R	163rd ARW	bl/w	40632	172nd AW	bl	
91510	KC-135T	22nd ARW	y/bk	40633	62nd AW	gn/r	
91511	KC-135T	319th ARW	w	40637	459th AW	y/bk	
91512	KC-135T	92nd ARW	gn	40638	305th AMW	bl	
91513	KC-135T	92nd ARW	bl	40640	172nd AW	bl	
91514	KC-135E	55th Wg	bl	40643	62nd AW	gn/r	
91515	KC-135R	22nd ARW	y/pr	40644	305th AMW	bl	
91516	KC-135R	163rd ARW	bl/w	40645	459th AW	y/bk	
91517	KC-135R	18th Wg	w	40646	305th AMW	bl	
91518	C-135K	15th ABW		40649	305th AMW	bl	
91519	KC-135R	171st ARW	y/bk	FY65			
91520	KC-135T	92nd ARW	bl	50216	459th AW	y/bk	
91521	KC-135R	168th ARW	bl/y	50217	305th AMW	bl	
91522	KC-135R	107th ARW	bl	50218	62nd AW	gn/r	
91523	KC-135T	92nd ARW	bk	50219	97th AMW	r/y	
				50220	305th AMW	bl	
Lockheed C-141 Starlifter				50221	305th AMW	bl	
19th AS/60th AMW, Travis AFB,				50222	164th AW	r	
California (bk/r & bk/si);				50224	305th AMW	bl	
62nd AW, McChord AFB, Washington:				50225*	452nd AMW	r/y	
4th AS (gn/r), 7th AS (gn/bl)				50226	459th AW	y/bk	
& 8th AS (gn/si);				50229	452nd AMW	r/y	
57th AS/97th AMW, Altus AFB,				50230	62nd AW	gn/r	
Oklahoma (r/y);				50231	60th AMW		
155th AS/164th AW, Memphis,				50232	445th AW	w/r	
Tennessee ANG (r);				50234	62nd AW	gn/si	
183rd AS/172nd AW, Jackson Int'l				50235	62nd AW	gn/si	
Airport, Mississippi ANG (bl);				50237	445th AW	w/r	
305th AMW, McGuire AFB,				50238	62nd AW	gn/si	
New Jersey:				50239	62nd AW	gn/bl	
6th AS, 13th AS & 18th AS (bl);				50240	62nd AW	gn/bl	
412th TW, Edwards AFB,				50241	62nd AW	gn/r	
California [ED];				50242	305th AMW	bl	
16th AS/437th AW, Charleston AFB,				50243	97th AMW	r/y	
South Carolina (y/bl);				50244	62nd AW	gn/si	
445th AW AFRC, Wright-Patterson				50245*	452nd AMW	r/y	
AFB, Ohio:				50248	452nd AMW	r/y	
89th AS & 356th AS (w/r);				50249	445th AW	w/r	
452nd AMW AFRC, March ARB,				50250	445th AW	w/r	

Notes	Type			Notes	Type		
	50251	62nd AW	gn/bl		60181*	452nd AMW	r/y
	50254	60th AMW	bk/r		60182	452nd AMW	r/y
	50256	445th AW	w/r		60183	62nd AW	gn/r
	50257	452nd AMW	r/y		60184	62nd AW	gn/bl
	50258	459th AW	y/bk		60185	172nd AW	bl
	50259	62nd AW	gn/si		60187	62nd AW	gn/si
	50260	62nd AW			60190	172nd AW	bl
	50261	445th AW	gy/r		60191	172nd AW	bl
	50263	305th AMW	bl		60192	437th AW	y/bl
	50266	305th AMW	bl		60193	452nd AMW	r/y
	50267	62nd AW	gn/r		60194	305th AMW	bl
	50269	437th AW	y/bl		60195	62nd AW	gn/r
	50271*	459th AW	y/bk		60196	305th AMW	bl
	50273	305th AMW	bl		60197	62nd AW	gn/r
	50276	305th AMW	bl		60198	62nd AW	gn/si
	50279	305th AMW	bl		60199	445th AW	w/r
	50280	305th AMW	bl		60201	452nd AMW	r/y
	59401	437th AW	y/bl		60202	305th AMW	bl
	59403	62nd AW	gn/si		60206	62nd AW	gn/bl
	59408	305th AMW	bl		60209	62nd AW	gn/si
	59409	445th AW	w/r		67944	62nd AW	gn/r
	59411	305th AMW	bl		67946	97th AMW	r/y
	59412	445th AW	w/r		67947	437th AW	y/bl
	59413	305th AMW	bl		67948	305th AMW	bl
	59414*	452nd AMW	r/y		67949	62nd AW	gn/bl
	FY66				67950	445th AW	w/r
	60130	172nd AW	bl		67951	62nd AW	gn/r
	60131	437th AW	y/bl		67952*	452nd AMW	r/y
	60132	445th AW	w/r		67953	445th AW	w/r
	60133	305th AMW	bl		67954	445th AW	w/r
	60134	445th AW	w/r		67955	62nd AW	n/si
	60136	452nd AMW	r/y		67956	62nd AW	gn/bl
	60137	62nd AW	m		67957	452nd AMW	r/y
	60139	164th AW	r		67959	445th AW	w/r
	60140	62nd AW	gn/r		*FY67*		
	60144	305th AMW	bl		70001	62nd AW	gn/r
	60146	305th AMW	bl		70002	62nd AW	gn/bl
	60147	62nd AW			70003	437th AW	y/bl
	60148	60th AMW	bk/r		70004	437th AW	y/bl
	60149	62nd AW	gn/r		70007	62nd AW	gn/bk
	60151	452nd AMW	r/y		70010	437th AW	y/bl
	60152*	452nd AMW	r/y		70011	437th AW	y/bl
	60153	459th AW	y/bk		70012	437th AW	y/bl
	60155	437th AW	y/bl		70013	437th AW	y/bl
	60156	62nd AW	gn/bl		70014	437th AW	y/bl
	60157	164th AW	r		70015	452nd AMW	r/y
	60158	62nd AW	gn/bl		70016	305th AMW	bl
	60159	62nd AW	gn/si		70018	62nd AW	gn/bl
	60160	62nd AW	gn/r		70019	305th AMW	bl
	60161	97th AMW	r/y		70020	305th AMW	bl
	60162	305th AMW	bl		70021	164th AW	r
	60163	305th AMW	bl		70022	97th AMW	r/y
	60164	172nd AW	bl		70024*	164th AW	r
	60165	62nd AW	gn/bl		70026	437th AW	y/bl
	60166	305th AMW	bl		70027	459th AW	y/bk
	60167	452nd AMW	r/y		70028	62nd AW	gn/si
	60168	305th AMW	bl		70029	164th AW	r
	60169	305th AMW	bl		70031	445th AW	gy/r
	60171	62nd AW	gn/r		70165	437th AW	y/bl
	60174	459th AW	y/bk		70166	305th AMW (VIP)	
	60175	62nd AW	gn/si				
	60177	445th AW	w/r				

Lockheed P-3 Orion

CinCAFSE, NAF Sigonella, Italy;
CinCLANT/VP-30, NAS Jacksonville, Florida;
CinCPAC/ETD, NAS Barbers Point, Hawaii;
CNO/VP-30, NAS Jacksonville, Florida;
NAF Keflavik, Iceland;
NAS Bermuda;
NAWC 23, Dallas/Love Field, Texas;
NAWC-AD, NAS Patuxent River, Maryland;
Navy Research Lab, Patuxent River, Maryland;
NWTPSPM, NAS Point Mugu, California;
VP-1, NAS Whidbey Island, Washington [YB];
VP-4, NAS Barbers Point, Hawaii [YD];
VP-5, NAS Jacksonville, Florida [LA];
VP-8, NAS Brunswick, Maine [LC];
VP-9, NAS Barbers Point, Hawaii [PD];
VP-10, NAS Brunswick, Maine [LD];
VP-16, NAS Jacksonville, Florida [LF];
VP-26, NAS Brunswick, Maine [LK];
VP-30, NAS Jacksonville, Florida [LL];
VP-40, NAS Whidbey Island, Washington [QE];
VP-45, NAS Jacksonville, Florida [LN];
VP-46, NAS Whidbey Island, Washington [RC];
VP-47, NAS Barbers Point, Hawaii [RD];
VP-62, NAS Jacksonville, Florida [LT];
VP-64, NAS Willow Grove, Pennsylvania [LU];
VP-65, NAS Point Mugu, California [PG];
VP-66, NAS Willow Grove, Pennsylvania [LV];
VP-69, NAS Whidbey Island, Washington [PJ];
VP-92, NAS Brunswick, Maine [LY];
VP-94, NAS New Orleans, Louisiana [PZ];
VPU-1, NAS Brunswick, Maine;
VPU-2, NAS Barbers Point, Hawaii;
VQ-1, NAS Whidbey Island, Washington [PR];
VQ-2, NAF Rota, Spain;
VQ-11, NAS Brunswick, Maine;
VX-1, NAS Patuxent River, Maryland

Serial	Code	Type	Unit
148883		NP-3D	NAWC-AD
149674		RP-3A	NRL
149675		VP-3A	CinCPAC
149676		VP-3A	CNO
150495		UP-3A	NAF Keflavik
150496		VP-3A	CNO
150499	[337]	NP-3D	NWTSPM
150511		VP-3A	CinCAFSE
150515		VP-3A	VP-30
150521	[341]	NP-3D	NWTSPM
150522	[340]	NP-3D	NWTSPM
150524	[335]	NP-3D	NWTSPM
150525	[336]	NP-3D	NWTSPM
150526	[PR-01]	UP-3A	VQ-1
150605		UP-3A	CinCPAC
151367		UP-3A	NAS Bermuda
151376		TP-3A	CinCPAC
151392	[LL-20]	TP-3A	VP-30
152150		NP-3D	NAWC-AD
152169		UP-3A	VPU-2
152719	[LV-719]	EP-3J	VP-66
152727	[PR-43]	UP-3B	VQ-1
152739		NP-3B	NAWC 23
153433	[PR-44]	UP-3B	VQ-1
153442		EP-3B	NRL
153443		RP-3D	NWTPSPM
153450		P-3B	VPU-1
154577		P-3B	VPU-1
154585	[SP]	P-3B	VPU-2
154587		RP-3D	NRL
154589		EP-3B	NRL
156507	[PR-31]	EP-3E	VQ-1
156508	[LK-508]	P-3C	VP-26
156509	[509]	P-3C	VPU-1
156510	[LL-44]	P-3C	VP-30
156511	[PR-32]	EP-3E	VQ-1
156514	[PR-33]	EP-3E	VQ-1
156515	[LF-515]	P-3C	VP-16
156516	[LL-38]	P-3C	VP-30
156517	[PR-34]	EP-3E	VQ-1
156518	[LL-49]	P-3C	VP-30
156520	[10]	P-3C	VQ-2
156521		P-3C	
156522	[LL-46]	P-3C	VP-30
156523	[LL-39]	P-3C	VP-30
156525	[11]	P-3C	VQ-2
156527	[LT-527]	P-3C	VP-62
156528	[PR-36]	EP-3E	VQ-1
156529	[24]	EP-3E	VQ-2
156530	[LL-45]	P-3C	VP-30
157310	[LA-310]	P-3C	VP-5
157311	[LA-311]	P-3C	VP-5
157312	[LN-312]	P-3C	VP-45
157313	[LD-313]	P-3C	VP-10
157314	[LD-314]	P-3C	VP-10
157315	[LD-315]	P-3C	VP-10
157316	[23]	EP-3E	VQ-2
157317		P-3C	
157318	[PR-35]	EP-3E	VQ-1
157319	[LK-319]	P-3C	VP-26
157320	[21]	EP-3E	VQ-2
157321	[LK-321]	P-3C	VP-26
157322	[322]	P-3C	VP-40
157323		P-3C	
157324	[YD]	P-3C	VP-4
157325	[25]	EP-3E	VQ-2
157326	[22]	EP-3E	VQ-2
157327	[LD-327]	P-3C	VP-10
157328	[LL-42]	P-3C	VP-30
157329	[YD-329]	P-3C	VP-4
157330	[LC-330]	P-3C	VP-8
157331	[LL-47]	P-3C	VP-30
158204		P-3C	NAWC-AD
158205	[YB-205]	P-3C	VP-1
158206	[JA-03]	P-3C	VX-1
158207	[LC-207]	P-3C	VP-8
158208		P-3C	
158209	[YB-209]	P-3C	VP-1
158210	[LD-210]	P-3C	VP-11
158211	[211]	P-3C	VP-1
158212	[212]	P-3C	VP-1
158214	[LL-48]	P-3C	VP-30
158215	[QE-215]	P-3C	VP-40
158216	[216]	P-3C	VP-1
158217	[RC]	P-3C	VP-46
158218	[YD-218]	P-3C	VP-4
158219	[LN-219]	P-3C	VP-45
158220		P-3C	VP-47
158221	[221]	P-3C	VP-46
158222	[222]	P-3C	VP-69
158223	[YD-223]	P-3C	VP-4
158224	[LK-224]	P-3C	VP-26
158225	[PD-225]	P-3C	VP-9
158226	[LT-226]	P-3C	VP-62
158227	[227]	RP-3D	NRL
158563	[LA-563]	P-3C	VP-5
158564	[LK-564]	P-3C	VP-26
158565	[LN-565]	P-3C	VP-45
158566	[LA-566]	P-3C	VP-5
158567	[LF-567]	P-3C	VP-16
158568	[LC-568]	P-3C	VP-8
158569	[LA-569]	P-3C	VP-5
158570	[LN-570]	P-3C	VP-45

USN/USMC

158571	[LA-571]	P-3C	VP-5
158572	[LA-572]	P-3C	VP-5
158573	[LD-573]	P-3C	VP-10
158574		P-3C	NAWC-23
158912		P-3C	NAWC-AD
158913	[YD-913]	P-3C	VP-4
158914	[914]	P-3C	VP-40
158915	[915]	P-3C	VP-40
158916	[LD-916]	P-3C	VP-10
158917	[LC-917]	P-3C	VP-8
158918		P-3C	
158919	[LN-919]	P-3C	VP-45
158920	[LF-920]	P-3C	VP-16
158921	[LY-921]	P-3C	VP-92
158922	[LA-922]	P-3C	VP-5
158923	[LC-923]	P-3C	VP-8
158924	[LF-924]	P-3C	VP-16
158925	[LD-925]	P-3C	VP-10
158926	[LD-926]	P-3C	VP-10
158927	[927]	P-3C	VP-16
158929		P-3C	
158931		P-3C	
158932	[LN-932]	P-3C	VP-45
158933	[933]	P-3C	VP-10
158934		P-3C	
158935	[LL-43]	P-3C	VP-30
159318	[LA-318]	P-3C	VP-5
159319	[LK-319]	P-3C	VP-26
159320	[LC-320]	P-3C	VP-8
159321	[YD-321]	P-3C	VP-4
159322	[LD-322]	P-3C	VP-10
159323	[PM-323]	P-3C	VP-91
159324	[PD-324]	P-3C	VP-9
159326	[326]	P-3C	VP-40
159327	[PD-327]	P-3C	VP-9
159328	[328]	P-3C	VP-40
159329		P-3C	
159503	[503]	P-3C	VP-16
159504	[SP]	P-3C	VPU-2
159506	[506]	P-3C	VPU-1
159507	[QE-507]	P-3C	VP-40
159511		P-3C	
159512	[LL-16]	P-3C	VP-30
159513	[LL-18]	P-3C	VP-30
159514	[LL-19]	P-3C	VP-30
159884	[LL-14]	P-3C	VP-30
159885		P-3C	
159886	[LL-15]	P-3C	VP-30
159887	[JA-04]	P-3C	VX-1
159889	[LL-41]	P-3C	VP-30
159890		P-3C	
159891	[LF-891]	P-3C	VP-16
159894	[LA-894]	P-3C	VP-5
160283	[YB-283]	P-3C	VP-1
160284	[LL-17]	P-3C	VP-30
160286	[286]	P-3C	VP-26
160287	[LF-287]	P-3C	VP-16
160288		P-3C	VPU-2
160290		P-3C	NAWC-AD
160291	[JA-05]	P-3C	VX-1
160292		P-3C	VPU-1
160293	[293]	P-3C	VPU-2
160610	[LF-610]	P-3C	VP-16
160611	[LT-611]	P-3C	VP-62
160612	[LV-612]	P-3C	VP-66
160761	[LU-761]	P-3C	VP-64
160762	[LY-762]	P-3C	VP-92
160763	[LV-763]	P-3C	VP-66
160764	[LF-764]	P-3C	VP-16
160765	[LK-765]	P-3C	VP-26
160766	[PJ-766]	P-3C	VP-69
160767	[767]	P-3C	VP-66
160768	[LU-768]	P-3C	VP-64
160769	[LC-769]	P-3C	VP-8
160770		P-3C	VPU-1
160999	[LP-999]	P-3C	VQ-11
161000	[000]	P-3C	
161001	[LU-001]	P-3C	VP-64
161002	[LN-002]	P-3C	VP-45
161003	[PJ-003]	P-3C	VP-69
161004	[LD-004]	P-3C	VP-10
161005	[LU-005]	P-3C	VP-64
161006	[LL-51]	P-3C	VP-30
161007	[LU-007]	P-3C	VP-64
161008	[LU-008]	P-3C	VP-64
161009	[LL-50]	P-3C	VP-30
161010	[LK-010]	P-3C	VP-26
161011	[LK-011]	P-3C	VP-26
161012		P-3C	
161013	[LV-013]	P-3C	VP-66
161014	[LV-014]	P-3C	VP-66
161121	[PJ-121]	P-3C	VP-69
161122	[LU-122]	P-3C	VP-64
161123		P-3C	
161124	[LA-124]	P-3C	VP-5
161125	[LV-125]	P-3C	VP-66
161126	[PR-50]	P-3C	VQ-1
161127	[LV-127]	P-3C	VP-66
161128	[LF-128]	P-3C	VP-16
161129	[LV-129]	P-3C	VP-66
161130	[130]	P-3C	VP-1
161131	[LV-131]	P-3C	VP-66
161132		P-3C	
161329	[PG-329]	P-3C	VP-65
161330		P-3C	
161331	[LY-331]	P-3C	VP-92
161332	[PG-332]	P-3C	VP-65
161333	[LY-333]	P-3C	VP-92
161334	[LY-334]	P-3C	VP-92
161335	[LY-335]	P-3C	VP-92
161336	[LY-336]	P-3C	VP-92
161337	[LT-337]	P-3C	VP-62
161338	[LN-338]	P-3C	VP-45
161339	[YD-339]	P-3C	VP-40
161340	[LN-340]	P-3C	VP-45
161404	[LY-404]	P-3C	VP-92
161405		P-3C	VX-1
161406	[PG-406]	P-3C	VP-65
161407	[PG-407]	P-3C	VP-65
161408	[LK-408]	P-3C	VP-26
161409	[LY-409]	P-3C	VP-92
161410		P-3C	NAWC 23
161411	[PG-411]	P-3C	VP-65
161412	[PG-412]	P-3C	VP-65
161413	[PG-413]	P-3C	VP-65
161414	[PG-414]	P-3C	VP-65
161415		P-3C	VP-30
161585	[LY-585]	P-3C	VP-92
161586	[LY-586]	P-3C	VP-92
161587	[587]	P-3C	VP-69
161588	[PZ-588]	P-3C	VP-94
161589	[RD-589]	P-3C	VP-47
161590	[PG-590]	P-3C	VP-65
161591	[PZ-591]	P-3C	VP-94
161592	[PZ-592]	P-3C	VP-94
161593	[PZ-593]	P-3C	VP-94
161594	[PZ-594]	P-3C	VP-94
161595	[PZ-595]	P-3C	VP-94
161596	[PZ-596]	P-3C	VP-94
161763		P-3C	
161764	[QE-764]	P-3C	VP-40
161765	[PJ-765]	P-3C	VP-69
161766		P-3C	
161767	[PD-767]	P-3C	VP-9
162314	[QE-314]	P-3C	VP-40
162315	[315]	P-3C	VP-40
162316	[316]	P-3C	VPU-1
162317	[317]	P-3C	VP-46

162318		P-3C	
162770		P-3C	NAWC-AD
162771	[YD-771]	P-3C	VP-4
162772	[772]	P-3C	VP-46
162773	[773]	P-3C	VP-40
162774		P-3C	
162775	[PD-775]	P-3C	VP-9
162776	[LN-776]	P-3C	VP-45
162777	[LT-777]	P-3C	VP-62
162778	[LL-31]	P-3C	VP-30
162998	[RD-998]	P-3C	VP-47
162999	[YD-999]	P-3C	VP-4
163000	[PJ-000]	P-3C	VP-69
163001	[LT-001]	P-3C	VP-62
163002	[LT-002]	P-3C	VP-62
163003	[LT-003]	P-3C	VP-62
163004	[LT-004]	P-3C	VP-62
163005	[LT-005]	P-3C	VP-62
163006	[JA-06]	P-3C	VX-1
163289	[LT-289]	P-3C	VP-62
163290	[PJ-290]	P-3C	VP-69
163291		P-3C	
163292	[LF-292]	P-3C	VP-16
163293	[LA-293]	P-3C	VP-5
163294		P-3C	
163295		P-3C	

Boeing E-6 Mercury

Boeing, McConnell AFB, Kansas;
VQ-3 & VQ-4, Sea Control Wing 1
 (SCW-1), Tinker AFB, Oklahoma

162782	E-6A	VQ-4
162783	E-6B	VQ-3
162784	E-6A	VQ-3
163918	E-6B	VQ-3
163919	E-6B	VQ-3
163920	E-6A	VQ-3
164386	E-6A	VQ-3
164387	E-6B	VQ-3
164388	E-6B	VQ-3
164404	E-6A	VQ-4
164405	E-6A	VQ-4
164406	E-6B	Boeing
164407	E-6A	VQ-4
164408	E-6A	VQ-4
164409	E-6B	VQ-4
164410	E-6A	VQ-4

McDonnell Douglas C-9B Skytrain II/DC-9-32*

VMR-1, Cherry Point MCAS, North Carolina;
VR-46, Atlanta, Georgia [JS];
VR-51, Glenview NAS, Illinois [RV];
VR-52, Willow Grove NAS, Pennsylvania [JT];
VR-56, Norfolk NAS, Virginia [JU];
VR-57, North Island NAS, California [RX];
VR-58, Jacksonville NAS, Florida [JV];
VR-59, Dallas, Texas [RY];
VR-60, Memphis NAS, Tennessee [RT];
VR-61, Whidbey Island NAS, Washington [RS];
VR-62, South Weymouth NAS, Massachusetts [JW]

159113	[RX]	VR-57
159114	[JS]	VR-46
159115	[RX]	VR-57
159116	[RX]	VR-57
159117	[JU]	VR-56
159118	[JU]	VR-56
159119	[JU]	VR-56
159120	[JU]	VR-56
160046		VMR-1
160047		VMR-1
160048	[JV]	VR-58
160049	[JV]	VR-58
160050	[JV]	VR-58
160051	[JV]	VR-58

161266	[RY]	VR-59
161529	[RY]	VR-59
161530	[RY]	VR-59
162753	[JT]	VR-52
162754	[JT]	VR-52
163036*	[JT]	VR-52
163037*	[JT]	VR-52
163208*	[RY]	VR-59
163511*	[JS]	VR-46
163512*	[JT]	VR-52
163513*	[JV]	VR-58
164605*	[RS]	VR-61
164606*	[RS]	VR-61
164607*	[RS]	VR-61
164608*	[RS]	VR-61

Boeing TC-18F

Sea Control Wing 1 (SCW-1),
 Tinker AFB, Oklahoma

165342
165343

Grumman C-20D Gulfstream III/ C-20G Gulfstream IV*

VR-1, NAF Washington, Maryland;
VR-48, NAF Washington, Maryland [JR];
VR-51, MCAF Kaneohe Bay, Hawaii

163691		VR-1
163692		VR-1
165093*	[JR]	VR-48
165094*	[JR]	VR-48
165151*		VR-51
165152*		VR-51

Lockheed C-130 Hercules

NAWC-AD, NAS Patuxent River, Maryland;
VR-53, Martinsburg, West Virginia [WV];
VR-54, New Orleans NAS, Louisiana [CW];
VR-55, Moffett Field NAS, California [RU];
VR-62, Brunswick NAS, Maine [JW];
VMGR-152, Futenma MCAS, Japan [QD];
VMGR-234, NAS Fort Worth, Texas [QH];
VMGR-252, Cherry Point MCAS, North Carolina
 [BH];
VMGRT-253, Cherry Point MCAS, North Carolina
 [GR];
VMGR-352, El Toro MCAS, California [QB];
VMGR-452, Stewart Field, New York [NY]

147572	[QB]	KC-130F	VMGR-352
147573	[QD]	KC-130F	VMGR-152
148246	[GR]	KC-130F	VMGRT-253
148247	[QD]	KC-130F	VMGR-152
148248	[QD]	KC-130F	VMGR-152
148249	[GR]	KC-130F	VMGRT-253
148890	[GR]	KC-130F	VMGRT-253
148891	[BH]	KC-130F	VMGR-252
148893	[QD]	KC-130F	VMGR-152
148894	[BH]	KC-130F	VMGR-252
148895	[BH]	KC-130F	VMGR-252
148896	[BH]	KC-130F	VMGR-252
148897	[BH]	KC-130F	VMGR-252
148898	[BH]	KC-130F	VMGR-252
148899	[BH]	KC-130F	VMGR-252
149788	[BH]	KC-130F	VMGR-252
149789	[BH]	KC-130F	VMGR-252
149791	[QB]	KC-130F	VMGR-352
149792	[QB]	KC-130F	VMGR-352
149795	[QB]	KC-130F	VMGR-352
149796	[QB]	KC-130F	VMGR-352
149798	[QB]	KC-130F	VMGR-352
149799	[QD]	KC-130F	VMGR-152
149800	[QB]	KC-130F	VMGR-352
149803	[GR]	KC-130F	VMGRT-253
149804	[GR]	KC-130F	VMGRT-253

USN/USMC

149806		KC-130F	NAWC		163591	[NY]	KC-130T	VMGR-452
149807	[QD]	KC-130F	VMGR-152		163592	[NY]	KC-130T	VMGR-452
149808	[BH]	KC-130F	VMGR-252		164105	[NY]	KC-130T	VMGR-452
149811	[GR]	KC-130F	VMGRT-253		164106	[NY]	KC-130T	VMGR-452
149812	[QD]	KC-130F	VMGR-152		164180	[NY]	KC-130T	VMGR-452
149815	[QB]	KC-130F	VMGR-352		164181	[NY]	KC-130T	VMGR-452
149816	[QD]	KC-130F	VMGR-152		164441	[QH]	KC-130T	VMGR-234
150684	[GR]	KC-130F	VMGRT-253		164442	[NY]	KC-130T	VMGR-452
150686	[BH]	KC-130F	VMGR-252		164597	[NY]	KC-130T-30	VMGR-452
150687	[GR]	KC-130F	VMGRT-253		164598	[QH]	KC-130T-30	VMGR-234
150688	[GR]	KC-130F	VMGRT-253		164762		C-130T	NAWC-AD
150689	[QB]	KC-130F	VMGR-352		164763		C-130T	NAWC-AD
150690	[QD]	KC-130F	VMGR-152		164993	[CW]	C-130T	VR-54
151891		TC-130G	*Blue Angels*		164994	[WV]	C-130T	VR-53
160013	[QD]	KC-130R	VMGR-152		164995	[CW]	C-130T	VR-54
160014	[QD]	KC-130R	VMGR-152		164996	[WV]	C-130T	VR-53
160015	[QB]	KC-130R	VMGR-352		164997	[WV]	C-130T	VR-53
160016	[QB]	KC-130R	VMGR-352		164998	[WV]	C-130T	VR-53
160017	[QB]	KC-130R	VMGR-352		164999	[QH]	KC-130T	VMGR-234
160018	[QD]	KC-130R	VMGR-152		165000	[QH]	KC-130T	VMGR-234
160019	[QD]	KC-130R	VMGR-152		165158	[CW]	C-130T	VR-54
160020	[QD]	KC-130R	VMGR-152		165159	[CW]	C-130T	VR-54
160021	[QB]	KC-130R	VMGR-352		165160	[CW]	C-130T	VR-54
160022	[QB]	KC-130R	VMGR-352		165161	[RU]	C-130T	VR-55
160240	[QB]	KC-130R	VMGR-352		165162	[QH]	KC-130T	VMGR-234
160625	[BH]	KC-130R	VMGR-252		165163	[QH]	KC-130T	VMGR-234
160626	[BH]	KC-130R	VMGR-252		165313	[JW]	C-130T	VR-62
160627	[BH]	KC-130R	VMGR-252		165314	[JW]	C-130T	VR-62
160628	[BH]	KC-130R	VMGR-252		165315	[NY]	KC-130T	VMGR-452
162308	[QH]	KC-130T	VMGR-234		165316	[NY]	KC-130T	VMGR-452
162309	[QH]	KC-130T	VMGR-234		165348	[JW]	C-130T	VR-62
162310	[QH]	KC-130T	VMGR-234		165349	[JW]	C-130T	VR-62
162311	[QH]	KC-130T	VMGR-234		165350	[RU]	C-130T	VR-55
162785	[QH]	KC-130T	VMGR-234		165351	[RU]	C-130T	VR-55
162786	[QH]	KC-130T	VMGR-234		165352	[NY]	KC-130T	VMGR-452
163022	[QH]	KC-130T	VMGR-234		165353	[NY]	KC-130T	VMGR-452
163023	[QH]	KC-130T	VMGR-234		165378	[RU]	C-130T	VR-55
163310	[QH]	KC-130T	VMGR-234		165379	[RU]	C-130T	VR-55
163311	[QH]	KC-130T	VMGR-234					

US based US Coast Guard Aircraft

Lockheed HC-130H Hercules
USCGS Barbers Point, Hawaii;
USCGS Clearwater, Florida;
USCGS Elizabeth City, North Carolina;
USCGS Kodiak, Alaska;
USCGS Sacramento, California

1500	Elizabeth City
1501	Elizabeth City
1502	Elizabeth City
1503	Elizabeth City
1504	Elizabeth City
1601	Sacramento
1602	Barbers Point
1603	Sacramentot
1700	Kodiak
1701	Kodiak
1702	Barbers Point
1703	Sacramento
1704	Barbers Point
1705	Sacramento
1706	Kodiak
1707	Kodiak
1708	Kodiak
1709	Sacramento
1710	Kodiak
1711	Barbers Point
1712	Clearwater
1713	Clearwater
1714	Barbers Point
1715	Clearwater
1716	Clearwater
1717	Clearwater
1718	Clearwater
1719	Clearwater
1720	Clearwater
1790	Sacramento

Grumman G1159A Gulfstream III
USCG Andrew's AFB, Maryland
01

Aircraft in Government or Military Service with Civil Registrations

Serial	Type (other identity)	Owner/operator, location	Notes
UNITED KINGDOM			
G-AZXA	Beech C55 Baron	FR Aviation, Bournemouth	
G-BLVI	Slingsby T.67M Firefly 2	Hunting Aircraft Ltd, Newton/Cranwell	
G-BNSO	Slingsby T.67M Firefly 2	Hunting Aircraft Ltd/JEFTS, Barkston Heath	
G-BNSP	Slingsby T.67M Firefly 2	Hunting Aircraft Ltd/JEFTS, Barkston Heath	
G-BNSR	Slingsby T.67M Firefly 2	Hunting Aircraft Ltd/JEFTS, Barkston Heath	
G-BUUA	Slingsby T.67M Firefly 2	Hunting Aircraft Ltd/JEFTS, Newton	
G-BUUB	Slingsby T.67M Firefly 2	Hunting Aircraft Ltd/JEFTS, Newton	
G-BUUC	Slingsby T.67M Firefly 2	Hunting Aircraft Ltd/JEFTS, Newton	
G-BUUD	Slingsby T.67M Firefly 2	Hunting Aircraft Ltd/JEFTS, Newton	
G-BUUE	Slingsby T.67M Firefly 2	Hunting Aircraft Ltd/JEFTS, Newton	
G-BUUF	Slingsby T.67M Firefly 2	Hunting Aircraft Ltd/JEFTS, Newton	
G-BUUG	Slingsby T.67M Firefly 2	Hunting Aircraft Ltd/JEFTS, Newton	
G-BUUI	Slingsby T.67M Firefly 2	Hunting Aircraft Ltd/JEFTS, Newton	
G-BUUJ	Slingsby T.67M Firefly 2	Hunting Aircraft Ltd/JEFTS, Newton	
G-BUUK	Slingsby T.67M Firefly 2	Hunting Aircraft Ltd/JEFTS, Newton	
G-BUUL	Slingsby T.67M Firefly 2	Hunting Aircraft Ltd/JEFTS, Newton	
G-BVHC	Grob G.115D-2 Heron	Shorts Bros/NFGF, Plymouth	
G-BVHD	Grob G.115D-2 Heron	Shorts Bros/NFGF, Plymouth	
G-BVHE	Grob G.115D-2 Heron	Shorts Bros/NFGF, Plymouth	
G-BVHF	Grob G.115D-2 Heron	Shorts Bros/NFGF, Plymouth	
G-BVHG	Grob G.115D-2 Heron	Shorts Bros/NFGF, Plymouth	
G-BVXW	Short SC7 Skyvan 3A-100	Hunting Aircraft Ltd, Weston-on-the-Green	
G-BWXA	Slingsby T.67M Firefly 260	Hunting Aircraft Ltd/JEFTS, Barkston Heath	
G-BWXB	Slingsby T.67M Firefly 260	Hunting Aircraft Ltd/JEFTS, Barkston Heath	
G-BWXC	Slingsby T.67M Firefly 260	Hunting Aircraft Ltd/JEFTS, Barkston Heath	
G-BWXD	Slingsby T.67M Firefly 260	Hunting Aircraft Ltd/JEFTS, Barkston Heath	
G-BWXE	Slingsby T.67M Firefly 260	Hunting Aircraft Ltd/JEFTS, Barkston Heath	
G-BWXF	Slingsby T.67M Firefly 260	Hunting Aircraft Ltd/JEFTS, Barkston Heath	
G-BWXG	Slingsby T.67M Firefly 260	Hunting Aircraft Ltd/JEFTS, Barkston Heath	
G-BWXH	Slingsby T.67M Firefly 260	Hunting Aircraft Ltd/JEFTS, Barkston Heath	
G-BWXI	Slingsby T.67M Firefly 260	Hunting Aircraft Ltd/JEFTS, Barkston Heath	
G-BWXJ	Slingsby T.67M Firefly 260	Hunting Aircraft Ltd/JEFTS, Barkston Heath	
G-BWXK	Slingsby T.67M Firefly 260	Hunting Aircraft Ltd/JEFTS, Barkston Heath	
G-BWXL	Slingsby T.67M Firefly 260	Hunting Aircraft Ltd/JEFTS, Barkston Heath	
G-BWXM	Slingsby T.67M Firefly 260	Hunting Aircraft Ltd/JEFTS, Barkston Heath	
G-BWXN	Slingsby T.67M Firefly 260	Hunting Aircraft Ltd/JEFTS, Barkston Heath	
G-BWXO	Slingsby T.67M Firefly 260	Hunting Aircraft Ltd/JEFTS, Barkston Heath	
G-BWXP	Slingsby T.67M Firefly 260	Hunting Aircraft Ltd/JEFTS, Barkston Heath	
G-BWXR	Slingsby T.67M Firefly 260	Hunting Aircraft Ltd/JEFTS, Barkston Heath	
G-BWXS	Slingsby T.67M Firefly 260 [6]	Hunting Aircraft Ltd/JEFTS, Barkston Heath	
G-BWXT	Slingsby T.67M Firefly 260	Hunting Aircraft Ltd/JEFTS, Barkston Heath	
G-BWXU	Slingsby T.67M Firefly 260	Hunting Aircraft Ltd/JEFTS, Barkston Heath	
G-BWXV	Slingsby T.67M Firefly 260	Hunting Aircraft Ltd/JEFTS, Barkston Heath	
G-BWXW	Slingsby T.67M Firefly 260	Hunting Aircraft Ltd/JEFTS, Barkston Heath	
G-BWXX	Slingsby T.67M Firefly 260	Hunting Aircraft Ltd/JEFTS, Barkston Heath	
G-BWXY	Slingsby T.67M Firefly 260	Hunting Aircraft Ltd/JEFTS, Barkston Heath	
G-BWXZ	Slingsby T.67M Firefly 260	Hunting Aircraft Ltd/JEFTS, Barkston Heath	
G-FCAL	Cessna 441 Conquest	FR Aviation, Bournemouth	
G-FFRA	Dassault Falcon 20DC (N902FR)	FR Aviation, Bournemouth	
G-FPLA	Beechcraft Super King Air B200	FR Aviation, Bournemouth	
G-FPLB	Beechcraft Super King Air B200	FR Aviation, Bournemouth	
G-FRAD	Dassault Falcon 20E (G-BCYF)	FR Aviation, Bournemouth	
G-FRAE	Dassault Falcon 20E (N910FR)	FR Aviation, Bournemouth	
G-FRAF	Dassault Falcon 20E (N911FR)	FR Aviation, Bournemouth	
G-FRAH	Dassault Falcon 20DC (N900FR)	FR Aviation, Bournemouth	
G-FRAI	Dassault Falcon 20E (N901FR)	FR Aviation, Bournemouth	
G-FRAJ	Dassault Falcon 20E (N903FR)	FR Aviation, Bournemouth	
G-FRAL	Dassault Falcon 20DC (N904FR)	FR Aviation, Bournemouth	
G-FRAM	Dassault Falcon 20DC (N907FR)	FR Aviation, Bournemouth	
G-FRAO	Dassault Falcon 20DC (N906FR)	FR Aviation, Bournemouth	

Civil Registrations

Notes	Serial	Type (other identity)	Owner/operator, location
	G-FRAP	Dassault Falcon 20DC (N908FR)	FR Aviation, Bournemouth
	G-FRAR	Dassault Falcon 20DC (N909FR)	FR Aviation, Bournemouth
	G-FRAS	Dassault Falcon 20C (117501)	FR Aviation, Bournemouth
	G-FRAT	Dassault Falcon 20C (117502)	FR Aviation, Bournemouth
	G-FRAU	Dassault Falcon 20C (117504)	FR Aviation, Bournemouth
	G-FRAW	Dassault Falcon 20ECM (117507)	FR Aviation, Bournemouth
	G-FRAX	Cessna 441 Conquest	FR Aviation, Bournemouth
	G-FRAZ	Cessna 441 Conquest	FR Aviation, Bournemouth
	G-FRBA	Dassault Falcon 20C	FR Aviation, Bournemouth
	G-FRBY	Beech E55 Baron	FR Aviation, Bournemouth
	G-HONG	Slingsby T.67M Firefly 2	Hunting Aircraft Ltd/JEFTS, Newton
	G-KONG	Slingsby T.67M Firefly 2	Hunting Aircraft Ltd/JEFTS, Newton
	G-MAFA	Cessna F406 Caravan II	Directflight, Prestwick
	G-MAFB	Cessna F406 Caravan II	Directflight, Prestwick
	G-PIGY	Short SC7 Skyvan 3A-100	Hunting Aircraft Ltd, Weston-on-the-Green
	G-SFPA	Cessna F406 Caravan II	Scottish Fisheries Protection Agency, Prestwick
	G-SFPB	Cessna F406 Caravan II	Scottish Fisheries Protection Agency, Prestwick
	G-XXEA	Sikorsky S-76C	Air Hanson/The Royal Flight, Blackbushe

ALGERIA

Notes	Serial	Type (other identity)	Owner/operator, location
	7T-VPA	Dassault Falcon 900 (81)	Ministry of Defence, Boufarik
	7T-VPB	Dassault Falcon 900 (82)	Ministry of Defence, Boufarik
	7T-VPR	G.1159C Gulfstream IVSP (1288)	Ministry of Defence, Boufarik
	7T-VPS	G.1159C Gulfstream IVSP (1291)	Ministry of Defence, Boufarik
	7T-VRB	G.1159A Gulfstream III (368)	Ministry of Defence, Boufarik
	7T-VRD	G.1159A Gulfstream III (399)	Ministry of Defence, Boufarik

BAHRAIN

Notes	Serial	Type (other identity)	Owner/operator, location
	A9C-BA	Boeing 727-2M7	Govt of Bahrain
	A9C-BB	G.1159A Gulfstream III	Govt of Bahrain
	A9C-BG	G.1159 Gulfstream IIIT	Govt of Bahrain

BRUNEI

Notes	Serial	Type (other identity)	Owner/operator, location
	V8-001	Gulfstream V (V8-009)	Brunei Govt, Bandar Seri Bergawan
	V8-007	Gulfstream V (82)	Brunei Govt, Bandar Seri Bergawan
	V8-AC1	Boeing 747SP-21 (V8-JBB/ V8-JP1)	Brunei Govt, Bandar Seri Bergawan
	V8-AL1	Boeing 747-430	Brunei Govt, Bandar Seri Bergawan
	V8-AM1	Airbus A.340-211 (V8-BKH/ V8-JP1)	Brunei Govt, Bandar Seri Bergawan
	V8-BKH	Airbus A.340-212 (V8-PJB)	Brunei Govt, Bandar Seri Bergawan
	V8-JBB	Airbus A.340-213	Brunei Govt, Bandar Seri Bergawan
	V8-MJB	Boeing 767-27GER	Brunei Govt, Bandar Seri Bergawan

BULGARIA

Notes	Serial	Type (other identity)	Owner/operator, location
	LZ-BTQ	Tupolev Tu-154M	Bulgarian Govt, Sofia

BURKINA FASO

Notes	Serial	Type (other identity)	Owner/operator, location
	XT-BBE	Boeing 727-14	Govt of Burkina Faso, Ouagadougou

CAMEROON

Notes	Serial	Type (other identity)	Owner/operator, location
	TJ-AAW	G.1159A Gulfstream III	Govt of Cameroon, Yaounde

CROATIA

Notes	Serial	Type (other identity)	Owner/operator, location
	9A-CRO	Canadair CL.601 Challenger	Croatian Govt, Zagreb
	9A-CRT	Canadair CL.601 Challenger (9A-CRO)	Croatian Govt, Zagreb

CZECH REPUBLIC

Notes	Serial	Type (other identity)	Owner/operator, location
	OK-BYA	Canadair CL.601-3A Challenger	Czech Govt, Praha/Kbely
	OK-BYF	Let L-410UVP-E	Czech Govt, Praha/Kbely
	OK-BYJ	Yakovlev Yak-40	Czech Govt, Praha/Kbely
	OK-BYK	Yakovlev Yak-40	Czech Govt, Praha/Kbely
	OK-BYZ	Tupolev Tu-154M	Czech Govt, Praha/Kbely

Serial	Type (other identity)	Owner/operator, location	Notes
EGYPT			
SU-AXJ	Boeing 707-366C	Egyptian Govt, Cairo	
SU-BGM	G.1159C Gulfstream IV	Egyptian Air Force/Govt, Cairo	
SU-BGU	G.1159A Gulfstream III	Egyptian Air Force/Govt, Cairo	
SU-BGV	G.1159A Gulfstream III	Egyptian Air Force/Govt, Cairo	
SU-BNC	G.1159C Gulfstream IV	Egyptian Air Force/Govt, Cairo	
SU-BND	G.1159C Gulfstream IV	Egyptian Air Force/Govt, Cairo	
SU-GGG	Airbus A.340-211	Egyptian Govt, Cairo	
FRANCE			
F-GPAA	Dassault Falcon 20ECM (117505/G-FRAV)	AVDEF, Nimes-Garons	
F-GPAB	Dassault Falcon 20E (G-FRAC)	AVDEF, Nimes-Garons	
F-SEBK	Aérospatiale ATR-42-320 (264)	CNET, Rennes	
F-ZBAB	Cessna F406 Caravan II (0025)	Douanes Francaises	
F-ZBBB	Cessna F406 Caravan II (0039)	Douanes Francaises	
F-ZBCE	Cessna F406 Caravan II (0042)	Douanes Francaises	
F-ZBCF	Cessna F406 Caravan II (0077)	Douanes Francaises	
F-ZBCG	Cessna F406 Caravan II (0066)	Douanes Francaises	
F-ZBCH	Cessna F406 Caravan II (0075)	Douanes Francaises	
F-ZBCI	Cessna F406 Caravan II (0070)	Douanes Francaises	
F-ZBCJ	Cessna F406 Caravan II (0074)	Douanes Francaises	
F-ZBDY	Cessna 404 Titan (0815)	Douanes Francaises	
F-ZBEF	AS355F-1 Twin Ecureuil (5236)	Douanes Francaises	
F-ZBEJ	AS355F-1 Twin Ecureuil (5003)	Douanes Francaises	
F-ZBEK	AS355F-1 Twin Ecureuil (5298)	Douanes Francaises	
F-ZBEL	AS355F-1 Twin Ecureuil (5299)	Douanes Francaises	
F-ZBEP	Cessna F406 Caravan II (0006)	Douanes Francaises	
F-ZBES	Cessna F406 Caravan II (0017)	Douanes Francaises	
F-ZBFA	Cessna F406 Caravan II (0001)	Douanes Francaises	
GREECE			
SX-ECH	Dassault Falcon 900	Greek Govt/Olympic Airways, Athens	
ISRAEL			
4X-COV	Hawker 800XP	Israeli Govt, Tel Aviv	
ITALY			
I-CNEF	Dassault Falcon 200	Italian Govt/Soc. CAI, Roma-Ciampino	
I-DIES	Dassault Falcon 900	Italian Govt/Soc. CAI, Roma-Ciampino	
I-FICV	Dassault Falcon 900	Italian Govt/Soc. CAI, Roma-Ciampino	
I-NUMI	Dassault Falcon 900	Italian Govt/Soc. CAI, Roma-Ciampino	
I-SAME	Dassault Falcon 50	Italian Govt/Soc. CAI, Roma-Ciampino	
I-SOBE	Dassault Falcon 200	Italian Govt/Soc. CAI, Roma-Ciampino	
IVORY COAST			
TU-VAA	Fokker 100	Ivory Coast Govt, Abidjan	
JORDAN			
JY-HKJ	L.1011 TriStar 500	Govt of Jordan, Amman	
JY-RAY	G.1159C Gulfstream IVSP	Govt of Jordan, Amman	
JY-RNA	Extra EA-300S	Royal Jordanian Falcons, Amman	
JY-RNC	Extra EA-300S	Royal Jordanian Falcons, Amman	
JY-RND	Extra EA-300S	Royal Jordanian Falcons, Amman	
JY-RNE	Extra EA-300S	Royal Jordanian Falcons, Amman	
JY-RNG	Extra EA-300S	Royal Jordanian Falcons, Amman	
KAZAKHSTAN			
P4-NSN	Boeing 757-2M6	Govt of Kazakhstan, Almaty	
KUWAIT			
9K-AGC	McDD MD.83	Kuwaiti Govt, Safat	
9K-AJA	G.1159C Gulfstream IV	Kuwaiti Govt/Kuwaiti Airways, Safat	
9K-AJB	G.1159C Gulfstream IV	Kuwaiti Govt/Kuwaiti Airways, Safat	
9K-AJC	G.1159C Gulfstream IV	Kuwaiti Govt/Kuwaiti Airways, Safat	
9K-ALD	Airbus A.310-308	Kuwaiti Govt, Safat	
KYRGYZSTAN			
EX-65119	Tupolev Tu.134A-3	Govt of Kyrgyzstan, Bishkek	
EX-85294	Tupolev Tu.154B	Govt of Kyrgyzstan, Bishkek	
EX-85718	Tupolev Tu.154M	Govt of Kyrgyzstan, Bishkek	
EX-85762	Tupolev Tu.154M	Govt of Kyrgyzstan, Bishkek	

Civil Registrations

Notes	Serial	Type (other identity)	Owner/operator, location
	LITHUANIA		
	LY-AMB	L.1329 Jetstar 731	Lithuanian Govt, Vilnius
	MOROCCO		
	CNA-NL	G.1159 Gulfstream IITT	Govt of Morocco, Rabat
	CNA-NR	Boeing 707-3W6C	Govt of Morocco, Rabat
	CNA-NS	Boeing 707-138B	Govt of Morocco, Rabat
	CNA-NU	G.1159A Gulfstream III	Govt of Morocco, Rabat
	CNA-NV	G.1159A Gulfstream III	Govt of Morocco, Rabat
	CN-TNA	Dassault Falcon 100	Govt of Morocco, Rabat
	NAMIBIA		
	V5-NAM	Dassault Falcon 900B	Govt of Namibia, Windhoek
	NETHERLANDS		
	PH-KBX	Fokker 70	Dutch Royal Flight, Schiphol
	PH-SBK	Beechcraft Super King Air 200	MLD 2 MOTU, Maastricht
	NIGERIA		
	5N-AGV	G.1159 Gulfstream II	Federal Govt of Nigeria, Lagos
	5N-FGE	Dassault Falcon 900	Federal Govt of Nigeria, Lagos
	5N-FGO	Dassault Falcon 900	Federal Govt of Nigeria, Lagos
	5N-FGP	G.1159A Gulfstream III	Federal Govt of Nigeria, Lagos
	OMAN		
	A4O-AB	G.1159C Gulfstream IV	Govt of Oman, Seeb
	A4O-AC	G.1159C Gulfstream IV	Govt of Oman, Seeb
	A4O-SO	Boeing 747SP-27	Govt of Oman, Seeb
	A4O-SP	Boeing 747SP-27	Govt of Oman, Seeb
	PAKISTAN		
	AP-BEH	Boeing 737-33A	Govt of Pakistan, karachi
	QATAR		
	A7-AAA	Boeing 707-3P1C	Qatari Govt, Doha
	A7-AAD	Dassault Falcon 900	Qatari Govt, Doha
	A7-AAE	Dassault Falcon 900	Qatari Govt, Doha
	A7-AAF	Airbus A.310-304	Qatari Govt, Doha
	A7-HHK	Airbus A.340-211	Qatari Govt, Doha
	RUSSIA		
	RA-65904	Tupolev Tu.134A	Russian Govt, Moscow
	RA-85629	Tupolev Tu.154M	Russian Govt, Moscow
	RA-85630	Tupolev Tu.154M	Russian Govt, Moscow
	RA-85631	Tupolev Tu.154M	Russian Govt, Moscow
	RA-85645	Tupolev Tu.154M	Russian Govt, Moscow
	RA-85651	Tupolev Tu.154M	Russian Govt, Moscow
	RA-85653	Tupolev Tu.154M	Russian Govt, Moscow
	RA-85658	Tupolev Tu.154M	Russian Govt, Moscow
	RA-85659	Tupolev Tu.154M	Russian Govt, Moscow
	RA-85666	Tupolev Tu.154M	Russian Govt, Moscow
	RA-85675	Tupolev Tu.154M	Russian Govt, Moscow
	RA-85686	Tupolev Tu.154M	Russian Govt, Moscow
	RA-86466	Ilyushin Il.62M	Russian Govt, Moscow
	RA-86467	Ilyushin Il.62M	Russian Govt, Moscow
	RA-86468	Ilyushin Il.62M	Russian Govt, Moscow
	RA-86536	Ilyushin Il.62M	Russian Govt, Moscow
	RA-86537	Ilyushin Il.62M	Russian Govt, Moscow
	RA-86540	Ilyushin Il.62M	Russian Govt, Moscow
	RA-86553	Ilyushin Il.62M	Russian Govt, Moscow
	RA-86554	Ilyushin Il.62M	Russian Govt, Moscow
	RA-86559	Ilyushin Il.62M	Russian Govt, Moscow
	RA-86561	Ilyushin Il.62M	Russian Govt, Moscow
	RA-86710	Ilyushin Il.62M	Russian Govt, Moscow
	RA-86711	Ilyushin Il.62M	Russian Govt, Moscow
	RA-86712	Ilyushin Il.62M	Russian Govt, Moscow
	RA-96012	Ilyushin Il.96-300	Russian Govt, Moscow
	HZ-103	G.1159C Gulfstream IV	Royal Saudi AF, No 1 Sqn, Riyadh
	HZ-105	BAe 125-800	Royal Saudi AF, No 1 Sqn, Riyadh
	HZ-108	G.1159A Gulfstream III	Royal Saudi AF, No 1 Sqn, Riyadh
	HZ-109	BAe 125-800B	Royal Saudi AF, No 1 Sqn, Riyadh

Civil Registrations

Serial	Type (other identity)	Owner/operator, location	Notes
HZ-110	BAe 125-800B	Royal Saudi AF, No 1 Sqn, Riyadh	
HZ-114	Lockheed VC-130H Hercules	Royal Saudi AF, No 1 Sqn, Riyadh	
HZ-115	Lockheed VC-130H Hercules	Royal Saudi AF, No 1 Sqn, Riyadh	
HZ-116	Lockheed VC-130H Hercules	Royal Saudi AF, No 1 Sqn, Riyadh	
HZ-117	Lockheed L.100-30 Hercules	Royal Saudi AF, No 1 Sqn, Riyadh	
HZ-124	Airbus A.340-211	Royal Embassy of Saudi Arabia, Riyadh	
HZ-128	Lockheed L.100-30 Hercules	Royal Saudi AF, No 1 Sqn, Riyadh	
HZ-129	Lockheed L.100-30 Hercules	Royal Saudi AF, No 1 Sqn, Riyadh	
HZ-AFA2	Canadair CL.604 Challenger	Saudi Royal Flight, Jeddah	
HZ-AFN	G.1159A Gulfstream III	Saudi Govt, Jeddah	
HZ-AFR	G.1159A Gulfstream III	Saudi Govt, Jeddah	
HZ-AFT	Dassault Falcon 900	Saudi Govt, Jeddah	
HZ-AFU	G.1159C Gulfstream IV	Saudi Govt, Jeddah	
HZ-AFV	G.1159C Gulfstream IV	Saudi Govt, Jeddah	
HZ-AFW	G.1159C Gulfstream IV	Saudi Govt, Jeddah	
HZ-AFX	G.1159C Gulfstream IV	Saudi Govt, Jeddah	
HZ-AFY	G.1159C Gulfstream IV	Saudi Govt, Jeddah	
HZ-AFZ	Dassault Falcon 900	Saudi Govt, Jeddah	
HZ-AIF	Boeing 747SP-68	Saudi Govt, Jeddah	
HZ-AIJ	Boeing 747SP-68	Saudi Royal Flight, Jeddah	
HZ-HM1A	Boeing 747-3G1	Saudi Royal Flight, Jeddah	
HZ-HM1B	Boeing 747SP-68	Saudi Royal Flight, Jeddah	
HZ-HM4	Boeing 737-268	Saudi Royal Flight, Jeddah	
HZ-HM5	L.1011 TriStar 500	Saudi Royal Flight, Jeddah	
HZ-HM6	L.1011 TriStar 500	Saudi Royal Flight, Jeddah	
HZ-MS3	G.1159A Gulfstream III	Armed Forces Medical Services, Riyadh	
HZ-MS4	G.1159A Gulfstream III	Armed Forces Medical Services, Riyadh	
HZ-MS6	Lockheed L.100-30 Hercules	Armed Forces Medical Services, Riyadh	
HZ-MS7	Lockheed C-130H Hercules	Armed Forces Medical Services, Riyadh	
HZ-MS8	Lockheed C-130H-30 Hercules	Armed Forces Medical Services, Riyadh	
HZ-MS09	Lockheed L.100-30 Hercules	Armed Forces Medical Services, Riyadh	
HZ-MS019	Lockheed C-130H Hercules	Armed Forces Medical Services, Riyadh	
HZ-MSD	G.1159A Gulfstream III	Armed Forces Medical Services, Riyadh	

SLOVAKIA

OM-BYE	Yakovlev Yak-40	Slovak Govt, Bratislava/Ivanka	
OM-BYL	Yakovlev Yak-40	Slovak Govt, Bratislava/Ivanka	
OM-BYO	Tupolev Tu.154M	Slovak Govt, Bratislava/Ivanka	
OM-BYR	Tupolev Tu.154M	Slovak Govt, Bratislava/Ivanka	

SLOVENIA

S5-BAA	Gates LearJet 35A	Slovenian Govt, Ljubljana	
S5-BAB	Gates LearJet 24D	Slovenian Govt, Ljubljana	

SOUTH AFRICA

ZS-NAN	Dassault Falcon 900	South African Air Force, No 21 Sqn, Waterkloof	

SWITZERLAND

HB-GII	Beechcraft Super King Air 350C	Flugwaffe, Flugswaffenbrigade 31, Dübendorf	

SYRIA

YK-AYA	Tupolev Tu.134A	Govt of Syria, Damascus	

TURKEY

TC-ATA	G.1159C Gulfstream IV	Govt of Turkey, Istanbul	
TC-GAP	G.1159C Gulfstream IV	Govt of Turkey, Istanbul	

TURKMENISTAN

EZ-B021	BAe 1000B	Govt of Turkmenistan, Ashkhabad	

UGANDA

5X-UOI	G.1159A Gulfstream III	Govt of Uganda, Entebbe	

UKRAINE

UR-76413	Ilyushin Il-76MD	Ukrainian Air Force, Uzin	
UR-76537	Ilyushin Il-76MD	Ukrainian Air Force, Uzin	
UR-76624	Ilyushin Il-76MD	Ukrainian Air Force, Uzin	
UR-76687	Ilyushin Il-76MD	Ukrainian Air Force, Uzin	
UR-78820	Ilyushin Il-76MD	Ukrainian Air Force, Uzin	

Civil Registrations

Notes	Serial	Type (other identity)	Owner/operator, location
	UNITED ARAB EMIRATES		
	A6-AUH	Dassault Falcon 900	Govt of Abu Dhabi
	A6-ESH	Boeing 737-2W8	Govt of Sharjah
	A6-HHH	G.1159C Gulfstream IV	Dubai Air Wing
	A6-PFD	Airbus A.300C4-620	Govt of Abu Dhabi
	A6-SHZ	Airbus A.300B4-620	Govt of Abu Dhabi
	A6-SMM	Boeing 747SP-31	Govt of Dubai
	A6-SMR	Boeing 747SP-31	Govt of Dubai
	A6-UAE	Dassault Falcon 900	Govt of Abu Dhabi
	A6-ZKM	Dassault Falcon 900	Govt of Abu Dhabi
	A6-ZSN	Boeing 747SP-Z5	Govt of Dubai
	UNITED STATES		
	N88JA	Gates LearJet 35A	Phoenix Aviation/US Navy, Sigonella
	N94	BAe 125-800A (C-29A) (88-0269)	Federal Aviation Administration, Oklahoma
	N95	BAe 125-800A (C-29A) (88-0270)	Federal Aviation Administration, Oklahoma
	N96	BAe 125-800A (C-29A) (88-0271)	Federal Aviation Administration, Oklahoma
	N97	BAe 125-800A (C-29A) (88-0272)	Federal Aviation Administration, Oklahoma
	N98	BAe 125-800A (C-29A) (88-0273)	Federal Aviation Administration, Oklahoma
	N99	BAe 125-800A (C-29A) (88-0274)	Federal Aviation Administration, Oklahoma
	N350JF	Gates LearJet 35A	Phoenix Aviation/US Navy, Sigonella
	YUGOSLAVIA		
	YU-BJG	Gates LearJet 25B	Govt of Yugoslavia, Belgrade
	YU-BKR	Gates LearJet 25D	Govt of Yugoslavia, Belgrade
	YU-BNA	Dassault Falcon 50 (72102)	Govt of Yugoslavia, Belgrade
	YU-BPZ	Dassault Falcon 50 (72101)	Govt of Yugoslavia, Belgrade

Swiss Air Force Learjet 35A T-781 based at Dubendorf. *PRM*

Military Aviation Sites on the Internet

The list below is not intended to be a complete list of military aviation sites on the Internet. The sites listed cover Museums, Locations, Air Forces, Companies and Organisations that are mentioned elsewhere in 'Military Aircraft Markings'. Sites listed are in English or contain sufficient English to be reasonably easily understood. Each site address is believed to be correct at the time of going to press. Additions are welcome, via the usual address found at the front of the book, or via e-mail to prmavia@cwcom.net

Names of sites	Internet Dial (all prefixed 'http://')
MILITARY SITES – UK	
No 8 Sqn	www.gwyn.demon.co.uk/8sqn/index.html
No 23 Sqn	www.ebrown.demon.co.uk/23Sqn/homepage.html
Blue Eagles Home Page	www.deltaweb.co.uk/eagles
DERA	www.dera.gov.uk/dera.htm
Fleet Air Arm	www.royal-navy.mod.uk/today/faa.htm
Ministry of Defence	www.mod.uk/
RAF College Cranwell	www.cranwell.raf.mod.uk/index.htm
RAF Kinloss	www.surflink.co.uk/users/raf/
RAF Lyneham	www.lyneham.raf.mod.uk/
RAF St Athan	ourworld.compuserve.com/homepages/st_athan/
RAF Valley	www.ecafe.org/~paul/valley.htm
Red Arrows	www.deltaweb.co.uk/reds/redhome.htm
Royal Air Force	www.raf.mod.uk/
Royal Air Force Careers	www.open.gov.uk/raf/rafhome.htm
Royal Auxiliary Air Force	www.rauxaf.mod.uk/
MILITARY SITES – US	
37th AS Home Page	www.usafe.af.mil/bases/ramstein/37als/blueta1.htm
86th AW Home Page	www.usafe.af.mil/bases/ramstein/ramstein.htm
100th ARW Home Page	www.mildenhall.af.mil/100arw/100arw.htm
106th Rescue Wing, New York ANG	www.infoshop.com/106rescue/
Air Combat Command	www.acc.af.mil/
Air Force Flight Test Center (Edwards AFB)	www.edwards.af.mil/
Air Force Reserve Command	www.afrc.af.mil/
Air National Guard	www.ang.af.mil/
AMARC - up to date list of aircraft	www.dm.af.mil/amarc/freedom.htm
Aviano Air Base	www.aviano.af.mil/
Holloman Air Force Base	www.holloman.af.mil/
Hurricane Hunters Home Page (53rd WRS)	www.hurricanehunters.com/
Liberty Wing Home Page (48th FW)	www.lakenheath.af.mil/
NASA	www.nasa.gov/
Nellis Air Force Base	www.nellis.af.mil/
RAF Mildenhall Home Page	www.mildenhall.af.mil/
Spangdahlem Air Base	www.spangdahlem.af.mil/
Travis Air Force Base	www.travis.af.mil/
The Thunderbirds	www.nellis.af.mil/thunderbirds/
USAF	www.af.mil/
USAF Europe	www.usafe.af.mil/
USAF World Wide Web Sites	www.af.mil/sites/
US Army	www.army.mil/
US Marine Corps	www.usmc.mil/
US Navy	www.navy.mil/
US Navy Patrol Squadrons (unofficial)	www.vpnavy.com/
Whiteman Air Force Base	www.whiteman.af.mil/
MILITARY SITES – ELSEWHERE	
8 Wing Trenton (Canadian Forces)	www.8wing.trenton.dnd.ca/
301 Sqn KLu	www.301sqn.com/
315 Sqn KLu	www.geocities.com/Pentagon/Quarters/8440/
407 Sqn Canadian Forces	mars.ark.com/~407ops/index.html
Armée de l'Air	www.defense.gouv.fr/air/index.html
Armée de l'Air (unofficial)	www.mygale.org/06/airmil/index.shtml
Aeronautica Militare	www.aero-mil.difesa.it/
Austrian Armed Forces (in German)	www.bmlv.gv.at/
Belgian Air Force	www.mil.be/luchtmacht/baf/homeuk.htm
Brazilian Air Force	www.mat.ufrgs.br/~rudnei/FAB/english.html
Canadian Forces	www.achq.dnd.ca/
East European Air Forces (unofficial)	mm.iit.uni-miskolc.hu/Data/Winx/

Military Aviation Internet

Names of sites	*Internet Dial (all prefixed 'http://')*
Finnish Defence Force	www.mil.fi/english/
Forca Aerea Portuguesa	www.emfa.pt/
Frecce Tricolori	users.iol.it/gromeo/
Hellenic Army Aviation	www.evansb.gr/haa/
Indian Air Force	www.bharat-rakshak.com/IAF/
Israeli Defence Force/Air Force	www.idf.il/
Japan Air Self Defence Force	www.jda.go.jp/jasdf/indexE.htm
JbG-38 (in German)	members.xoom.com/jabog38/homepage.htm
Luftforsvaret	www.mil.no/luftforsvaret/index.html
Luftwaffe	www.bundeswehr.de/bundeswehr/streitkraefte/luftwaffe/luftwaffe.htm
NATO	www.nato.int
Royal Australian Air Force	www.adfa.oz.au/DOD/RAAF/
Royal Danish Air Force	users.cybercity.dk/~ccc6161/denmark/rdaf.htm
Royal Netherlands AF (unofficial)	web.inter.NL.net/hcc/D.vanDolderen/
Royal New Zealand AF	www.airforce.mil.nz/
Royal Thai Air Force	www.rtaf.mi.th
Singapore Air Force	www.mindef.gov.sg/rsaf/
South African AF Site (unofficial)	www.geocities.com/CapeCanaveral/Lab/2789/saaf.htm
Spanish Air Force (unofficial)	www.geocities.com/Pentagon/2112/
Swedish Air Force	www.mil.se/FM/flyg/index_e.html
Swedish Military Aviation (unofficial)	www.canit.se/%7Egriffon/aviation/
Swiss Armed Forces	www.vbs.admin.ch/internet/e/armee/index.htm
Turkish General Staff (Armed Forces)	www.tsk.mil.tr/

AIRCRAFT & AERO ENGINE MANUFACTURERS

Aérospatiale	www.aerospatiale.fr/
Aero Vodochody Ltd	www.ctx.cz/aero/
Allison Engine Company	www.allison.com/
Bell Helicopter Textron	www.bellhelicopter.textron.com/index.html
Boeing	www.boeing.com/
Bombardier	www.bombardier.com/
British Aerospace	www.bAe.co.uk/
CFM International	www.cfm56.com/
Daimler-Benz Aerospace AG	www.dasa.com/
Dassault	www.dassault-aviation.com/
Embraer	www.embraer.com/
Fairchild Dornier	www.fairchilddornier.com/
Fokker	www.fokker.com/fokker.html
General Electric	www.ge.com/
GKN Westland	www.gknplc.com/aerospace/helicopter.html
Gulfstream Aerospace	www.gulfstreamaircraft.com/
Kaman Aerospace	www.kamanaero.com/
LET	www.let.cz/
Lockheed Martin	www.lmco.com/
Lockheed Martin Skunk Works	www.lmsw.external.lmco.com/lmsw/html/index.html
Northrop Grumman	www.northgrum.com/
Pilatus Britten-Norman	www.britten-norman.com/
Raytheon (Beech, Hawker)	www.raytheon.com/rac/
Rolls-Royce	www.rolls-royce.com/
SAAB	www.saab.se/
Sikorsky	www.sikorsky.com/

UK AVIATION MUSEUMS

Aviation Museums in Great Britain	www.rdg.ac.uk/AcaDepts/sn/wsn1/dept/av/gb.html
Brooklands Museum	www.motor-software.co.uk/brooklands/index.html
Caernarfon Air World	www.planefacts.ndirect.co.uk/caernarfonairworld.htm
City of Norwich Aviation Museum	www.mth.uea.ac.uk/~h720/aviation/conam.html
De Havilland Heritage Museum	www.netlink.co.uk/users/aeroflt/mus/mosqmus.htm
Flambards Village Theme Park	www.flambards.co.uk/
Fly-In Guide to Aviation Museums in the UK	www.avnet.co.uk/greenawa/museums.html
The Helicopter Museum	ds.dial.pipex.com/ihm/
Imperial War Museum, Duxford	iwm.iwm.org.uk/duxford.htm
Imperial War Museum, Duxford (unofficial)	dspace.dial.pipex.com/town/square/rcy85/
Imperial War Museum, Lambeth	chide.museum.org.uk/imperial.war/imperial.war.index.html
The Jet Age Museum	www.argonet.co.uk/education/noel.gac/
Lincs Aviation Heritage Centre	www.pipswan.demon.co.uk/lahc.htm
Midland Air Museum	www.discover.co.uk/~mam/
Museum of Berkshire Aviation	www.prole.demon.co.uk/mba/mba.htm

Names of sites	Internet Dial (all prefixed 'http://')
Museum of Flight, East Fortune	www.nms.ac.uk/flight/main.htm
Museum of Science & Industry, Manchester	www.msim.org.uk/
Newark Air Museum	www.emnet.co.uk/Museums/NewarkAir/
North East Aircraft Museum	members.tripod.com/~BDaugherty/neam.html
RAF Cosford Aerospace Museum	www.rafmuseum.org.uk/flat/cosford/
RAF Manston Spitfire & Hurricane Memorial	www.spitfire-museum.com/
RAF Museum, Hendon	www.rafmuseum.org.uk/
Science Museum, South Kensington	www.nmsi.ac.uk/on-line/flight/
Yorkshire Air Museum, Elvington	www.pocklington.gov.uk/YAM/index.html

AVIATION SOCIETIES

Air Britain	www.air-britain.com/
Air Britain Merseyside	members.xoom.com/ABM/welcome.html
Air North	www.airnorth.demon.co.uk/index.html
Cleveland Tailwatchers	members.aol.com/philc2/ctwhome.html
East London Aviation Society	dspace.dial.pipex.com/westrowops/
Friends of Leeming Aviation Group	www.crakehal.demon.co.uk/aviation/flag.htm
Gatwick Aviation Society	www.totavia.com/hawkeye
Royal Aeronautical Society	www.raes.org.uk/
St Athan Aviation group	dspace.dial.pipex.com/westrowops/stamu.htm
Scramble (Dutch Aviation Society)	www.scramble.nl/
Solent Aviation Society	freespace.virgin.net/anthony.gordon/
Spitfire Society	www.ncl.ac.uk/~nsgg/s_soc1.htm
Turnhouse Aviation Group	wkweb1.cableinet.co.uk/j.woodrow/turnhouse/
Ulster Aviation Society	www.d-n-a.net/users/dnetrAzQ/

OPERATORS OF HISTORIC AIRCRAFT

B-17 Preservation Ltd	www.deltaweb.co.uk/sallyb/
Battle of Britain Memorial Flight	www.raf.mod.uk/on_display/bbmf.html
Catalina Online	www.users.dircon.co.uk/~catalina
De Havilland Aviation	www.inter-plane.com/dehavilland/
Eastern Stearman	www.btinternet.com/~eastern.stearman/
Intrepid Aviation	www.deltaweb.co.uk/intrepid/
Old Flying Machine Company	www.evoke.co.uk/ofmc/
Swordfish Heritage Trust	www.yeovilton.org.uk/
The Fighter Collection	www.avnet.co.uk/tfc/

SITES RELATING TO SPECIFIC TYPES OF MILITARY AIRCRAFT

The Avro Shackleton Page	www.home.aone.net.au/shack_one/
B-24 Liberator	www.b24bestweb.com/
B-52 Stratofortress Association	www.stratofortress.org/
Blackburn Buccaneer	ourworld.compuserve.com/
	homepages/andrewbrooks1/
Dassault Mirages	www.decollage.com/mirage/mirages.htm
EE Canberra	www.netcomuk.co.uk/~lesb/canberra.html
Eurofighter Typhoon	www.eurofighter-typhoon.com
F-4 Phantom II Society	www.f4phantom.org/
F-16: The Complete Reference	allserv.rug.ac.be/~svhastel/
F-20 Tigershark	inote.com/~jaemoon/f20/
F-86 Web Page	www.geocities.com/CapeCanaveral/
	Launchpad/8608/
F-105 Thunderchief	www.geocities.com/Pentagon/7002/
The Gripen	www.gripen.saab.se/
The Harrier	members.aol.com/stonker/harrier/harrier1.htm
International F-104 Society	www.avdigest.com/f104/f104.html
The Lightning	homepages.enterprise.net/garry/light.html
Lockheed C-130 Hercules	www.tmvp.demon.co.uk/70sqn_raf_lyneham/
	page3.html
Lockheed SR-71 Blackbird	www.wvi.com/~lelandh/sr-71~1.htm
The MiG-21 Page	gramercy.ios.com/~tkraft/mig.htm
P-3 Orion Research Group	home.wxs.nl/~p3orin/
P-51 Mustang	www.p51mustang.com/
Swiss F-18 Hornet site (unofficial)	www.geocities.com/CapeCanaveral/Lab/6063/
Thunder & Lightnings (Postwar British Aircraft)	www.totavia.com/jetman/
Vulcan 558 Club	www.vulcan558club.demon.co.uk/
Vulcan Restoration Trust	www.XL426.com
The XM655 Association	www.jetman.dircon.co.uk/xm655/

MISCELLANEOUS

Aerodata	dspace.dial.pipex.com/aerodata/
Aeroflight	www.netlink.co.uk/users/aeroflt/
The 'AirNet' Links Site	www.howardcurtis.mcmail.com/

Military Aviation Internet

Names of sites	Internet Dial (all prefixed 'http://')
AirSpeed	www.airspeed.ndirect.co.uk/
The Aviator's Network	www.aviators.net/
British Aviation Forum Infromation	www.comet3.demon.co.uk/baif/
Chinese Military Aviation	www.concentric.net/~Jetfight/
David Hastings' Military Aviation Page	users.ox.ac.uk/~daveh/Military/
f4Aviation	www.ffour.force9.co.uk/
Farnborough Movements & Photographs	www.geocities.com/CapeCanaveral/hangar/1937/
Military Aircraft Database	www.csd.uwo.ca/~pettypi/elevon/gustin_military/
Military Aviation	www.crakehal.demon.co.uk/aviation/aviation.htm
Polish Aviation Site	aviation.pol.pl/
RAF Northolt (unofficial)	www.netcomuk.co.uk/~landair/
Russian Aviation Page	aeroweb.lucia.it/~agretch/RAP.html
The Spotter's Nest	www.spotters.it/

Rolls-Royce operates Spitfire XIX PS853 from Filton. *PRM*

This Meteor NF11 WM167/G-LOSM is kept in immaculate condition by Jet Heritage at Bournemouth. *PRM*

This former Army Air Corps Chipmunk WK512/G-BXIM is now privately owned. *Daniel J. March*

XD693 is the only airworthy example of the Jet Provost T1. *PRM*

In 'Yellowjacks' paint scheme, Gnat XR991/G-MOUR is based at North Weald by Intrepid Aviation. *PRM*

Tony Hulls keeps Lightning T5 XS458 in airworthy condition at Cranfield. *PRM*

Eurofighter Typhoon prototype 98+30, the first to fly with the ES-200 engine. *PRM*

Portuguese AF A-7P Corsair II 15512 is flown by 304 Sqn from Monte Real. *PRM*